University of Michigan
Physics 135
Fall 2013 / Winter 2014

Physics for the Life Sciences I

University of Michigan Ann Arbor

— **Wiley Custom Learning Solutions** —

ISBN 978-1-118-81213-6

Printed and bound by Quad/Graphics.

V10003674_081518

Contents

Contents

Equalities denoted by $\equiv$ are exact.

Length

1 metre $\equiv$ 39.37 inches = 3.281 feet
1 inch $\equiv$ 2.54 centimetres
1 foot $\equiv$ 30.48 centimetres
1 kilometre $\equiv$ 10^3 metres = 0.6214 miles
1 mile $\equiv$ 5280 feet = 1.609 kilometres
1 angstrom $\equiv$ 10^{-10} metres
1 nanometre $\equiv$ 10^{-9} metres
1 micrometre = 1 micron = 10^{-6} metres

Area

1 in.^{2} $\equiv$ 6.4516 cm^2
1 ft^2 = 9.29 $\times$ 10^{-2} m^2
1 cm^2 $\equiv$ 10^{-4} m^2 = 0.155 in.^{2} = 1.076 $\times$ 10^{-3} ft^2
1 m^2 $\equiv$ 10^4 cm^2 = 10.76 ft^2

Volume

1 in.^{3} = 16.39 cm^3
1 ft^3 = 2.832 $\times$ 10^{-2} m^3
1 cm^3 $\equiv$ 10^{-6} m^3 = 6.102 $\times$ 10^{-2} in.^{3}
   = 3.531 $\times$ 10^{-5} ft^3
1 m^3 $\equiv$ 10^6 cm^3 = 35.31 ft^3
1 litre $\equiv$ 10^{-3} m^3 = 0.264 gallons
1 gallon = 3.786 liters = 231 in.^{3}

Time

1 hour $\equiv$ 60 minutes $\equiv$ 3600 seconds
1 day $\equiv$ 24 hours $\equiv$ 1440 minutes
   $\equiv$ 8.64 $\times$ 10^4 seconds
1 year = 365.24 days = 3.156 $\times$ 10^7 seconds

Mass

1 gram $\equiv$ 10^{-3} kilograms = 6.852 $\times$ 10^{-5} slugs
   = 6.024 $\times$ 10^{23} u
1 kilogram $\equiv$ 10^3 grams = 6.852 $\times$ 10^{-2} slugs
   = 6.024 $\times$ 10^{26} u
1 slug = 14.59 kilograms
1 u = 1.66 $\times$ 10^{-27} kilograms

Mass density

1 gm cm^{-3} $\equiv$ 10^3 kg m^{-3} = 1.94 slug ft^{-3}
1 slug ft^{-3} = 0.5153 gm cm^{-3}
   = 5.153 $\times$ 10^2 kg m^{-3}

Speed

1 cm s^{-1} $\equiv$ 10^{-2} m s^{-1} $\equiv$ 3.6 $\times$ 10^{-2} km h^{-1}
1 m s^{-1} = 3.6 km h^{-1} = 2.24 mi h^{-1}
1 ft s^{-1} = 30.48 cm s^{-1} = 0.3048 m s^{-1}
   = 1.097 km h^{-1}
1 mi h^{-1} = 0.447 m s^{-1} = 1.609 km h^{-1}
   = 1.467 ft s^{-1}
1 km h^{-1} = 0.2778 m s^{-1} = 0.6214 mi h^{-1}

Angle and Angular Speed

180 degrees $\equiv$ π radians
1 radian = 57.3 degrees
1 degree = 1.745 χ 10^{-2} radians
1 rad s^{-1} = 0.159 rev s^{-1} = 9.549 rev min^{-1}
1 rev min^{-1} = 0.0167 rev s^{-1} = 0.1047 rad s^{-1}

Force

1 pound = 4.448 newtons = 4.448 $\times$ 10^5 dynes
1 newton $\equiv$ 10^5 dynes = 0.2248 pounds
1 dyne $\equiv$ 10^{-5} newtons = 2.248 $\times$ 10^{-6} pounds

Pressure

1 atmosphere = 1.013 $\times$ 10^5 pascals
   = 14.7 lb in.$^{-2}$
1 pascal $\equiv$ 10 dyn cm^{-2} = 1.450 $\times$ 10^{-4} lb in.$^{-2}$
   = 7.501 $\times$ 10^{-4} cm Hg
1 cm Hg = 1.333 $\times$ 10^4 dyn cm^{-2}
   =1.316 $\times$ 10^{-2} atmosphere
   = 1.333 $\times$ 10^3 pascals
1 in. H$_2$O = 1.868 mm Hg = 249.1 pascals
1 lb in.$^{-2}$ = 6.895 $\times$ 10^3 pascals
   = 6.805 $\times$ 10^{-2} atmosphere
1 lb ft^{-2} = 47.88 pascals
1 torr $\equiv$ 1 mm Hg = 133.3 pascals
1 bar = 10^5 pascals

Viscosity and Flow Resistance

1 Pa s $\equiv$ 10 poise
1 Pa s m^{-3} = 0.750 $\times$ 10^{-8} torr s cm^{-3}

Energy

1 joule $\equiv$ 10^7 ergs = 0.2390 calorie = 0.7376 ft lb
1 calorie = 4.184 joules
1 kcal $\equiv$ 10^3 calories
1 joule = 6.24 $\times$ 10^{18} electron volts
1 electron volt = 1.602 $\times$ 10^{-19} joule
1 kWh = 3.6 $\times$ 10^6 joules
1 BTU = 1.054 $\times$ 10^3 joules
1 ft lb = 1.356 joules

Mass Energy Conversion

1 u = 931 $\times$ 10^6 electron volts $\equiv$ 931 MeV

Power

1 watt $\equiv$ 10^{-3} kilowatts = 0.7376 ft lb s^{-1}
   = 1.341 $\times$ 10^{-3} horsepower
1 horsepower $\equiv$ 550 ft lb s^{-1} = 7.457 $\times$ 10^2 watts
1 kilowatt $\equiv$ 10^3 watts = 1.341 horsepower

Magnetic Field

1 gauss = 10^{-4} tesla

Prefixes used to define multiples of S.I. units. These may be used with any of the basic S.I. units or with units derived from them

Fraction	Prefix	Symbol	Example
10^{-18}	atto	a	
10^{-15}	femto	f	
10^{-12}	pico	p	
10^{-9}	nano	n	1 nanosecond = 1 ns $= 10^{-9}$ seconds
10^{-6}	micro	μ	
10^{-3}	milli	m	1 millimetre = 1 mm $= 10^{-3}$ metres
10^{-2}	centi	c	1 centimetre = 1 cm $= 10^{-2}$ metres
10^{-1}	deci	d	
10	deka	da	
10^2	hecto	h	
10^3	kilo	k	1 kilogram = 1 kg $= 10^3$ grams
10^6	mega	M	
10^9	giga	G	
10^{12}	tera	T	

The Greek Alphabet

A	α	alpha
B	β	beta
Γ	γ	gamma
Δ	δ	delta
E	ε	epsilon
Z	ζ	zeta
H	η	eta
Θ	θ	theta
I	ι	iota
K	κ	kappa
Λ	λ	lambda
M	μ	mu
N	ν	nu
Ξ	ξ	xi
O	o	omicron
Π	π	pi
P	ρ	rho
Σ	σ	sigma
T	τ	tau
Υ	υ	upsilon
Φ	ϕ	phi
X	χ	chi
Ψ	ψ	psi
Ω	ω	omega

Motion with Constant Acceleration

$$v = v_0 + a\Delta t$$
$$\Delta x = v_0 \Delta t + \tfrac{1}{2}a(\Delta t)^2$$
$$\bar{v} = \tfrac{1}{2}(v_0 + v)$$
$$\Delta x = \tfrac{1}{2}(v_0 + v)\Delta t$$
$$v^2 = v_0^2 + 2a\Delta x$$

GENERAL PHYSICS

SUPPLEMENTS

Student Study Guide and Solutions Manual for General Physics 2nd Edition
Morton M. Sternheim, University of Massachusetts, Amherst
Joseph W. Kane, University of Massachusetts, Amherst

Developed for student use with this text, including objectives, reviews, examples, new concepts and terms, quizzes and exams, as well as solutions for approximately 25% of the problems in the text.

Experiments in Physics—A Laboratory Manual for Scientists and Engineers
Daryl W. Preston, California State University at Hayward

A laboratory manual designed to be used in the calculus-based general physics course. The experiments follow the order of topics in traditional texts. Optional material is provided as well as flexibility in the choice of experiments.

For The Instructor
Instructor's Manual for *Physics 2nd Edition, includes solutions to all exercises and problems* and *transparency masters from which overhead transparencies may be made, in the text. A computerized text bank is also available, for MACIN-TOSH and IBM compatible computers.*

GENERAL PHYSICS

SECOND EDITION

MORTON M. STERNHEIM

Department of Physics and Astronomy
University of Massachusetts
Amherst, Massachusetts

JOSEPH W. KANE

Digital Equipment Corporation

WILEY

JOHN WILEY & SONS

    General physics/Morton M. Sternheim, Joseph W. Kane.—2nd ed.

Cover Photo: @ Michael Melford / Getty Images, Inc
Cover Design: Laura Nicholls

Acquisitions Editor: Cliff Mills
Managing Editor: Joan Kalkut
Production Manager: Katy Rubin
Production Supervisor: Nancy Prinz
Manufacturing Manager: Lorraine Fumoso
Photo Research Manager: Stella Kupferberg

Library of Congress Cataloging in Publication Data:

Sternheim, Morton M., 1933-
    General physics/Morton M. Sternheim, Joseph W. Kane. —2nd ed.
    Includes bibliographical references.
    ISBN 9780471522782
    1. Physics. I. Kane, Joseph W., 1938-. II. Title.
QC23.S84   1991
530—dc20

Printed in the United States of America

20 19 18 17 16 15

90-40174
CIP

To Suzy, Laura, Bill, and Pat.   JWK

To my wife, Helen, and my children, Laura, Amy, and Jeffrey.   MMS

PREFACE

General Physics is an introduction to physics for science majors with some background in calculus. Like our earlier text, *Physics,* it is intended to appeal to students with a wide range of interests and needs. However, it differs in that we have rewritten and added numerous topics which can most effectively be presented and understood with the aid of somewhat more advanced mathematical tools.

Ideally, students using this text will have completed at least one semester of calculus at the outset, but this is not essential. The derivative is introduced in discussing kinematics in Chapter One. Integrals are used only sparingly until Electricity and Magnetism is reached near the middle of the book. Calculations involving calculus are carried out with a good deal of detail and discussion. A few minor omissions may be appropriate if the students begin their calculus along with the physics.

Both our books differ in several ways from many other physics texts. First, the specific needs of science majors, including those in the life sciences, have influenced which physics topics are included or emphasized. Thus we cover some topics no longer of great current interest to many physicists, such as geometric optics, the mechanics of fluids, and acoustics, and minimize historical material and contemporary physics areas with little impact on other sciences. Second, we make extensive use of examples involving biological, chemical, geophysical, and astronomical systems, as well as alternative energy sources. Finally, we devote entire sections and chapters to applications of physics, covering subjects such as nerve conduction, ionizing radiation, and nuclear magnetic resonance. These features help to motivate students while demonstrating the widespread utility of physics and the unity of science.

General Physics contains 31 chapters, grouped into nine units. To accommodate varying needs and tastes, there is more material than can usually be covered in a two-semester or three-quarter course. Chapters that may be treated lightly or omitted entirely include Chapter Eight, Elastic Properties of Materials; Chapter Eighteen, Nerve Conduction; Chapter Twenty-Five, Special Relativity; Chapter Twenty-Nine, The Structure of Matter; and Chapter Thirty-One, Ionizing Radiation. Most of the chapters end with Supplementary Topics sections containing either applications of physics or traditional topics that can be omitted without loss of continuity. This arrangement assists the instructor in selecting what to include or to emphasize and also helps the student to distinguish the basic principles of physics from more peripheral material.

The changes made in the units of mechanics, thermal physics, and fluids in the present book are relatively minor. We use calculus in our discussions of kinematics, the center of gravity, moments of inertia, work and energy, area and polar moments of inertia, simple harmonic motion, the adiabatic expansion of an ideal gas, and Poiseuille's law. In Electricity and Magnetism, a significant amount of new material has been added, including finding fields and potentials by integration. Gauss' and Ampere's laws are present as Supplementary Topics. In Wave Motion, we use trigonometric functions to represent waves. In Chapter Twenty-Eight, Quantum Mechanics and Atomic Structure, we introduce and solve the Schrödinger equation in one dimension, and consider the hydrogen atom wave functions.

Throughout *General Physics,* we present the appropriate calculus-based derivations within the main discussion; the few such derivation included in *Physics* are located in the Supplementary Topics. SI units are used exclusively. Each chapter has a checklist of terms to define or explain, and exercises keyed to the sections. There are also problems, which are unkeyed; occasional more difficult ones are preceded by an asterisk. Exercises and problems involving calculus are preceded by a ^{c}. There are also exercises and problems for the Supplementary Topics.

This second edition of *General Physics* incorporates the improvements we made in the recent third edition of *Physics.* We have strengthened the pedagogic aspects wherever possible by clarifying our developments, adding examples, exercises, and problems. We have also kept the book up to date and have sought to increase its appeal for students with a wide range of interests. This has meant revising or adding many sections and subsections devoted to topics in basic physics and to applications of the fundamental principles in science and technology. Much of this new material is based on very recent developments or events. We think that both students and teachers will find it very stimulating.

In improving the pedagogy, we looked carefully at each section to make sure that there were varied examples, exercises, and problems at different levels of difficulty. We have added more than 50 examples and nearly 300 exercises and problems, as well as revising some of the older items. We also rewrote sections and paragraphs scattered throughout the book where we thought we could improve the discussion or could clarify topics that are difficult for students.

Clearly physics underlies much of what is happening today in other sciences and in technology. In keeping with our basic philosophy, the additions are aimed at making the book interesting and useful for students majoring in all areas of the biological and physical sciences. We have expanded and updated some earlier discussions of applications such as tomography, NMR, and PET scans (Chapters 23, 29, 31), and of nuclear safety and accidents (Chapter 30). Completely new materials include Coriolis forces and wind patterns (Chapter 7); large-scale atmospheric motions and monsoons (Chapter 12); models for the earth's crust (Chapter 13); hysteresis and magnetic disk-storage (Chapter 20); auditory localization by barn owls (Chapter 22); reflectance, rainbows (Chapter 23); direct observations of quantum jumps, barrier penetration and tunneling, scanning tunneling electron microscope (Chapter 28); superconductivity (Chapters 17, 29); superstrings (Chapter 30); and radon in the home (Chapter 31).

We thank the students and faculty colleagues who have helped us in so many ways. Kandula S. R. Sastry (University of Massachusetts) and Elizabeth P. Nickles (Albany College of Pharmacy) made many valuable suggestions. We are also grateful to H. Michael Sommermann (Westmont College, Santa Barbara, CA), Mildred Moe (University of California—Irvine), Frances Anderson (College of St. Thomas, St. Paul, MN), James A. Coleman (American International College, Springfield, MA), D. Harrison (University of Toronto, Toronto, Ontario), and Dennis Collins (Grossmont College, El Cajon, CA) for their comments. We are indebted to the competent and cooperative editorial and production staffs at John Wiley & Sons for their valuable assistance. Most of all, we thank our families for their ongoing patience, help, and encouragement.

MORTON M. STERNHEIM

JOSEPH W. KANE

PROLOGUE
PHYSICS AND
THE SCIENCE STUDENT

"Why should I study physics?" Sometimes asked with emotional overtones ranging from anguish to anger, this is one of the questions most frequently heard by physics teachers. It seems appropriate therefore to begin this book by attempting an answer.

One reason this question is asked so often is that many people who have not studied physics—and some who have—lack a clear notion of what physics is. Dictionaries are not much help. A typical short dictionary definition says that physics is the branch of science that deals with matter, energy, and their interactions. This is vague and general enough to include what is usually considered to be chemistry; in any case, it does not give any real feeling for what is involved. Longer dictionary entries usually expand the definition by noting that physics includes subfields such as mechanics, heat, electricity, and so forth. They give no clues as to why some subfields of science are included and others are not.

A better approach to defining physics is to ask what physicists are concerned about. Physicists attempt to understand the basic rules or *laws* that govern the operation of the natural world in which we live. Since their activities and interests evolve with time, the basic science called physics also changes with time. Many of the most active contemporary subfields of physics were undreamed of a generation or two ago. On the other hand, some parts of what are now considered to be chemistry or engineering were once considered to be physics. This is because physicists sometimes gradually abandon a field once the basic principles are known, leaving further developments and practical applications to others.

The fact that physics deals with the basic rules governing how the world works lets us see why people with varied interests may find the study of physics interesting and useful. For example, a historian who wants to understand the origins of our contemporary society will find significance in the story of the development of physics and its relationship to other human activities. Similarly, a philosopher concerned about concepts of space and time will profit greatly from understanding the revolutionary twentieth-century advances in physics. However, since we have written this book primarily for students majoring in the sciences, we have not stressed the historical or philosophical aspects of physics. Instead, we have tried to make clear in every chapter the connection between physics and other areas of science. We have learned that science majors find this approach more appropriate, since it makes clear the relevance and usefulness of studying physics.

An obvious impact of physics on both the life and physical sciences is in the area of instrumentation. Physical principles underlie the operation of light and electron microscopes, of X-ray machines and nuclear magnetic resonance spectrometers, of oscilloscopes and nuclear radiation monitors. Physics is also fundamental to a true understanding of chemistry, biology, and the earth sciences. The physical laws governing the behavior of molecules, atoms, and nuclei are the basis for all of chemistry and biochemistry. At the macroscopic level, the effects of forces of various types strongly influence the shapes of anatomical and human-built structures. Physiology offers many examples of physical processes and principles; diffusion within cells, the regulation of body temperature, the motion of fluids within the circulatory system, and electrical signals in nerves are just a few. In exercise science, activities ranging from running and jumping to karate can be analyzed and sometimes optimized by the application of physical principles. In the course of developing and illustrating the basic principles of physics, we discuss these applications and many others.

A few remarks about how one studies physics may be helpful. More than any other science, physics is a logical and deductive discipline. In any subfield of physics, there are just a few fundamental concepts or laws derived from experimental measurements. Once one has mastered these basic ideas, the applications are usually straightforward conceptually, even though the details may sometimes become complicated. Consequently, it is important to focus one's attention on the basic principles and to avoid memorizing a mass of facts and formulas.

Most of the basic laws of physics can be expressed rather concisely in the form of mathematical equations. This is a great convenience, since a tremendous amount of information is implicitly contained in a single equation. However, this also means that any serious attempt to learn or apply physics necessitates using a certain amount of mathematics. *General Physics* assumes a reasonable level of facility with high school algebra and basic geometry. Also, students should ideally have had some calculus before starting to use this text, although they may take it concurrently. An understanding of what derivatives and integrals mean is important, although not a great deal of skill in applying these concepts is needed. A mathematical review in Appendix B reviews key algebra and geometry topics and also lists the derivatives and integrals required for the examples and problems.

In summary, we believe that science majors will benefit in two major ways from studying physics. They will gain an understanding of the basic laws that govern everything in our world, from the subatomic to the cosmic scale, and will also learn much that will be important in their later work. The study of physics as a basic science is not particularly easy, but we believe it is rewarding, particularly for students planning further training in related sciences. We hope that all who use this book will agree.

M. M. S.

J. W. K.

CONTENTS

UNIT EIGHT
ATOMS AND MOLECULES   719

UNIT NINE
THE ATOMIC NUCLEUS   787

UNIT ONE

UNIT ONE

CHAPTER 1
MOTION IN A
STRAIGHT LINE

The most basic and obvious result of physical interactions is motion: a brick falls, an eardrum vibrates, a compass needle swings into line with a magnetic field, a meter needle moves on a scale, a radioactive nucleus emits a beta particle. Most of our understanding of nature is derived from our observations of motions and our efforts to relate them to their causes. Accordingly, we begin our study of physics by developing the ideas needed for a quantitative discussion of motion, starting in this chapter with the case of an object moving in a straight line.

Physics, like many other sciences, is largely based on quantitative measurements. These measurements must be correlated or interpreted in some way; often they are compared with theoretical predictions. To the extent that theory and experiment are in accord, we say that we have some understanding of the phenomena in question. A quantitative discussion of motion requires measurements of times and distances, so we must first consider the *standards*, *units*, and *errors* involved in physical measurements.

1.1 | MEASUREMENTS, STANDARDS, UNITS, AND ERRORS

Quantitative physical measurements must be expressed by numerical comparison to some agreed-upon set of standards. If you say a lecture lasted 53 minutes, you mean that it went on for the same length of time as it took for the wall clock to make some number of ticks. Here the quantity being measured has the *dimensions* of time, the *unit* for the measurement is the minute, and the clock is the *standard*. It is a *secondary standard*, since the minute is not defined by the properties of that one clock. All such measuring devices are calibrated directly or indirectly in terms of *primary standards* of length, time, and mass established by the international scientific community.

These primary standards are redefined from time to time as measurements become more precise. For example, the unit of length—the *metre*— was defined in 1889 as the length of a particular platinum–iridium bar kept under controlled conditions. This standard was discarded in 1960 because replication and preservation were inconvenient and subject to inaccuracies. The length standard is now based on the wavelength of the orange-red light emitted by atoms of krypton 86 in an electric discharge tube. Standards have also been defined for the units of time and mass (Fig. 1.1).

It is not accidental that standards have been set up for length, time, and mass. All mechanical quantities can be expressed in terms of some combination of these three fundamental dimensions, which we will denote as L, T, and M, respectively. For example, a velocity is a distance divided by a time, so its dimensions are L/T.

Systems of Units | *Metric units* have long been used in everyday matters everywhere except in the English-speaking countries, where *British units* were the norm. The British Commonwealth countries recently converted to the metric system, and the United States has slowly begun that complex process. In scientific work, metric units are used worldwide. Accordingly, in this text we will only use the internationally accepted set of metric units called the *Système Internationale* (*S.I.*). The *metre*, *kilogram*, and *second* are its basic units of length,

British length units (foot, yard, mile) and force unit (pound). Some fairly common non-S.I. units are defined for reference in Appendix C.

Representative lengths and times of various magnitudes are listed in S.I. units in Tables 1.1 and 1.2, respectively. The numbers appear in powers of 10, or "scientific notation," which is reviewed in Appendix B.1. Note that many of the quantities in these tables look extremely large or small. For this reason, we will often use power-of-10 multiples or submultiples of S.I. units constructed with the aid of standard prefixes, tabulated for easy reference on the inside front cover of this text. For example, the distance between two cities is usually measured in kilometres, where 1 kilometre is 10^3 metres. The dimensions of this book are more conveniently ex-

mass, and time, respectively. In older texts, an earlier version of this system is referred to as the *m.k.s. system*. Older texts also sometimes used *c.g.s. units*, built on the *centimetre*, *gram*, and *second*: 1 centimetre is 0.01 metre, and 1 gram is 0.001 kilogram. The centimetre and gram are considered acceptable submultiples of the basic S.I. unit, but most other c.g.s. units are now obsolete. In this text, we mention in passing just a few more commonly encountered remnants of this system. We will also show how to convert into S.I. units the

TABLE 1.1

Representative lengths in metres	
Atomic nucleus	10^{-15}
Sodium atom, diameter	10^{-11}
C—C bond	1.5×10^{-10}
DNA, diameter	2×10^{-9}
Microfilament, thickness	4×10^{-9}
Hemoglobin	7×10^{-9}
Cell membrane	10^{-8}
Small virus, diameter	2×10^{-8}
Small bacterium, diameter	2×10^{-7}
Visible light, wavelength	$4–7 \times 10^{-7}$
Mitochondria, diameter	$0.5–1.0 \times 10^{-6}$
Large bacterium, diameter	10^{-6}
Mammalian liver cell, diameter	2×10^{-5}
Sea urchin egg	7×10^{-5}
Giant amoeba, diameter	2×10^{-4}
Small crustacean	10^{-3}
Ostrich egg, diameter	4×10^{-2}
Mouse	10^{-1}
Human	$1–2 \times 10^{0}$
Blue whale	3×10^{1}
Brooklyn Bridge	10^{3}
Earth, diameter	1.3×10^{7}
Sun, diameter	1.2×10^{9}
Earth–sun, distance	1.3×10^{11}
Our galaxy, diameter	10^{22}
Distance to the farthest galaxies ever observed	10^{28}

TABLE 1.2

Representative times in seconds

Nuclear events	$10^{-23} - 10^{-10}$
Atomic events: light absorption, electronic excitation	$10^{-15} - 10^{-9}$
Chemical events	$10^{-9} - 10^{-6}$
Chains of biochemical reactions	$10^{-8} - 10^{2}$
Quick contraction of striated muscle (wink)	10^{-1}
Fastest cell division	5×10^{2}
Typical bacterial generation time	3×10^{3}
Typical protozoan generation time	10^{5}
Small mammal generation time	4×10^{7}
Large mammal lifetime	$4 \times 10^{8}–4 \times 10^{9}$
Lifetime of a lake	$10^{10} - 10^{12}$
Age of mammals	3×10^{15}
Age of vertebrates	10^{16}
Age of life	$>10^{17}$
Age of the earth	2×10^{17}

pressed in centimetres than in metres, while the thickness of this page is roughly 0.1 millimetre, or 100 micrometers (1 millimetre = 10^{-3} metre, 1 micrometre = 10^{-6} metre).

Conversion of Units | Although we only use

S.I. units, we occasionally need to convert quantities from one set of units to another. It is easy to do this correctly, even in complicated cases, with the aid of a trick involving "multiplying by one." For example, suppose we need to convert 100 feet (100 ft) into the equivalent number of metres (m). From the conversion factors listed on the inside front cover,

$$1 \text{ ft} = 0.3048 \text{ m}$$

Now we divide both sides by 1 ft, just as if the unit (feet) were an algebraic quantity:

$$\frac{1 \text{ ft}}{1 \text{ ft}} = \frac{0.3048 \text{ m}}{1 \text{ ft}}$$

The feet cancel on the left, leaving us a way of writing the quantity 1,

$$1 = \frac{0.3048 \text{ m}}{1 \text{ ft}}$$

If we multiply 100 ft by 1, nothing is changed, so we find

$$100 \text{ ft} = (100 \text{ ft})(1)$$
$$= (100 \text{ ft}) \left(\frac{0.3048 \text{ m}}{1 \text{ ft}} \right)$$
$$= 30.48 \text{ m}$$

Note that the ft units in the numerator and denominator cancel, leaving the desired unit, m. The virtue of multiplying by 1 is that this eliminates any doubt as to whether we should multiply or divide by the conversion factor. For instance, we can divide 1 ft = 0.3048 m by 0.3048 m to obtain another way of writing 1,

$$1 = \frac{1 \text{ ft}}{0.3048 \text{ m}}$$

However, if we multiply 100 ft by this factor, the units do not cancel properly.

Sometimes a quantity involves two or more units that must be converted. For example, a volume might be measured in cubic metres, or m^3, and a velocity in kilometres per hour, or km h^{-1}. (Note that we use negative exponents with units exactly as we would with algebraic quantities, so 1 h^{-1} = 1/h.) A factor of 1 is used for each conversion in the following examples.

Example 1.1

A small swimming pool is 20 ft long, 10 ft wide, and 5 ft deep. Its volume is the product of these distances, or (20 ft)(10 ft)(5 ft) = 1000 ft³. What is the volume in cubic metres (m^3)?

Here we must convert feet to metres three times, corresponding to changing the units for length, width, and depth. Using 1 ft = 0.3048 m,

$$1000 \text{ ft}^3 (1)^3 = 1000 \text{ ft}^3 \frac{(0.3048 \text{ m})^3}{(1 \text{ ft})^3}$$
$$= 1000(0.3048)^3 \text{ m}^3 = 28.3 \text{ m}^3$$

Example 1.2

Convert a velocity of 60 mi h^{-1} (miles per hour) to metres per second (m s^{-1}).

To carry out this conversion, we need a factor of 1 to convert hours to seconds and another to convert miles to metres. Since 1 h = 60 min = 3600 s, dividing by 3600 s gives

$$1 = \frac{1 \text{ h}}{3600 \text{ s}}$$

Also, 1 mi = 1.609 km = 1609 m, so

$$1 = 1609 \text{ m mi}^{-1}$$

Multiplying 60 mi h^{-1} by 1 twice gives

$$(60 \text{ mi h}^{-1})(1)(1) = (60 \text{ mi h}^{-1})\left(\frac{1 \text{ h}}{3600 \text{ s}}\right)(1609 \text{ m mi}^{-1})$$

$$= 60\left(\frac{1609}{3600}\right) \text{ m s}^{-1} = 26.8 \text{ m s}^{-1}$$

Types of Errors | Measurements and predictions

are both subject to errors. Measurement errors are of two types, *random* and *systematic*. The meaning of these terms is best understood with the aid of an example: the time T required for a weight on a string to swing back and forth once when released from a given point.

If someone uses a stopwatch to measure T and repeats the experiment several times, each result will be slightly different from the others. Usually, most of the measurements will be close to the average of all the measurements. The variation in results about this average arises from the inability of the observer to start and stop the watch exactly the same way each time. The error introduced by this inability is *random* and can be reduced by taking the average of many measurements.

Even when many measurements are made, the average result for T will be too small if the watch runs slow. This *systematic* error can be reduced by using a better watch or by comparing the watch used with a more accurate one and adjusting the results accordingly.

A systematic error may also result from the observer's reaction time. The observer may systematically start or stop the watch too early or too late. This error can be reduced by doing a more complex experiment. For example, the timing device may be started and stopped using a light beam and a photoelectric cell similar to those used in automatic door openers. Naturally, this apparatus will also have systematic and random errors, but they will be smaller than before.

Both systematic and random errors are present in all experiments. Reducing these errors generally requires increasingly elaborate apparatus and time-consuming procedures. High-precision measurements and measurements of small effects require

that great attention be given to identifying and reducing these errors.

Theoretical predictions usually have errors arising from various sources. A theoretical formula often contains measured quantities such as the mass of an electron or the speed of light, and there is some error associated with these measurements. For example, we will later obtain a formula for the period of a pendulum, the time T in our discussion above. Theoretical predictions made with this formula depend on the accuracy of our present knowledge of the acceleration due to gravity. Also, like most theoretical formulas, this formula depends on the validity of several approximations. Among these are the absence of friction and air resistance and the assumption that the pendulum does not swing very far from its rest position.

In all careful scientific work the numerical accuracy must be stated with precision. However, it is customary in textbooks to avoid the difficulties of a complete error analysis in doing numerical examples by using the rules for *significant figures*. This means that in the statement "the length of a rod is 2.43 metres" the last digit (3) is somewhat uncertain; the exact length might turn out to be closer to 2.42 or 2.44 m. In the examples, exercises, and problems in this text, all numbers should be treated as known to three significant figures. For example, 2.5 and 3 should be interpreted in calculations as 2.50 and 3.00, respectively. Significant figures are reviewed in Appendix B.3.

1.2 | DISPLACEMENT; AVERAGE VELOCITY

Quantitative discussions of motion are based on measurements and calculations of *positions*, *displacements*, *velocities*, and *accelerations*. In this and the following two sections, we use simple examples to introduce these concepts for motion along a straight line; we give their extensions to curved paths in the next chapter. We consider only *translational* motion, in which every part of an object moves in the same direction, and there is no rotation. Rotation will be discussed in Chapter Five.

The average velocity is defined in terms of the *displacement*, or the change in the position of an object that occurs in a specified interval of time. To illustrate what this means, suppose that a car is moving north along a straight highway with marker posts every 100 m, and that it is observed to pass one of these posts every 5 s, as in Fig. 1.2a. During any one of these 5-s intervals, the displacement is 100 m; in a 10-s interval, it is 200 m; and so on.

The displacement of an object is not the same as the distance it has traveled. Suppose you walk 10 m north, and then turn around and walk 10 m south. You have walked a total distance of 20 m. However, your displacement is the net change in your position, or zero in this case.

Displacements have a direction as well as a magnitude. The displacements in successive time intervals for the car in Fig. 1.2 are all directed along the highway, or north. Specifying the direction is simple for motion along a straight path. It becomes a bit more complex with curved paths.

The *average velocity* of the car during a specific time interval is the displacement divided by the time elapsed:

$$\text{average velocity} = \frac{\text{displacement}}{\text{time elapsed}}$$

The average velocity is proportional to the displacement, and it has the same direction. This definition is illustrated by the following example.

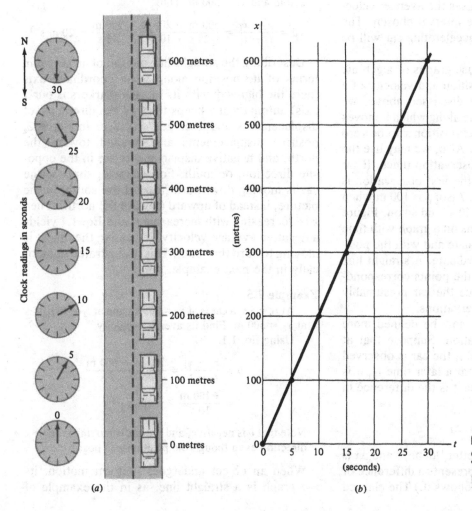

Figure 1.2. (a) The position of a car as observed at 5-s intervals. The speedometer reading is constant. (b) A graph of the position *x* versus time *t*.

Example 1.3

What is the average velocity of the car in Fig. 1.2a during the interval that the clock reading changes from 10 s to 25 s?

From the figure, we see that the car travels 500 m − 200 m = 300 m during the 15-s period, so

$$\text{average velocity} = \frac{300 \text{ m}}{15 \text{ s}} = 20 \text{ m s}^{-1}$$

The direction of the average velocity is northward.

Because the car in this example moves equal distances in equal times, the average velocity will be the same no matter what time interval is chosen. In this situation the motion is said to be *uniform*, and the driver will observe the speedometer reading to remain constant. Motion that is not uniform is said to be *accelerated*. In such cases the average velocity does depend on the time interval chosen. The speedometer reading of an accelerating car will be changing in time.

Often it is convenient to use graphs or algebraic formulas to describe the position and velocity of a moving object. For the car discussed above, we may designate the straight line along which it moves as an ''x axis'' and choose its position x to be zero at the post marked 0 metres. Also, we may use the symbol t to represent the observation times. If we arbitrarily take t = 0 when the first observation is made, then x is zero at t = 0. Also, x is 100 m when t = 5 s, x is 200 m when t = 10 s, and so on. Figure 1:2b shows these observations on a graph with time t along the horizontal coordinate and with the position x along the vertical coordinate. A straight line has been drawn connecting the points corresponding to the observations, since the car presumably moves steadily between observations.

The average velocity can now be defined more symbolically using this notation. Suppose that at some time which we will call t_1 the car is observed to be at position x_1 and that at a later time t_2, it is located at x_2. The displacement is the difference in positions,

$$\Delta x = x_2 - x_1$$

(The symbol Δ is the Greek letter ''delta,'' and Δx is read ''delta x.'' Δ usually represents a difference or change of the quantity that follows it.) The elapsed

time between the observations is the difference

$$\Delta t = t_2 - t_1$$

In this notation, the average velocity $\bar{v}$ is the displacement divided by the elapsed time,

$$\bar{v} = \frac{\Delta x}{\Delta t} = \frac{x_2 - x_1}{t_2 - t_1} \tag{1.1}$$

Note that this definition of the average velocity holds whether or not $\bar{v}$ is constant in time.

We now repeat the preceding example to show how this notation is used.

Example 1.4

Using Eq. 1.1, again find the average velocity of the car in Fig. 1.2 during the period from t = 10 to 25 s.

Here t_1 is 10 s and t_2 is 25 s; from the graph, x_1 = 200 m and x_2 = 500 m. Thus

$$\bar{v} = \frac{x_2 - x_1}{t_2 - t_1} = \frac{500 \text{ m} - 200 \text{ m}}{25 \text{ s} - 10 \text{ s}} = \frac{300 \text{ m}}{15 \text{ s}} = 20 \text{ m s}^{-1}$$

Describing the straight-line motion of an object in terms of its position along some coordinate axis (here the highway with its labeled markers is our x axis) automatically keeps track of the directions of displacements and average velocities. In Fig. 1.2, positive displacements are directed toward the north, and negative displacements are in the opposite direction, or south. For example, suppose the car is moving downward (toward the south) in the picture, instead of upward (toward the north). Then x is decreasing with increasing t, and Eq. 1.1 yields a negative average velocity, indicating the object is moving toward the south. This is illustrated numerically in the next example.

Example 1.5

At t_1 = 5 s, a car is at x_1 = 600 m; and at t_2 = 15 s, it is at x_2 = 500 m. Find its average velocity.

Using Eq. 1.1,

$$\bar{v} = \frac{x_2 - x_1}{t_2 - t_1} = \frac{500 \text{ m} - 600 \text{ m}}{15 \text{ s} - 5 \text{ s}}$$

$$= \frac{-100 \text{ m}}{10 \text{ s}} = -10 \text{ m s}^{-1}$$

Note that $\bar{v}$ is negative, and the car is moving in the −x direction even though the position x is positive.

When an object undergoes uniform motion, its x–t graph is a straight line, as in the example of

Fig. 1.2. If the motion is accelerated, the graph is not a straight line, and the average velocity depends on the particular time interval chosen. For example, in Fig. 1.3, a car starting from rest travels a short distance in the first second and a longer distance in the next second as it speeds up. In this situation the average velocity will be less in the first second of the motion than in later seconds. This is illustrated by the following example.

Example 1.6

A car moves as shown in Fig. 1.3. Find its average velocity from $t = 0$ to $t = 1$ s and from $t = 1$ to $t = 2$ s.

To calculate the average velocities, we need the positions at $t = 0$, 1, and 2 s. From Fig. 1.3, these are 0, 1,

and 4 m, respectively. From $t = 0$ to 1 s, the average velocity is

$$\bar{v} = \frac{\Delta x}{\Delta t} = \frac{1 \text{ m} - 0 \text{ m}}{1 \text{ s} - 0 \text{ s}} = 1 \text{ m s}^{-1}$$

From $t = 1$ to 2 s,

$$\bar{v} = \frac{\Delta x}{\Delta t} = \frac{4 \text{ m} - 1 \text{ m}}{2 \text{ s} - 1 \text{ s}} = 3 \text{ m s}^{-1}$$

As anticipated, the average velocity is greater in the later time interval because the car is accelerating.

We see later in this chapter that sometimes we can describe the motion of an object by an algebraic equation. The use of such an equation is illustrated in the next example.

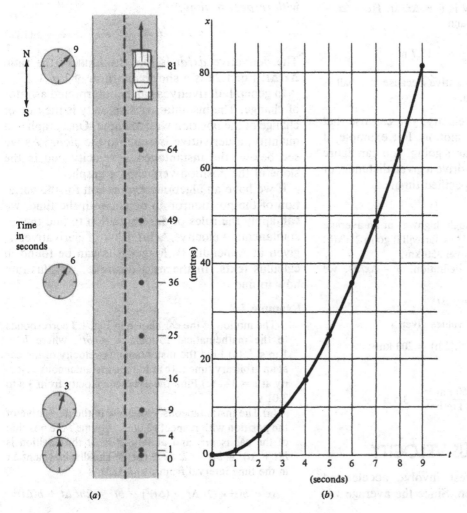

Figure 1.3. (a) The positions of an accelerating car at 1-s intervals are represented by solid circles. (b) The position–time graph for the car.

Example 1.7

A ball is dropped from a 50-m tall building at time $t = 0$ s. Its height x above the ground at a time t after it is released is given by the formula $x = (50 \text{ m}) - (4.9 \text{ m s}^{-2})t^2$. (a) When will the ball land? (b) What is its average velocity during the fall?

(a) We must substitute $x = 0$ to find the time t when the ball lands. Replacing x by 0, $x = (50 \text{ m}) - (4.9 \text{ m s}^{-2})t^2$ becomes

$$0 = (50 \text{ m}) - (4.9 \text{ m s}^{-2})t^2$$

Solving for t^2,

$$t^2 = \frac{50 \text{ m}}{4.9 \text{ m s}^{-2}} = 10.20 \text{ s}^2$$

Taking the square root, we have two solutions, $t = 3.19$ s and $t = -3.19$ s. The ball must land *after* it is released, so $t = 3.19$ s is the correct solution.

(b) The average velocity is $\bar{v} = \Delta x/\Delta t$. Here $\Delta x = (0 \text{ m}) - (50 \text{ m}) = -50$ m, and

$$\bar{v} = \frac{\Delta x}{\Delta t} = \frac{-50 \text{ m}}{3.19 \text{ s}} = -15.7 \text{ m s}^{-1}$$

The average velocity is negative because the ball is moving in the $-x$ direction.

If you know the average velocity, you can use that information to discuss the motion. For example, if you know how fast your car is going, you can figure out how long it will take to drive a given distance, or how far you can go in a specified time.

Example 1.8

A car moves along a straight highway at an average velocity of 100 km h^{-1}. (a) How far will it go in 2 h? (b) How long will it take to travel 350 km?

(a) Using the velocity definition, $\bar{v} = \Delta x/\Delta t$, we solve for Δx:

$$\Delta x = \bar{v}\ \Delta t$$

Substituting the numerical values given,

$$\Delta x = (100 \text{ km h}^{-1})(2 \text{ h}) = 200 \text{ km}$$

(b) From the definition,

$$\Delta t = \frac{\Delta x}{\bar{v}} = \frac{350 \text{ km}}{100 \text{ km h}^{-1}} = 3.5 \text{ h}$$

1.3 | INSTANTANEOUS VELOCITY

Most situations of interest involve accelerated rather than uniform motion. Since the average ve-

locity depends on the time interval if the motion is accelerated, it is often more useful to characterize the motion by the *instantaneous velocity*—the velocity at a particular instant in time. For example, when we say that an accelerating car is moving at 10 m s^{-1}, we are referring to its instantaneous velocity at the present moment.

A more rigorous definition of the instantaneous velocity v is that it is the limit of the average velocity $\bar{v} = \Delta x/\Delta t$ as Δt approaches zero. In the mathematical notation, this is written as

$$v = \lim_{\Delta t \to 0} \frac{\Delta x}{\Delta t} \qquad (1.2)$$

This equation is the definition of the *derivative* of x with respect to t, dx/dt. Thus the instantaneous velocity of an object is the derivative of its position with respect to time,

$$v = \frac{dx}{dt} \qquad (1.2a)$$

The derivative dx/dt is just the limit of the ratio $\Delta x/\Delta t$; Eq. 1.2a is a shorthand form of Eq. 1.2.

In general, derivatives can be interpreted as rates of change. The instantaneous velocity is the rate of change of the position with the time. On a graph of a quantity, a derivative is equal to the *slope*. As we see below, the instantaneous velocity equals the slope of the position-versus-time graph.

If we have an algebraic expression for the variation of the position of an object with the time, we can apply the rules of differentiation to find the instantaneous velocity. A brief list of derivatives is given in Appendix B; longer lists can be found in calculus texts. In the next example, we illustrate how to find v.

Example 1.9

The motion of the car shown in Fig. 1.3 corresponds to the mathematical formula $x = bt^2$, where $b = 1$ m s^{-2}. (a) Find the instantaneous velocity of the car at an arbitrary time t. (b) Find the instantaneous velocity at $t = 3$ s. (c) Find the average velocity from 3 s to 3.01 s.

(a) The instantaneous velocity v is the derivative of the position with respect to time. At time t the position of the car is bt^2, and at time $t + \Delta t$ the position is $b(t + \Delta t)^2 = b[t^2 + 2t\ \Delta t + (\Delta t)^2]$. The displacement Δx in the time interval from t to $t + \Delta t$ is

$$\Delta x = b[t^2 + 2t\ \Delta t + (\Delta t)^2] - bt^2 = 2bt\ \Delta t + b(\Delta t)^2$$

Thus the average velocity over this time interval is

$$\bar{v} = \frac{\Delta x}{\Delta t} = \frac{2bt\,\Delta t + b(\Delta t)^2}{\Delta t} = 2bt + b\,\Delta t$$

If we take the limit as $\Delta t \to 0$, then $b\,\Delta t \to 0$, and we find that the instantaneous velocity at t is

$$v = 2bt$$

The same result is found immediately if we use Eq. B.22 in Appendix B, $(d/dt)t^n = nt^{n-1}$; with $n = 2$, $(d/dt)t^2 = 2t$. (The factor b just multiplies the derivative of t^2.) From now on we will use differentiation formulas rather than working from the definition of the derivative.

(b) Substituting $t = 3$ s in $v = 2bt$, the instantaneous velocity at that time is

$$v = 2(1 \text{ m s}^{-2})(3 \text{ s}) = 6 \text{ m s}^{-1}$$

(c) When $t = 3$ s, the car is located at $x = bt^2 = (1 \text{ m s}^{-2})(3 \text{ s})^2 = 9$ m. At $t = 3.01$ s, $x = (1 \text{ m s}^{-2})(3.01 \text{ s})^2 = 9.0601$ m. Thus the average velocity $\bar{v}$ from 3 s to 3.01 s is

$$\bar{v} = \frac{9.0601 \text{ m} - 9 \text{ m}}{3.01 \text{ s} - 3 \text{ s}} = 6.01 \text{ m s}^{-1}$$

The average velocity for the small time interval of 0.01 s is very close to the instantaneous velocity at $t = 3$ s, $v = 6$ m s^{-1}. In fact, for the shorter time interval from 3s to 3.001 s, we find that $\bar{v}$ is 6.001 m s^{-1}, even closer to the instantaneous value. This is what we expect from the definition of v.

Like the displacement and the average velocity, the instantaneous velocity can be either positive or negative. Positive values correspond to motion toward increasing x, or in the $+x$ direction. If v is negative, the object is moving in the $-x$ direction.

From now on, when we refer to the velocity or any other rate of change, we mean the instantaneous value, unless we use the word "average" explicitly. Note that the distinction between the average and instantaneous velocity disappears for the special case of uniform motion.

Many common words have different or more restricted meanings to physicists. In everyday usage, *speed* and *velocity* have the same meaning. However, in physics texts, a distinction is made between the two terms. The speed is defined as the magnitude of the instantaneous velocity, so it is always positive or zero. An equivalent definition of speed is the distance traveled divided by the elapsed time.

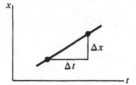

Figure 1.4. The x–t graph for an object undergoing uniform motion. The slope of the line is defined to be $\Delta x/\Delta t$, which is the velocity.

The difference between the velocity and the speed is illustrated by the next example.

Example 1.10

A man walks 10 km due east in 2 h. He then walks 10 km due west in 2 h. For the total 4-h trip, find his (a) average velocity; (b) average speed.

(a) After 4 hours, the man has returned to his starting point. Thus his displacement is zero, and his average velocity is $\bar{v} = \Delta x/\Delta t = (0 \text{ km})/(4 \text{ h}) = 0$.

(b) The man has walked 10 km + 10 km = 20 km. His average speed is the distance traveled divided by the elapsed time, $(20 \text{ km})/(4 \text{ h}) = 5$ km h^{-1}.

Graphical Interpretation of Velocity

A position-versus-time graph provides direct information about the velocity. As we have seen, a straight-line graph corresponds to a constant velocity or uniform motion, while a curved graph corresponds to a changing velocity. Furthermore, the velocity is equal to the slope of the x–t graph. In the straight-line graph of Fig. 1.4, the slope of the line is defined to be $\Delta x/\Delta t$, which is just the velocity. In the curved x–t graph of Fig. 1.5, the slope at point P is defined to be that of the straight-line tangent to the curve at P. The velocity at P is equal to the slope, since the curve and the tangent line have the same rate of increase with time at that point in the motion.

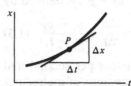

Figure 1.5. The slope of the x–t curve at P is equal to the slope $\Delta x/\Delta t$ of the straight-line tangent to the curve at P. The velocity at P is equal to the slope of the curve at that point.

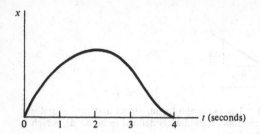

Figure 1.6.   Position-versus-time graph of an object (Example 1.11). The velocity is greatest where x is changing most rapidly.

All this is not as difficult or abstract as it may seem. We know that if x is increasing, the velocity is positive. When x is decreasing, v is negative. The faster x changes, the greater the velocity. This is easy to see on a graph, as in the next example.

Example 1.11

Figure 1.6 shows the x–t graph for a moving object. At what time does the object have (a) the largest positive velocity; (b) zero velocity; (c) the most negative velocity?

(a) At $t = 0$, the x–t curve is rising more rapidly than at any other time. The slope and v are positive and have their largest positive value at that time.

(b) At $t = 2$ s, x has its greatest value. The curve is flat there; x is neither increasing or decreasing. Hence the slope and v are zero.

(c) After $t = 2$ s, the x is decreasing, so v is negative. At $t = 3$ s, the curve is falling most rapidly, so v has its most negative value.

1.4 | ACCELERATION

Like the position, the velocity can change with time. The rate at which the velocity changes is the *acceleration*. Again we can discuss either the average or instantaneous rate of change.

The *average acceleration* $\bar{a}$ from time t_1 to t_2, if the velocity changes by $\Delta v = v_2 - v_1$, is defined by

$$\bar{a} = \frac{\text{change in velocity}}{\text{time elapsed}} = \frac{\Delta v}{\Delta t} = \frac{v_2 - v_1}{t_2 - t_1} \quad (1.3)$$

If we measure velocity in metres per second and time in seconds, $\bar{a}$ will have the units of metres per second per second (usually abbreviated as m s^{-2} and read as "metres per second squared"). An average acceleration of 1 m s^{-2} corresponds to an

average increase in the velocity of 1 m s^{-1} each second. We will illustrate this definition with an example.

Example 1.12

A car accelerates from rest to 30 m s^{-1} in 10 s. What is its average acceleration?

From the definition,

$$\bar{a} = \frac{\Delta v}{\Delta t} = \frac{30 \text{ m s}^{-1} - 0}{10 \text{ s}} = 3 \text{ m s}^{-2}$$

This corresponds to an increase in the velocity of 3 m s^{-1} in each second of the 10-s time interval.

The *instantaneous acceleration a* is defined as a limit much as the instantaneous velocity is defined. The instantaneous acceleration at time t is the derivative of the velocity with respect to time at that instant,

$$a = \lim_{\Delta t \to 0} \frac{\Delta v}{\Delta t} = \frac{dv}{dt} \quad (1.4)$$

On a graph of the velocity of an object versus time, the instantaneous acceleration is equal to the slope of the curve. These ideas are illustrated in the following examples.

Example 1.13

An object moves according to the formula $x = (b + ct^3)$. What is the instantaneous acceleration at time t?

The instantaneous acceleration is defined as the derivative of the velocity, so we must first find v. From the definition,

$$v = \frac{dx}{dt} = \frac{d}{dt}(b + ct^3) = 3ct^2$$

Then

$$a = \frac{dv}{dt} = \frac{d}{dt}(3ct^2) = 6ct$$

This is the instantaneous acceleration at time t.

Example 1.14

Figure 1.7 shows the velocity-versus-time graph for a car. Describe its acceleration qualitatively.

From A to B, the velocity is increasing, the slope is positive, and the car is accelerating. However, the slope is becoming progressively smaller, so the acceleration is decreasing. From B to C, the velocity is constant and the slope and the acceleration are zero. From C to D, the velocity is decreasing, so the acceleration is

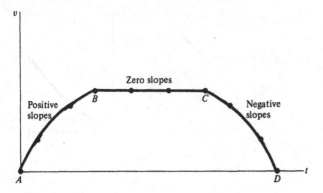

Figure 1.7. The velocity-versus-time graph for a car. The slope and acceleration are positive from A to B, zero from B to C, and negative from C to D.

negative. This *deceleration* increases in magnitude as the car slows.

It is important to realize that *the signs or directions of the velocity and acceleration need not be the same.* For an object moving in a straight line, the acceleration can be in the same direction as the velocity, or opposite to it. If we are in a car that is moving along a straight road with an increasing speed, our acceleration is forward, or in the *same* direction as the velocity. If we have chosen our $+x$ direction so v is positive, then a is also positive in this case. However, if the car is slowing, then the acceleration is in the direction *opposite* to the velocity, and it is negative.

Example 1.15

The velocity of a slowing car is given by the equation

$$v = (20 \text{ m s}^{-1}) - (3 \text{ m s}^{-2})t$$

Find the average acceleration from $t = 1$ s to $t = 3$ s.
At $t = 1$ s, the velocity is

$$v = (20 \text{ m s}^{-1}) - (3 \text{ m s}^{-2})(1 \text{ s}) = 17 \text{ m s}^{-1}$$

At $t = 3$ s, the velocity is

$$v = (20 \text{ m s}^{-1}) - (3 \text{ m s}^{-2})(3 \text{ s}) = 11 \text{ m s}^{-1}$$

Thus the average acceleration is

$$\bar{a} = \frac{\Delta v}{\Delta t} = \frac{11 \text{ m s}^{-1} - 17 \text{ m s}^{-1}}{3 \text{ s} - 1 \text{ s}} = -3 \text{ m s}^{-2}$$

The negative sign indicates that $\bar{a}$ is in the $-x$ direction, or opposite to the velocity.

If you know the acceleration of an object, you can determine the change in its velocity.

Example 1.16

A rock falls off a cliff and moves with a constant acceleration of 9.8 m s^{-2}. How fast will it be moving after 5 s?

The acceleration is constant, so $a = \Delta v/\Delta t$. Solving for Δv,

$$\Delta v = a \, \Delta t = (9.8 \text{ m s}^{-2})(5 \text{ s}) = 49 \text{ m s}^{-1}$$

Since the rock was initially at rest, its velocity after 5 s is 49 m s^{-1}.

1.5 | FINDING THE MOTION OF AN OBJECT

So far we have calculated velocities from position changes and accelerations from velocity changes. However, it is often true that it is the acceleration of an object that is either measured or predicted theoretically, and we wish to know the corresponding velocity and position changes. For example, when an animal jumps vertically from the earth's surface, it is subject to a constant acceleration due to gravity, which determines the motion of the animal while it is off the ground. In this section, we see how to find the subsequent motion of an object given its acceleration and its initial position and velocity.

Consider an object initially moving with a velocity v_0. If the object undergoes a constant acceleration a for a time Δt, then from the definition of the acceleration, $a = \Delta v/\Delta t$, or $\Delta v = a \, \Delta t$. Hence the velocity has changed by an amount Δv to a value

$$v = v_0 + a \, \Delta t \qquad (1.5)$$

This result has an interesting and useful interpretation in terms of the acceleration-versus-time graph (Fig. 1.8a). The product of the height a and width Δt of the shaded rectangle is its area $a \, \Delta t$, which is equal to the velocity change. *Thus the change in velocity equals the area under the a–t graph over the time interval chosen.* The area is considered to be positive if it lies above the time axis and negative if it lies below. This result is quite general and is not restricted to constant acceleration situations.

Note that when we refer to the "area" in Fig. 1.8,

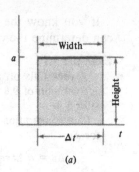
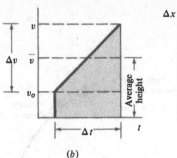
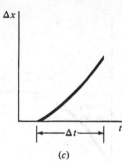

Figure 1.8. Motion with constant acceleration. (a) The acceleration a is constant over the time interval Δt. (b) The graph of $v = v_0 + a\,\Delta t$. The average velocity is $\bar{v} = \frac{1}{2}(v_0 + v)$. (c) The displacement-versus-time graph.

(a)   (b)   (c)

its dimensions are not the usual ones for area, length × length, or L^2. Rather, the dimension are those of $a\,\Delta t$, or $(L/T^2)(T) = L/T$, as expected for a velocity.

If we draw a graph of the velocity versus time as given by Eq. 1.5, we obtain a straight line (Fig. 1.8b). The average velocity for the time interval Δt is $\bar{v} = v_0 + \Delta v/2 = v_0 + (v - v_0)/2$, or

$$\bar{v} = \tfrac{1}{2}(v_0 + v) \qquad (1.6)$$

This displacement or change in position that occurs during the time interval Δt is related to the average velocity through the definition $\bar{v} = \Delta x/\Delta t$. Thus $\Delta x = \bar{v}\,\Delta t$, or

$$\Delta x = \tfrac{1}{2}(v_0 + v)\Delta t \qquad (1.7)$$

Alternatively, if we substitute $v = v_0 + a\,\Delta t$ in this equation, we find

$$\Delta x = v_0\,\Delta t + \tfrac{1}{2}a(\Delta t)^2 \qquad (1.8)$$

Similarly, we can rewrite Eq. 1.5 as $\Delta t = (v - v_0)/a$ and substitute for Δt in Eq. 1.7 to give

$$\Delta x = \tfrac{1}{2}(v_0 + v)\left(\frac{v - v_0}{a}\right) = \frac{v^2 - v_0^2}{2a}$$

or

$$v^2 = v_0^2 + 2a\,\Delta x \qquad (1.9)$$

Again, our algebraic results have a direct graphical correspondence. The shaded area under the v–t graph in Fig. 1.8b has an average height $\bar{v}\,\Delta t$, which is equal to Δx as given by Eq. 1.7. (Alternatively, the sum of the triangular and rectangular areas re-

duces to Eq. 1.8. See Problem 1-92.) *Thus the displacement is equal to the area under the* v-t *graph over the time interval* Δt. This is also true when the acceleration is not constant. As before, areas above the time axis are considered positive, and areas below are negative. Note that here the area has the dimensions of $v\,\Delta t$ or $(L/T)T = L$.

Equation 1.5 for the velocity and Eq. 1.8 for the displacement completely describe the motion of an object with a given initial velocity and position and a constant acceleration. Equations 1.6, 1.7, and 1.9 contain equivalent information, and are sometimes handy for solving problems. For example, Eq. 1.9 is useful when the initial and final velocity and acceleration are given but not the elapsed time. The constant acceleration formulas are listed in Table 1.3 and on the front endpapers for convenient reference. Their use is illustrated by the examples below and in the next section.

Example 1.17

A car initially at rest at a traffic light accelerates at 2 m s^{-2} when the light turns green. After 4 s, what are its velocity and position?

Since we know the acceleration a, the elapsed time Δt, and the initial velocity $v_0 = 0$, we can use Eqs. 1.5

TABLE 1.3
Motion with constant acceleration

$v = v_0 + a\,\Delta t$	(1.5)
$\Delta x = v_0\,\Delta t + \tfrac{1}{2}a(\Delta t)^2$	(1.8)
$\bar{v} = \tfrac{1}{2}(v_0 + v)$	(1.6)
$\Delta x = \tfrac{1}{2}(v_0 + v)\Delta t$	(1.7)
$v^2 = v_0^2 + 2a\,\Delta x$	(1.9)

and 1.8 to find the velocity and displacement. Thus

$$v = v_0 + a \, \Delta t = 0 + (2 \text{ m s}^{-2})(4 \text{ s}) = 8 \text{ m s}^{-1}$$
$$\Delta x = v_0 \, \Delta t + \tfrac{1}{2}a(\Delta t)^2 = 0 + \tfrac{1}{2}(2 \text{ m s}^{-2})(4 \text{ s})^2 = 16 \text{ m}$$

After 4 s the car has reached a velocity of 8 m s^{-1} and is 16 m from the light.

Note that we could also have found Δx from Eq. 1.7, using our result for v. Constant acceleration problems and physics problems in general can often be solved in more than one way.

Example 1.18

A car reaches a velocity of 20 m s^{-1} with an acceleration of 2 m s^2. How far will it travel while it is accelerating if it is (a) initially at rest; (b) initially moving at 10 m s^{-1}?

(a) Here we know the initial and final velocities as well as the acceleration. Equation 1.9 contains these known quantities plus the displacement Δx. Solving for Δx, with $a = 2$ m s^{-2}, $v = 20$ m s^{-1}, and $v_0 = 0$, we find

$$\Delta x = \frac{v^2 - v_0^2}{2a} = \frac{(20 \text{ m s}^{-1})^2}{2(2 \text{ m s}^{-2})} = 100 \text{ m}$$

We could also have solved this problem by using $v = v_0 + a \, \Delta t$ to find Δt and then substituting the elapsed time into Eq. 1.8. (The reader should work out this solution as an exercise.)

(b) Proceeding as above but with $v_0 = 10$ m s^{-1},

$$\Delta x = \frac{v^2 - v_0^2}{2a}$$
$$= \frac{(20 \text{ m s}^{-1})^2 - (10 \text{ m s}^{-1})^2}{2(2 \text{ m s}^{-2})} = 75 \text{ m}$$

The distance required to reach the desired velocity is shorter than in part (a) because the car is initially in motion.

Example 1.19

A car accelerates from rest with a constant acceleration of 2 m s^{-2} onto a highway where traffic is moving at a steady 24 m s^{-1}. (a) How long will it take for the car to reach a velocity of 24 m s^{-1}? (b) How far will it travel in that time? (c) The driver does not want the vehicle behind to come closer than 20 m nor force it to slow down. How large a break in traffic must the driver wait for?

(a) The time needed for the car to reach the velocity $v = 24$ m s^{-1} starting from rest satisfies $v = v_0 + a \, \Delta t$,

or

$$\Delta t = \frac{v - v_0}{a} = \frac{24 \text{ m s}^{-1}}{2 \text{ m s}^{-2}} = 12 \text{ s}$$

(b) Using Eq. 1.8, the distance traveled by the car in 12 s is

$$\Delta x = v_0 \, \Delta t + \tfrac{1}{2}a(\Delta t)^2$$
$$= 0 + \tfrac{1}{2}(2 \text{ m s}^{-2})(12 \text{ s})^2 = 144 \text{ m}$$

(c) The vehicle behind is moving at a constant velocity $v_0 = 24$ m s^{-1}, so $a = 0$. Using Eq. 1.8, in 12 s it moves a distance

$$\Delta x = v_0 \, \Delta t + \tfrac{1}{2}a(\Delta t)^2$$
$$= (24 \text{ m s}^{-1})(12 \text{ s}) + 0 = 288 \text{ m}$$

Since the entering car travels 144 m in this time, the oncoming vehicle gains $(288 - 144)$ m, or 144 m. If it is to come no closer than 20 m, then the break in traffic must be at least $(144 + 20)$ m, or 164 m.

The car in this example reaches 24 m s^{-1}, or about 86 km h^{-1} (54 mi h^{-1}) in 12 s, which is a fairly brisk acceleration. A less powerful car would take longer to reach this speed and would require a longer break in traffic.

The above examples illustrate the procedures for solving constant acceleration problems and physics problems in general. We identify which quantities are known and which are to be found and determine the equation or equations relating these quantities. If necessary, we then solve algebraically for one unknown in terms of known quantities. Numerical values are usually best substituted in the final step rather than at an earlier stage. This tends to minimize the arithmetic labor and also facilitates checking for errors.

A useful check on any problem is provided by the dimensions of the final result. If the unknown is a length, then the result should be in length units such as metres or kilometres; if not, an error has been made somewhere. Note, for example, that in parts (b) and (c) of Example 1.19 the time units cancel and the distances are in metres as required.

To summarize, we have found that given the initial position and velocity, we can find the velocity at a later time from the acceleration, and the position from the velocity. The equations listed in Table 1.3 can be used to find the motion of objects undergoing a constant acceleration. When the acceleration is not constant, the average acceleration may often be used in the constant acceleration equations to find an approximate description of the motion. We do this in analyzing vertical jumping in the Supplementary Topics at the end of this chapter. Alternatively, we can use integration techniques if we know an explicit formula for the acceleration. This is also considered in the Supplementary Topics.

1.6 | THE ACCELERATION OF GRAVITY AND FALLING OBJECTS

Until now, our discussion of motion has been based on definitions and their consequences. Specifically, we have considered the mathematical relationships arising from the definitions of velocity and acceleration, but we have made no statements about how the natural world works. However, to discuss the motion of falling objects, we must use some information first obtained by Galileo from careful experimental observations.

We know from everyday experience that unsupported objects tend to fall toward the ground. The speed at impact often increases if the distance dropped increases. Thus it is evident that falling objects undergo an acceleration, which we attribute to *gravity*, the gravitational attraction of the earth. Nevertheless, two essential aspects of this gravitational acceleration are not so readily observed.

Suppose gravity is the only factor affecting the motion of an object falling near the earth's surface, and air resistance is either absent or negligibly small. So long as the object's distance from the surface of the earth is small compared to the earth's radius, it is found that:

1   *The gravitational acceleration is the same for all falling objects*, no matter what their size or composition.
2   *The gravitational acceleration is constant*. It does not change as the object falls.

Neither of these statements squares entirely with our everyday experience. Coins fall faster than bits of paper, which contradicts statement 1. Objects dropped from great heights reach a maximum or *terminal* velocity, which contradicts statement 2. However, both these effects result from air resis-

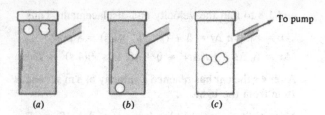

Figure 1.9.   (*a*) A coin and a piece of paper are released simultaneously from the top of a container. (*b*) If the container has air in it, the coin hits the bottom first. (*c*) If most of the air is pumped out of the container, both objects reach the bottom at the same time.

tance. A coin and scrap of paper fall together in a vacuum (Fig. 1.9), and an object falling at high altitude has a constant acceleration until entering the atmosphere.

The acceleration of gravity near the surface of the earth is denoted by g; it is approximately equal to

$$g = 9.8 \text{ m s}^{-2}$$

Small variations in g occur as a result of changes in latitude, elevation, and the density of local geological features.

In this chapter, we neglect such variations in g. In addition, except in the next example, we usually assume that air resistance is unimportant. This allows us to use the constant acceleration equations to find the motion of falling objects.

The next example illustrates that the signs or directions of the velocity and acceleration can be related in various ways.

Example 1.20
A sky diver steps out of an airplane. She falls with an increasing speed until she reaches a terminal (maximum) velocity and maintains that velocity for several seconds. Then she opens her parachute and gradually slows to a smaller terminal velocity. A few seconds later she lands on the ground. What is the direction of her acceleration during each phase of her motion?

The sky diver's initial acceleration after she has left the airplane is *downward* and equal in *magnitude* to g. Her velocity is also downward, so a is in the *same* direction as v. Gradually, as her speed increases, the air resistance increases. Her acceleration diminishes in magnitude but remains in the same direction until her speed is constant and a is zero. When she opens her chute, the air resistance increases again, and she begins to slow down. Her acceleration is now *opposite* to

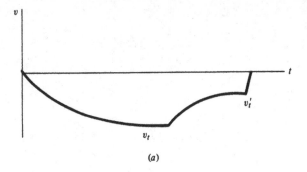

(a)

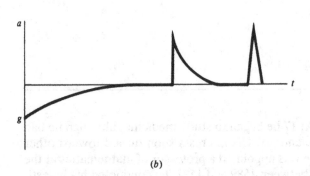

(b)

Figure 1.10. Example 1.20. (a) A sky diver steps out of a plane at $t = 0$. Her velocity increases in magnitude until a terminal velocity v_t is reached. Once her parachute opens, the increased air resistance reduces her velocity in magnitude to v_t'. Her velocity rapidly decreases in magnitude to zero once she touches the ground. (b) The corresponding acceleration.

her motion, or *upward*. Eventually her speed again becomes constant, and a is again zero. Finally, she reaches the ground, and her velocity is reduced to zero in a very short time. During this brief time interval, she experiences a large acceleration that is *upward*, or *opposite* to her downward motion.

In numerical problems, we frequently choose an origin and a $+x$ direction. In this example, if we take $x = 0$ at the ground and $+x$ to be upward, the position x is positive until the sky diver reaches the ground. Her velocity v is always downward or in the $-x$ direction, so it is always negative (Fig. 1.10). Her acceleration is downward or negative when she has just left the plane, but it is upward or positive during the periods when her motion is slowing.

In the next example, we use the constant acceleration equations to predict the motion of a falling object when air resistance is neglected.

Example 1.21

A ball is dropped from a window 84 m above the ground (Fig. 1.11). (a) When does the ball strike the ground? (b) What is the velocity of the ball when it strikes the ground?

In this type of problem, we can choose the coordinate system so that the positive x direction is either up or down. Let us choose positive values of x in the upward direction.

Since the ball is dropped with zero initial velocity, $v_0 = 0$. The gravitational acceleration is constant and in the $-x$ direction, so the equations of Table 1.3 can be applied using $a = -g = -9.8$ m s^{-2}.

(a) The ball strikes the ground when $\Delta x = -84$ m. This happens after a time interval Δt, which satisfies

$$\Delta x = \tfrac{1}{2}a(\Delta t)^2$$

or

$$(\Delta t)^2 = \frac{2 \, \Delta x}{a}$$

Thus

$$\Delta t = \sqrt{\frac{2 \, \Delta x}{a}} = \sqrt{\frac{2(-84 \text{ m})}{-9.8 \text{ m s}^{-2}}} = 4.14 \text{ s}$$

The positive root is used because the ball hits the ground after it is released, not before.

(b) Using Eq. 1.5 with $\Delta t = 4.14$ s and $v_0 = 0$,

$$v = a \, \Delta t = (-9.8 \text{ m s}^{-2})(4.14 \text{ s}) = -40.6 \text{ m s}^{-1}$$

This example can also be done when the $+x$ direction is chosen to be downward. Then the accel-

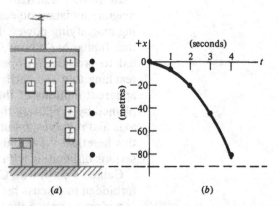

(a)   (b)

Figure 1.11. (a) A freely falling ball released with no initial velocity. Note that it falls through successively larger distances in each second. (b) The x–t graph for the ball in Example 1.21, taking $x = 0$ at the window.

Galileo was born in Pisa. At 17 he began to study medicine, although he had also shown talent in music and art. His interests soon turned toward other branches of science, and he was appointed a professor of mathematics at the University of Pisa. There, between 1589 and 1592, he conducted his investigations of motion, which are the basis for this chapter.

The Greek philosopher Aristotle (384–322 B.C.) had taught that heavy objects fall faster than light ones. Galileo performed a series of experiments on objects rolling down smooth inclines and concluded that, in the ideal frictionless case, all objects have the same acceleration. Furthermore, he showed that the distance varies as the time squared, which implies that the acceleration is constant. Galileo is considered to have shown the importance of experimentation in science.

In 1608, Galileo heard that two spectacle lenses used together would magnify a distant object, and he soon built a series of telescopes of increasing magnifying power. He discovered that our moon has mountain ranges, that Jupiter has moons, and that the sun has spots. But his observations also led to problems. Copernicus (1473–1543) had earlier doubted Aristotle's teaching that the earth is the center of the universe. He showed that the apparent motions of the sun, stars, and planets could be most simply explained by supposing that the earth itself is a planet that rotates daily on its axis and revolves annually about the sun. Galileo's observations supported this heretical view that the earth is not unique. Consequently, he ran into serious difficulties with the authorities.

Galileo's clash with Church dogma lasted for nearly two decades. Initially forbidden to discuss his ideas, he was later ordered to describe the Copernican ideas as only a theory. However, Galileo's analysis and presentation of the existing facts were so complete and convincing that, at age 70, he was tried for disregarding the earlier order. After the trial, he was kept under house arrest for the remaining 12 years of his life.

eration is $a = g = +9.8$ m s^{-2}, and the ball hits the ground when $\Delta x = +84$ m. With these values, the same result is found for Δt. The velocity v when the ball hits the ground is positive because $+x$ is now downward. The choice of the positive x direction has no effect on our physical results, but we must correctly interpret the signs in our answers.

Objects Thrown Straight Up
The motion of a ball or other object thrown straight up raises some interesting and potentially confusing points. The ball experiences the constant downward gravitational acceleration throughout its motion. This is true while the ball is going up, at the instant it reaches its greatest height, and as it is coming down.

However, the velocity is continually changing. Initially it is directed upward. As the ball rises, the magnitude of v uniformly decreases, until the velocity becomes zero at the instant the ball is at its highest point. The ball then begins to move downward, with v steadily increasing in magnitude.

One way to understand the fact that $v = 0$ at the highest point is to note that when a quantity has a maximum or minimum value, its rate of change or derivative is zero. Thus the maximum value of x occurs where $v = dx/dt = 0$. Alternatively, if we take the upward direction to be positive, v is positive on the way up and negative on the way down. Since v changes sign, it has to be zero at some instant. This occurs, in fact, when the ball is at its highest point.

The fact that v = 0 *at the highest point reached is the key to solving many vertical motion problems.*

The motion of an object thrown upward is illustrated by the v–t and x–t graphs in Fig. 1.12. At A the object is moving upward, in the $+x$ direction. At B it is instantaneously at rest at the highest point in its motion, and at C it is moving downward. Thus, v is initially positive, then zero for an instant, and negative afterward. By contrast, *the acceleration is equal to the slope of the* v-t *graph, or to* −g, *at all times.*

We can see from Fig. 1.12 that the motion is *symmetric* about its highest point (point B). The upward velocity 1 s before the peak and the downward velocity 1 s after the peak have the same magnitude. Consequently the time the object takes to traverse

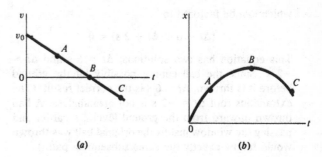

Figure 1.12. (a) v–t and (b) x–t graphs for an object thrown straight up from $x = 0$. The velocity is zero at the instant the object reaches its greatest height (point B), but the acceleration is always $-g$.

any given portion of the path will be the same going up and coming down.

These features of the motion are illustrated by the next example.

Example 1.22
A ball is thrown upward at 19.6 m s^{-1} from a window 58.8 m above the ground. (a) How high does it go? (b) When does it reach its highest point? (c) When does it strike the ground?

Again choosing $+x$ upward, $v_0 = 19.6$ m s^{-1} and $a = -g = -9.8$ m s^{-2}.

(a) As the ball rises, its velocity decreases uniformly until $v = 0$ at the peak; we want to find the height at which this occurs. From Eq. 1.9, using $v = 0$,

$$\Delta x = \frac{v^2 - v_0^2}{2a} = \frac{0 - (19.6 \text{ m s}^{-1})^2}{2(-9.8 \text{ m s}^{-2})} = 19.6 \text{ m}$$

Thus the ball reaches a maximum height 19.6 m above the window, or $(58.8 + 19.6)$ m = 78.4 m above the ground.

(b) Using Eq. 1.5 and the fact that $v = 0$ at the peak height,

$$t = \frac{v - v_0}{a} = \frac{0 - 19.6 \text{ m s}^{-1}}{-9.8 \text{ m s}^{-2}} = 2 \text{ s}$$

The peak is reached in 2 s.

(c) The ball hits the ground when $\Delta x = -58.8$ m, or after a time interval Δt, which satisfies

$$\Delta x = v_0 \Delta t + \tfrac{1}{2}a(\Delta t)^2$$
$$-58.8 \text{ m} = (19.6 \text{ m s}^{-1}) \Delta t + \tfrac{1}{2}(-9.8 \text{ m s}^{-2})(\Delta t)^2$$

Dividing by 4.9 m s^{-2} and rearranging terms, this becomes

$$(\Delta t)^2 - (4 \text{ s})(\Delta t) - 12 \text{ s}^2 = 0$$

which can be factored to

$$(\Delta t - 6 \text{ s})(\Delta t + 2 \text{ s}) = 0$$

This equation has two solutions, $\Delta t = 6$ s and $\Delta t = -2$ s. Since the ball cannot possibly hit the ground before it is thrown, $\Delta t = 6$ s is the correct result. (The extraneous root $\Delta t = -2$ s is not meaningless. A ball thrown upward from the ground level 2 s earlier and passing the window just as the original ball was thrown would follow exactly the same subsequent path.)

1.7 | MODELS IN PHYSICS

Real problems sometimes are so complex that an exact solution is either impossible or else requires very difficult measurements or calculations. A rough estimate of the correct solution can often be found with a *mathematical model* obtained by making simplifying assumptions and approximations.

We used a model in the preceding section when we considered falling objects and neglected air resistance. For a rock or a coin falling at low speeds, this is a good approximation. However, if the speed is high, air resistance is more important, and a model that neglects it can be misleading in its predictions. Also, as we saw, it would be very inaccurate to ignore air resistance for something as light as a scrap of paper.

Mathematical models can show what factors are important in a problem and provide a qualitative understanding that may not be obtainable from a more exact approach. Their predictions may indicate whether a more elaborate effort is worth attempting and may suggest lines of attack for such an effort. However, textbooks—including this one—and other sources are not always fully explicit in stating their assumptions and in distinguishing models from exact treatments. Thus a moderate amount of skepticism is a healthy thing to acquire.

SUMMARY
Physical quantities are stated in terms of units. To convert units from one system to another, we multiply by 1 and cancel units as though they were algebraic quantities.

The motion of an object along a straight line is described by its position, velocity, and acceleration. The velocity is the time rate of change of the position. The average velocity is the change in position or displacement divided by the elapsed time,

$$\bar{v} = \frac{\Delta x}{\Delta t}$$

The instantaneous velocity is the limit of the average velocity $\bar{v} = \Delta x / \Delta t$ as Δt approaches zero, or the derivative of x with respect to t,

$$v = \frac{dx}{dt}$$

Similarly, the average acceleration is the velocity change divided by the elapsed time,

$$\bar{a} = \frac{\Delta v}{\Delta t}$$

The instantaneous acceleration is the derivative of v with respect to t,

$$a = \frac{dv}{dt}$$

On an x–t graph, the slope is equal to the instantaneous velocity; on a v–t graph, the slope is equal to the instantaneous acceleration.

Often the acceleration can be calculated theoretically or measured experimentally. If the initial position and velocity are known, their later values can then be found from the acceleration. In the special case where the acceleration is constant, we have found the equations of motion. These are listed in Table 1.3 for convenient reference. Whether or not the acceleration is constant, the displacement equals the area under the v–t graph, and the velocity change equals the area under the a–t graph. Areas above the time axis are positive, and areas below the time axis are negative.

Objects falling without appreciable air resistance near the earth's surface all experience a common, constant acceleration g. An object initially thrown upward also has this acceleration. Its velocity steadily decreases in magnitude until it becomes zero at the highest point reached.

Checklist
Define or explain:

dimensions	m.k.s. system
standards	c.g.s. system
units	British units
S.I.	random errors

systematic errors	average acceleration
significant figures	instantaneous
translational motion	acceleration
displacement	constant acceleration
average velocity	formulas
uniform motion	gravitational
accelerated motion	acceleration
instantaneous velocity	terminal velocity
slope	mathematical model

REVIEW QUESTIONS

(Answers are given in this chapter just before the supplementary topics.)

Q1-1 The officially recognized set of units for scientific work is the _____ .

Q1-2 Experimental data usually contain _____ and _____ errors.

Q1-3 The best way to convert units is to multiply by a factor of _____ for each unit that must be converted.

Q1-4 The change in position is called the _____ .

Q1-5 The average velocity is the ratio _____ / _____ .

Q1-6 The instantaneous velocity is the average velocity evaluated for _____ .

Q1-7 The average acceleration is the _____ divided by the _____ .

Q1-8 On an $x-t$ graph, the slope equals the _____ .

Q1-9 On a $v-t$ graph, the slope equals the _____ .

Q1-10 The velocity change equals the area under the _____ graph.

Q1-11 The displacement equals the area under the _____ graph.

Q1-12 In air, a rock falls faster than a feather because of _____ .

Q1-13 When an object thrown straight upward reaches its greatest height, its velocity is _____ and its acceleration is _____ .

EXERCISES

The students to ~~...~~ the exercises
~~...~~ nis o~~...~~ general under-
~~cepts be~~fore attempting the prob-
to most of the odd-numbered exer-

cises and problems are given at the end of the book, usually to three significant figures. If your answers differ slightly in the last place, this may be due to differences in rounding off intermediate results, rather than to an error in your work. Solutions to half the odd-numbered exercises appear in the Study Guide. Exercises and problems preceded by a [c] may require the use of calculus.

Section 1.1 | Measurements, Standards, Units, and Errors

1-1 An acre is 43,560 ft^2. How large is this in square metres (m^2)?

1-2 Convert 40 mi h^{-1} to metres per second (m s^{-1}).

1-3 A gallon is 231 cubic inches (in.^{3}), and a litre is 1000 cm^3. How many litres are there in a gallon?

1-4 A furlong is 220 yards, and a fortnight is 14 days. If a snail moves at 2 m h^{-1}, what is this in furlongs per fortnight?

1-5 A cell membrane is 70 angstrom (Å) units thick. If an angstrom unit is 10^{-10} m, what is the membrane thickness in (a) metres; (b) micrometres?

1-6 If two quantities have different dimensions, can they be (a) multiplied; (b) added? Give examples to support your answers.

1-7 In the United States land is measured in acres (1 acre = 43,560 ft^2). In most other countries it is measured in hectares (1 hectare = 10^4 m^2). How large is a 100-acre farm in hectares?

1-8 The volumes of reservoirs are sometimes measured in acre-feet; that is, a lake with an area of 1 acre and an average depth of 1 ft contains 1 acre-foot of water. If a lake has an area of 100 acres an average depth of 20 ft, find its volume (a) in acre-feet; (b) in cubic feet; (c) in cubic metres (1 acre = 43,560 ft^2).

1-9 Suppose you wanted to know the area of a rectangular room and had a cloth tape measure available to determine its dimensions. What are some random and systematic errors that might affect your result?

1-10 A driver wishes to check the speedometer by traveling at a constant speed along a highway with markers placed every kilometre and having a passenger note the time intervals with a wristwatch. Discuss the random and systematic errors involved.

1-11 If a dollar is 7.2 francs and a 0.75-litre bottle of wine costs 20 francs, how much does it cost in dollars per quart?

1-12 A U.S. gallon is 231 in.³. An Imperial gallon, used sometimes in England and in the British Commonwealth, is 277.42 in.³. In Niagara Falls, New York, gasoline is $1.08 (U.S.) per U.S. gallon. Across the international bridge in Niagara Falls, Ontario, gasoline is $1.80 (Canadian) per Imperial gallon. If $1.00 (Canadian) = $0.72 (U.S.), on which side is gasoline cheaper, and by what percentage?

Section 1.2 | Displacement; Average Velocity

1-13 A car travels 30 km in 45 min on a straight highway. What is its average velocity in kilometres per hour (km h⁻¹)?

1-14 A pilot wishes to fly 2000 km in 4 h. What average velocity in metres per second is required to accomplish this?

1-15 Sketch the position-versus-time graph for a car that starts from rest and is driven 1 km to a store. (Describe the motion in words.)

1-16 A car travels in a straight line at 40 km h⁻¹ for 1 h and at 60 km h⁻¹ for 2 h. (a) How far does it travel? (b) Find the average velocity.

1-17 A woman wants to drive 100 km in 2 h. If she averages 40 km h⁻¹ for the first 1.5 h, what average velocity must she maintain for the remaining time?

1-18 A man runs a 42-km marathon in 2.5 h. Find the average velocity in (a) kilometres per hour (km h⁻¹); (b) metres per second (m s⁻¹).

1-19 A sprinter runs the 100 m dash in 9.8 s. (a) What is the sprinter's average velocity? (b) Since the runner starts from rest, the velocity cannot be constant. Sketch the approximate velocity-versus-time graph for the runner. Explain the assumptions made.

1-20 Light travels at 3 × 10⁸ m s⁻¹. A light-year is the distance light travels in 1 year, or 365 days. Find the distance in kilometres to the nearest star, which is 4 light-years away from us.

1-21 A falling object moves so that its height x above the ground at time t is given by the equation $x = 100$ m $- (4.9$ s⁻²$)t^2$. Find its average

velocity from (a) $t = 0$ to $t = 2$ s; (b) $t = 2$ to $t = 4$ s.

1-22 A ball thrown straight upward has a height x above the ground which is given by the equation $x = (19.6$ m s⁻¹$)t - (4.9$ m s⁻²$)t^2$. Find the average velocity from (a) $t = 0$ to $t = 2$ s; (b) $t = 2$ to 4 s.

1-23 From the position-versus-time graph of Fig. 1.13, find the average velocity from $t = 0$ s to (a) $t = 10$ s; (b) $t = 20$ s; (c) $t = 40$ s.

1-24 A baseball reaches a batter at 40 m s⁻¹. If home plate is 0.3 m across, how long will the ball be over the plate?

1-25 In 1970, a record was set when a swimmer swam 100 m in 51.9 s. What was his average velocity in km h⁻¹?

Section 1.3 | Instantaneous Velocity

1-26 In a period of 4 h, a man walks 10 km north, turns around, and walks 6 km south. Find his (a) average velocity; (b) average speed.

1-27 John drives 100 km at 100 km h⁻¹ and then drives an additional 100 km at 80 km h⁻¹. Mary makes the same 200-km trip at a constant speed of 90 km h⁻¹. (a) If they leave at the same time, who (if either) will complete the trip first? (b) By how much time will he or she beat the other driver?

1-28 In Fig. 1.13, what is the instantaneous velocity at (a) $t = 5$ s; (b) $t = 15$ s; (c) $t = 25$ s; (d) $t = 35$ s?

1-29 Draw the instantaneous velocity-versus-time graph corresponding to Fig. 1.13.

1-30 Figure 1.14 shows the position of a pendulum versus time. In the interval $t = 0$ to T, when is the velocity (a) zero; (b) positive; (c) negative?

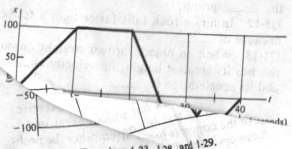

Figure 1.13. Exercises 1-23, 1-28, and 1-29.

1-60 A rock falls from a cliff 60 m high. (a) Find the average velocity during the first 3 s of its fall. (b) At what instant of time is the instantaneous velocity equal to the average velocity of part (a)? (c) How long does it take for the rock to fall to the ground?

1-61 A boy standing beside a tall building throws a ball straight up with an initial velocity of 15 m s^{-1}. (a) How high will the ball rise? (b) How long will it take for the ball to reach its maximum height? (c) Another boy reaches out of a window 6 m above the initial position of the ball and attempts to catch the ball. At what times will the ball pass him?

1-62 A rock dropped from the top of a tower strikes the ground in 4 s. (a) Find the velocity of the rock just before it strikes the ground. (b) Find the height of the tower.

1-63 A stone is thrown vertically downward from a bridge with an initial velocity of 10 m s^{-1}. It strikes the water in 3 s. (a) What is the velocity of the stone as it strikes the water? (b) What is the height of the bridge above the water?

1-64 A stone dropped from a bridge strikes the water in 5 s. (a) What is the velocity of the stone when it strikes the water? (b) What is the height of the bridge?

1-65 The hammer of a pile driver strikes the top of a pipe with a velocity of 7 m s^{-1}. From what height did the hammer fall?

1-66 A sandbag dropped from a balloon strikes the ground in 15 s. What was the height of the balloon if it was initially (a) at rest in the air; (b) descending with a velocity of 20 m s^{-1}?

1-67 A box falls from an elevator that is ascending with a velocity of 2 m s^{-1}. It strikes the bottom of the elevator shaft in 3 s. (a) How long will it take the box to reach its maximum height? (b) How far from the bottom of the shaft was the box when it fell off the elevator? (c) What is the height of the elevator when the box is at its highest point?

1-68 Repeat Example 1-21 with the $+x$ direction downward.

1-69 Repeat Example 1-22 with the $+x$ direction downward.

1-70 A car moving at 30 m s^{-1} (108 km h^{-1}) collides head on with a stone wall. From what height would the car have to fall to achieve the same results?

1-71 One ball is thrown straight up from a bridge, and another is thrown straight down. Just before they hit the water, which has the larger acceleration? (Neglect air resistance.)

1-72 In 1971, Apollo 15 astronaut David Scott dropped a hammer and a feather on the moon. The feather fell a distance of 0.73 m in the first second. (a) Did the hammer fall a larger or smaller distance in that second? Explain. (b) What is the acceleration due to gravity on the moon?

1-73 A physics student measures her reaction time by having a friend drop a metre stick between her fingers. The metre stick falls 0.3 m before she catches it. (a) What is her reaction time? (b) Estimate the minimum average speed of nerve impulses going from her eye to her brain and then back to her hand.

1-74 A ball is thrown straight up with an initial velocity of 30 m s^{-1}. (a) How far will it travel in the first second after it is released? (b) What is its velocity after 1 s? (c) What is its acceleration after 1 s?

PROBLEMS

The occasional problems preceded by an asterisk are the most difficult. Answers to most of the odd-numbered problems are given in the back of the book. Solutions to half the odd-numbered problems appear in the Study Guide.

1-75 Figure 1.18 shows the position-versus-time graph for an object. Consider the intervals from 0 to T_1, T_1 to T_2, and so on. (a) During which time

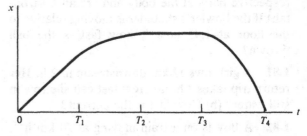

Figure 1.18.

interval is the object at rest? (b) During which time interval is it moving with constant velocity? (c) During which time interval does it have a positive velocity? (d) During which time interval does it have a negative velocity? (e) During which time interval does it have a positive acceleration? (f) During which time interval does it have a negative acceleration?

1-76 A car traveling at 20 m s^{-1} hits a stone wall. The driver, who is wearing a shoulder harness and seat belt, moves forward 1.0 m as the car stops. Assuming her acceleration is uniform, find (a) her average velocity during the collision; (b) her acceleration.

1-77 We saw that when you throw an object upward, in the absence of air resistance, it takes as long for the object to come down again as to reach its highest point. Are these times equal when there is air resistance? Explain.

1-78 Galileo concluded that falling objects have a constant acceleration because their distance varies with the square of the elapsed time: $x = ct^2$. Is this equation valid when air resistance is present? If not, explain qualitatively how the equation would have to be modified.

1-79 At the instant a bowler releases the ball, her hand is moving horizontally with a speed of 6 m s^{-1} relative to her body. If she is moving forward at a speed of 1 m s^{-1}, what is the velocity of the ball with respect to the floor?

1-80 When a bowling ball is released, a bowler's hand is moving relative to his forearm at 0.82 m s^{-1}. The forearm is moving relative to the upper arm at 0.55 m s^{-1}, and the upper arm is moving at 5.26 m s^{-1} relative to the shoulder. (The velocities refer to the outermost ends of the respective parts of the body and are all horizontal.) If the bowler's shoulder is moving relative to the floor at 1.43 m s^{-1}, how fast is the ball thrown?

1-81 A girl rows 12 km downstream in 2 h. Her return trip takes 3 h. (a) How fast can she row in still water? (b) How fast is the current?

1-82 A boy is on a train moving at 70 km h^{-1}. Relative to the ground, how fast is he moving if he runs at 15 km h^{-1} (a) toward the front of the train; (b) toward the rear?

1-83 The position-versus-time graph for a pendulum is shown in Fig. 1.14. Sketch the velocity-versus-time and acceleration-versus-time graphs for the motion.

1-84 A sled starting from rest slides down a hill with uniform acceleration. It travels 12 m in the first 4 s. When will the sled have a velocity of 4 m s^{-1}?

1-85 A racing car initially at rest accelerates for one-quarter of a kilometre and then brakes to a stop in an additional one-half kilometre. (a) Sketch an approximate velocity-versus-time graph. (b) Sketch an acceleration-versus-time graph.

1-86 Plane A, flying at 500 m s^{-1}, is 10,000 m directly behind plane B, moving in the same direction at 400 m s^{-1}. The pilot of plane A fires a missile that accelerates at 100 m s^{-2}. How long will it take for the missile to reach plane B? (Neglect the effects of the gravitational acceleration.)

1-87 A dog running at 10 m s^{-1} is 30 m behind a rabbit moving at 5 m s^{-1}. When will the dog catch up with the rabbit? (Both velocities remain constant.)

1-88 A rocket-powered experimental sled carrying a test pilot is brought to rest from 200 m s^{-1} over a distance d. If the pilot is not to be subjected to an acceleration greater than six times that of gravity, what is the minimum value of d?

*1-89 The world record for the 100-m dash is 9.95 s, and for the 60-m dash it is 6.45 s. Assume a sprinter accelerates at a constant rate up to a maximum velocity that is maintained for the remainder of the race, no matter how long it is. (a) Find the acceleration. (b) What is the duration of the acceleration period? (c) What is the maximum velocity? (d) The record for the 200-m dash is 19.83 s, while for the 1000-m run it is about 133.9 s. Are these times consistent with the assumptions made?

1-90 A sandbag is dropped from an ascending balloon that is 300 m above the ground and is ascending at 10 m s^{-1}. (a) What is the maximum height of the sandbag? (b) Find the position and velocity of the sandbag after 5 s. (c) How long does it take for the sandbag to reach the ground from the time it was dropped?

*1-91 In the television show "The Six Million Dollar Man," Colonel Austin had superhuman capabilities. In one episode he tries to catch a man fleeing in a sports car. The distance between them is 100 m when the car begins to accelerate with a constant acceleration of 5 m s^{-2}. Colonel Austin runs at a constant speed of 30 m s^{-1}. Show that he cannot catch the car, and find his distance of closest approach.

1-92 In Fig. 1.8b, the shaded area has a triangular portion (above the v_0 line) and a rectangular portion. Show that the sum of their areas reduces to the right-hand side of Eq. 1.8.

1-93 (a) A magazine article states that cheetahs are the fastest sprinters in the animal world and that a cheetah was observed to accelerate from rest to 70 km h^{-1} in 2 s. What average acceleration in m s^{-2} does this require? (b) The article also says the cheetah covered 60 m during that 2-s interval. How large a constant acceleration is implied by this statement? Does it agree with your result in (a)? (c) Accelerations substantially greater than g are difficult for an animal or an automobile to attain, because there is a tendency to slip even on very rough ground with larger acceleration. Given this information, can you guess which number is wrong in the article?

1-94 A rock is dropped into a well and a splash is heard 3 s later. If sound travels in air at 344 m s^{-1}, how deep is the well?

1-95 A lightning flash is seen, and 5 s later thunder is heard. Assuming they are produced simultaneously, how far away is the flash? (In air, sound travels at 344 m s^{-1} and light at 3.00×10^8 m s^{-1}.)

1-96 An estimate of the difficulties involved in space exploration beyond the solar system can be seen from the following calculation. (a) The distance to the moon from the earth is 3.84×10^8 m. Present-day spaceships require about 24 hours to reach the moon. What is the average velocity of these spaceships? (b) The nearest star to our solar system is about 4 light-years away, where a light-year is the distance traveled by light in 1 year (365 days) and the speed of light is 3.00×10^8 m s^{-1}. How many years would it take to reach this star if the spaceship had the velocity calculated in (a)?

^{c}1-97 A mass on the end of a spring moves so that its position is given by $x = A \sin (2\pi t/T)$. (a) Show that the motion repeats after a time T. (T is called the period.) (b) What is the greatest distance the mass moves from $x = 0$? (c) Find the instantaneous velocity as a function of time. (d) Find the instantaneous acceleration as a function of time. (e) Show that a is proportional to $-x$ and find the constant of proportionality.

^{c}1-98 An object falling through a fluid has a velocity at a time t given by $v = v_f(1 - e^{-t/T})$. ($e = 2.718. \ldots$ is the base of natural logarithms. See Appendix B.10.) (a) Find the velocities at $t = 0$, T, and ∞. (b) Explain why v_f is called the terminal velocity. (c) Show that the instantaneous acceleration is $(v_f - v)/T$. (d) Give a qualitative explanation of your results.

^{c}1-99 The position of an object moving along the x axis is given by $x = A + Bt^2 - Ct^3$, where A, B, and C are positive numbers. At time t, find (a) the velocity; (b) the acceleration. (c) At what time is the value of x greatest?

^{c}1-100 A swimmer can swim at a velocity v in still water. She swims upstream a distance d against the current, which has a velocity u. She then swims back to her starting point. (a) How long does it take her to make the round-trip? (b) What is her average speed for the trip? (c) For what value of u is her average speed the greatest?

ANSWERS TO REVIEW QUESTIONS

Q1-1, Système Internationale (S.I.); Q1-2, random, systematic; Q1-3, one; Q1-4, displacement; Q1-5, displacement, elapsed time; Q1-6, an extremely short time; Q1-7, velocity change, elapsed time; Q1-8, instantaneous velocity; Q1-9, instantaneous acceleration; Q1-10, a–t; Q1-11, v–t; Q1-12, air resistance; Q1-13, 0, g (downward).

SUPPLEMENTARY TOPICS

1.8 | VERTICAL JUMPING

We can use the equations for constant acceleration to analyze the relative jumping ability of various animals. Table 1.4 lists the heights recorded for some animals jumping vertically. Note that the jumping height for the human is less than the record for the high jump, which is about 2 m. This is because a man 1.8 m tall is already in a position to clear a bar at about half his height by rotating his body to a horizontal position. The method of human jumping called the Western Roll (Fig. 1.19) is not used by other animals, so the heights listed in Table

Figure 1.19. High jumpers using (a) the traditional Western Roll and (b) the newer Fosbury Flop technique. In both cases the athlete keeps as much of his weight below the bar as possible. [(a) RIA Novosti / Alamy Limited; (b) Ian Walton / Getty Images, Inc.]

TABLE 1.4

Acceleration distances d and vertical heights h for several animals. All distances are in metres.

	Acceleration Distance (d)	Vertical Height (h)
Human	0.5	1.0
Kangaroo	1.0	2.7
Bushbaby	0.16	2.2
Frog	0.09	0.3
Locust	0.03	0.3
Flea	0.0008	0.1

1.4 are the appropriate ones to use for comparing jumping abilities.

Animals make standing jumps by folding their legs and extending them rapidly. Usually the acceleration distance d is somewhat shorter than the animal's legs. Once off the ground the animal experiences only the acceleration of gravity, so the constant acceleration formulas apply. We can also analyze the takeoff phase if we make the approximation that the acceleration a_t during takeoff is constant. This approximation is used in the following example.

Example 1.23

Using the data in Table 1.4, find (a) the takeoff velocity v_t for a human and (b) the takeoff acceleration a_t.

(a) Let the coordinate x stand for the position of the person's midpoint, and chose the $+x$ direction upward (Fig. 1.20). To find the takeoff velocity, we consider the airborne phase of the jump. During this phase, the acceleration is $-g$ and the velocity changes from $v_0 = v_t$ to $v = 0$. The height changes by $\Delta x = h = 1$ m, so $v^2 = v_0^2 + 2a \, \Delta x$ becomes

$$0 = v_t^2 - 2gh$$

or

$$v_t^2 = 2gh$$

Thus

$$v_t = \sqrt{2gh} = \sqrt{(2)(9.8 \text{ m s}^{-2})(1 \text{ m})}$$
$$= 4.4 \text{ m s}^{-1}$$

(b) We will assume that during the takeoff phase the acceleration a_t is constant. The velocity increases from $v_0 = 0$ to $v = v_t$, and the height changes by $\Delta x = d = 0.5$ m. Thus during the takeoff phase, $v^2 = v_0^2 + 2a \, \Delta x$

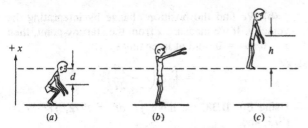

Figure 1.20. Positions during vertical jumping: (a) crouched, with $v = 0$; (b) fully extended at takeoff, with $v = v_t$; (c) maximum height, with $v = 0$. The coordinate x indicates the height of the person's midpoint.

becomes

$$v_t^2 = 2a_t d$$

Comparing this with $v_t^2 = 2gh$, we find

$$a_t = \frac{h}{d} g$$

$$= \frac{1 \text{ m}}{0.5 \text{ m}} (9.8 \text{ m s}^{-2}) = 19.6 \text{ m s}^{-2}$$

The takeoff accelerations and times are vastly different for different animals. A human jumping with the same acceleration as a flea would reach a height of more than 50 m! Despite these great differences, in Chapter Six we see that the total energy that a given amount of muscle can supply in a single jump is roughly the same in all animals.

1.9 | FINDING THE MOTION USING INTEGRATION

The acceleration of a swinging pendulum or of a mass oscillating on a spring is continually changing in magnitude and direction. In such situations, we cannot use the uniform acceleration formulas to find the changes in position and velocity even approximately. We show now that if the acceleration is a known function of time, it can be integrated to find the velocity. The velocity can then be integrated to find the position.

From the definition of the average acceleration, $\bar{a} = \Delta v / \Delta t$, the change in the velocity Δv in the time interval between t and $t + \Delta t$ is $\Delta v = \bar{a} \Delta t$. On an a–t graph (Fig. 1.21a), $a \Delta t$ is the area of the colored rectangular strip, where a is the acceleration at t. If

Δt is small, the average acceleration $\bar{a}$ approximately equals the acceleration a at the beginning of the interval, so $\Delta v \simeq a \Delta t$. Thus the total change in velocity between the times t_1 and t_2 is the sum of the velocity changes,

$$v_2 - v_1 \simeq \Sigma \, a \, \Delta t$$

Here Σ (capital Greek sigma) is the conventional symbol for summation.

In the limit where Δt aproaches zero, the total area of the strips becomes exactly equal to the area under the a–t curve (Fig. 1.21b). (We saw this earlier for the special case of constant acceleration.) Also, from the definition of an integral as the limit of a sum, we have

$$v_2 - v_1 = \int_{t_1}^{t_2} a \, dt \qquad (1.10)$$

When a is constant, it can be taken out of the integral. Then the integral becomes

$$v_2 - v_1 = a \int_{t_1}^{t_2} dt = a[t]_{t_1}^{t_2} = a(t_2 - t_1)$$

With $\Delta t = t_2 - t_1$ and $\Delta v = v_2 - v_1$, this reduces to $\Delta v = a \, \Delta t$, the constant acceleration relationship.

The position can be found from the velocity in a similar fashion. The position change Δx in a time interval Δt is $\bar{v} \Delta t$. The total position change from t_1 to t_2 is equal to the area under the v–t curve and to the integral

$$x_2 - x_1 = \int_{t_1}^{t_2} v \, dt \qquad (1.11)$$

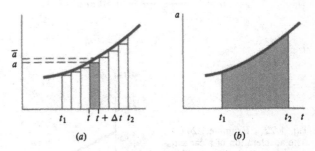

Figure 1.21. (a) the area of the colored strip is $a \, \Delta t$. In the limit where Δt approaches zero, $\bar{a}$ is equal to the acceleration a at time t. Hence $\Delta v = \bar{a} \, \Delta t = a \, \Delta t$, and the velocity change equals the area of the strip. (b) The total velocity change equals the area under the curve from t_1 to t_2.

If v is constant, it can be taken out of the integral. The equation then becomes $x_2 - x_1 = v(t_2 - t_1)$, or $\Delta x = v \, \Delta t$, as expected.

We illustrate the use of these results with an example of an accelerating car.

Example 1.24

A car starts from rest at time $t = 0$. It moves with an acceleration which diminishes linearly to zero according to the formula $a = a_0(1 - t/T)$, where $a_0 = 2$ m s^{-2} and $T = 10$ s (Fig. 1.22a). (a) What is the velocity of the car when the acceleration reaches zero at $t = T$? (b) How far does the car move during the acceleration period? (c) What is the average velocity from $t = 0$ to $t = T$?

(a) The velocity at time $t = 0$ is zero. At a later time t, the velocity is the integral of the acceleration from 0 to t. Since we want the velocity at time t, we use t' as the integration variable. Thus

$$v = \int_0^t a_0\left(1 - \frac{t'}{T}\right)dt' = a_0 \int_0^t \left(1 - \frac{t'}{T}\right)dt'$$

Now according to Eq. B.38 in Appendix B.12, $\int t'^n \, dt' = t'^{n+1}/(n + 1)$. Thus $\int dt' = t'$, $\int t' \, dt' = t'^2/2$, and v is given by

$$v = a_0\left[t' - \frac{t'^2}{2T}\right]_0^t = a_0\left(t - \frac{t^2}{2T}\right)$$

This is the velocity at any time t during the acceleration period (Fig. 1.22b). Substituting $t = T$ into this result, the velocity at the end of the acceleration period is

$$v = a_0\left(T - \frac{T^2}{2T}\right) = \frac{a_0 T}{2}$$

Using $a_0 = 2$ m s^{-2} and $T = 10$ s, we have

$$v = \frac{(2 \text{ m s}^{-2})(10 \text{ s})}{2} = 10 \text{ m s}^{-1}$$

(b) We find the position change by integrating the velocity. If we measure x from the starting point, then $x = 0$ at $t = 0$, and at later times

$$x = \int_0^t a_0\left(t' - \frac{t'^2}{2T}\right)dt'$$

Using Eq. B.38, we have $\int t' \, dt' = t'^2/2$, $\int t'^2 \, dt' = t'^3/3$, and

$$x = a_0\left[\frac{t'^2}{2} - \frac{t'^3}{6T}\right]_0^t = a_0\left(\frac{t^2}{2} - \frac{t^3}{6T}\right)$$

This is the distance the car has traveled up to time t (Fig. 1.22c). At $t = T$,

$$x = a_0\left(\frac{T^2}{2} - \frac{T^3}{6T}\right) = \frac{a_0 T^2}{3}$$

$$= \frac{(2 \text{ m s}^{-2})(10 \text{ s})^2}{3} = 66.7 \text{ m}$$

The car traveled 66.7 m while accelerating.

(c) The average velocity is the displacement divided by the elapsed time,

$$\bar{v} = \Delta x/\Delta t = (66.7 \text{ m})/(10 \text{ s}) = 6.67 \text{ m}$$

Note that $\bar{v}$ *is not* equal to the average of the initial and final velocities, $\frac{1}{2}(0 + a_0 T/2) = \frac{1}{2}(10 \text{ m s}^{-1}) = 5 \text{ m s}^{-1}$ (Fig. 1.22b). The average velocity is usually different from the average of the initial and final velocities when the acceleration is not constant.

EXERCISES ON SUPPLEMENTARY TOPICS

Section 1.8 | Vertical Jumping

1-101   A salmon jumps vertically out of the water at an initial velocity of 6 m s^{-1}. (a) How high will it jump? (b) How long will the salmon be out of the water?

Fig. 1.22. Example 1.24 (a) The acceleration of a car satisfies $a = a_0(1 - t/T)$. (b) The velocity of the car versus time if it starts from rest at $t = 0$. Note the average velocity is more than half the final velocity. (c) Its position versus time.

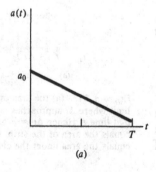

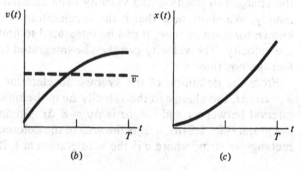

1-102 How high will a woman jump if her take-off velocity is the same as that of the flea?

1-103 From Table 1.4, compute the average takeoff acceleration and takeoff velocity for a locust, assuming the acceleration is constant. Compare these results with that for the human of Example 1.23.

1-104 An astronaut wearing a space suit can jump 0.5 m vertically at the surface of the earth. The gravitational acceleration on Mars is 0.4 times that on the earth. If his takeoff velocity is the same, how high can the astronaut jump on Mars?

1-105 If a human could achieve a takeoff acceleration equal to that of the flea, how high could she jump? (Assume the acceleration distance is still 0.5 m.)

1-106 Compute the takeoff times for the human, bushbaby, and flea of Table 1.4.

Section 1.9 | Finding the Motion Using Integration

^c**1-107** The velocity of an object is $v = bt^2$. If the object is at the origin at $t = 0$, where is it at $t = T$?

^c**1-108** An object has an acceleration $a = kt$, where $k = 3$ m s^{-3}. At $t = 0$ s, it is at the origin and has a velocity $v_0 = 10$ m s^{-1}. (a) What is the velocity at $t = 10$ s? (b) What is the position at this time?

PROBLEMS ON SUPPLEMENTARY TOPICS

^c**1-109** The velocity of a small object starting from rest at $t = 0$ and falling through a fluid is found to obey the formula $v = v_f(1 - e^{-bt})$, where b is a constant. ($e = 2.718$. . . is the base of the natural logarithms. See Appendix B.10.) Find the position at time $t > 0$ if the object is at the origin at $t = 0$.

^c**1-110** Using integration techniques, derive the uniform acceleration formulas for v and for Δx, Eqs. 1.5 and 1.8.

*^c**1-111** A protein molecule in water is effectively weightless because the buoyancy of the water balances the gravitational attraction. If the molecule is set in motion, it eventually comes to rest because of the resistance of the fluid to its motion. The acceleration is opposite to the velocity

and proportional to its magnitude, $a = -cv$. Find the subsequent velocity if the initial velocity at $t = 0$ is v_0. [*Hint:* Find dv/v and integrate.]

^c**1-112** We defined the average velocity $\bar{v}$ as the displacement Δx divided by the elapsed time Δt. Show that $\bar{v}$ is also equal to the *time-averaged* instantaneous velocity:

$$\bar{v} = \frac{\int_{t_1}^{t_2} v \, dt}{\int_{t_1}^{t_2} dt}$$

^c**1-113** The preceding problem notes that the average velocity $\bar{v}$ equals the time-averaged instantaneous velocity. A *position-averaged* velocity $\bar{v}'$ can be defined by

$$\bar{v}' = \frac{\int_{x_1}^{x_2} v \, dx}{\int_{x_1}^{x_2} dx}$$

Except in special cases, $\bar{v}$ and $\bar{v}'$ are not equal. Consider an object dropped from $x_1 = 0$ at $t_1 = 0$. Then $a = g$, and $v = gt = (2gx)^{1/2}$. Show that with $v_2 = at_2$, (a) $\bar{v} = v_2/2$; (b) $\bar{v}' = 2v_2/3$.

^c**1-114** Two observers study the motion of an object along the ground. The first observer is at rest relative to the ground and observes the object to have a velocity $v_1(t)$ at time t. The second observer is moving at a constant velocity u away from the first and observes the velocity of the object to be $v_2(t)$. (a) How are v_1 and v_2 related? (b) Find $x_1(t) - x_2(t)$, assuming that both are zero at time $t = 0$. (Do not assume that v_1 and v_2 are constant.) (c) Find $a_1(t)$ and $a_2(t)$.

^c**1-115** An object moving at the end of a spring has an acceleration $a = A \cos \omega t$, where A and ω are constants. For a full oscillation, the position of the object averages out to $x = 0$. At time $t = 0$ its velocity is zero. (a) Find the velocity v at time t. (b) Find the position at time t.

Additional Reading

Alfred M. Bork and Arnold B. Arons, Resource Letter Col R-1 on Collateral Reading in Physics, *American Journal of Physics*, vol. 35, 1967, p. 1. A bibliography.

Marjorie Nicholson, Science and Literature, *American Journal of Physics*, vol. 33, 1965, p. 175. A bibliography.

Arnold B. Arons and Alfred M. Bork, *Science and Ideas*, Prentice-Hall, Inc., Englewood Cliffs, N.J., 1964. An anthology.

American Foundation for Continuing Education, *The Mystery of Matter*, Oxford University Press, New York, 1965. An anthology.

National Science Foundation, *Exploring the Universe*, McGraw-Hill Book Co., New York, 1963. An anthology.

W. F. Magie, *Source Book in Physics*, McGraw-Hill Book Co., New York, 1935. An anthology.

L. B. Macurdy, Standards of Mass, *Physics Today*, vol. 4, April 1951, p. 7.

D. Brouwer, The Accurate Measurement of Time, *Physics Today*, vol. 4, August 1951, p. 6.

Robert A. Nelson, Foundations of the International System of Units (SI), *The Physics Teacher*, vol. 19, 1981, p. 596.

P. Giacomo, The New Definition of the Meter, *The American Journal of Physics*, vol. 52, 1984, p. 607.

E. Richard Cohen and Barry N. Taylor, The Fundamental Physical Constants, *Physics Today*, August 1989, part 2, p. 8. Latest best values.

Stillman Drake, *Discoveries and Opinions of Galileo*, Doubleday and Co., Garden City, New York, 1957.

Giorgio de Santillana, *The Crime of Galileo*, University of Chicago Press, Chicago, 1955.

James Hansen, The Crime of Galileo, *Science 81*. March 1981, p. 14.

R. B. Lindsay, Galileo Galilei, 1564–1642, and the Motion of Falling Bodies, *American Journal of Physics*, vol. 10, 1942, p. 285.

Sir James Gray, *How Animals Move*, Cambridge University Press, Cambridge, 1953. Pages 69–80 discuss jumping.

R. McNeill Alexander, *Animal Mechanics*, University of Washington Press, Seattle, 1968, Pages 28–33 discuss jumping.

David P. Willoughby, Running and Jumping, *Natural History*, vol. 83, March 1974, p. 68. Comparisons of various animals.

J. B. Rafert and R. N. Nicklin, Velocity Measurement of Humans by Computers, *The Physics Teacher*, vol. 22, 1984, p. 213.

Scientific American articles:

Herbert Butterfield, The Scientific Revolution, September 1960, p. 173.

P. A. M. Dirac, The Physicist's Picture of Nature, May 1963, p. 45.

Freeman J. Dyson, Mathematics in the Physical Sciences, September 1964, p. 128.

Allen V. Astin, Standards of Measurement, June 1968, p. 50.

Lord Ritchie-Calder, Conversion to the Metric System, July 1970, p. 17.

Barry N. Taylor, Donald N. Langenberg, and William H. Parker, The Fundamental Physical Constants, October 1970, p. 62.

J. E. Ravetz, The Origins of the Copernican Revolutions, October 1966, p. 88.

Stillman Drake, Galileo's Discovery of the Law of Free Fall, May 1973, p. 84.

Stillman Drake, The Role of Music in Galileo's Experiments, June 1975, p. 98.

Lawrence S. Lerner and Edward A. Gosselin, Galileo and the Specter of Bruno, November 1986, p. 126.

Owen Gingerich, The Galileo Affair, August 1982, p. 132. Galileo's conflict with the church.

Jearl Walker, How to Analyze a City Traffic-Light System from the Outside Looking In, *The Amateur Scientist*, March 1983, p. 138.

CHAPTER 2
MOTION IN
TWO DIMENSIONS

Although many of the principles of mechanics can be illustrated by objects moving in a straight line, their applications often involve more complex motions. Animals leaping forward, thrown or struck balls, and figure skaters all move in a vertical or horizontal plane. The definitions of position, velocity, and acceleration and their interrelations can be extended from the one-dimensional case to the more general situation if these quantities are represented by *vectors*. Vectors are mathematical objects having both a magnitude and a direction and are used to represent many other physical quantities in addition to the ones needed to describe motion. By contrast, some physical quantities, such as temperature and time, have no direction and are represented by ordinary numbers, or *scalars*.

In the first section we introduce vectors and explain some of the rules for manipulating them. We then restate the definitions of the previous chapter in vector language and show that motion in a plane is equivalent to a pair of one-dimensional motions. This permits us to carry over the results of the preceding chapter and to discuss the motion of projectiles.

2.1 | AN INTRODUCTION TO VECTORS

In this section we introduce vectors and show how to add and subtract them. While vectors are written with an arrow over the symbol ($\vec{A}$), in print they are denoted with boldface type, as in **A**, **s**, and **v**. The magnitude of the vector **A** is written as A or $|\mathbf{A}|$. A vector is pictured in a diagram by an arrow with a length proportional to its magnitude and oriented to indicate its direction. For example, in Fig. 2.1, **A**,

B, and **C** each have different directions, and **C** is longer or greater in magnitude than **A**.

Addition of Vectors | The concept of vector addition is illustrated by an example involving two vectors representing displacements. Suppose someone walks a certain distance in one direction and then turns and walks another distance in a second direction. The net change in position or displacement will depend on the magnitudes and directions of the two displacements. Let us denote the first displacement by **A** and the second by **B**. The net displacement **C** is the sum of **A** and **B**,

$$\mathbf{C} = \mathbf{A} + \mathbf{B}$$

The procedure for finding **C** is shown in Fig. 2.1. Note that the order of the vectors in the sum is irrelevant: **A** + **B** and **B** + **A** are the same thing. When there are three or more vectors to be summed, two vectors are added first, then the next, and so on. Again, the order of the vectors is irrelevant; for example, in Fig. 2.2, **A** + **B** + **C** = **B** + **A** + **C**.

The following example shows how the magnitude of **A** + **B** depends on the relative directions of **A** and **B**.

Example 2.1

A person walks 1 km due east. If the person then walks a second kilometre, what is the final distance from the starting point if the second kilometre is walked (a) due east; (b) due west; (c) due south?

We will call the first displacement **A** and the second, **B**. Using the procedures outlined above, we construct the sum **C** = **A** + **B** for the three cases (Fig. 2.3).

(a) Since **A** and **B** are in the same direction, $C = A + B = 2A = 2$ km. **C** is directed due east.

Figure 2.1.   (*a*) The vectors **A** and **B** representing two displacements. (*b*) To add **B** to **A**, we place its tail at the head of **A**. (Moving a vector does not change it so long as the direction and magnitude are not altered.) (*c*) The sum **C** = **A** + **B** is a vector from the tail of the first vector. **A**, to the head of the second vector, **B**. **C** represents the net displacement. (*d*) The order in which the vectors are added does not matter: **A** + **B** = **B** + **A**.

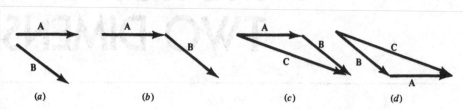

(*a*)   (*b*)   (*c*)   (*d*)

(b) Here the vectors are opposite, so $C = A - B = 0$.

(c) From the Pythagorean theorem, $C^2 = A^2 + B^2 = 2A^2$, so

$$C = \sqrt{2}\, A = \sqrt{2} \text{ km}$$

From Fig. 2.3*c*, **C** points toward the southeast.

Multiplication of a Vector By a Scalar

Multiplication of a vector by a scalar is defined so that the usual rules of algebra apply. If $2\mathbf{A} = \mathbf{A} + \mathbf{A}$ is to hold, then we must interpret $2\mathbf{A}$ as a vector in the same direction as **A** but with twice the length.

For example, if **A** is a 2-km displacement due north, 2**A** is a 4-km displacement due north, and 5**A** is a 10-km displacement due north.

Vector Subtraction

Subtraction of vectors is also defined so that the usual algebraic rules apply. In order that $\mathbf{A} - \mathbf{A} = 0$ holds, $-\mathbf{A}$ must be interpreted as a vector equal in magnitude to A but opposite in direction. Thus if **A** is a 2-km displacement due north, $-\mathbf{A}$ is a 2-km displacement due south and $-3\mathbf{A}$ is a 6-km displacement due south. The vector difference $\mathbf{C} = \mathbf{B} - \mathbf{A} = \mathbf{B} + (-\mathbf{A})$ is evaluated by adding the vector $-\mathbf{A}$ to the vector **B** as in Fig. 2.4.

Vector Components

A vector in a given plane is specified by two pieces of information, its magnitude and its direction. Equivalently, the vector can be specified by two other quantities, its *components* along a pair of perpendicular axes. These components are often useful in vector calculations.

The procedure for finding the components of a vector is shown in Fig. 2.5. The vector **A** is redrawn

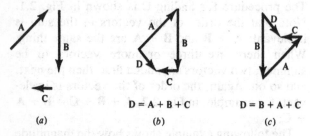

(*a*)   (*b*)   (*c*)

D = A + B + C   D = B + A + C

Figure 2.2.   (*a*) Three vectors, **A**, **B**, and **C**. (*b*) and (*c*) Two possible orderings in computing the sum **D** of the three vectors.

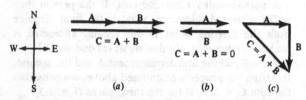

(*a*)   (*b*)   (*c*)

C = A + B   C = A + B = 0   C = A + B

Figure 2.3.   The sum of two displacement vectors that are equal in magnitude and (*a*) parallel; (*b*) opposite or antiparallel; and (*c*) perpendicular.

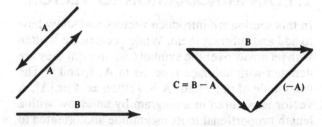

C = B − A   (−A)

Figure 2.4.   The vector $\mathbf{C} = \mathbf{B} - \mathbf{A}$ is found by adding $-\mathbf{A}$ to **B**.

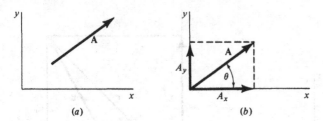

Figure 2.5. (a) A vector **A** and perpendicular x and y axes. (b) The components of **A** are A_x and A_y.

from the origin of the x–y axes, and the components of **A**, denoted by A_x and A_y, are constructed by drawing the dashed lines at right angles to the axes. Expressions relating the components to the magnitude of **A** and its angle θ (theta) with the x axis can be obtained using some properties of right triangles.

Figure 2.6 shows a right triangle with sides a, b, and c. These satisfy the Pythagorean relation,

$$a^2 + b^2 = c^2 \qquad (2.1)$$

The sine, cosine, and tangent of the angle θ are defined by

$$\sin \theta = \frac{\text{opposite side}}{\text{hypotenuse}} = \frac{a}{c}$$

$$\cos \theta = \frac{\text{adjacent side}}{\text{hypotenuse}} = \frac{b}{c}$$

$$\tan \theta = \frac{\text{opposite side}}{\text{adjacent side}} = \frac{a}{b}$$

Thus in Fig. 2.5b, the components A_x and A_y satisfy

$$A_x^2 + A_y^2 = A^2 \qquad (2.2)$$

Also,

$$\cos \theta = \frac{A_x}{A}, \qquad \sin \theta = \frac{A_y}{A} \qquad (2.3)$$

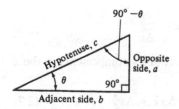

Figure 2.6. A right triangle.

or

$$A_x = A \cos \theta, \qquad A_y = A \sin \theta \qquad (2.4)$$

A_x is positive when it is directed in the $+x$ direction and negative when it is directed toward the $-x$ direction. Similarly A_y can be positive or negative, as we see in the next example.

Example 2.2

Find the components of the vectors **A** and **B** in Fig. 2.7 if $A = 2$ and $B = 3$.

Using trigonometric tables or an electronic calculator, we find that $\cos 30° = 0.866$ and $\sin 30° = 0.500$. Thus

$$A_x = A \cos \theta = 2 \cos 30° = 2(0.866) = 1.73$$
$$A_y = A \sin \theta = 2 \sin 30° = 2(0.500) = 1.00$$

From Fig. 2.7b, B_x is positive and B_y is negative. With $\cos 45° = \sin 45° = 0.707$,

$$B_x = 3 \cos 45° = 3(0.707) = 2.12$$
$$B_y = -3 \sin 45° = -3(0.707) = -2.12$$

The sum of two or more vectors can be calculated conveniently in terms of components. To do this, we define the *unit vector* $\hat{x}$ (read "x-hat"), a vector of length 1 in the $+x$ direction. Similarly, $\hat{y}$ is a unit vector in the $+y$ direction. With these unit vectors, a vector **A** with components A_x and A_y can be written as

$$\mathbf{A} = A_x\hat{x} + A_y\hat{y}$$

If a vector **B** is also written as

$$\mathbf{B} = B_x\hat{x} + B_y\hat{y}$$

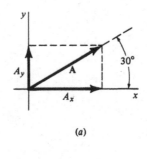
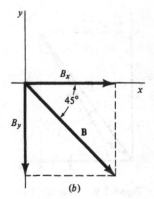

Figure 2.7. Example 2.2.

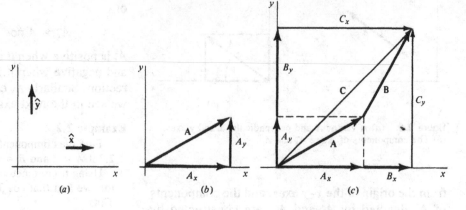

Figure 2.8. (a) $\hat{x}$ and $\hat{y}$ are unit vectors, vectors of length one directed along the coordinate axes. (b) A vector **A** can be constructed from its components A_x and A_y. (c) **C** = **A** + **B** in components is $C_x = A_x + B_x$, $C_y = A_y + B_y$.

the sum **C** = **A** + **B** is

$$\mathbf{C} = (A_x + B_x)\hat{x} + (A_y + B_y)\hat{y} \qquad (2.5)$$

The components of **C** *are the sums of the components of* **A** *and* **B** *(Fig. 2.8). This is illustrated by the following example.*

Example 2.3

In Fig. 2.9, **A** = $2\hat{x} + \hat{y}$ and **B** = $4\hat{x} + 7\hat{y}$. (a) Find the components of **C** = **A** + **B**. (b) Find the magnitude of **C** and its angle θ with the x axis.

(a) Using Eq. 2.5,

$$\mathbf{C} = (2 + 4)\hat{x} + (1 + 7)\hat{y} = 6\hat{x} + 8\hat{y}$$

Thus $C_x = 6$, and $C_y = 8$.

(b) From the Pythagorean theorem,

$$C^2 = C_x^2 + C_y^2 = 6^2 + 8^2 = 100$$

so $C = 10$. From Fig. 2.9, we see that the angle θ

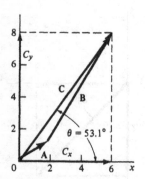

Figure 2.9. Example 2.3.

satisfies

$$\tan \theta = \frac{C_y}{C_x} = \frac{8}{6} = 1.333$$

Using a calculator, we find $\theta = 53.1°$.

2.2 | THE VELOCITY IN TWO DIMENSIONS

In two dimensions, position, velocity, and acceleration are represented by vectors. Their definitions are very similar to those for motion along a straight line, and their x components are related to each other in the same way as are x, v, and a for straight-line motion. Since this is also true for the y components, *a problem involving motion in a plane is effectively a pair of one-dimensional motion problems.*

Figure 2.10 shows an object moving in a plane labeled with x and y axes. The object could be a car, an animal, or a red blood cell, and it is represented symbolically by a point. If the displacement in a time interval Δt is denoted by the vector $\Delta\mathbf{s}$, then the *average velocity* of the object is parallel to $\Delta\mathbf{s}$ and is given by

$$\bar{\mathbf{v}} = \frac{\Delta\mathbf{s}}{\Delta t} \qquad (2.6)$$

We can write $\Delta\mathbf{s}$ in terms of its components in the x and y direction,

$$\Delta\mathbf{s} = \Delta x\hat{x} + \Delta y\hat{y} \qquad (2.7)$$

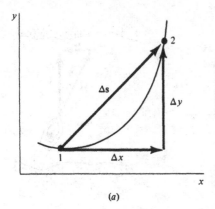

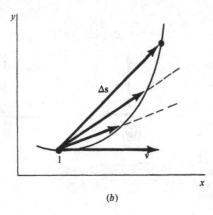

Figure 2.10. (a) An object moves along a path in a plane. At time t_1, it is at point 1, and at t_2 it is at point 2. The average velocity is parallel to Δs. (b) As the time interval $t_2 - t_1$ becomes smaller, so does the displacement Δs. The average velocity $\bar{v} = \Delta s/\Delta t$ approaches the instantaneous velocity v at t_1, which is tangent to the path at point 1.

Then the average velocity can also be written in terms of its components,

$$\bar{v} = \frac{\Delta x}{\Delta t}\hat{x} + \frac{\Delta y}{\Delta t}\hat{y} \qquad (2.8)$$

Thus the components of $\bar{v}$ are

$$\bar{v}_x = \frac{\Delta x}{\Delta t}, \qquad \bar{v}_y = \frac{\Delta y}{\Delta t} \qquad (2.9)$$

Each component of the average velocity looks like a one-dimensional average velocity.

Since the average velocity in a plane is equivalent to two one-dimensional average velocities, everything stated in the preceding chapter about the average and instantaneous velocities holds here for each component. For example, the *instantaneous velocity* v is the limit of the average velocity as the time interval Δt approaches zero. In component form

$$v = v_x\hat{x} + v_y\hat{y} \qquad (2.10)$$

Here $v_x = dx/dt$ and $v_y = dy/dt$ are the rates of change of the x and y coordinates of the object with respect to the time. Again, the derivatives dx/dt and dy/dt are shorthand notations for the limits of $\Delta x/\Delta t$ and $\Delta y/\Delta t$ as Δt approaches zero. At any instant, v is directed along the tangent to the path or *trajectory* of the object (Fig. 2.10b). These ideas are illustrated by the following examples.

Example 2.4

A car travels halfway around an oval racetrack at a constant speed of 30 m s^{-1} (Fig. 2.11). (a) What are its instantaneous velocities at points 1 and 2? (b) It takes

40 s to go from 1 to 2, and these points are 300 m apart. What is the average velocity of the car during this time interval?

(a) The instantaneous velocity is tangent to the path of the car, and its magnitude is equal to the speed. Thus, at point 1 the velocity is directed in the $+y$ direction and $v_1 = 30$ m s$^{-1}\hat{y}$. Similarly, at point 2 the velocity is along the $-y$ direction, and $v_2 = (30$ m s$^{-1})(-\hat{y}) = -30$ m s$^{-1}\hat{y}$.

(b) The average velocity is the displacement divided by the elapsed time. The displacement is entirely along the x direction, so $\Delta s = (300$ m$)\hat{x}$. Since $\Delta t = 40$ s,

$$\bar{v} = \frac{\Delta s}{\Delta t} = \frac{300 \text{ m}}{40 \text{ s}}\hat{x} = 7.5 \text{ m s}^{-1}\hat{x}$$

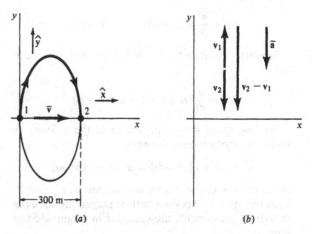

Figure 2.11. (a) A car goes halfway around an oval track. Its average velocity $\bar{v}$ during this interval points in the $+x$ direction. (b) The average acceleration $\bar{a}$ points in the $-y$ direction.

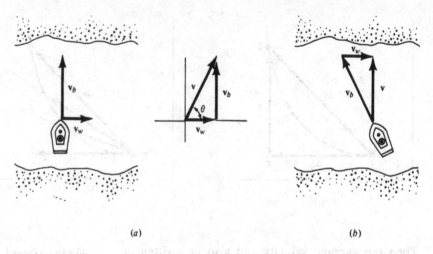

Figure 2.12. (a) The velocity of the boat relative to the shore is $\mathbf{v} = \mathbf{v}_b + \mathbf{v}_w$. If the boat is pointed toward the opposite shore, it will be deflected by the current. (b) The boat must be pointed upstream to go directly toward the opposite shore.

(a)   (b)

The average velocity during this time interval is directed along the $+x$ axis. Its magnitude is less than the speed of 30 m s^{-1} because the car does not travel in a straight line.

Example 2.5

An object moving in a circle about the origin has coordinates which vary in time according to

$$x = R \cos \omega t, \quad y = R \sin \omega t$$

where R and ω are constants. (a) Find the velocity components. (b) Show that the speed is constant in time.

(a) The velocity component v_x is dx/dt. Using Eq. B.26 in Appendix B, $(d/dt) \cos \omega t = -\omega \sin \omega t$,

$$v_x = \frac{d}{dt}(R \cos \omega t) = -\omega R \sin \omega t$$

Similarly, $(d/dt) \sin \omega t = \omega \cos \omega t$, and with $v_y = dy/dt$,

$$v_y = \frac{d}{dt}(R \sin \omega t) = \omega R \cos \omega t$$

(b) The speed is the magnitude of the velocity v. Using the Pythagorean theorem,

$$v^2 = v_x^2 + v_y^2 = \omega^2 R^2 (\sin^2 \omega t + \cos^2 \omega t)$$

Since $\sin^2 \theta + \cos^2 \theta = 1$ for any argument, $v^2 = \omega^2 R^2$. Thus the velocity has the constant magnitude ωR even though its components are changing in magnitude and sign.

Velocities are vectors and are added by using the rules for vector addition. When a boat moves relative to a moving stream, or a person walks on a moving vehicle, the motion relative to the ground is found by adding the velocity vectors.

Example 2.6

A boat moves at 10 m s^{-1} relative to the water in a river. It is pointed toward the opposite shore. There is a 5 m s^{-1} current (Fig. 2.12a). Find the magnitude and direction of the boat's velocity relative to the shore.

The boat is swept downstream by the current as it crosses the river. We must add the velocities $\mathbf{v}_b$ and $\mathbf{v}_w$ to find the velocity $\mathbf{v}$ of the boat relative to the shore. Since the velocities form a right triangle,

$$v^2 = v_b^2 + v_w^2 = (10 \text{ m s}^{-1})^2 + (5 \text{ m s}^{-1})^2 = 125 \text{ m}^2 \text{ s}^{-2}$$

$$v = 11.18 \text{ m s}^{-1}$$

The angle θ between the direction of the boat and the direction of the current is found from

$$\tan \theta = \frac{v_b}{v_w} = \frac{10}{5} = 2, \quad \theta = 63.4°$$

The boat does not move straight across the stream, and it will reach the opposite bank downstream of its starting point. For the boat to follow a direct line toward the opposite shore, the bow must be pointed somewhat upstream (Fig. 2.12b).

2.3 | THE ACCELERATION IN TWO DIMENSIONS

The acceleration of an object moving in a plane is defined much as in the one-dimensional case. Suppose that in a time interval $\Delta t = t_2 - t_1$ the velocity

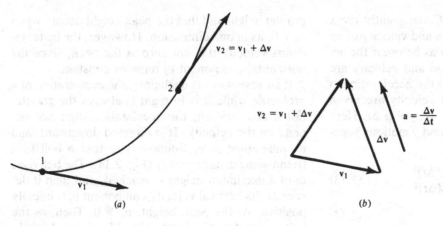

(a)

$v_2 = v_1 + \Delta v$

$v_2 = v_1 + \Delta v$

1

v_1

(b)

$a = \dfrac{\Delta v}{\Delta t}$

Δv

v_1

Figure 2.13. (a) The black curve represents the path of an object. The velocities at points 1 and 2 are vectors tangent to the trajectory at times t_1 and t_2. (b) The average acceleration $\bar{a}$ from t_1 to t_2 is parallel to Δv.

changes by $\Delta v = v_2 - v_1$. Then the *average acceleration* is

$$\bar{a} = \frac{\Delta v}{\Delta t} = \frac{v_2 - v_1}{t_2 - t_1} \qquad (2.11)$$

The *instantaneous acceleration* **a** is the limit of the average acceleration as the time interval Δt approaches zero (Fig. 2.13). In components,

$$a = a_x\hat{x} + a_y\hat{y} \qquad (2.12)$$

Here $a_x = dv_x/dt$ and $a_y = dv_y/dt$ are the rates of change of v_x and v_y.

The following example illustrates the calculation of the average acceleration.

Example 2.7

In Example 2.4, the velocity of the car changed from $v_1 = 30 \text{ m s}^{-1}\hat{y}$ to $v_2 = -30 \text{ m s}^{-1}\hat{y}$ in 40 s. What was the average acceleration of the car in that time interval?

The average acceleration is defined as the velocity change divided by the elapsed time:

$$\bar{a} = \frac{v_2 - v_1}{\Delta t} = \frac{(-30 \text{ m s}^{-1}\hat{y}) - (30 \text{ m s}^{-1}\hat{y})}{40 \text{ s}}$$

$$= -1.5 \text{ m s}^{-2}\hat{y}$$

Thus the average acceleration during the time the car goes from point 1 to point 2 is directed in the $-y$ direction, or downward in Fig. 2.11*b*.

Example 2.8

In example 2.5, an object moving in a circle was found to have the velocity components

$$v_x = -\omega R \sin \omega t \quad \text{and} \quad v_y = \omega R \cos \omega t$$

Find the acceleration components.

Using the definitions of the acceleration components, we have

$$a_x = \frac{dv_x}{dt} = \frac{d}{dt}(-\omega R \sin \omega t) = -\omega^2 R \cos \omega t$$

$$a_y = \frac{dv_y}{dt} = \frac{d}{dt}(\omega R \cos \omega t) = -\omega^2 R \sin \omega t$$

Note that if we apply the Pythagorean theorem, we find that a has a constant magnitude, $a = \omega^2 R$.

These examples illustrate two important points. If the velocity is constant, the acceleration is zero, since **a** is the rate of change of the velocity. However, when the *speed* is constant, the acceleration may or may not be zero. If an object moves at a constant speed along a curved path, its velocity is changing direction, and it is accelerating. We feel the effects of this acceleration when a car turns a corner quickly. *The acceleration is zero only when the speed and direction of motion are both constant.*

The second point is that the directions of the velocity and acceleration at any instant can be related in many ways. The magnitude and direction of **a** are determined by how **v** is changing. When a car moves along a straight road, the acceleration is parallel to the velocity if v is increasing and opposite if v is decreasing. When the motion is along a curved path, the acceleration is at some angle to the velocity. For instance, in Example 2.7, the average acceleration was at right angles to the average velocity.

2.4 | FINDING THE MOTION OF AN OBJECT

As we have stressed, a problem involving motion of an object in a plane is equivalent to a pair of straight-line motion problems. Consequently the x and y components of the position and velocity of an object can be calculated exactly as before if the acceleration and the initial position and velocity are known. In one dimension, when the acceleration is constant, the displacement and velocity are given by $\Delta x = v_0 \Delta t + \frac{1}{2}a(\Delta t)^2$ and $v = v_0 + a \Delta t$. Here similar equations hold for the x and y motions separately:

$$\Delta x = v_{0x} \Delta t + \tfrac{1}{2}a_x(\Delta t)^2$$
$$\Delta y = v_{0y} \Delta t + \tfrac{1}{2}a_y(\Delta t)^2 \qquad (2.13)$$

$$v_x = v_{0x} + a_x \Delta t$$
$$v_y = v_{0y} + a_y \Delta t \qquad (2.14)$$

Each of the other constant acceleration equations tabulated on the front endpapers also leads to a pair of component equations for two-dimensional motion. As in one dimension, integration methods are required if the acceleration varies in time.

The use of these equations is illustrated in the next section.

2.5 | PROJECTILES

Kicked or thrown balls, jumping animals, and objects dropped from windows are all examples of *projectiles. If air resistance is neglected, the motion of a projectile is influenced only by the constant gravitational acceleration.* Given the initial position and velocity, the subsequent position and velocity can be found using the constant acceleration equations.

To use these equations for the motion of a projectile, let us choose the x axis to be horizontal and the $+y$ axis to be directed upward. Then $a_x = 0$ and $a_y = -g$, and Eqs. 2.13 and 2.14 become

$$\Delta x = v_{0x} \Delta t, \qquad \Delta y = v_{0y} \Delta t - \tfrac{1}{2}g(\Delta t)^2 \quad (2.15)$$
$$v_x = v_{0x}, \qquad v_y = v_{0y} - g \Delta t \qquad (2.16)$$

The Δx and v_x equations show that the horizontal motion is uniform, and the Δy and v_y equations show that the vertical motion is that of an object acting only under the influence of gravity.

These equations contain a great deal of information and let us solve many types of problems. Note that the projectile hits the ground when y equals the ground height and that the peak height occurs when $v_y = 0$, as in one dimension. However, the instantaneous velocity v is not zero at the peak, since the horizontal component v_x remains constant.

If air resistance is negligible, the acceleration of a projectile while it is in flight is always the gravitational acceleration; the acceleration does not depend on the velocity. It is directed downward, and its magnitude is g. Suppose you toss a ball to a friend some distance away (Fig. 2.14). The ball rises until a maximum height is reached, and then it descends. Its vertical velocity component v_y is initially positive. At the peak height, $v_y = 0$. Then, as the ball comes down, v_y is negative. However, throughout its motion, the ball has a vertical acceleration $a_y = -g$. The acceleration remains the same, although v_y changes magnitude and sign. Similarly, the horizontal velocity component is constant throughout, and $a_x = 0$.

Two interesting examples of projectile motion are often shown as lecture demonstrations. In one of these, two steel balls are simultaneously released from a stand above the floor. Ball 1 is projected horizontally by a spring, while ball 2 is allowed to drop from rest. The problem is to predict which ball will hit the floor first.

Although this problem sounds hard initially, its solution is apparent once we realize that both balls have the same initial vertical velocity and position components and the same acceleration. Consequently, the equations for the vertical motion of the two balls are the same, and they must hit the floor simultaneously (Fig. 2.15). This illustrates clearly the idea that motion in the horizontal and vertical directions are independent.

The second demonstration is a bit more elaborate. A projectile is fired by a "cannon" pointed at a stuffed animal (Fig. 2.16). Just as the projectile leaves the cannon, the stuffed animal is released and falls. Somewhat surprisingly, the projectile strikes the animal in midair. The point is that if there were no gravitational acceleration, the projectile would travel in a straight line. However, since both the projectile and the stuffed animal experience the same gravitational acceleration, both fall at the same rate relative to where they would have been otherwise. Hence, if the cannon is aimed di-

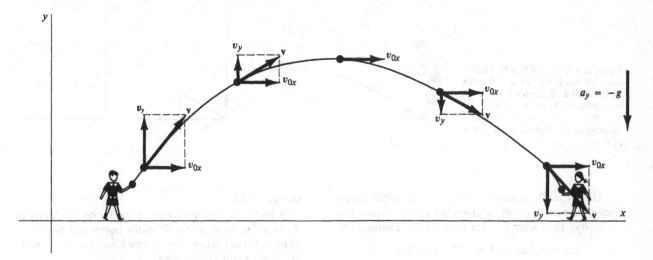

Figure 2.14. When a ball is thrown, v_y is initially positive. It is zero at the highest point reached and negative on the way down. Throughout the motion, v_x retains its initial value, and the acceleration is downward with a magnitude g.

rectly at the animal, the only effect of the gravitational acceleration is that they meet somewhat below where the animal was initially.

The following examples illustrate the solution of quantitative projectile motion problems.

Example 2.9

A diver leaps from a tower with an initial horizontal velocity component of 7 m s^{-1} and an upward velocity component of 3 m s^{-1}. Find the components of her position and velocity after 1 s.

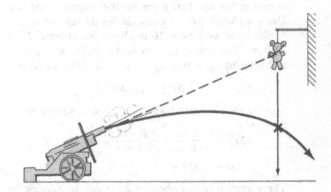

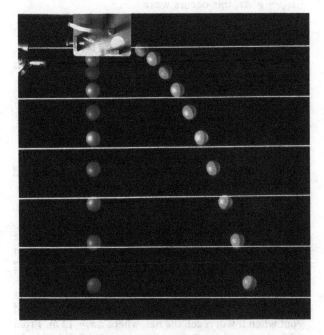

Figure 2.15. Multiple exposure photographs show that a ball dropped from rest and one projected forward fall at the same rate. (Richard Megna / Fundamental Photographs)

Figure 2.16. The projectile and stuffed animal fall together when simultaneously released. They collide at the point indicated with a cross.

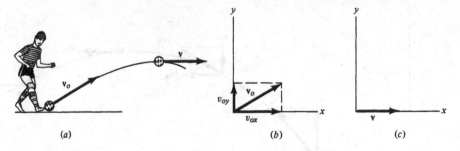

Figure 2.17. (*a*) A ball kicked from ground level has $v_y = 0$ at its highest point. Example 2.11. (*b*) Components of the initial velocity. (*c*) Components of the velocity at the highest point. Note $v_y = 0$.

(*a*)   (*b*)   (*c*)

The projectile equations of motion tell us the subsequent motion of the diver given her initial position and velocity. Thus after 1 s, her position has changed by

$$\Delta x = v_{0x}\,\Delta t = (7\text{ m s}^{-1})(1\text{ s}) = 7\text{ m}$$

$$\Delta y = v_{0y}\,\Delta t - \tfrac{1}{2}g(\Delta t)^2$$
$$= (3\text{ m s}^{-1})(1\text{ s}) - \tfrac{1}{2}(9.8\text{ m s}^{-2})(1\text{ s})^2$$
$$= -1.9\text{ m}$$

She is 7 m away from the board horizontally and 1.9 m below it. Her velocity components after 1 s are

$$v_x = v_{0x} = 7\text{ m s}^{-1}$$

$$v_y = v_{0y} - g(\Delta t)$$
$$= (3\text{ m s}^{-1}) - (9.8\text{ m s}^{-2})(1\text{ s})$$
$$= -6.8\text{ m s}^{-1}$$

Example 2.10

A ball is thrown horizontally from a window 10 m above the ground and hits the ground 40 m away. How fast was the ball thrown?

The key to solving this problem is noting that the ball hits the ground when *y* is at the ground height. The equation for Δy then gives us the elapsed time, Δt. Once we know Δt, the equation for Δx tells us v_{0x}.

Since the window is 10 m above the ground, $\Delta y = -10$ m. The ball is thrown horizontally, so $v_{0y} = 0$. Substituting $v_{0y} = 0$ in $\Delta y = v_{0y} - \tfrac{1}{2}g(\Delta t)^2$, we have

$$\Delta y = -\tfrac{1}{2}g(\Delta t)^2$$

Solving for $(\Delta t)^2$ and taking the positive square root,

$$(\Delta t)^2 = \frac{-2\,\Delta y}{g} = \frac{-2(-10\text{ m})}{9.8\text{ m s}^{-2}} = 2.041\text{ s}^2$$

$$\Delta t = 1.429\text{ s}$$

The *x* motion is described by $\Delta x = v_{0x}\,\Delta t$. Solving for v_{0x}, we find the initial velocity of the ball:

$$v_{0x} = \frac{\Delta x}{\Delta t} = \frac{40\text{ m}}{1.429\text{ s}} = 28.0\text{ m s}^{-1}$$

Example 2.11

A ball is kicked from ground level with a velocity of 25 m s^{-1} at an angle of 30° to the horizontal direction. (Fig. 2.17) (a) When does it reach its greatest height? (b) Where is it at that time?

(a) From Fig. 2.17*b*, the initial velocity has components

$$v_{0x} = v_0 \cos 30° = (25\text{ m s}^{-1})(0.866) = 21.7\text{ m s}^{-1}$$

$$v_{0y} = v_0 \sin 30° = (25\text{ m s}^{-1})(0.500) = 12.5\text{ m s}^{-1}$$

The greatest height is reached when $v_y = 0$. Using $v_y = v_{0y} - g\,\Delta t$, this occurs when

$$\Delta t = \frac{v_{0y} - v_y}{g} = \frac{12.5\text{ m s}^{-1} - 0}{9.8\text{ m s}^{-2}} = 1.28\text{ s}$$

(b) With Eqs. 2.15, the displacement after 1.28 s is given by

$$\Delta x = v_{0x}\,\Delta t = (21.7\text{ m s}^{-1})(1.28\text{ s}) = 27.8\text{ m}$$

$$\Delta y = v_{0y}\,\Delta t - \tfrac{1}{2}g(\Delta t)^2$$
$$= (12.5\text{ m s}^{-1})(1.28\text{ s}) - \tfrac{1}{2}(9.8\text{ m s}^{-2})(1.28\text{ s})^2$$
$$= 7.97\text{ m}$$

Thus the ball is 7.97 m above a point on the ground 27.8 m from where it was kicked.

Example 2.12

A tennis ball is served horizontally from 2.4 m above the ground at 30 m s^{-1} (Fig. 2.18). (a) The net is 12 m away and 0.9 m high. Will the ball clear the net? (b) Where will the ball land?

(a) To find the height of the ball at the net, we must first use the equations for the horizontal motion to find out when it will reach the net, where $\Delta x = 12$ m. From this time, we can determine the height. Solving $\Delta x = v_{0x}\,\Delta t$ for Δt,

$$\Delta t = \frac{\Delta x}{v_{0x}} = \frac{12\text{ m}}{30\text{ m s}^{-1}} = 0.4\text{ s}$$

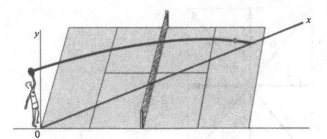

Figure 2.18. A tennis ball is served horizontally. Example 2.12.

Using $\Delta t = 0.4$ s and $v_{0y} = 0$, the vertical displacement is

$$\Delta y = v_{0y} \Delta t - \tfrac{1}{2}g(\Delta t)^2$$
$$= -\tfrac{1}{2}(9.8 \text{ m s}^{-2})(0.4 \text{ s})^2 = -0.78 \text{ m}$$

Since the ball was initially 2.4 m above the ground, it is now $(2.4 - 0.78)$ m = 1.62 m above the ground, so it easily clears the net.

(b) The ball lands when $\Delta y = -2.4$ m. Once we have found this time interval, we can find the horizontal displacement from the equation for Δx. Substituting $v_{0y} = 0$ in $\Delta y = v_{0y} \Delta t - \tfrac{1}{2}g(\Delta t)^2$, we find

$$\Delta y = -\tfrac{1}{2}g(\Delta t)^2$$
$$(\Delta t)^2 = \frac{-2 \Delta y}{g} = \frac{-2(-2.4 \text{ m})}{9.8 \text{ m s}^{-2}} = 0.490 \text{ s}^2$$
$$\Delta t = 0.700 \text{ s}$$

Hence the distance the ball travels horizontally before it lands is

$$\Delta x = v_{0x} \Delta t = (30 \text{ m s}^{-1})(0.700 \text{ s}) = 21.0 \text{ m}$$

Projectiles in Athletics | The preceding example illustrates how the projectile motion formulas can be used to analyze a tennis serve. A serve should clear the net by a small but safe margin and land just inside the service court. If a beginner serves the ball rather slowly, the ball will not clear the net unless it is served slightly above the horizontal direction. More advanced players can serve horizontally or slightly below the horizontal, since the ball moves faster and has a flatter trajectory. While a player can determine his or her own best serving angle by trial and error, the projectile motion formulas can be used to predict this angle given

the initial speed. The advice given in textbooks on tennis is sometimes based on this kind of analysis. Many other athletic events involving projectiles that are thrown, kicked, or struck can be discussed using the projectile motion formulas.

SUMMARY

In two dimensions, position, velocity, and acceleration have both magnitude and direction, so they are represented by vectors. In diagrams, vectors are designated by arrows. To find the sum $\mathbf{C} = \mathbf{A} + \mathbf{B}$, we draw the tail of $\mathbf{B}$ from the head of $\mathbf{A}$; $\mathbf{C}$ is then a vector from the tail of $\mathbf{A}$ to the head of $\mathbf{B}$. Multiplying a vector by a positive scalar or ordinary number increases its magnitude by that factor without altering its direction; multiplying by a negative scalar reverses its direction as well as changing the magnitude.

Many calculations involving vectors are simplified by choosing a convenient pair of x-y axes and finding the vector components. If $\mathbf{A}$ makes an angle θ with respect to the positive x direction, then its components are $A_x = A \cos \theta$ and $A_y = A \sin \theta$. Adding the x components of two or more vectors gives the x component of their sum. Similarly, adding the y components gives the y component of the sum.

The velocity and acceleration in a plane are defined by restating the one-dimensional definitions in vector form: $\mathbf{v} = d\mathbf{s}/dt$ and $\mathbf{a} = d\mathbf{v}/dt$. Also, the x components of these quantities are related to each other exactly as in one dimension, as are the y components, so motion in a plane is effectively a pair of one-dimensional motions. Therefore, if we know the acceleration and the initial position and velocity, the subsequent motion can be found much as in one dimension.

The maximum height a projectile reaches is found by setting $v_y = 0$. The projectile lands when y equals the ground height. The vertical acceleration component is $-g$ throughout, and the horizontal velocity component is constant at its initial value.

Checklist

Define or explain:

vector	addition of vectors
scalar	subtraction of vectors

vector components   acceleration in two
unit vector   dimensions
velocity in two   projectile
  dimensions

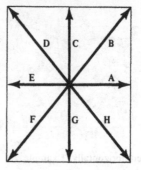

Figure 2.19.   Exercise 2-1.

REVIEW QUESTIONS

Q2-1   What is the difference between a scalar
and a vector?

Q2-2   How do we represent vectors in writing
and in textbooks?

Q2-3   If **A** is parallel to **B**, what is the magnitude of **A** + **B**? Of **A** − **B**? Of 2**A**?

Q2-4   If **A** is perpendicular to **B**, what is the
magnitude of **A** + **B**?

Q2-5   The average velocity in a plane is the
_____ divided by the _____ .

Q2-6   The average acceleration in a plane is the
_____ divided by the _____ .

Q2-7   The acceleration is zero when both the
_____ and _____ of the velocity are constant.

Q2-8   Motion in a plane is equivalent to a pair
of _____ .

Q2-9   The motion of a projectile is influenced
only by the _____ (assuming air resistance is
negligible).

Q2-10   The time when a projectile hits the
ground is found from the equations for the _____
motion.

Q2-11   When a projectile is at its greatest height,
the _____ component of the velocity is zero.

Q2-12   The _____ component of the velocity of
a projectile remains constant throughout its
motion.

Q2-13   The vertical component of the acceleration of a projectile is _____ , and the horizontal
component is _____ .

EXERCISES

Section 2.1 | An Introduction to Vectors

2-1   Figure 2.19 shows a collection of vectors
that can be combined in various ways. For exam-
ple, **A** + **C** = **B**. Find (a) **E** + **C**; (b) **A** +.**F**;
(c) **A** + **D**; (d) **E** + **A**; (e) **E** + 2**A**; (f) **A** − **B**;
(g) **B** − **A**; (h) **C** − **A**.

2-2   In Fig. 2.20, for what value of θ will **C** =
A + **B** have (a) a minimum magnitude, and (b) a
maximum magnitude? (c) Find C when $\theta = 90°$.

2-3   A vector has an x component of −10 and a
y component of +3. (a) Draw a set of x–y axes
and show the vector. (b) Calculate the magnitude
and direction of the vector.

2-4   **A** = $3\hat{x} + 2\hat{y}$, and **B** = $4\hat{x} − \hat{y}$. Find the
magnitude of (a) **A** + **B**; (b) **A** − **B**; (c) 2**B**.

2-5   **A** = $2\hat{x} + 4\hat{y}$. Find the magnitude and direction of (a) **A**; (b) −**A**.

2-6   If $\theta = 72°$ in Fig. 2.20, find (a) the direction
and magnitude of **C** = **A** + **B** by constructing a
drawing using a ruler and a protractor; (b) the
direction and magnitude of **C** using the component method.

2-7   For the vectors **A** and **B** in Fig. 2.21, find
(a) **A** + **B**; (b) **B** − **A**; (c) **A** − **B**.

2-8   Using components for the vectors in Fig.
2.22, find the direction and magnitude of
E = **A** + **B** + **C** + **D**.

2-9   Using components for the vectors in Fig.
2.22, find the direction and magnitude of
F = **A** − **C** + **B** − 2**D**.

2-10   A woman walks 10 km north, turns toward
the northwest, and walks 5 km further. What is
her final position?

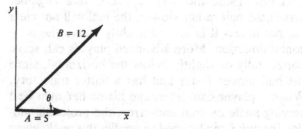

Figure 2.20.   Exercises 2-2 and 2-6.

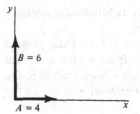

Figure 2.21. Exercise 2-7.

2-11 A ship sets out to sail 100 km north but is blown by a severe storm to a point 200 km east of its starting point. How far must it sail, and in what direction, to reach its intended destination?

2-12 One person walks northeast at 3 km h⁻¹, and another heads south at 4 km h⁻¹. How far apart are they after 2 h?

2-13 For the vectors in Fig. 2.23, find the magnitude and direction of (a) $D = A + B + C$; (b) $E = A - B - C$.

2-14 For the vectors in Fig. 2.24, find the magnitude and direction of (a) $D = A + B + C$; (b) $E = A - B - C$.

Section 2.2 | The Velocity in Two Dimensions

2-15 A car goes around a circular track 500 m in diameter at a constant speed of 20 m s⁻¹. (a) How long does it take for the car to go halfway around the track? (b) What is its average velocity in that time interval?

2-16 A car goes around a circular track with a radius of 1000 m at a constant speed of 10 m s⁻¹. (a) How long does it take the car to go once completely around the track? (b) What is the average velocity of the car over this time interval?

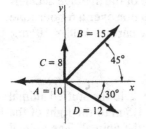

Figure 2.22. Exercises 2-8 and 2.9.

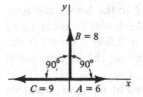

Figure 2.23. Exercise 2-13.

2-17 A ball is thrown at 30 m s⁻¹ at an angle of 20° to the horizontal direction. Find the horizontal and vertical components of its initial velocity.

2-18 A plane flies for 3 h and reaches a point 600 km north and 800 km east of its starting point. Find the direction and magnitude of its average velocity.

2-19 A plane flies south at 500 km h⁻¹ for 2 h and then flies west at 500 km h⁻¹ west for 1 h. (a) What is its average speed? (b) What are the magnitude and direction of its average velocity?

2-20 A ship is sailing north at 10 m s⁻¹. A man runs east across it at 8 m s⁻¹. (a) How far has he moved relative to the water after 3 s? (b) In what direction has he moved?

2-21 An object has its position given by the formula $r = ptx + qt^2y$, where p and q are constants. Find its instantaneous velocity components as functions of time.

Section 2.3 | The Acceleration in Two Dimensions

2-22 A car initially traveling due north goes around a semicircle having a radius of 500 m at a constant speed of 20 m s⁻¹. (a) How long does this take? (b) What is the magnitude and direction of the average acceleration?

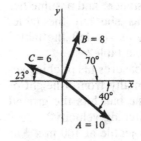

Figure 2.24. Exercise 2-14.

2-23   A rifle pointed at 30° to the horizontal fires a bullet at 250 m s^{-1}. If the bullet is accelerated uniformly in the barrel for 0.006 s, find (a) the magnitude of the acceleration; (b) its horizontal and vertical components.

2-24   A tennis ball is served by a player, bounces in the opponent's court, and is hit by the opponent toward the first player. Describe the direction and magnitude of the acceleration during each part of the motion.

2-25   The earth rotates about the sun once each year on an approximately circular path. Find the magnitude of the average acceleration associated with this motion over a 6-month interval. (The average distance from the earth to the sun is 1.50×10^{11} m.)

ᶜ2-26   Find the instantaneous acceleration of the object in Exercise 2-21.

Section 2.4 | Finding the Motion of an Object and Section 2.5 | Projectiles

2-27   A ball is thrown from a rooftop at a 45° angle above the horizontal and a few seconds later hits the ground. At what point in its motion does it have its (a) greatest velocity; (b) smallest velocity; (c) greatest acceleration?

2-28   A soccer ball is kicked into the air. What is its acceleration (a) as it rises; (b) at the top; (c) on the way down?

2-29   A hunter aims a rifle at an angle of 20° above the horizontal. She fires a bullet while simultaneously dropping another bullet from the level of the rifle. Which bullet will hit the ground first?

2-30   An inspired physics teacher runs across a lecture table and right off the end. Exactly 0.5 s later, she lands on the floor 2 m from the end of the table. Neglect air resistance, and assume her velocity was horizontal as she left the table. (a) What was her velocity as she left the table? (b) What is the height of the table?

2-31   A baseball player measures his pitching velocity by throwing horizontally from a height of 5 m above the ground. The ball hits the ground 25 m away. What is his pitching velocity?

2-32   A cannon fires a projectile at 100 m s^{-1} at an angle of 30° above the horizontal. How high

will the projectile be when its horizontal distance from the cannon is 200 m?

2-33   A football kicked into the air from ground level hits the ground 30 m from where it started after 4 s. (a) Find its average velocity while in the air. (b) Find its average acceleration while in the air.

2-34   A ball is thrown horizontally at 20 m s^{-1} from a window 15 m above the ground. (a) When will it hit the ground? (b) Where will it land?

2-35   A rifle pointed at 30° above the horizontal fires a bullet at 500 m s^{-1}. The rifle barrel is 0.7 m long. (a) Find the average acceleration in the rifle barrel. (b) Find the horizontal and vertical components of this acceleration.

2-36   A snowball is thrown from 2 m above the ground at a velocity of 10 m s^{-1} directed at 30° above the horizontal. (a) Find its horizontal and vertical position after 1 s. (b) Find its velocity components after 1 s.

2-37   (a) How long will the snowball of the preceding exercise be in the air? (b) Where will it land?

2-38   A baseball is hit at 40 m s^{-1} at an angle of 30° to the horizontal. (a) How high will it go? (b) When will it reach that height? (c) What will be its horizontal distance from the batter at that time?

2-39   For the baseball in the preceding exercise, find (a) the horizontal distance it will travel; (b) the total time it will be in the air. (Neglect the fact that the ball is struck from slightly above ground.)

2-40   A rifle is aimed directly at a target 200 m away at the same height as the rifle. If the bullet leaves the muzzle at 500 m s^{-1}, by how much will it miss the target?

2-41   The earth revolves about its axis every 24 hours. Find the magnitude of the average acceleration of a point on the equator over a 6-hour time interval. (The radius of the earth is 6.38×10^6 m.)

PROBLEMS

2-42   Suppose that in Fig. 2.15 the stuffed animal is initially 1 m above and 1.5 m to the right of the cannon that is pointed at the animal. The animal starts to fall as the cannonball is fired at 10 m s^{-1}.

(a) What are the initial horizontal and vertical velocity components of the cannonball? (b) How long does it take for the horizontal coordinate of the ball to change by 1.5 m? (c) What are the vertical positions of the ball and the animal at that time?

2-43 One ball is thrown horizontally with a velocity v_0 from a height h, and another is thrown straight down with the same initial speed. (a) Which ball will land first? (b) Which ball will have the greater speed as it is about to land?

2-44 A boy throws a ball so that it rises 1 m while traveling 7 m horizontally and then begins to drop. What were the initial speed and direction of the ball?

2-45 A man points his boat due east and rows at 4 km h^{-1} relative to the water. The river flows south at 2 km h^{-1}, and it is 1 km wide. (a) How fast is the man moving relative to the shore? (b) Where will he land? (c) How long will his trip take?

2-46 A woman wishes to go directly across a river that is 1 km wide. The river flows south at 2 km h^{-1}, and she can row at 4 km h^{-1} relative to the water. (a) In what direction should she row relative to the water? (b) How long will it take her to reach the other side?

2-47 A snowball is thrown from the ground at a building 30 m away. It hits the building 20 m above the height from which it was thrown. Its initial horizontal velocity component was 30 m s^{-1}. What was the initial vertical velocity component?

2-48 A tennis ball is served horizontally at a height of 2.4 m, 12 m from a net that is 0.9 m high. (a) If it is to clear the net by at least 0.2 m, what is its minimum initial velocity? (Neglect air resistance.) (b) If it clears the net by 0.2 m, where will it land?

2-49 Some books advise serving a tennis ball at an angle below the horizontal direction. To see if this is sound advice, suppose a ball is struck at an angle of 5° downward at a height of 2.4 m with the relatively high speed of 30 m s^{-1}. How high will it

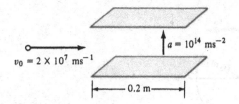

Figure 2.25. Problem 2-50.

be when it reaches the net 12 m away? (The net is 0.9 m high. Neglect air resistance.)

2-50 The screens of cathode ray tubes in television sets and oscilloscopes emit light when they are struck by rapidly moving electrons. Electrical deflecting plates are used to control where the electrons strike. In Fig. 2.25, electrons with an initial horizontal velocity of 2×10^7 m s^{-1} experience a vertical acceleration of 10^{14} m s^{-2} while they are between the plates, which are 0.2 m long. (a) How long will the electrons be between the plates? (b) In what direction will the electrons be moving after they leave the plates? (c) How far will the electrons be deflected vertically as they leave the plates?

*2-51 A tennis ball is served 2.5 m above the ground at an angle of 5° above the horizontal direction with an initial speed of 30 m s^{-1}. (a) When will it hit the ground? (b) How far will it travel?

2-52 A ski jumper leaves a slope at an angle of 20° above the horizontal direction. She lands 3.5 s later at a point 20 m below her takeoff point. (a) What was her initial speed? (b) How far does she travel horizontally?

2-53 A boy standing 10 m from a building can just barely reach the roof 12 m above him when he throws a ball at the optimum angle with respect to the ground. Find the initial velocity components of the ball.

2-54 Derive a formula for the maximum height reached by a projectile in terms of its initial velocity components.

*2-55 Show that the horizontal and vertical displacement components for a projectile satisfy an equation of the form $\Delta y = a \Delta x + b(\Delta x)^2$, so that the trajectory is a *parabola*.

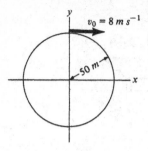

Figure 2.26. Problem 2-57.

c2-56 A point on the rim of a rolling wheel has its position given by $x = R \sin \omega t + \omega R t$, $y = R \cos \omega t + R$. (a) Sketch the path followed by the point. (This curve is called a cycloid.) (b) Find the instantaneous velocity and acceleration components at time t. (c) Find the magnitudes of v and a at time t.

c2-57 A runner goes around a circular track of radius 50 m at a constant speed of 8 m s^{-1} (Fig. 2.26). Assume she starts to run clockwise at $t = 0$ s from $x = 0$ m, $y = 50$ m. For $t > 0$, find the components of her (a) position; (b) velocity; (c) acceleration.

c2-58 (a) Show that the acceleration of an object undergoing circular motion at constant speed is directed toward the center of the circle. (b) Is this true if the speed is not constant? Explain.

c2-59 An object has an acceleration $\mathbf{a} = p\hat{\mathbf{x}} + qt\hat{\mathbf{y}}$, where p and q are constants. It starts from rest at the origin at $t = 0$. Using integration techniques (Sec. 1.9), for $t > 0$ find (a) its velocity; (b) its position.

ANSWERS TO REVIEW QUESTIONS

Q2-1, scalar has magnitude only, vector also has direction; **Q2-2**, arrows over symbols, boldface type; **Q2-3**, $A + B$, $A - B$, $2A$; **Q2-4**, $(A^2 + B^2)^{1/2}$; **Q2-5**, displacement, elapsed time; **Q2-6**, velocity change, elapsed time; **Q2-7**, magnitude, direction; **Q2-8**, one-dimensional motions; **Q2-9**, gravitational acceleration; **Q2-10**, vertical; **Q2-11**, vertical; **Q2-12**, horizontal, **Q2-13**, $-g$, 0.

SUPPLEMENTARY TOPICS
2.6 | PROJECTILES IN BIOMECHANICS

Many applications of projectile motion occur in athletics and in animal motion. Here we explore some further aspects of this subject.

In applications of projectile motion, it is convenient to have a formula for the horizontal distance traveled or *range*, R. To obtain this formula, consider a projectile launched from a flat surface (Fig. 2.27). The projectile lands after an elapsed time Δt when Δy returns to zero. The range can be found from the equation for Δx once this elapsed time is known.

With $\Delta y = 0$, we can rewrite $\Delta y = v_{0y} \Delta t - \frac{1}{2}g(\Delta t)^2$ as

$$(v_{0y} - \tfrac{1}{2}g \, \Delta t)\Delta t = 0$$

The solutions of this equation are $\Delta t = 0$, which corresponds to the instant the projectile was launched, and

$$\Delta t = \frac{2v_{0y}}{g} \qquad (2.17)$$

which gives the elapsed time the projectile is in motion.

Using this elapsed time in $\Delta x = v_{0x} \, \Delta t$, the range is

$$R = \frac{2v_{0x} v_{0y}}{g}$$

If the initial velocity of the projectile is at a *launch angle* θ_0 to the ground (Fig. 2.27), $v_{0x} = v_0 \cos \theta_0$ and $v_{0y} = v_0 \sin \theta_0$. Then the range can be expressed as

$$R = \frac{2v_0^2 \sin \theta_0 \cos \theta_0}{g} \qquad (2.18)$$

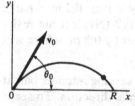

Figure 2.27. A projectile with a velocity v_0 launched at an angle θ_0 to the horizontal has a range R.

Alternatively, using the trigonometric identity $\sin 2\theta_0 = 2 \sin \theta_0 \cos \theta_0$,

$$R = \frac{v_0^2}{g} \sin 2\theta_0 \qquad (2.19)$$

Two interesting features of projectile motion can be extracted from these equations. First, $\sin \theta_0 = \cos (90° - \theta_0)$, so replacing θ_0 by its complement $90° - \theta_0$ in Eq. 2.18 leaves the range unchanged. For example, footballs punted at 30° or at 60° launch angles will land at the same spot. However, the ball kicked at 60° will have a higher trajectory and will stay in the air longer, giving the kicking team more time to run down the field (Fig. 2.28). Second, the sine has its maximum value of +1 when its argument is 90°, so the range is a maximum in Eq. 2.19 when $2\theta = 90°$ or $\theta = 45°$. *The maximum range on flat ground occurs when the launch angle is 45°* (Fig. 2.28).

The calculation of the range is somewhat more complicated when the takeoff and landing heights are not equal. However, we can see from Fig. 2.29 that a shot put thrown from *above* ground level will have its greatest range with a launch angle *less* than 45°. Conversely, an object thrown from *below* its landing point will have its longest range for an angle *greater* than 45° (see Problem 2-73).

If air resistance is significant, then the analysis of the motion becomes rather complicated. Nevertheless, we can see generally what will happen. Air resistance opposes the motion and tends to reduce the velocity. More specifically, it produces an acceleration opposite to $\mathbf{v}$. As a projectile rises, air resistance steadily diminishes the vertical velocity

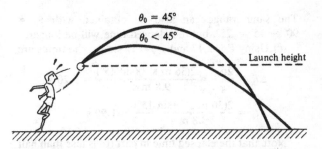

Figure 2.29. A shot put is thrown from above ground level. The trajectories for a launch angle of 45° and a smaller launch angle cross at a point below the launch height. The flatter trajectory has a longer range. In general, the launch angle that will produce the largest range is less than 45° if the landing point is below the launch point.

component. Thus the maximum height reached by the projectile is reduced. Also, v_x decreases steadily throughout the motion. If the motion continues long enough, v_x becomes small, and the motion is nearly vertical. Thus the symmetry of the trajectory is destroyed. The projectile is closer to the vertical direction as it falls than as it rises. This is easily seen when a football is kicked high in the air or when a golf ball is hit a long distance.

The following example illustrates how the range formulas can be used to analyze a situation in athletics.

Example 2.13

A baseball player can throw a ball at 36 m s^{-1}. (a) What is the greatest distance he can throw the ball, assuming it is caught at the same height at which he releases it? (b) If he wishes to throw the ball half this maximum distance in the shortest possible time, at what angle should he throw it? (c) What are the elapsed times in the two situations?

(a) The maximum range occurs for a launch angle of 45°, or $\sin 2\theta_0 = 1$ in Eq. 2.19. Thus

$$R = \frac{v_0^2}{g} = \frac{(36 \text{ m s}^{-1})^2}{9.8 \text{ m s}^{-2}} = 132 \text{ m}$$

(b) Solving Eq. 2.19 for $\sin 2\theta_0$ and using $R = (132 \text{ m})/2 = 66 \text{ m}$,

$$\sin 2\theta_0 = \frac{gR}{v_0^2} = \frac{(9.8 \text{ m s}^{-2})(66 \text{ m})}{(36 \text{ m s}^{-1})^2} = 0.5$$

$$2\theta_0 = 30°$$

$$\theta_0 = 15°$$

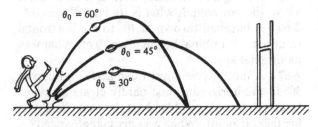

Figure 2.28. Footballs kicked with the same initial speed from ground level with launch angles of 30° and 60° have the same range. The maximum range occurs when the launch angle is 45°.

The same range can also be obtained with $\theta_0 = 90° - 15° = 75°$, but the elapsed time will be longer.

(c) Using Eq. 2.17 and $v_{0y} = v_0 \sin \theta_0$, the times are

$$\Delta t_a = \frac{2v_{0y}}{g} = \frac{2(36 \text{ m s}^{-1})(\sin 45°)}{9.8 \text{ m s}^{-2}} = 5.20 \text{ s}$$

$$\Delta t_b = \frac{2(36 \text{ m s}^{-1})(\sin 15°)}{9.8 \text{ m s}^{-2}} = 1.90 \text{ s}$$

Note that the elapsed time in part (b) is less than half that in (a), even though the range is halved, because the trajectory is much flatter. The time for *two* of the shorter throws is less than Δt_a by $(5.20 \text{ s}) - 2(1.90 \text{ s}) = 1.40 \text{ s}$. Rather than throwing directly to the plate, an outfielder frequently throws to a player who relays the ball to home plate. This makes the accuracy less critical and often saves time. (Allowing for the time to make the second throw reduces the savings, while air resistance effects increase them.)

Horizontal Jumping

In Section 1.8, we saw that the constant acceleration formulas can be used to analyze vertical jumping by animals. Similarly, the projectile motion formulas can be used to discuss horizontal jumping, since they accurately describe the motion while the animal is in the air if air resistance is negligible.

Although a 45° launch angle produces the maximum range on flat ground for a given initial speed (Fig. 2.30), an animal may customarily jump at some other angle for reasons related to its needs or structure. For example, locusts often jump into the air and then start flying. In this case the range of the jump is clearly irrelevant, but the time duration may be significant. Whether or not they begin to fly, locusts usually jump at about 55°.

Figure 2.30. Frogs frequently jump with a launch angle of approximately 45°, the angle that produces the maximum range on flat ground.

The calculation of the takeoff velocity is illustrated in the following example.

Example 2.14

What is the takeoff speed of a locust if its launch angle is 55° and its range is 0.8 m?

Since we know R and θ_0, we can find v_0 from

$$R = \frac{v_0^2}{g} \sin \theta_0 \cos \theta_0$$

With $\sin 55° = 0.819$ and $\cos 55° = 0.574$,

$$v_0^2 = \frac{gR}{2 \sin \theta_0 \cos \theta_0} = \frac{(9.8 \text{ m s}^{-2})(0.8 \text{ m})}{2(0.819)(0.574)}$$

$$= 8.3 \text{ m}^2 \text{ s}^{-2}$$

$$v_0 = 2.9 \text{ m s}^{-1}$$

EXERCISES ON SUPPLEMENTARY TOPICS

Section 2.6 | Projectiles in Biomechanics

2-60 A football is kicked at 20 m s^{-1} from ground level. Find its range if the launch angle is (a) 30°; (b) 60°; (c) 45°.

2-61 In the preceding exercise, how long will the football be in the air in each of the three cases?

2-62 An astronaut wearing his spacesuit can broad jump 2 m on the earth. How far can he jump on a planet where the gravitational acceleration is half that at the surface of the earth?

2-63 A girl wishes to throw a snowball at another child. If she can throw the snowball at 20 m s^{-1}, how far can she stand from the other child and still reach him?

2-64 A rifle is fired horizontally from the top of a tall mountain. Using a sketch, show the effect of the earth's curvature on the range of the bullet.

2-65 A kangaroo can jump 8 m. If it takes off at 45° to the horizontal, what is its takeoff speed?

2-66 A baseball thrown at 10° to the horizontal returns to its original height after 70 m. What was its original speed?

2-67 A motorcycle stunt rider leaves a ramp at 30° to the horizontal, just barely clears a row of trucks 36 m wide, and lands at the same height as his takeoff point. What was his takeoff speed?

2-68 A rifle is aimed slightly above a target 200 m away at the same height as the rifle. The bullet leaves the muzzle at 500 m s^{-1} and strikes the center of the target. At what angle to the horizontal is the rifle barrel?

2-69 A football is kicked 60 m on a level field. If the launch angle is 60°, how large is its initial velocity?

2-70 A rescue ship is to fire a shell trailing a lifeline to a distressed vessel located at a distance of 300 m. The initial velocity of the shell is 100 m s^{-1}. What are the possible launch angles? (Neglect the effect of the trailing lifeline.)

2-71 A mortar shell is fired at a ground-level target 500 m distant with an initial velocity of 90 m s^{-1}. What is its launch angle? (Mortars are fired at large launch angles.)

2-72 A football is kicked from ground level on a level field with an initial velocity v_0 and a launch angle θ_0. Find the velocity v and the angle θ at which it hits the ground.

PROBLEMS ON SUPPLEMENTARY TOPICS

2-73 With the aid of a sketch, show that the maximum range for an object launched at a given speed from below its landing point occurs for a launch angle greater than 45°.

2-74 (a) Explain why the maximum range for a man doing a standing broad jump is not obtained for a takeoff angle of 45°. (b) Should the angle be less than or greater than 45°? Explain.

2-75 A frog can jump 0.9 m with a takeoff angle of 45°. (a) What initial velocity does this require? (b) With this same initial velocity directed vertically, how high could a frog jump? (c) The maximum height jumped by frogs is 0.3 m. What are some possible explanations for this difference?

2-76 A flea can jump 0.03 m. (a) If the takeoff angle is 70°, what is the initial velocity? (b) If the flea achieves this velocity in a takeoff distance of 8×10^{-4} m, what is its average acceleration during takeoff?

2-77 A boy can throw a ball a maximum horizontal distance of 60 m. Assuming he can throw equally hard in the vertical direction, how high can he throw a ball?

*2-78 Show that for a ball kicked on level ground, the ratio of the maximum height reached to the range is $\frac{1}{4} \tan \theta_0$.

*2-79 The curvature of the earth becomes important in projectile calculations when the distance traveled R is a significant fraction of the radius of the earth, R_E. Ignoring any possible variations in g, show that (a) the extra time the projectile is in motion is approximately given by $\Delta t \simeq \Delta y/v_{0y} \simeq (R^2/2R_E)/v_{0y}$; (b) the fractional error $\Delta R/R$ is given by $\Delta R/R = v_{0x}^2/gR_E$.

2-80 Using the equation in the preceding problem, find the fractional error in the range of a projectile due to the curvature of the earth if the projectile is fired with a launch angle of 45° and an intended range of 100 km. (The average radius of the earth is 6.38×10^6 m.)

c2-81 (a) Explain why the launch angle θ which gives the maximum range must satisfy $dR/d\theta = 0$. (b) Using this requirement, show that a 45° launch angle produces the maximum range on flat ground.

Additional Reading

Sir James Gray, *How Animals Move*, Cambridge University Press, Cambridge, 1953. Pages 69–80 discuss jumping.

R. McNeill Alexander, *Animal Mechanics*, University of Washington Press, Seattle, 1968. Pages 28–33 discuss jumping.

David F. Griffing, *The Dynamics of Sports—Why That's the Way the Ball Bounces*, Mohican, Loudonville, Ohio, 1982. Basic physics applied to track and field, swimming, water skiing, football, etc.

Scientific American articles:

Stillman Drake and James MacLachlan, Galileo's Discovery of the Parabolic Trajectory, March 1975, p. 102.

Cornelius T. Leondes, Inertial Navigation for Aircraft, March 1970, p. 80.

Graham Hoyle, The Leap of the Grasshopper, January 1958, p. 30.

Miriam Rothschild et al., The Flying Leap of the Flea, November 1973, p. 92.

CHAPTER 3
NEWTON'S
LAWS OF MOTION

Having learned how to describe motion, we can now turn to the more fundamental question of what causes motion. An object is set into motion when it is pushed or pulled or subjected to a *force*. The discussion of forces and their effects is the central topic in mechanics.

Although there are many kinds of forces in nature, the effects of any force are described accurately by three general laws of motion first stated fully by Sir Isaac Newton (1642–1727). Guided by earlier astronomical observations and making several giant steps of intuition, Newton developed the laws of motion and also the expression for the gravitational attraction between two objects. He then showed that the orbital motions of the planets and the moon were in quantitative agreement with the predictions he made using these laws.

Newton's work represented a tremendous step forward in our understanding of the natural world and exerted a great influence on science and on the way people viewed science. For over two centuries, Newton's laws of motion served as the foundation of mechanics, with later workers finding full agreement between theory and experiment for a wide range of phenomena. Even though twentieth-century advances have shown that Newton's laws are inadequate at the atomic scale and at velocities comparable to the speed of light, 3×10^8 m s^{-1}, they provide an extremely accurate framework for discussing the motions of macroscopic objects at ordinary velocities. Thus, they are fully adequate for most applications in fields such as astronomy, biomechanics, geology, and engineering. The twentieth-century modifications of mechanics are discussed in later units.

3.1 | FORCE, WEIGHT, AND GRAVITATIONAL MASS

If we push or pull an object, we are exerting a force on it. Forces have both magnitudes and directions, so they are vector quantities. It is found that the *net* or *total* force on an object is the vector sum of all the forces acting on the object. For example, if two forces equal in magnitude but opposite in direction act on an object, there is no net force (Fig. 3.1a).

Forces that are exerted only when two objects are in contact are referred to as *contact forces*. Examples are the force exerted by a compressed spring on an attached object, the upward force exerted by a table on a book resting upon it, and the force exerted on a bone by a contracting muscle. Other forces, including gravitational, magnetic, and electric forces, can be exerted between objects that are not in contact. For example, the earth is kept in a nearly circular orbit by the gravitational attraction of the sun. However, the underlying origin of the contact forces that objects exert on each other lies in electrical and magnetic forces acting among the constituent atomic particles, so this distinction is not clear-cut.

To make quantitative statements about forces, we must define a force unit. One way to do this is to use a spring to measure the gravitational force on an object adopted as a standard. If the spring is compressed, a pointer moves along a calibrated dial. When the standard is placed on a plate mounted on the spring, the pointer moves a certain distance. The standard object is then said to exert a force of one unit on the spring. The same reading will always be obtained if this procedure is performed at

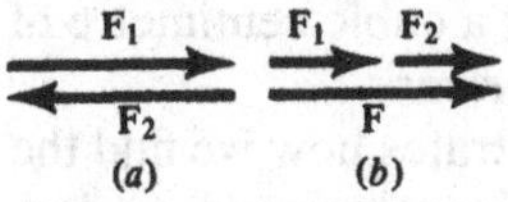

Figure 3.1. Forces have both magnitudes and directions and are vector quantities. (*a*) $\mathbf{F}_1$ and $\mathbf{F}_2$ are equal in magnitude but opposite, so their sum is zero. (*b*) Since $\mathbf{F}_1$ and $\mathbf{F}_2$ are equal, the net force is $\mathbf{F} = \mathbf{F}_1 + \mathbf{F}_2 = 2\mathbf{F}_1$.

points on the earth's surface where the gravitational acceleration is the same. Other forces can then be measured by determining the compression of the spring once the dial has been calibrated using multiple copies of the standard object. In Section 3.6, we see that the force unit can also be defined by measuring the acceleration of a standard object.

The S.I. force unit is the *newton* (N), and the British unit is the *pound* (lb). To three significant figures, these units are related by

$$1 \text{ N} = 0.225 \text{ lb}$$

We will use the S.I. unit exclusively.

A particularly important force is the gravitational force on an object, which is referred to as its *weight* **w**. The weight of a fairly heavy man might be 1000 N, or 225 lb.

Closely related to the weight is the *gravitational mass m* of an object, which is defined as the weight divided by the gravitational acceleration g at the location of the object:

$$m = \frac{w}{g} \qquad (3.1)$$

The gravitational force pulls an object downward along the direction it will fall if it is not supported. Thus the weight **w** is parallel to the gravitational acceleration **g**, and Eq. 3.1 can be written in vector form as

$$\mathbf{w} = m\mathbf{g} \qquad (3.2)$$

The S.I. unit of gravitational mass is the *kilogram* (kg). With Eq. 3.2, the force and mass units are related by

$$1 \text{ N} = (1 \text{ kg})(1 \text{ m s}^{-2}) = 1 \text{ kg m s}^{-2}$$

For example, a man who weighs 1000 N on the earth has a gravitational mass of

$$\frac{w}{g} = \frac{1000 \text{ N}}{9.8 \text{ m s}^{-2}} = 102 \text{ kg}$$

TABLE 3.1

Representative masses in kilograms

Electron	9×10^{-31}
Proton	2×10^{-27}
Oxygen atom	3×10^{-26}
Insulin molecule (a small protein)	10^{-23}
Penicillin molecule	10^{-18}
Giant amoeba	10^{-8}
Ant	10^{-5}
Hummingbird	10^{-2}
Dog	10^{1}
Human	10^{2}
Elephant	10^{4}
Blue whale	10^{5}
Oil tanker	10^{8}
Moon	7×10^{22}
Earth	6×10^{24}
Sun	2×10^{30}
Our galaxy	2×10^{41}

An object with a gravitational mass of 1 kg weighs $w = mg = (1 \text{ kg})(9.8 \text{ m s}^{-2}) = 9.8 \text{ N}$. Since $1 \text{ N} = 0.225 \text{ lb}$, its weight is $(9.8)(0.225 \text{ lb}) = 2.2 \text{ lb}$. This is a handy conversion factor to remember: a 1-kg mass has a weight of approximately 2.2 lb.

The mass, denoted dimensionally by M, completes the basic set of physical dimensions. All mechanical quantities can be written in terms of the dimensions of length, time, and mass. Table 3.1 shows the masses of some representative objects.

In this section, we have introduced two major concepts, force and gravitational mass. A force is any push or pull on an object. The gravitational force on an object is referred to as its weight, and the gravitational mass of an object is its weight divided by the gravitational acceleration. We explore the relationships among forces and masses in the following sections.

3.2 | DENSITY

When we talk about the properties of materials in a general way, rather than about specific objects, it is often convenient to refer to the mass per unit volume or the *density*. If a sample of a material has a mass m and a volume V, the density is given by the ratio

$$\rho = \frac{mass}{volume} = \frac{m}{V} \qquad (3.3)$$

(The symbol ρ is the Greek letter "rho.") In S.I. units, densities are measured in kilograms per cubic metre (kg m^{-3}). For example, if a block of wood has a mass of 50 kg and a volume of 0.1 m^3, its density is $\rho = m/V = (50 \text{ kg})/(0.1 \text{ m}^3) = 500 \text{ kg m}^{-3}$.

Table 3.2 lists the densities of some materials. Note that the density varies with the temperature and the pressure, especially for gases.

Closely related is the concept of the *relative density* or *specific gravity*, which is defined as the ratio of the density of a substance to that of water at 0°C (Celsius). The relative density can be found readily from Table 3.2, since the density of water at 0°C is 1000 kg m^{-3}. For example, the relative density of mercury is the dimensionless number 13,600/1000 = 13.6. From the conversion factor given in the table,

TABLE 3.2

Some representative densities in kilograms per cubic metre. Densities of materials are at atmospheric pressure and 0°C, except as noted. (At 0°C, 1 cm^3 of water has a mass of 1 gram.)

Interstellar space	$10^{-18} - 10^{-21}$
Best laboratory vacuum	10^{-17}
Hydrogen (H$_2$)	0.0899
Air, at 0°C and 1 atmosphere	1.29
at 100°C and 1 atmosphere	0.95
at 0°C and 50 atmospheres	6.5
Water, at 0°C and 1 atmosphere	1,000
at 100°C and 1 atmosphere	958
at 0°C and 50 atmospheres	1,002
Whole blood, at 25°C	1,059.5
Mercury	13,600
Aluminum	2,700
Iron, steel	7,800
Copper	8,900
Lead	11,300
Gold	19,300
The earth, density of core	9,500
The sun, density at center	1.6×10^5
White dwarf stars	$10^8 - 10^{15}$
Atomic nuclei	10^{17}
Neutron stars	10^{17}

we also see, for example, that a cubic centimetre of mercury has a mass of 13.6 grams.

The following example illustrates how we find the mass of an object from its dimensions and its density.

Example 3.1

A cylindrical aluminum rod has a radius of 1.2 cm and a length of 2 m. What is its mass?

Table 3.2 lists the density of aluminum. Thus with the definition of the density, $\rho = m/V$, we can find the mass of the rod once we have its volume. For a cylinder, $V = \pi r^2 l$. Converting the radius to metres, the mass is

$$m = \rho V = \rho \pi r^2 l = (2700 \text{ kg m}^{-3})\pi(0.012 \text{ m})^2(2 \text{ m})$$
$$= 2.44 \text{ kg}$$

3.3 | NEWTON'S FIRST LAW

According to the Aristotelian view that dominated medieval ideas about motion, all objects move only if some force causes the motion to occur. Thus a wagon detached from the horse that was pulling it would quickly come to rest because no force is pulling it along. The modern view is that the cart slows down and stops because of frictional forces acting upon it. This view is summarized in Newton's first law, which states that

Every object continues in a state of rest, or of uniform motion in a straight line, unless it is compelled to change that state by forces acting upon it.

An equivalent statement of the first law is that if there is no force on an object, or if there is no net force when two or more forces act on the object, then

(1) an object at rest remains at rest, and
(2) an object in motion continues to move with constant velocity.

The first law holds true in the form stated only for measurements made by certain observers. A girl riding on a merry-go-round sees objects not subjected to any net force undergo rather complex motions, while a boy at rest on the ground sees them at rest or moving with constant velocity. Thus Newton's first law as stated is true for the boy at rest but not for the girl. The point is that the girl is accelerating, since her velocity is changing, and Newton's first law as stated does not hold true for someone who is accelerating.

The first law leads us to define an *inertial* coordinate system or reference frame as one in which Newton's first law holds true as stated. Strictly speaking, the boy in the preceding example is not quite in an inertial frame, since he is standing on the earth, which is revolving daily on its axis, rotating annually about the sun, and moving with the solar system relative to the distant stars. Usually these effects can be ignored, and the earth can be treated as an inertial frame. However, the earth's daily revolution does affect the large-scale motions of the atmosphere and the oceans.

A coordinate system moving at a constant velocity relative to an inertial frame is itself an inertial frame. To see this, consider an observer standing on the ground and another in a car moving at a constant velocity. If both observers measure the velocity of a moving object, their measurements will differ by their *constant* relative velocity. Hence they will agree on whether the motion of the object is accelerated, and Newton's first law will work equally well for both observers.

From this discussion, we see that cars or airplanes moving at constant velocities relative to the ground are inertial reference frames, while accelerating vehicles, merry-go-rounds, and playground swings are not. As a further illustration, consider the driver of an accelerating car. She feels the back of her seat exerting a force on her. Relative to the ground, she is accelerating, but relative to the car, she is not. The first law is consistent with the measurements of an observer at rest on the ground: the state of motion of the driver is being changed by forces acting on her. The first law does not work in the frame of the accelerating car, since there is a force on the driver, but she remains at rest.

Friction | The fact that friction is often present led Aristotle and others to conclude that a force is required to sustain motion. For example, if you briefly push a box and let it slide, it gradually slows and comes to rest. You have to keep pushing the box to keep it moving, suggesting that in general, objects do not move unless you exert a force. However, the box will slide more easily on a waxed wooden floor than on a rough concrete surface. The force you must exert to keep it moving is less on the smoother surface, and it will be small if the box and floor are very smooth. Thus there is no specific force you must exert on the box so that it maintains a constant velocity. Rather, the floor exerts a frictional force on the box that tends to change its motion. You must provide an opposing force to keep the velocity constant. In the absence of friction or any other force, an object moves with a constant velocity.

3.4 | EQUILIBRIUM

Newton's first law tells us that the state of motion of an object remains unchanged whenever the net force on the object is zero. This can happen if no forces act on an object. More commonly, it occurs because two or more forces acting on an object add to zero or "balance." When the state of motion of an object remains unchanged even though two or more forces act upon it, the object is said to be in *equilibrium*.

Right now, assuming you are sitting at rest in your chair, the net force on you is zero. However, your weight—the gravitational force exerted by the earth—is pulling you downward. This force is offset by upward forces exerted on you by the chair and the floor. This is an illustration of equilibrium.

The first law applies to objects in uniform motion as well as objects at rest. Consider a car moving with a constant speed and direction. The velocity of the car is constant, so there is no *net* force on it. There are, of course, forces acting upon the car, but they add up to zero. The car is in equilibrium.

The statement that the net force on a car moving at a constant velocity is zero is quite contrary to the Aristotelian concept that forces are required to maintain motion. It is also contrary to the intuitive ideas about motion that people often develop before they study physics. The observation that an object is moving at a constant velocity and therefore cannot have a net force acting upon it is a crucial element in analyzing many physics problems and applications.

The simplest kind of equilibrium situation is one where two forces act on an object. When you stand

Figure 3.2. Since the woman is in equilibrium, the force **N** exerted by the floor is equal in magnitude to her weight **w** and opposite in direction.

motionless, you experience the downward gravitational pull of the earth, your weight **w**. The weight is balanced by an upward force exerted on you by the floor. This force is perpendicular or normal to the floor, so it is called a *normal force*. (The symbol **N** is generally used for normal forces. Its magnitude N should not be confused with the conventional abbreviation N for the force unit, the newton.)

Example 3.2

A woman has a mass of 60 kg. She is standing on a floor and remains at rest (Fig. 3.2). Find the normal force exerted on her by the floor.

The net force **w** + **N** on the woman must be zero. Thus the upward normal force must have the same magnitude as her weight, which acts downward. Symbolically, **w** + **N** = 0, and **w** = −**N**. Her weight is

$$w = mg = (60 \text{ kg})(9.8 \text{ m s}^{-2}) = 588 \text{ N}$$

Hence the normal force has a magnitude of $N = 588$ N.

Often three or more forces act on an object in equilibrium. This is the case for the traffic light in Fig. 3.3. It remains at rest, so the vector sum of its weight and the forces exerted by the cables must be zero. Similarly, the sled in Fig. 3.4 is moving with a

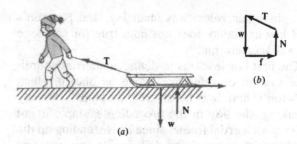

Figure 3.4. (*a*) A sled moving with a constant velocity. Forces acting on it include the weight **w**, a normal force **N**, a frictional force **f** retarding its motion, and a force **T** exerted by the rope. (*b*) The vector sum of the forces is zero because the sled is in equilibrium.

constant velocity, so the net force on it must be zero. The vector sum of the forces on the cart in the next example is also zero.

Example 3.3

An ice cream vendor (Fig. 3.5*a*) exerts a force of 40 N to overcome friction and push his cart at a constant velocity. The cart has a mass of 150 kg. Find the forces acting on the cart.

The vertical forces acting on the cart are its weight **w**, which acts downward, and an upward normal force **N** exerted on the cart by the floor. The vendor exerts a horizontal force **F** to the left. The frictional force **f** opposes the motion, and is directed toward the right. The net force on the cart is the sum **w** + **N** + **F** + **f**, and it is equal to zero since the cart is moving with a constant velocity. We add the force vectors by placing the tail of one at the head of the preceding vector. Since the sum is zero, we must come back to the tail of the first vector when all four forces are added (Fig. 3.5*b*).

Since the horizontal and vertical forces are at right

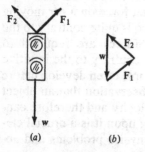

Figure 3.3. (*a*) A traffic light suspended by two cables is in equilibrium under the action of three forces. (*b*) The vector sum of the forces is zero.

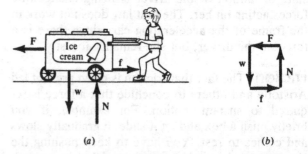

Figure 3.5. (*a*) A vendor pushes an ice cream cart at a constant velocity. (*b*) The vector sum of the forces acting on the cart is zero, since it is in equilibrium.

angles, the figure in Fig. 3.5*b* is a rectangle. Its opposite sides are equal, so

$$f = F = 40 \text{ N}$$
$$N = w = mg = (150 \text{ kg})(9.8 \text{ m s}^{-2}) = 1470 \text{ N}$$

Types of Equilibrium

There are three types of equilibrium: *unstable*, *stable*, and *neutral*. These are best defined with the aid of an example.

Suppose a ball is placed exactly at the crest of a hill (point *A* in Fig. 3.6). It may remain at rest there briefly, but if a slight breeze moves it a bit, the ball will rapidly accelerate down the hill. This is *unstable equilibrium*: a small displacement leads to an unbalanced force that further increases the displacement from the equilibrium location.

Conversely, in the depression at *B*, the ball will roll back if disturbed. This is *stable equilibrium*: a small displacement leads to an unbalanced force that tends to restore the object to the equilibrium position.

Finally, on the flat area near *C*, there is still no unbalanced force even if the ball is displaced slightly. It is in equilibrium at any location near *C*. This is *neutral equilibrium*.

Our discussion of equilibrium has dealt so far only with translational motion, motion in which each point in an object moves in the same direction. However, objects can also rotate. The rotational state of motion will be unchanged if there is no net twisting effect or *torque* on the object. We discuss rotational equilibrium in the next chapter. In this chapter, we assume the forces are applied so there is no net torque. This is always the case if the forces are all applied at a common point or so that their *lines of action* cross at a common point. In Fig. 3.3, for example, the lines of action of the tension forces and the weight meet at the top of the light.

We noted in the preceding section that two inertial observers will agree on whether the motion of an object is accelerated. For example, consider two observers of the traffic light in Fig. 3.3. A driver stopped at the light finds that the light is stationary, so that it must be equilibrium. Another driver approaching the light at a constant velocity relative to the first driver observes that the light is moving at a constant velocity relative to her. She also concludes that the light is in equilibrium, since its velocity is

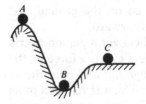

Figure 3.6. A ball at the crest of a hill is in unstable equilibrium. In the depression, it is in stable equilibrium. On the level plain, it is in neutral equilibrium.

constant. The drivers agree that the light is in equilibrium, even though they measure different velocities for it. Both drivers find that there is no net force on the light.

To summarize, an object is in translational equilibrium if the vector sum of the forces on it is zero. The type of equilibrium—stable, unstable, or neutral—is determined by noting how the forces change when the object is displaced slightly from its original state of rest or uniform motion.

3.5 | NEWTON'S THIRD LAW

We turn now to Newton's third law, deferring the second law until the next section. The third law relates the forces that two objects exert on each other, and it is familiar in a general way from our everyday experiences. For example, suppose you are at rest in a swimming pool. If you push a wall with your legs, the wall exerts a force that propels you further into the pool. The *reaction* force the wall exerts on you is opposite in direction to the force you exert on the wall (Fig. 3.7). Similarly, in order for you to start walking forward, your feet

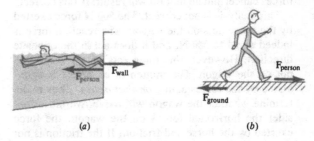

Figure 3.7. The force on the person is equal in magnitude and opposite in direction to the force on (*a*) the wall and (*b*) the ground.

must exert a backward force on the ground; the ground, in turn, pushes you forward.

Newton observed that whenever a person exerts a force on an object, the object exerts a force on the person that is *equal in magnitude and opposite in direction*. This relationship, which is referred to as the third law of motion, holds true whether or not the person or the object accelerates. The two forces acting between a person and an object, or between two objects, are called *action* and *reaction* forces.

The general statement of the third law is

*If one object exerts a force **F** on a second, then the second object exerts an equal but opposite force −**F** on the first.*

For example, if you push a chair with a horizontal force of 10 N, the chair exerts a force on you of 10 N in the opposite direction. If the earth exerts a downward 5-N gravitational force on a book, then the book exerts an upward 5-N force on the earth.

It is important to realize that in each case the two forces—the action and reaction forces—act on different objects, so their effects do *not* cancel out. When you push the chair, it starts to move unless there is a sufficiently large frictional force exerted by the floor to prevent this. Or if a book is not subjected to any force other than gravity, it will fall toward the earth. In other words, *only the forces acting on a particular object can affect its state of motion*; the forces exerted *by* an object will affect the motion of *other* objects.

Example 3.4

A student considers a problem in which a horse pulls a wagon, exerting a force of 500 N. The wagon is initially at rest. The student argues that the reaction to this force is 500 N in the opposite direction, so that the forces cancel and no motion will result. Is this correct?

This analysis is not correct. The 500-N force exerted by the horse acts on the *wagon*. The reaction force is indeed equal to 500 N, and it does act in the opposite direction. However, this force acts on the *horse* and not on the wagon. The motion of an object is determined by the forces acting *on that object*. Thus to determine whether the wagon will move, we must consider the horizontal forces on the wagon: the force exerted by the horse and friction. If the friction is not large enough to balance the force applied by the horse, the wagon will begin to move. Without more information about the frictional force, the problem cannot be analyzed any further.

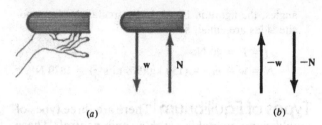

Figure 3.8. (*a*) Forces on a book in equilibrium. (*b*) The reaction to the weight of the book is a force −**w** on the earth. The reaction to the normal force is a force −**N** the book exerts on the hand.

Sometimes forces are equal in magnitude and opposite in direction, but they are nevertheless *not* action–reaction pairs in the sense of the third law. This often happens when an object is in equilibrium, and forces therefore cancel as a consequence of the *first* law. We illustrate this point with a simple example.

Example 3.5

A student holds a book so that it does not move (Fig. 3.8). The book weighs 20 N. Find (a) the forces acting on the book, and (b) the reactions to those forces.

(a) The forces acting on the book are its weight (down) and a normal force (up) due to the student's hand. As in the case of the woman standing on a floor (Example 3.2), the net force on the book must be zero since it remains at rest. Hence $N = w = 20$ N. This is a consequence of Newton's *first* law.

(b) The reactions to the weight and to the normal force act on other objects, not the book. The normal force is an upward force **N** exerted by the hand on the book. According to Newton's third law, the reaction is a downward force −**N** of 20 N on the *hand*. The weight **w** of the book is a downward force exerted by the earth. The reaction to this force is an upward 20-N force (−**w**) on the *earth* exerted by the book.

The student will be aware of the reaction force the book exerts on her hand, pushing it down. However, the upward force on the earth is not very apparent. The reason for this is the very large *mass* of the earth. This will be discussed in the next section.

3.6 | NEWTON'S SECOND LAW

Newton's first law states that when no net force acts on an object, it stays at rest or in motion with a constant velocity. The second law tells us what happens when this force is not zero.

Newton observed that when there is a net force on an object, it accelerates along the direction of that force. He also found that the net force and acceleration are proportional in magnitude. For example, if you exert twice as large a net force on a particular object, you will double its acceleration.

If two quantities are proportional, one is equal to some number or *proportionality constant* times the other. Thus we can relate the net force **F** and the acceleration **a** by *Newton's second law*,

$$\mathbf{F} = m\mathbf{a} \qquad (3.4)$$

The proportionality constant m is called the *inertial mass* of the object. We shall see in Section 3.10 that all the experimental evidence indicates that the inertial mass is equal to the gravitational mass defined in Section 3.1. This is a remarkable property of nature. It also permits us to use the single term *mass* for both the inertial or the gravitational masses.

The mass of an object is a measure of the amount of matter it comprises or, in other words, its inertia. The greater the mass of an object, the less effect a given force will have on its motion. For example, two identical bricks have twice the mass of one brick. If a force **F** produces a certain acceleration when applied to one brick, it produces half as large an acceleration when applied to the pair. Mass is related to, but very different from, weight. The weight of an object is the gravitational force on the object, and it is a vector quantity; mass is a scalar quantity.

The next example illustrates how the mass of an object determines its acceleration for a given force.

Example 3.6

A child pushes a sled across a frozen pond with a horizontal force of 20 N. Assume friction is negligible. (a) If the sled accelerates at 0.5 m s^{-2}, what is its mass? (b) Another child with a mass of 60 kg sits on the sled. What acceleration will the same force produce now?

(a) The sled does not move vertically, so its weight and the normal force exerted by the ice cancel. Thus the net force on the sled is the 20-N force exerted by the child. From the second law, **F** = m**a**, the mass is

$$m = \frac{F}{a} = \frac{20 \text{ N}}{0.5 \text{ m s}^{-2}}$$

$$= \frac{20 \text{ kg m s}^{-2}}{0.5 \text{ m s}^{-2}} = 40 \text{ kg}$$

Note that the units m s^{-2} cancel, so that the mass m is in kilograms, as expected.

(b) The total mass of the passenger and sled is 60 kg + 40 kg = 100 kg. Thus the acceleration is now

$$a = \frac{F}{m} = \frac{20 \text{ N}}{100 \text{ kg}} = 0.2 \text{ m s}^{-2}$$

The same force produces a smaller acceleration when applied to a more massive object.

We can see now why the equality of the action and reaction forces is sometimes not immediately apparent. Since **a** = **F**/m, the acceleration resulting from a given force varies inversely with the mass of the object. For example, suppose your weight is w. This means the earth is pulling you downward with a force of magnitude w. According to the third law, you are also pulling the earth upward with an equally large force. For example, if you step off a chair, you experience a downward acceleration $a = w/m = g = 9.8$ m s^{-2}. The earth also accelerates upward, but since its mass M is huge, this acceleration $a = w/M$ is undetectably small. Similarly, when a small car and a large truck collide, the forces on the two vehicles are equal in magnitude, but the car experiences a much larger acceleration than does the truck.

3.7 | THE SIGNIFICANCE OF NEWTON'S LAWS OF MOTION

Newton's three laws of motion are very fundamental statements about the physical world. All of mechanics may be viewed as Newton's laws applied in direct or indirect ways to a variety of forces and systems. Although we introduce many other quantities and concepts in our discussions of mechanics in the following chapters, none are so basic as Newton's laws of motion. Accordingly, before going on to discuss specific forces and examples of how one uses Newton's laws, we list these laws together here for emphasis and for convenient reference.

Newton's first law of motion: *When there is no net force on an object, (1) an object at rest remains at rest; and (2) an object in motion continues to move with a velocity that is constant in magnitude and direction.*

Born in 1642, the year of Galileo's death, Newton made the crucial advances needed to complete our understanding of motion. He also made major contributions to optics and mathematics.

Newton was a thin, frail baby and was raised by his grandmother after his widowed mother remarried when he was 2 years old. His difficult childhood may have contributed to his later psychotic tendencies. Throughout his brilliant career, he was extremely anxious when his work was published and irrationally violent whenever his ideas were challenged. He suffered at least two nervous breakdowns.

As an undergraduate at Cambridge (1661–1665), Newton soon mastered the literature of science and mathematics and began to enter unexplored regions. He formulated the binomial theorem and the basic concepts of calculus. During this period and the years immediately following, he also began to do research on optics and on planetary motion. He deduced that the force on a planet due to the sun must vary as $1/r^2$. Some 20 years later, he would extend this idea to the universal law of gravitation.

Although Newton's work was known only to a limited circle because of his reluctance to publish his research, he was appointed a professor at Cambridge in 1669. He developed the first reflecting telescope in order to circumvent the distortions inherent in lenses. When this telescope received an enthusiastic reception from the Royal Society of London, he was encouraged to present his other research in optics to the Society in 1672. Robert Hooke, the leading authority on optics, disagreed with some of Newton's ideas. This led to bitter disputes, with Newton finally withdrawing into isolation for some years.

Newton's greatest achievements were his advances in mechanics. Although many of his results were obtained quite early in his career, he did not present his theory of planetary motion until he was urged to do so in 1684 by Edmond Halley, an astronomer who had heard of Newton's work.

Newton's classic work, *Principia Mathematica*, appeared in 1687. Written in Latin, it contained the three laws of motion and the universal law of gravitation. This treatise constituted one of the foundations of modern science and made Newton internationally famous. It also effectively marked the end of Newton's active research, with his attention gradually turning to politics, theology, and scientific priority disputes.

Newton became master of the mint, a well-paying and normally undemanding job. However, he took the position seriously and was especially zealous in sending counterfeiters to the gallows. He also assumed the role of the leader of English science, becoming president of the Royal Society in 1703; in 1705, he became the first scientist to be knighted. Unfortunately, he repeatedly used his position to carry on bitter arguments with various scientists. The most prolonged of these was a 25-year battle with Leibniz (which ended with Newton's death in 1727) over credit for the development of the calculus. It is now agreed that Leibniz independently developed the calculus after Newton had, but before Newton published his results.

Newton's second law of motion: *The force* **F** *needed to produce an acceleration* **a** *is*

$$\mathbf{F} = m\mathbf{a} \qquad (3.4)$$

where m is the mass of the object.

Newton's third law of motion: *If one object exerts a force* **F** *on a second, then the second object exerts an equal but opposite force* −**F** *on the first.*

Note that in the form given, Newton's laws may be applied only with respect to inertial coordinate systems.

3.8 | SOME EXAMPLES OF NEWTON'S LAWS

We now give several examples of how Newton's laws of motion are used. In each case, we employ a systematic procedure for relating the acceleration of an object or objects to the forces present.

1 For each object, we draw a careful sketch showing the forces acting *on* that object.
2 We then apply Newton's second law **F** = *m***a** to *each object separately*. If there are *n* forces

$\mathbf{F}_1, \mathbf{F}_2, \ldots, \mathbf{F}_n$ acting on an object, the net force **F** is the sum of the forces, and we have

$$\mathbf{F} = \mathbf{F}_1 + \mathbf{F}_2 + \cdots + \mathbf{F}_n = m\mathbf{a}$$

In component form, this is

$$F_x = F_{1x} + F_{2x} + \cdots + F_{nx} = ma_x \quad (3.5)$$
$$F_y = F_{1y} + F_{2y} + \cdots + F_{ny} = ma_y \quad (3.6)$$

3 As in the earlier chapters, we usually do not substitute numerical values immediately. Instead we solve the equations for the unknown quantities symbolically and then substitute the numbers if they are given. This procedure facilitates checking for algebra and physics errors and often reduces the amount of arithmetic required.
4 We include the units of the numerical quantities and see that the final answer has the correct dimensions.

We use these steps in the examples below and in later chapters as well.

Example 3.7

An elevator has a mass of 1000 kg. (a) It accelerates upward at 3 m s^{-2}. What is the force T exerted by the

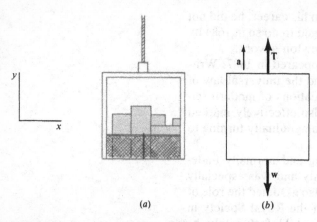

(a)

(b)

Figure 3.9. (a) The elevator and cable. (b) The force of the cable on the elevator, **T**, and the weight of the elevator, **w**. When the elevator is accelerating upward, **T** is greater than **w**.

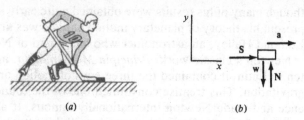

(a)

(b)

Figure 3.10. (a) A hockey player hits a puck. (b) Force diagram for the puck. Since the acceleration is horizontal, the net vertical force component is zero, and the normal force **N** has the same magnitude as the weight **w**.

cable on the elevator? (b) What is the force T if the acceleration is 3 m s^{-2} downward?

(a) The forces on the elevator are its weight **w** and the upward force **T** resulting from the cable (Fig. 3.9). Using Eq. 3.6 with two forces present,

$$F_{1y} + F_{2y} = ma_y$$

With $F_{1y} = T$ and $F_{2y} = -w = -mg$, this becomes

$$T - mg = ma_y$$

or

$$T = m(g + a_y) \qquad \text{(i)}$$

Then with $a_y = 3$ m s^{-2} and $m = 1000$ kg,

$$T = (1000 \text{ kg})(9.8 \text{ m s}^{-2} + 3 \text{ m s}^{-2})$$
$$= 12,800 \text{ N}$$

Note that T is greater than the weight mg. The cable must support the weight of the elevator and also provide the extra force needed for the acceleration.

(b) Equation i holds true no matter what the magnitude or sign of a_y. When **a** is directed downward, $a_y = -3$ m s^{-2}, and Eq. i gives

$$T = m(g + a_y)$$
$$= (1000 \text{ kg})(9.8 \text{ m s}^{-2} - 3 \text{ m s}^{-2}) = 6800 \text{ N}$$

Note that T is now less than the weight mg, since the elevator is being allowed to accelerate downward.

Example 3.8

An ice hockey player strikes a puck of mass 0.17 kg with his stick, accelerating it along the ice from rest to a speed of 20 m s^{-1} over a distance of 0.5 m (Fig. 3.10).

What force must he exert if the frictional force between the puck and the ice is negligible? (Assume the acceleration is constant.)

To solve this problem, we find the acceleration and then apply Newton's second law. From the constant acceleration formulas in Table 1.3, we have $v^2 = v_0^2 + 2a \, \Delta x$. With $v_0 = 0$,

$$a = \frac{v^2}{2 \, \Delta x} = \frac{(20 \text{ m s}^{-1})^2}{2(0.5 \text{ m})} = 400 \text{ m s}^{-2}$$

Then the net force on the puck is

$$F = ma = (0.17 \text{ kg})(400 \text{ m s}^{-2}) = 68 \text{ N}$$

This net force of 68 N in the direction of acceleration is the force **S** the player's stick must exert on the puck. This follows since the only other forces acting on the puck are its weight (downward) and a normal force (upward) due to the ice. These two forces must exactly cancel, since the acceleration has no vertical component, and $F_y = ma_y = 0$.

Suppose two people pull the ends of a rope with oppositely directed forces, $\mathbf{F}_1$ and $\mathbf{F}_2$. The rope also exerts forces $-\mathbf{F}_1$ and $-\mathbf{F}_2$ on the people, in accordance with the third law of motion. From the second law, we know $F_1 - F_2 = ma$, where m is the mass of the rope and a is its acceleration. If that acceleration is zero, or if the mass of the rope is so small that we can idealize the rope as having zero mass, then $F_1 - F_2 = 0$. In this special situation the forces *exerted by the rope* on the two people are equal in magnitude, and the rope can be thought of as simply transmitting a force from one person to the other; it is as though they were holding each other's hands and pulling. The force at any point in the rope is referred to as the *tension*. It is the same everywhere in the rope only if the rope is unaccel-

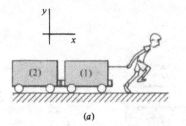

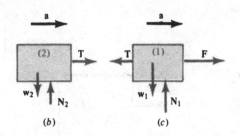

Figure 3.11. (a) The system in Example 3.9. (b) and (c) show the force diagrams of cars 2 and 1, respectively.

erated or if it is idealized as massless. The tension at any point in the rope can be measured in principle by cutting it there and inserting a spring balance.

Example 3.9

A child pulls a train of two cars with a horizontal force **F** of 10 N. Car 1 has a mass $m_1 = 3$ kg, and car 2 has a mass $m_2 = 1$ kg (Fig. 3.11). The mass of the string connecting the cars is small enough so it can be set equal to zero, and friction can be neglected. (a) Find the normal forces exerted on each car by the floor. (b) What is the tension in the string? (c) What is the acceleration of the train?

In this problem, there is a system of several objects. The three objects of interest are the two cars and the string connecting them. When Newton's second law **F** = m**a** is applied to each object, a set of equations results that must be solved simultaneously.

The fact that the string is massless means that the net force **F** = m**a** on the string must be zero. As we have explained, this implies that the forces *it exerts* on the two cars are equal in magnitude, so we have labeled its tension force by the same symbol **T** in the force diagrams for each of the cars.

(a) Since $a_y = 0$ for each car, $F_y = ma_y = 0$, so

$$N_2 - w_2 = 0$$

and

$$N_1 - w_1 = 0$$

Thus the normal forces exerted by the floor are

$$N_2 = w_2 = m_2 g = (1 \text{ kg})(9.8 \text{ m s}^{-2}) = 9.80 \text{ N}$$
$$N_1 = w_1 = m_1 g = (3 \text{ kg})(9.8 \text{ m s}^{-2}) = 29.4 \text{ N}$$

(b) For both cars, $a_x = a$; so for car 1, $F_x = m_1 a_x$ becomes

$$F - T = m_1 a \qquad \text{(i)}$$

Both T and a are unknowns, so we cannot find them from this one equation alone; as many equations as there are unknowns are needed to solve a problem.

The second equation relating T and a is obtained by applying $F_x = m_2 a_x$ to car 2:

$$T = m_2 a \qquad \text{(ii)}$$

This gives $a = T/m_2$. Substituting this for a in Eq. i,

$$F - T = m_1 \left(\frac{T}{m_2} \right)$$

Solving for T,

$$T = \frac{F}{1 + \dfrac{m_1}{m_2}} = \frac{10 \text{ N}}{1 + \dfrac{3 \text{ kg}}{1 \text{ kg}}} = 2.5 \text{ N}$$

(c) Now we can find a from Eq. ii:

$$a = \frac{T}{m_2} = \frac{2.5 \text{ N}}{1 \text{ kg}} = 2.5 \text{ m s}^{-2}$$

Note that if we had considered the train as a single object of mass $m = m_1 + m_2 = (3 + 1)$ kg = 4 kg, we could immediately have found the acceleration from $a = F/m = 10$ N/4 kg = 2.5 m s^{-2}. However, the normal and tension forces can only be found by considering the individual cars and not the system as a whole.

Example 3.10

A block of mass $m_1 = 20$ kg is free to move on a horizontal surface. A rope, which passes over a pulley, attaches it to a hanging block of mass $m_2 = 10$ kg (Fig. 3.12). Assuming for simplicity that the pulley and rope masses are negligible and that there is no friction, find (a) the forces on the blocks and (b) their acceleration. (c) If the system is initially at rest, how far has it moved after 2 s?

This problem is similar to the preceding problem of the two cars, although here one mass moves horizontally and one moves vertically. Again, the fact that the rope and pulley are massless implies that the force exerted by the rope on m_1 is equal in magnitude to the force exerted by the rope on m_2. Accordingly we denote both forces by the same symbol **T**.

(a) We first apply **F** = m**a** to the block on the surface. Since it has no vertical acceleration component,

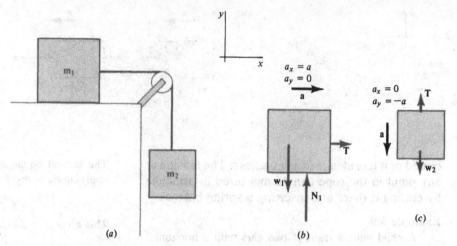

Figure 3.12. (b) and (c) are force diagrams for the two blocks when they are connected as shown in (a). *(a)*

the net vertical force component must be zero. Thus the normal force N_1 on block 1 due to the surface is

$$N_1 = w_1 = m_1 g = (20 \text{ kg})(9.8 \text{ m s}^{-2}) = 196 \text{ N}$$

The system is accelerating with an unknown acceleration a. Block 1 has $a_x = a$, so $F_x = m_1 a_x$ becomes

$$T = m_1 a \qquad \text{(i)}$$

Note that both T and a are unknown, so we cannot find either until we consider the motion of m_2.

We now apply Newton's second law to block 2. Since it is accelerating downward, $a_y = -a$, and $F_y = m_2 a_y$ becomes

$$T - w_2 = -m_2 a \qquad \text{(ii)}$$

This equation also involves the two unknowns, T and a. Since the number of equations now equals the number of unknowns, we can solve for T and a. From Eq. i we have $a = T/m_1$. Substituting this in Eq. ii gives

$$T - w_2 = -m_2 \frac{T}{m_1}$$

Solving for T,

$$T = \frac{w_2}{1 + \dfrac{m_2}{m_1}} = \frac{m_2 g}{1 + \dfrac{m_2}{m_1}} = \frac{(10 \text{ kg})(9.8 \text{ m s}^{-2})}{1 + \dfrac{10 \text{ kg}}{20 \text{ kg}}}$$

$$= 65.3 \text{ N}$$

(b) Using Eq. i, the acceleration is

$$a = \frac{T}{m_1} = \frac{65.3 \text{ N}}{20 \text{ kg}} = 3.27 \text{ m s}^{-2}$$

(c) Since the system is initially at rest and uniformly accelerated, the distance it moves in 2 s is

$$\Delta x = \tfrac{1}{2} a (\Delta t)^2 = \tfrac{1}{2}(3.27 \text{ m s}^{-2})(2 \text{ s})^2 = 6.54 \text{ m}$$

Thus if we know the initial position and velocity, we can find the subsequent motion from the forces.

Example 3.11

A parachutist of weight **w** strikes the ground with her legs flexed and comes to rest with an upward acceleration of magnitude $3g$. Find the force exerted on her by the ground during landing (Fig. 3.13).

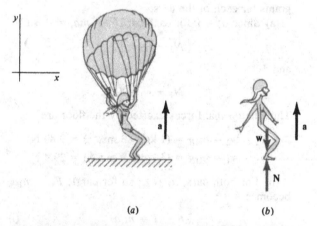

Figure 3.13. (a) A parachutist comes to rest with an acceleration of $3g$. (b) The forces on her are a normal force **N** due to the ground and her weight **w**.

The forces on the woman are her weight **w** and a normal force **N** due to the ground. With $m = w/g$ and $a = 3g$, $F_y = ma_y$ becomes

$$N - w = ma = \left(\frac{w}{g}\right)(3g) = 3w$$

$$N = 4w$$

The force on her feet due to the ground is four times her weight. By contrast, if she is simply standing on the ground, the normal force equals her weight. Note that if she holds her legs more stiffly during landing, she will come to rest with a greater acceleration in a shorter distance, and the force on her feet will be greater.

3.9 | GRAVITATIONAL FORCES

Newton's study of planetary motion led him to infer the formula for the gravitational force between two masses. This formula is referred to as the *law of universal gravitation* and is regarded as a fundamental law of nature. Using this law along with the three laws of motion, Newton was able to derive the observed laws of planetary motion. In addition, he was able to account accurately for the motion of the moon around the earth and to provide a qualitative explanation of the tides in our oceans.

The law of universal gravitation states that all objects in the universe attract each other. For two uniform spheres, or for two objects of any shape that are so small compared to their separation that they may be considered as point particles, the law has a simple form. If two spheres or particles have gravitational masses m and m' and their centers are separated by a distance r, the forces between the two spheres have a magnitude

$$F = \frac{Gmm'}{r^2} \tag{3.7}$$

G is called the *gravitational constant* and has a measured value of

$$G = 6.67 \times 10^{-11} \text{ N m}^2 \text{ kg}^{-2}$$

The gravitational forces are directed along the line connecting the centers of the two spheres (Fig. 3.14). The magnitude of the gravitational force varies as $1/r^2$, so Eq. 3.7 is referred to as an *inverse square law*.

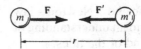

Figure 3.14. Two spheres exert attractive forces on each other. **F** and **F'** are equal in magnitude but opposite in direction, in accordance with Newton's third law of motion.

As noted, Eq. 3.7 applies directly to spheres and to particles. For more complex objects, the forces between all the pairs of particles in the objects must be summed to find the net gravitational forces on the objects. However, these net forces are still equal but opposite as required by the third law of motion.

The gravitational force exerted by the earth on an object is relatively large because of the large mass of the earth. In contrast, the gravitational force between two objects of moderate mass is very small and hard to detect, as is shown quantitatively in the next example.

Example 3.12

The centers of two 10-kg spheres are separated by 0.1 m. (a) What is their gravitational attraction? (b) What is the ratio of this attraction to the weight of one of the spheres?

(a) Using Newton's law of gravitation, the forces between the spheres have a magnitude

$$F = G\frac{mm'}{r^2} = (6.67 \times 10^{-11} \text{ N m}^2 \text{ kg}^{-2}) \frac{(10 \text{ kg})(10 \text{ kg})}{(0.1 \text{ m})^2}$$

$$= 6.67 \times 10^{-7} \text{ N}$$

The forces are directed along the line connecting the centers of the spheres.

(b) The weight of one of the spheres is

$$w = mg = (10 \text{ kg})(9.8 \text{ m s}^{-2}) = 98 \text{ N}$$

Thus the ratio of the gravitational forces between the spheres to the weight of a sphere is

$$\frac{F}{w} = \frac{6.67 \times 10^{-7} \text{ N}}{98 \text{ N}} = 6.81 \times 10^{-9}$$

The small size of this ratio explains why we do not notice the gravitational attractions among objects of ordinary size. However, the gravitational forces between two such objects can be observed and measured using very sensitive instruments.

In Chapter Five, we shall see how Newton's law of universal gravitation leads to an understanding of planetary and lunar motion and of the tides.

3.10 | WEIGHT

The weight of an object is the gravitational force it experiences. For an object near the surface of the earth, this force is mainly due to the earth's attraction.

Let us call the radius of the earth R_E and its mass M_E (Fig. 3.15). An object with a gravitational mass $\tilde{m}$ at the earth's surface is subjected to a gravitational force. From Eq. 3.7, this force is

$$F = G\frac{\tilde{m}M_E}{R_E^2} \qquad (3.8)$$

The acceleration g resulting from this force can be found from Newton's second law, $\mathbf{F} = m\mathbf{a}$, which contains the inertial mass m:

$$g = \frac{F}{m} = \frac{1}{m}\left(G\frac{\tilde{m}M_E}{R_E^2}\right)$$

If we assume that the inertial and gravitational masses are the same, then $\tilde{m}/m = 1$, and we find

$$g = G\frac{M_E}{R_E^2} \qquad (3.9)$$

This result says that the gravitational acceleration is the same for all objects. This is in agreement with experiments and justifies the assumption that the

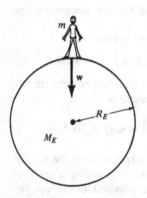

Figure 3.15. A person of mass m has a weight $w = GmM_E/R_E^2$ at the surface of the earth.

gravitational and inertial masses of an object are equal.

Note that the earth's radius R_E is 6380 km. Accordingly, the gravitational acceleration within a few metres or even a few kilometres of the surface will not differ appreciably from the value at the surface, 9.8 m s⁻².

As we have seen, mass and weight are related but quite different quantities. The mass of an object is an intrinsic property that is the same whether the object is in Chicago, on the moon, or in interstellar space. It is a measure of the amount of matter in the object and determines its inertia or its response to a force. The weight of an object varies from place to place and is the force resulting from gravity.

The mass of an object is determined *only* by the amount of matter present and is independent of its physical or chemical state. For example, if a cubic metre of oxygen gas at atmosphere pressure is cooled, it will liquefy and fill a volume of about 10^{-3} m³. Nevertheless, it will still have the same number of molecules and the same mass. Similarly, when a volume of hydrogen gas and another volume of oxygen gas combine to form liquid water, the volume is reduced by a large factor, but again the mass is unchanged. The following examples further illustrate the relationship between mass and weight.

Example 3.13

An astronaut weighs 700 N on the earth. What is his weight on planet X, which has a radius $R_X = R_E/2$ and a mass $M_X = M_E/8$?

On the earth, his weight is

$$w_E = \frac{GmM_E}{R_E^2}$$

where m is his mass. On planet X, his mass is the same, but his weight is

$$w_X = \frac{GmM_X}{R_X^2} = \frac{Gm(M_E/8)}{(R_E/2)^2}$$
$$= \frac{4}{8}\frac{GmM_E}{R_E^2} = \frac{1}{2}w_E$$

Thus his weight on planet X is $(\frac{1}{2})(700\ \text{N}) = 350$ N.

Example 3.14

Using the measured values of the gravitational acceleration g, the gravitational constant G, and the radius of the earth R_E, find the mass of the earth. (The radius of the earth is 6380 km = 6.38×10^6 m.)

We saw earlier that the gravitational force on an object of mass m at the surface of the earth is $w = mg$. With the universal law of gravitation, this force is also given by $F = GmM_E/R_E^2$. Hence

$$mg = \frac{GmM_E}{R_E^2}$$

Solving for M_E, the mass m cancels out, and we get

$$M_E = \frac{gR_E^2}{G} = \frac{(9.8 \text{ m s}^{-2})(6.38 \times 10^6 \text{ m})^2}{(6.67 \times 10^{-11} \text{ N m}^2 \text{ kg}^{-2})}$$
$$= 5.98 \times 10^{24} \text{ kg}$$

Thus the mass of the earth can be calculated from the measured quantities. It is then easy to calculate its average density, which provides a clue to its composition.

3.11 | EFFECTIVE WEIGHT

When an elevator starts to move upward, it accelerates briefly and then moves at a constant velocity until it approaches the desired floor. During the upward acceleration, we feel heavier than usual. Similarly, when the acceleration is downward, we have the feeling that our weight is reduced. Our weight is the gravitational force exerted on us by the earth, and that, of course, is not changed by our being in the elevator. However, our *perception* of our weight is determined by the forces exerted on us by the floor or chair or whatever is supporting us. These forces are not equal to our weight when we are accelerating.

We define the *effective weight* $\mathbf{w}^e$ of a person or an object as the total force that object exerts on a spring scale. According to Newton's third law of motion, this is equal in magnitude and opposite in direction to the force $\mathbf{S}$ the scale exerts on the person or object, so

$$\mathbf{w}^e = -\mathbf{S} \qquad (3.10)$$

While such a measurement may not always be feasible, this definition will be useful in understanding and calculating the effective weight of an accelerating object. The following example illustrates how the effective weight is found.

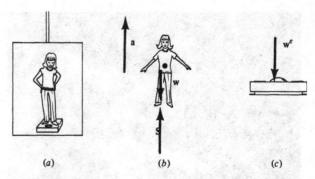

Figure 3.16. (*a*) A woman accelerating upward in an elevator. (*b*) The forces on the woman. (*c*) The woman exerts a force $\mathbf{w}^e$ on the spring scale. By Newton's third law, $\mathbf{S} = -\mathbf{w}^e$.

Example 3.15

A woman of mass m stands on a spring scale in an elevator. Find the effective weight of the woman if the elevator is accelerating upward at $0.2g$.

The forces acting on the woman are her weight $\mathbf{w} = m\mathbf{g}$ and the force $\mathbf{S}$ due to the spring scale (Fig. 3.16).

Using Newton's second law $\mathbf{F} = m\mathbf{a}$,

$$S - mg = ma, \qquad S = mg + ma$$

Since by definition the effective weight is equal in magnitude to the spring scale force S,

$$w^e = m(g + a) = mg(1 + 0.2) = 1.2mg$$

The effective weight of the woman is then 1.2 times her normal weight mg.

If the acceleration were downward, a similar calculation would show that the woman's effective weight is less than mg.

From Fig. 3.16, it is clear how to find the effective weight $\mathbf{w}^e$ in general. By definition, $\mathbf{w}^e = -\mathbf{S}$, where $\mathbf{S}$ is the force exerted by the scale. From Newton's second law, $\mathbf{S} + m\mathbf{g} = m\mathbf{a}$, or $-\mathbf{S} = m\mathbf{g} - m\mathbf{a}$. Thus,

$$\mathbf{w}^e = m\mathbf{g} - m\mathbf{a} \qquad (3.11)$$

An object in free fall has an acceleration $\mathbf{a}$ equal to $\mathbf{g}$, so its effective weight is zero. Since an artificial satellite in orbit around the earth is in free fall, an astronaut in such a satellite has zero effective weight, and will float freely about his spaceship if he is not tethered. However, even though his effective weight is zero, his mass has not changed (Fig. 3.17). If he carelessly pushes off hard from one wall and strikes the opposite wall headfirst, he will experi-

Figure 3.17.   An astronaut in free fall has a zero effective weight and perceives himself to be weightless. (Courtesy of NASA)

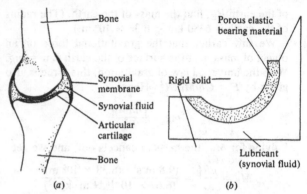

Figure 3.18.   Human joints are lubricated by synovial fluid squeezed through the porous cartilage lining the joint. (a) A typical human joint. (b) A model approximately equivalent to the joint. (From Duncan Dowson. "Lubrication in Human Joints." Verna Wright, ed., in *Lubrication and Wear in Joints*, Lippincott, Philadelphia, 1969.)

ence a large and unpleasant force as he abruptly decelerates.

3.12 | FRICTION

Friction is a force that always acts to resist the motion of one object sliding on another. Frictional forces are very important, since they make it possible for us to walk, use wheeled vehicles, and hold books. Microscopically, friction arises from many minute temporary bonds between the contact points of the two surfaces.

Frequently, we try to reduce the frictional forces that oppose some desired motion. This is often done with rollers or with wheels, since rolling peels the surfaces apart with a much smaller force than is required when they are torn apart by sliding.

Frictional forces in fluids are called *viscous forces*. They are often quite small compared to the friction between solid surfaces. Thus the use of lubricating liquids such as oil, which clings to the surfaces of metals, greatly reduces friction. Similarly, an air layer provides an almost frictionless support

for a hovercraft vehicle or an air track demonstration apparatus.

When we walk or run, we are not conscious of any friction in our knees or other leg joints. These and many other mammalian joints are well lubricated by *synovial fluid*, which is squeezed through the cartilage lining the joints when they move (Fig. 3.18). This lubricant tends to be absorbed when the joint is stationary, increasing the friction and making it easier to maintain a fixed position. This is an excellent example of the clever biological engineering that nature has employed. Other illustrations of lubrication in our bodies include the saliva we add to food as we chew it, and the mucus coatings in our heart, lungs, and intestines that minimize friction as these organs move in carrying out their functions.

To make quantitative statements about friction, we consider a block at rest on a horizontal surface (Fig. 3.18a, b). Since the block is at rest, the first law requires that the net force on the block be zero. The vertical forces are the weight **w** and the normal force **N**, so we must have $N = w$. In the horizontal direction, there is no applied force and no motion, so the frictional force must also be zero, according to the first law.

Now suppose we apply a small horizontal force **T** to the right (Fig. 3.19c). If the block *remains at rest*, the friction force f_s can no longer be zero, since the first law requires that the net force be zero, or $f_s = T$. If **T** is gradually increased, f_s increases also.

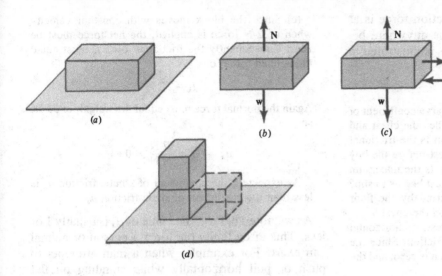

Figure 3.19. (a) A block at rest on a horizontal surface. (b) The force diagram. (c) The force diagram when a force **T** is applied. (d) The maximum static friction force is independent of the contact area.

Eventually when **T** becomes large enough, the block begins to slide. *Thus there is a maximum possible static friction force* $f_s(max)$.

Experimentally, it is found that $f_s(max)$ has the following properties:

1 $f_s(max)$ *is independent of the contact area.* For example, if we saw the block in half and stack one piece on the other (Fig. 3.18d), then $f_s(max)$ is unchanged.

2 *For a given pair of surfaces, $f_s(max)$ is proportional to the normal force N.*

3 The number relating $f_s(max)$ and N, called the *coefficient of static friction μ_s*, is defined by

$$f_s(max) = \mu_s N \qquad (3.12)$$

The coefficient μ_s depends on the nature of the two surfaces, on their cleanliness and smoothness, the amount of moisture present, and so forth. Typically, for metals on metals, μ_s is between 0.3 and 1.0. Values much above 1 are not encountered under ordinary circumstances. However, metals exposed to air form thin layers of oxide on their surfaces. If these are removed and the surfaces are brought into contact in a vacuum, large bonding forces come into play, making the value of μ_s quite large. When lubricating oils are used, μ_s is about 0.1 for metals on metals. For Teflon on metals, $\mu_s \simeq 0.04$. In a healthy hip joint, the synovial fluid reduces μ_s to the remarkably low value of 0.003.

4 *The force necessary to keep an object sliding at constant velocity is smaller than that required to start it moving.* For example, it is easier to keep a heavy table or box moving than it is to get it started. Thus the *sliding or kinetic friction force f_k is less than $f_s(max)$. It is independent of the contact area, and it satisfies*

$$f_k = \mu_k N \qquad (3.13)$$

Here μ_k is the *coefficient of kinetic friction* and is determined by the nature of the two surfaces.

5 μ_k *is nearly independent of the velocity*, and, since $f_k < f_s(max)$,

$$\mu_k < \mu_s \qquad (3.14)$$

It is important to note that these properties of frictional forces are *not* fundamental statements about the physical world in the same sense as Newton's laws of motion or the universal law of gravitation. Even though they give a good description of the frictional forces in common situations, they represent only an *approximation* to a complex problem. A more complete discussion would have to include the specific characteristics of the forces among the molecules making up the two surfaces. Friction is still an imperfectly understood phenomenon because of this complexity.

As we have noted, the static friction force is at most equal to f_s(max), but it can be anywhere between zero and this maximum. This is illustrated in the following examples.

Example 3.16

A 100-kg chest standing on a floor has a coefficient of static friction of 0.6. A boy approaches the chest and leans horizontally against it. (a) What is the frictional force exerted by the floor on the chest before the boy comes into contact with it? (b) What is the maximum force the boy can exert before the chest begins to slip? (c) What is the frictional force exerted by the floor when the boy exerts a 100-N force on the chest?

(a) Before the boy touches the chest, no horizontal forces act upon it, except possibly friction. Since the chest remains at rest, the net force on it is zero, and the frictional force must in fact be zero.

(b) The maximum frictional force is

$$f_s(\text{max}) = \mu_s N = \mu_s mg = (0.6)(100 \text{ kg})(9.8 \text{ m s}^{-2})$$
$$= 588 \text{ N}$$

The chest starts to slip when the boy exerts a 588-N force.

(c) If he exerts a 100-N force, which is less than f_s(max), the chest remains at rest. Hence the frictional force must equal 100 N, because the net horizontal force is zero.

Example 3.17

A 50-N block is on a flat, horizontal surface (Fig. 3.19). (a) If a horizontal force $T = 20$ N is applied and the block remains at rest, what is the frictional force? (b) The block starts to slide when T is increased to 40 N. What is μ_s? (c) The block continues to move at constant velocity if T is reduced to 32 N. What is μ_k?

(a) Since the block remains at rest when the force $\mathbf{T}$ is applied, the frictional force $\mathbf{f}_s$ must be equal but opposite to $\mathbf{T}$. Consequently

$$f_s = T = 20 \text{ N}$$

(b) Since the block just begins to slide when the applied force is increased to 40 N, the maximum frictional force must be

$$f_s(\text{max}) = 40 \text{ N}$$

The vertical forces must add to zero, so the normal force N is equal to the weight w, or 50 N. Hence

$$\mu_s = \frac{f_s(\text{max})}{N} = \frac{40 \text{ N}}{50 \text{ N}} = 0.8$$

(c) Since the block moves with constant velocity when a 32-N force is applied, the net force must be zero. Consequently the frictional force f_k must equal the applied force, or

$$f_k = 32 \text{ N}$$

Again the normal force must equal the weight, or 50 N, so

$$\mu_k = \frac{f_k}{N} = \frac{32 \text{ N}}{50 \text{ N}} = 0.64$$

As expected, the coefficient of kinetic friction μ_k is less than the coefficient of static friction μ_s.

As we noted before, the value of μ_s is usually 1 or less. This often limits the force a person or animal can exert. For example, when a man attempts to push or pull horizontally while standing on flat ground, the force he exerts is matched by an equally large reaction force acting on him. He will slip if that reaction force exceeds the maximum friction force, which will equal his weight if $\mu_s = 1$. On soft ground, animals with hooves or claws can dig in and somewhat increase the force they apply without slipping. Locomotives are made very heavy to increase the maximum friction force.

These ideas are used in the next example.

Example 3.18

In a comic strip, Superman extends his arm and brings a large speeding truck to a stop before it reaches his torso (Fig. 3.20). To see if this is consistent with the principles of physics, assume the truck is moving at 30 m s^{-1}, its mass M is 50,000 kg, and Superman's

Figure 3.20. Superman attempting to stop a speeding truck. Since the coefficient of friction for his feet on the road is not much larger than 1, he cannot exert a horizontal force much greater than his weight without slipping due to the equally large reaction force exerted on him by the truck. Despite his superstrength, his effort to stop the truck within an arm's length will fail badly.

mass m is 100 kg. If the force he exerts is limited by the frictional force between his feet and the ground, and $\mu_s = \mu_k = 1$, what is the minimum distance over which he can stop the truck?

The maximum force he can exert is $F = \mu_s N = \mu_s mg$, so

$$F = (1)(100 \text{ kg})(9.8 \text{ m s}^{-2}) = 980 \text{ N}$$

Thus the acceleration of the truck is at most

$$a = \frac{F}{M} = \frac{980 \text{ N}}{50,000 \text{ kg}} = 0.0196 \text{ m s}^{-2}$$

Using $v^2 = v_0^2 + 2a \, \Delta x$, with $v = 0$, the stopping distance is

$$\Delta x = \frac{-v_0^2}{2a} = -\frac{(30 \text{ m s}^{-1})^2}{2(0.0196 \text{ m s}^{-2})}$$

$$= -23,000 \text{ m} = -23 \text{ km}$$

Because Superman's maximum force is limited here to his weight, it takes him 23 km to stop the truck! (The minus sign arises because Δx and a are in opposite directions.)

The next example shows how the coefficient of static friction may be measured in an introductory physics laboratory.

Example 3.19

A block is at rest on an inclined plane (Fig. 3.21). The coefficient of static friction is μ_s. What is the maximum possible angle of inclination θ(max) of the surface for which the block will remain at rest?

In this problem it is convenient to choose the coordinate axes as shown. By definition, the normal force $\mathbf{N}$ is perpendicular to the surface, or in the $-x$ direction. Similarly, the frictional force $\mathbf{f}_s$ is parallel to the surface or along the y direction. From Fig. 3.21c, the components of the weight $\mathbf{w}$ are

$$w_x = w \cos \theta, \qquad w_y = -w \sin \theta$$

When the block remains at rest, the first law requires that the x and y components of the forces cancel. Thus

$$f_s = w \sin \theta$$
$$N = w \cos \theta$$

Taking the ratio of these equations, the weight w cancels, leaving

$$\frac{f_s}{N} = \frac{\sin \theta}{\cos \theta} = \tan \theta$$

When the block is about to slip, $f_s = f_s(\text{max}) = \mu_s N$ and $\theta = \theta(\text{max})$. Thus we find

$$\mu_s = \tan \theta(\text{max})$$

An arrangement of this type provides a simple way to measure the coefficient of static friction. The angle is gradually increased until the block will not stay in place. For example, if θ(max) = 37°, then $\mu_s = \tan 37° = 0.754$.

SUMMARY

The mass of an object is defined as the ratio of its weight w to the gravitational acceleration g. Since the inertia and gravitational masses are equal, it can also be defined as the net force on the object divided by the acceleration produced. The density of an object is its mass to volume ratio, $\rho = m/V$. Its relative density or specific gravity is the ratio of the density to that of water at 0°C and atmospheric pressure.

Newton's three laws of motion allow us to predict the motion of an object from the forces acting upon it. The first law states that in an inertial coordinate frame, the object remains at rest or in motion with constant velocity unless a net force is applied. When an object has no net force on it even though two or more forces act upon it, the object is said to

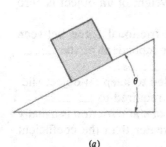

(a)

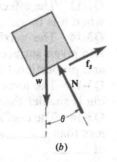

(b)

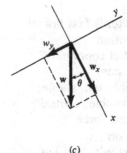

(c)

Figure 3.21. (a) A block on an inclined plane. (b) The forces on the block. (c) The components of the weight $\mathbf{w}$.

be in equilibrium. The type of equilibrium—stable, unstable, or neutral—is determined by noting whether the object tends to return to its original state of rest or uniform motion when it is disturbed slightly.

The second law states that the net force **F** needed to produce an acceleration **a** satisfies

$$\mathbf{F} = m\mathbf{a}$$

Here m is the mass or inertia of the object.

The third law states that if object A exerts a force B, then B exerts an equal and opposite force on A. Since the forces act on different objects, their effects do not cancel.

All objects exert gravitational forces on each other. The forces between two spheres or point particles are proportional to the products of their masses and inversely proportional to the square of their separation. The mass of an object is the same everywhere in the universe; its weight $w = mg$ depends on the acceleration due to gravity at that object's location. The perceived or effective weight also depends on the acceleration and is given by

$$\mathbf{w}^e = m(\mathbf{g} - \mathbf{a})$$

A person in free fall has zero effective weight.

When the force applied to an object resting on a surface exceeds the maximum static friction force $\mu_s N$, it starts to move. The force of sliding or kinetic friction $\mu_k N$ is usually smaller than the maximum static friction force. The coefficients μ_s and μ_k depend on the surfaces and are usually less than 1. The frictional forces between two surfaces are independent of their contact area.

Checklist
Define or explain:

force	Newton's first law of
contact force	motion
weight	inertial coordinate
newton	system
gravitational mass	equilibrium: stable,
kilogram	unstable, neutral
density	normal force
relative density	tension
specific gravity	Newton's third law

of motion	gravitational constant
action–reaction forces	inverse square law
Newton's second law of	effective weight
motion	friction force
inertial mass	coefficients of static and
law of universal	kinetic or sliding
gravitation	friction

REVIEW QUESTIONS

Q3-1 Forces exerted only when two objects are touching are called _____.

Q3-2 The weight of an object is the _____ force on that object.

Q3-3 The mass of an object is its weight divided by the _____.

Q3-4 The density is the ratio of the mass of an object to its _____.

Q3-5 A material with a specific gravity of 1 has the same density as _____.

Q3-6 According to Newton's first law, an object in motion with a constant velocity relative to an inertial frame has _____ acting on it.

Q3-7 If an object returns to its original resting place when moved slightly, it is in _____.

Q3-8 If object A exerts a force on object B, B exerts _____ on A.

Q3-9 The acceleration of an object is equal to the net force acting on the object divided by its _____.

Q3-10 The universal law of gravitation is referred to as an inverse square law because the gravitational force varies as _____.

Q3-11 The gravitational mass of an object equals its _____.

Q3-12 The _____ of an object is the same everywhere; its _____ depends on where the object is located in the universe.

Q3-13 The effective weight of an object is zero when it is in _____.

Q3-14 The maximum frictional force between two given surfaces is independent of the _____ and proportional to the _____.

Q3-15 The force needed to keep an object sliding is smaller than that required to _____.

Q3-16 The coefficient of static friction is usually less than _____ and greater than the coefficient of _____.

EXERCISES

Section 3.1 | Force, Weight, and Gravitational Mass

3-1 Find the direction and magnitude of the net force on the object in Fig. 3.22.

3-2 Find the direction and magnitude of the net force on the object in Fig. 3.23.

3-3 Find the direction and magnitude of the net force on the object in Fig. 3.24.

3-4 A man weighs 980 N. What is his mass in kilograms?

3-5 A woman has a mass of 50 kg. What is her weight in newtons?

3-6 What is the weight of a 1-kg steak?

3-7 Find the weight of 500 g of candy in (a) newtons; (b) pounds.

3-8 A candy bar weighs 1 ounce (1 oz) (16 oz = 1 lb). Find its mass in kilograms.

3-9 A woman weighs 120 lb. What is her mass in kilograms?

3-10 A large oil tanker weighs 200,000 tons, where 1 ton = 2000 lb. What is its mass in kilograms?

Section 3.2 | Density (See Table 3.2 for required densities.)

3-11 Sphere A has twice the mass and three times the radius of sphere B. What is the ratio of their densities?

3-12 Bricks with identical dimensions are made from lead and from aluminum. What is the ratio of their masses?

3-13 What is the mass of a litre of whole blood? (1 litre = 10^{-3} m^3)

3-14 Hydrogen atoms are the most common type of matter in many regions of interstellar space. A hydrogen atom has a mass of 1.67 ×

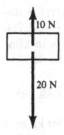

Figure 3.23. Exercise 3-2.

10^{-27} kg. If there is an average of one hydrogen atom in each cubic centimetre of an interstellar "gas cloud," what is the density of hydrogen in S.I. units?

3-15 (a) Using the solar and terrestrial data tabulated on the inside back cover of this book, calculate the average density of the sun. (b) Is this density consistent with that given for the sun in Table 3.2? Explain.

3-16 A cylindrical iron rod has a radius of 1 cm and a length of 20 cm. What is its mass?

3-17 The nucleus of a uranium atom is approximately described as a sphere of radius 8.7 × 10^{-15} m and of mass 3.5 × 10^{-25} kg. (a) What is its average density? (b) What is its specific gravity?

3-18 Neutron stars are a late stage in stellar evolution. A typical neutron star has a radius of 10^4 m and a mass of 2 × 10^{30} kg. (a) What is its average density? (b) Find the ratio of this density to the density of lead.

3-19 What is the specific gravity of water at a temperature of 0°C and a pressure of 50 atmospheres?

3-20 A gold foil has a thickness of 10 micrometres (1 μm = 10^{-6} m). What is the mass of a square of side 10 cm?

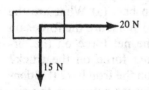

Figure 3.22. Exercise 3-1.

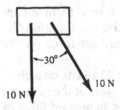

Figure 3.24. Exercise 3-3.

3-21   In the petroleum industry, a barrel is defined to be 42 gallons, where 1 gallon = 3.786 litres = 3.786×10^{-3} m^3. Find the mass in kilograms of one barrel of oil with a relative density of 0.8.

3-22   Find the density of gasoline if 5 kg has a volume of 7.35×10^{-3} m^3.

3-23   Battery acid has a density of 1290 kg m^{-3} and contains 35 percent sulfuric acid by weight. What is the mass of the sulfuric acid in 1 litre? (1 litre = 10^{-3} m^3 of battery acid.)

3-24   (a) Calculate the percentage change in the density of air when it is heated at atmospheric pressure from 0°C to 100°C. (b) Calculate the corresponding change for water.

3-25   (a) What is the specific gravity of lead? (b) What is the mass of a cube of lead whose side is 10 cm?

Section 3.3 | Newton's First Law and Section 3.4 | Equilibrium

3-26   For which of the following observers does Newton's first law of motion hold true in the form stated in this chapter? (a) A person on a plane moving at constant speed in a constant direction. (b) A parachutist who has just stepped out of an airplane. (c) A parachutist who has reached terminal velocity and is falling at constant speed. (d) The pilot of a plane that is taking off from a runway. Explain your reasoning.

3-27   A person is in a car traveling around a circular track. Do the observations of this person agree with Newton's first law as stated in this chapter? Does your answer depend on whether the speed is constant? Explain.

3-28   A car is moving at a constant speed on a straight road, which is at an angle of 10° to the horizontal direction. (a) Is it in equilibrium? (b) What forces act on the car?

3-29   A 2000-kg airplane is in level flight at constant velocity. (a) What is the net force on the plane? (b) What is the upward lift force on the plane due to the air?

3-30   A man with a mass of 80 kg sits on a chair of mass 10 kg. (a) Find the weights of the man and the chair. (b) The chair exerts an upward force of 700 N on the man. What force does the floor exert on his feet? (c) What force does the floor exert on the chair?

3-31   In Fig. 3.3, the cables are at an angle of 30° to the horizontal direction. How large are the forces $\mathbf{F}_1$ and $\mathbf{F}_2$ they exert on the traffic light if its weight is $\mathbf{w}$?

3-32   (a) A pencil is placed on its side on a table. If its cross section is hexagonal (six sided), what type of equilibrium is the pencil in? (b) What type of equilibrium is it if the pencil has a circular cross section? (c) Suppose the pencil is balanced on its point. What type of equilibrium is this?

3-33   Which type of equilibrium is illustrated by the traffic light in Fig. 3.3? Explain what will happen if it is slightly displaced horizontally or vertically.

3-34   A package of emergency supplies is parachuted from a plane. The air resistance force increases roughly as the velocity squared, so the package rapidly reaches a constant, maximum velocity directed straight down. (a) Once it reaches this velocity, is this package in equilibrium? (b) What will happen to its state of motion if a brief gust of wind pushes it sideways? (c) What will happen to its state of motion if there is a sudden brief downdraft of air?

3-35   A car goes around a circular track at a constant speed. Is it in equilibrium? Explain.

Section 3.5 | Newton's Third Law

3-36   A boat in a flowing river is tied by a rope to a post on a dock. (a) Draw a diagram showing all the forces acting on the boat. (b) Identify the horizontal forces acting on the boat and the associated reaction forces. (c) Identify the vertical forces acting on the boat and the associated reaction forces. (d) What is the net force on the boat?

3-37   A large airplane is pulled at constant velocity relative to the runway by a truck. The two are connected by an iron bar. (a) What are the forces on the airplane? (b) What are the forces on the truck? (c) What is the net force on the airplane? (d) What is the net force on the truck? (e) What is the net force on the iron bar? (f) Identify the action–reaction forces acting on the airplane, bar, and truck.

3-38 An airplane is flying horizontally with a constant velocity. The propellers are pushing backward on the air. (a) Is the airplane in equilibrium? (b) What forces are acting in the horizontal plane?

3-39 (a) A girl holds a ball motionless in her hand. Identify the forces acting on the ball and their reactions. (b) She throws the ball into the air. What are the forces on the ball while it is in the air? What are the reactions to these forces?

3-40 A car coasts to a stop on a flat, straight road. (a) What are the forces acting on the car? (b) What are the reactions to those forces?

Section 3.6 | Newton's Second Law

3-41 On a horizontal air track, a spring exerts an average force of 2 N on a cart of mass 0.4 kg. (a) Find the acceleration of the cart. (b) If the car accelerates from rest to 0.3 m s^{-1}, for how long a time is the force applied?

3-42 A box weighing 100 N falls from an airplane. As its speed increases, the air resistance force opposing its motion also increases. How large is the acceleration when the air resistance is 100 N?

3-43 A force **F** acts on a brick of mass m and an acceleration **a** results. If the force is halved and applied to two such bricks, what is the new acceleration?

3-44 What acceleration is produced when a 100-N net force is applied to a 10-kg rock?

3-45 What net force is needed to give a 1000-kg car an acceleration of 3 m s^{-2}?

3-46 A baseball of mass 0.15 kg is struck by a bat with a force of 5000 N. What is the acceleration of the ball?

Section 3.8 | Some Examples of Newton's Laws

3-47 An elevator of mass 900 kg accelerates upward at 3 m s^{-2}. What is the tension in the cable where it is attached to the elevator?

3-48 A horse can exert a horizontal force of 3.5×10^4 N on a rope that passes over a pulley to lift loads vertically. What is the acceleration of a load of weight (a) 3.5×10^4 N; (b) 3×10^4 N? (Neglect the masses of the rope and pulley.)

3-49 An elevator cable that is light in weight compared to the elevator car can support a weight of 10,000 N. If the elevator and occupants weigh 8000 N, what is the maximum possible vertical acceleration of the elevator?

3-50 A 60-kg man hangs from a light cable suspended from a helicopter. Find the tension in the cable if the acceleration is (a) 5 m s^{-2} upward; (b) 5 m s^{-2} downward.

3-51 A human femur will fracture if the compressional force is 2×10^5 N. A person of mass 60 kg lands on one leg, so that there is a compressional force on the femur. (a) What acceleration will produce fracture? (b) How many times the acceleration of gravity is this?

3-52 A 55-kg woman wishes to slide down a stationary rope that will support a force of 400 N. What is the minimum acceleration of the woman if she safely slides down the rope?

3-53 An engine with a mass of 4×10^4 kg pulls a train with a mass of 2×10^5 kg on a level track with an acceleration of 0.5 m s^{-2}. What would the acceleration be if the train had a mass of 10^5 kg?

3-54 In a collision, an automobile of mass 1000 kg stops with constant acceleration in 2 m from an initial speed of 20 m s^{-1}. (a) What is the acceleration of the car? (b) What is the net force on the car during the collision?

3-55 A tennis ball of mass 0.058 kg initially at rest is served at a velocity of 45 m s^{-1}. If the racket is in contact with the ball for 0.004 s, what is the net force on the ball during the serve? (Assume the acceleration is constant.)

Section 3.9 | Gravitational Forces

3-56 The moon is 3.9×10^5 km from the center of the earth. The mass of the moon is 7.3×10^{22} kg, and the mass of the earth is 6.0×10^{24} kg. How far from the earth's center are the gravitational forces on an object due to the earth and moon equal and opposite? (Assume the object is on the line connecting the earth and moon.)

3-57 The mass of the sun is 2.0×10^{30} kg, and the distance from the moon to the sun is 1.5×10^8 km. Using the data of the preceding exercise, find the ratio of the forces exerted by the earth and the sun on the moon.

3-58   When a rocket ship is at a distance R_E from the surface of the earth, the earth's gravitational attraction on the ship is 144,000 N. What is the earth's gravitational attraction when the ship is at a distance $3R_E$ from the surface? (R_E is the radius of the earth.)

3-59   (a) Find the average density of the earth. (b) Using the data in Table 3.2, explain whether its density is consistent with models that state that the earth has a large iron core.

Section 3.10 | Weight

3-60   Would you prefer to have a piece of gold that weighs 1 N on the earth or one that weighs 1 N on the moon? Explain. (Ignore shipping charges!)

3-61   If the radius of the earth were halved and its mass stayed constant, how would your weight change?

3-62   Find the acceleration due to gravity on a planet twice the mass of the earth and three times the radius of the earth.

3-63   The acceleration of gravity on the surface of Mars is 3.62 m s⁻². How much would a person who weighs 800 N on earth weigh on Mars?

3-64   The mass of Mars is 6.42×10^{23} kg and the acceleration of gravity on its surface is 3.62 m s⁻². What is the radius of Mars?

3-65   The acceleration of gravity at the surface of a planet is half that on the surface of the earth. If the radius of the planet is half the radius of the earth, how is its mass related to the mass of the earth?

3-66   Planet Y has a radius one-third times that of the earth, and a mass $(\frac{1}{3})^3 = \frac{1}{27}$ times that of the earth. On the surface of Planet Y, what is the weight of an astronaut with a mass of 70 kg?

3-67   On the moon, $g = 1.62$ m s⁻². An astronaut has a weight of 600 N on the earth. (a) What is her mass on the earth? (b) What is her mass on the moon? (c) What is her weight on the moon?

3-68   An airline stewardess has a mass of 50 kg. (a) What is her weight on the ground? (b) By what fraction does her weight change when she is in a plane 6.38 km above the ground? (The radius of the earth is 6380 km.)

Section 3.11 | Effective Weight

3-69   A fighter plane dives straight down with an acceleration of 3g. What is the magnitude and direction of the pilot's effective weight if his weight is w?

3-70   A racing car accelerates with an acceleration equal to g on a straight, flat track. If the driver has a mass of 60 kg, what is the magnitude and direction of her effective weight?

3-71   A car initially moving on a straight, flat road at 30 m s⁻¹ comes to a stop in 10 s. (a) Assuming the acceleration is constant, how large is it? (b) The driver has a mass m. What is the magnitude and direction of his effective weight as the car slows down?

3-72   An astronaut of mass m is in a spaceship that takes off straight up from the surface of the earth. Its acceleration is kept equal to 9.8 m s⁻². (a) What is the effective weight of the astronaut just after takeoff? (b) What is his effective weight when the spaceship is at a distance from the surface of the earth equal to the radius of the earth?

Section 3.12 | Friction

3-73   A horse weighing 7500 N is able to exert a horizontal force of 6500 N on a load. What is the coefficient of static friction between the horse's feet and the ground? (Assume the force exerted by the horse is limited by its tendency to slip.)

3-74   A refrigerator weighs 1000 N. A horizontal force of 200 N is applied, but the refrigerator does not move. (a) What is the frictional force? (b) What can we conclude about the coefficient of static friction?

3-75   A box weighing 100 N is at rest on a horizontal floor. The coefficient of static friction is 0.3. What is the minimum force needed to start the box in motion?

3-76   A box weighing 100 N is pushed on a horizontal floor. The coefficient of sliding friction is 0.2. What acceleration will result if a horizontal force of 40 N is applied?

3-77   On racing cars, surfaces called *spoilers* are sometimes placed so that there will be a downward force due to the air rushing over the car. What is their purpose?

3-78   A refrigerator of mass 120 kg is at rest on

a kitchen floor ($\mu_s = 0.4$ and $\mu_k = 0.2$). (a) If nobody touches the refrigerator, what is the frictional force exerted on the refrigerator by the floor? (b) A boy of mass 40 kg leans on the refrigerator, exerting a horizontal force on it equal to half his weight. What is the frictional force exerted by the floor on the refrigerator?

3-79 A sled weighing 1000 N is pulled along flat, snow-covered ground. The coefficient of static friction is 0.3, and the coefficient of sliding friction is 0.15. Find the force needed to (a) start the sled moving; (b) keep it moving at constant velocity.

3-80 A stone boat of total weight 60,000 N is used in a horse-pulling contest. The coefficient of static friction between the stone boat and the earth is 0.6, and the coefficient of sliding friction is 0.4. (a) What force must a pair of horses exert to start the stone boat moving? (b) What force must the horses exert to keep the stone boat moving at a constant velocity?

3-81 How can the adjustable inclined plane in Fig. 3.21 be used to measure the coefficient of kinetic friction for an object on the plane?

PROBLEMS

3-82 A planet of radius R is made up of a core of radius $R/2$ and density ρ and an outer shell of density $\rho/2$ (Fig. 3.25). What is the average density of the planet as a whole?

3-83 A 1000-kg automobile is traveling at 15 m s^{-1} and skids to a stop with constant acceleration in 100 m. What is the frictional force on the car?

3-84 A 0.5-kg ball is initially at rest. If a 10-N force is applied for 2 s, what is the final velocity of the ball?

3-85 A hockey player who weighs 800 N comes to rest from 10 m s^{-1} in 1 s. (a) What is his mass? (b) What is his average acceleration? (c) What force is required to provide this acceleration?

3-86 A runner's foot strikes the ground with a velocity of 10 m s^{-1} downward. If the effective mass of the foot and leg that is brought to rest is 9 kg, what is the force on the foot as it comes to rest with constant acceleration in (a) 0.03 m on a soft surface; (b) 0.005 m on a hard surface?

3-87 A woman of mass 55 kg steps off a rock, striking the ground at 5 m s^{-1}. (a) If she lands on her feet with her body held rigid, she stops in 0.15 m. What average force is exerted upward on the woman by the ground during the impact? (b) If she flexes her legs and body during impact, she stops in 0.5 m. What average force does she now experience during impact?

3-88 A boy is fishing with a line that will sustain a maximum force of 40 N. If he hooks a 3-kg fish, which can exert a force of 60 N for several seconds, what is the minimum acceleration with which the line must be played out during that time interval?

3-89 A subway train has three cars, each weighing 1.2×10^5 N. The frictional force on each car is 10^3 N, and the first car, acting as an engine, exerts a horizontal force of 4.8×10^4 N on the rails. (a) What is the acceleration of the train? (b) What is the tension in the coupling between the first and second cars? (c) What is the tension between the second and third cars?

3-90 In Fig. 3.26, the string and the pulley are massless, and there is no friction. If $m_1 = m_2 = $

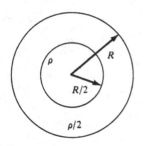

Figure 3.25. Problem 3-82.

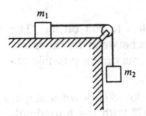

Figure 3.26. Problems 3-90, 3-91, 3-92, and 3-93.

5 kg, find (a) the tension in the string; (b) the acceleration.

3-91   Repeat the preceding problem if the coefficient of kinetic friction between the block and the surface is 0.2.

3-92   In Fig. 3.26, the string and the pulley are massless, and there is no friction. If $m_1 = 10$ kg and $m_2 = 5$ kg, find (a) the tension in the string; (b) the acceleration.

3-93   In Fig. 3.26, the string and the pulley are massless; $m_1 = 10$ kg and $m_2 = 5$ kg. The system remains at rest. Find (a) the tension in the string; (b) the minimum value of the coefficient of static friction between the block and the surface.

3-94   A wagon weighing 5×10^3 N is pulled along a muddy, horizontal road by a 500-kg horse. The coefficient of friction between the wagon wheels and the road is 0.2. (a) If the wagon is pulled at constant speed, what force must the horse exert on the ground to pull the wagon? (b) If the wagon is accelerated from rest to a velocity of 5 m s^{-1} in 5 s, what force must the horse exert on the ground?

3-95   The radius of the planet Venus is 6.1×10^3 km and that of the earth is 6.4×10^3 km. The mass of Venus is 82 percent of the earth's mass. What is the acceleration of gravity on the surface of Venus?

3-96   Two lead spheres of radius 0.1 m are in contact. (a) What is the mass of each sphere? (b) What is the gravitational force between them?

3-97   Neutron stars with a density comparable to that of atomic nuclei, 10^{17} kg m^{-3}, are believed to exist. Suppose two spheres of radius 0.01 m of such a density were somehow placed 1 m apart on the earth. (a) What would be the weight of each sphere? (b) What would be the gravitational attraction between them?

3-98   A 60-kg man wishes to run on ice. The coefficient of static friction between his shoes and the ice is 0.1. What is his maximum possible acceleration?

3-99   A girl of mass 40 kg skis down a slope, which is at an angle of 37° with the horizontal. (Neglect air resistance.) If the coefficient of ki-

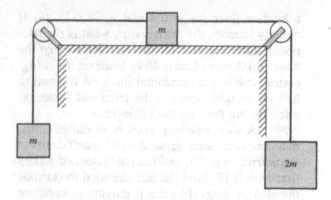

Figure 3.27.   Problems 3-100 and 3-101.

netic friction between her skis and the snow is 0.1, what is her acceleration?

3-100   In Fig. 3-27, the strings and pulleys are massless, and there is no friction. Find (a) the tensions in the strings; (b) the acceleration of the system.

3-101   Repeat the preceding problem if the coefficient of kinetic friction between the block on the surface and the surface is 0.1.

3-102   In Fig. 3-28, the string and pulley are massless, and there is no friction. Find (a) the tension in the string; (b) the acceleration.

3-103   In the preceding problem, $m_1 = 2$ kg and $m_2 = 3$ kg. Find (a) the tension in the string; (b) the acceleration. (c) If the system is released from rest, what are its velocity and position after 0.5 s?

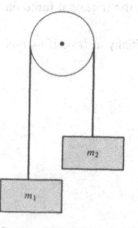

Figure 3.28.   Problems 3-102 and 3-103.

*3-104 Two people wish to push a food freezer weighing 2000 N up a ramp inclined at an angle of 37° with the horizontal. The coefficient of sliding friction between the freezer and ramp is 0.5. (a) What minimum force must the people exert to slide the freezer up the ramp? (b) What acceleration will the freezer have if it is released and slides down the ramp? (c) If it slides 4 m down the ramp and strikes a heavy object, coming to rest in 0.5 m, what average force does it exert on the heavy object?

*3-105 A man can exert a force of 700 N on a rope attached to a sled. The rope is at an angle of 30° with the horizontal. If the coefficient of kinetic friction between the sled and ground is 0.4, what is the maximum load on the sled that the man can pull at constant speed?

*3-106 A box weighing 600 N is at rest on a ramp at an angle of 37° with the horizontal. The coefficient of static friction between the box and ramp is 0.8. Find the minimum force required to move the box down the ramp if the force is applied (a) parallel to the ramp; (b) horizontally.

*3-107 In a ski jump, the slope is initially at an angle of 45° to the horizontal. If the coefficient of kinetic friction between the skis and the snow is 0.1, find (a) a skier's acceleration; (b) the velocity reached after 40 m on the ramp.

3-108 If there is no friction, what is the acceleration of the block in Fig. 3.29?

3-109 If the coefficient of sliding friction is 0.2, what is the acceleration of the block in Fig. 3.29?

ANSWERS TO REVIEW QUESTIONS

Q3-1, contact forces; **Q3-2**, gravitational; **Q3-3**, gravitational acceleration; **Q3-4**, volume; **Q3-5**, water at 0°C; **Q3-6**, no net force; **Q3-7**, stable equilibrium; **Q3-8**, an equal but opposite (reaction) force; **Q3-9**, mass; **Q3-10**, $1/r^2$; **Q3-11**, inertial mass; **Q3-12**, mass, weight; **Q3-13**, free fall; **Q3-14**, contact area, normal force; **Q3-15**, start it moving; **Q3-16**, one, kinetic or sliding friction.

Additional Reading

E. N. daCosta Andrade, *Sir Isaac Newton: His Life and Work*, Science Study Series, Doubleday and Co., Garden City, New York, 1958.

Richard S. Westfall, *Never at Rest*, Cambridge University Press, New York, 1981. A biography of Newton.

Herbert Butterfield, *The Origins of Modern Science*, Macmillan Publishing Company, New York, 1960. Chapters 8 and 10 discuss Newton's work.

Robert W. Zimmerman, The Measurement of Mass, *The Physics Teacher*, vol. 21, 1983, p. 354.

William J. Kaufman III, Listening for the Whisper of Gravity Waves, *Science 80*, May/June 1980, p. 64.

J. W. Beams, Finding a Better Value for G, *Physics Today*, vol. 24, May 1971, p. 34.

R. McNeill Alexander, *Animal Mechanics*, University of Washington Press, Seattle, 1968. Pages 55–66 discuss friction in animals.

E. H. Freitag, The Friction of Solids, *Contemporary Physics*, vol. 2, 1961, p. 198.

Ernest Rabinowitz, Friction (Resource Letter F-1), *American Journal of Physics*, vol. 31, 1963, p. 897. A bibliography.

John R. Cameron and James R. Skofronick, *Medical Physics*, John Wiley & Sons, Inc., New York, 1978. Friction in the body is discussed on page 27 and on pages 56–58.

Scientific American articles:

I. Bernard Cohen, Newton, December 1955, p. 73.

D. Sciama, Inertia, February 1957, p. 99.

Michael McCloskey, Intuitive Physics, April 1983, p. 122. Common misconceptions about the laws of motion.

Carl Gans, How Snakes Move, June 1970, p. 82.

W. A. Heiskane, The Earth's Gravity, September 1955, p. 164.

George Gamow, Gravity, March 1961, p. 94.

R. H. Dicke, The Eötvös Experiment, December 1961, p. 84.

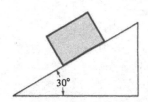

Figure 3.29. Problems 3-108 and 3-109.

Clifford C. Will, Gravitational Theory, November 1974, p. 24.

Stillman Drake, Newton's Apple and Galileo's Dialogue, August 1980, p. 150.

I. Bernard Cohen, Newton's Discovery of Gravity, March 1981, p. 166.

Daniel Z. Freedman, Supergravity and the Unification of the Laws of Physics, February 1978, p. 126.

T. C. Van Flandern, Is Gravity Getting Weaker, February 1976, p. 44.

Bryce S. DeWitt, Quantum Gravity, December 1983, p. 112.

Andrew D. Jeffries, Peter R. Saulson, Robert E. Spero, and Michael E. Zucher, Gravitational Wave Observatories, June 1987, p. 50.

F. Palmer, Friction, February 1956, p. 54.

Ernest Rabinowitz, Stick and Slip, May 1956, p. 109.

CHAPTER 4
STATICS

Statics is the study of the forces acting on an object that is in equilibrium and at rest. Even though no motion occurs, a number of interesting questions arise concerning these forces that can be answered with the aid of Newton's laws. For example, one can find the forces acting on various parts of engineering structures, such as bridges or buildings, or of biological structures, such as jaws, limbs, or backbones. Statics can be used to understand the force multiplication or *mechanical advantage* obtained with simple machines, such as the many levers found in the human body. It also addresses problems of balance and stability for objects as well as for animals. The range of questions answerable with statics makes it invaluable in fields as diverse as engineering, comparative anatomy, physical therapy, and orthodonture.

Our discussion of statics is based on an idealized object, the *rigid body*: an object extended in space that does not change its size or shape when subjected to a force. Real objects are made up of a large number of particles (atoms and molecules) held together by forces acting among the particles, and they may vibrate or bend when they are subjected to forces. However, objects such as baseballs, bones, and steel beams are often rigid enough so that these deformations are negligibly small.

A rigid body will be in equilibrium if two conditions are satisfied. The condition that the net force is zero is sufficient to ensure that a point particle at rest remains at rest; for a rigid body, this condition means that the body as a whole will not accelerate, or that it is in *translational equilibrium*. However, a rigid body will start to rotate if forces act so that there is a net turning effect, or *torque*. Thus the absence of a net torque is the second condition necessary for the equilibrium of a rigid body.

Applications of statics to questions of stability and balance also require the concept of the *center of gravity*. This is the point at which the weight of a rigid body may be considered to be concentrated.

4.1 | TORQUES

Suppose an object is subjected to two equal but opposite forces. The net force is zero, so the object is in translational equilibrium. Nevertheless, it may not be in rotational equilibrium. As an example, consider a lunch counter stool with a freely rotating seat (Fig. 4.1). If a child applies equal but opposite forces $\mathbf{F}_1$ and $\mathbf{F}_2 = -\mathbf{F}_1$ to opposite sides of the seat, it will begin to rotate. Thus the seat does not remain at rest even though $\mathbf{F} = \mathbf{F}_1 + \mathbf{F}_2 = 0$, and there is no net force.

Clearly, in addition to $\mathbf{F} = 0$, we require another equilibrium condition to exclude the possibility of rotational motion. The quantity that indicates the ability of a force to cause rotation is called the *torque*. *A rigid body is in rotational equilibrium when there is no net torque acting on it.* The torque τ depends on the force $\mathbf{F}$, the distance $\mathbf{r}$ from a point on the axis of rotation to the point where the force acts on the object, and the angle θ between $\mathbf{r}$ and $\mathbf{F}$ (Fig. 4.2). (τ is the Greek letter "tau.") Deferring the specification of the direction for several paragraphs, the magnitude of the torque about point P is

$$\tau = rF \sin \theta \qquad (4.1)$$

The dimensions of a torque are force times length, so the S.I. torque unit is a newton metre (N m).

Figure 4.1. Equal but opposite forces applied to opposite sides of the seat will cause it to start rotating. Hence it is not in equilibrium, even though the net force is zero.

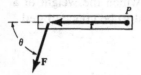

Figure 4.2. The torque on the rigid body about point P has a magnitude $\tau = rF \sin \theta$.

This expression for the torque can be illustrated in various ways. For example, suppose we need to unscrew a large nut that is rusted into place (Fig. 4.3). To maximize the torque, we use the longest wrench available and exert as large a force as possible. When $\theta = 90°$, $\sin \theta = 1$, which is the largest value of $\sin \theta$. Consequently, we should pull at right

angles to the wrench. Note that when θ is $0°$ or $180°$, $\sin \theta$ is zero and there is no torque.

Example 4.1

A mechanic holds a wrench 0.3 m from the center of a nut. How large is the torque applied to the nut if he pulls at right angles to the wrench with a force of 200 N?

Since he exerts the force at right angles to the wrench, the angle θ is $90°$, and $\sin \theta = 1$. Thus the torque is

$$\tau = rF \sin \theta = (0.3 \text{ m})(200 \text{ N})(1) = 60 \text{ N m}$$

Another example is provided by the screen door in Fig. 4.4. A spring opposes the rotation of the door and permits it to open through an angle ϕ that increases with the torque. We observe that the torque is greatest when the force is applied as far as possible from the hinge and at right angles to the door.

The magnitude of the torque, $\tau = rF \sin \theta$, can be rewritten as (Fig. 4.5a)

$$\tau = r_{\perp}F \qquad (4.2)$$

Here the subscript $\perp$ means perpendicular. That is, the magnitude of the torque is the product of the force and the perpendicular distance to the *line of action* of the force. The perpendicular distance or *lever arm* $r_{\perp} = r \sin \theta$ depends both on the distance from P to the point where the force acts and on the angle; it is greatest when $\theta = 90°$ and $\sin \theta = 1$. The torque can also be written (Fig. 4.5b) in terms of the force component $F_{\perp} = F \sin \theta$ perpendicular to **r**:

$$\tau = rF_{\perp} \qquad (4.3)$$

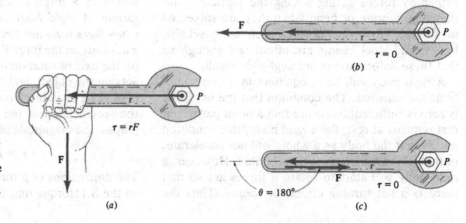

Figure 4.3. The torque has a magnitude $\tau = rF \sin \theta$. Accordingly it is a maximum when **r** and **F** are at right angles as in (*a*). The torque is zero when **r** and **F** are parallel ($\theta = 0°$) as in (*b*) or opposite ($\theta = 180°$) as in (*c*).

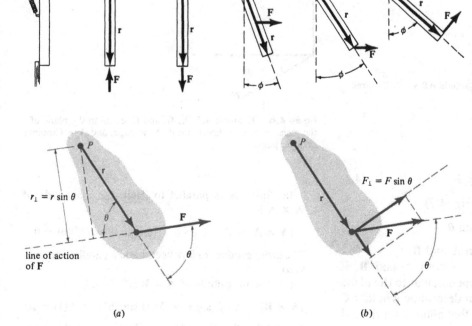

Figure 4.4. A top view of a screen door hinged at P. A spring resists opening of the door, so that the deflection angle ϕ increases with the applied torque. When a force **F** is applied opposite or parallel to **r**, no torque results. The greatest torque occurs when **F** is perpendicular to **r** and **r** is as large as possible.

$r_\perp = r \sin \theta$

line of action of **F**

(a)

$F_\perp = F \sin \theta$

(b)

Figure 4.5. The magnitude of the torque about P is $\tau = rF \sin \theta$. This can be rewritten as (a) $\tau = r_\perp F$, where $r_\perp = r \sin \theta$ is the lever arm. (b) Also, $\tau = rF_\perp$, where $F_\perp = F \sin \theta$.

Direction of the Torque

Specifying the direction of the torque is simplest for an object such as a wrench or door constrained to move about a given axis. Then only torques due to forces acting perpendicular to that axis have to be considered. A force (or a component of a force) parallel to the axis will have no effect on the state of rotational motion, because the hinges or other constraints will exert compensating torques.

In this kind of situation, we can draw two-dimensional pictures, as in Figs. 4.3 and 4.4, with the forces and the distance vectors **r** from a point P on the axis lying in a plane perpendicular to the axis of rotation. The torques that tend to produce a *counterclockwise* rotation are then said to be vectors directed along the axis outward from the page, and are conventionally taken to be *positive* (Fig. 4.6). In the figure, τ is shown as a circled dot representing the tip of an arrow. Similarly, torques causing *clockwise* rotations are directed along the axis into the page and are conventionally taken to be *negative*. Here τ is shown as a circled cross symbolizing the tail of an arrow.

A more general definition of the direction of the torque is needed for objects, such as balls or gymnasts, that are free to rotate about any axis. This definition, which reduces to that given previously for objects rotating about fixed axes, is given in terms of the *vector product* or *cross product* of two vectors.

The vector product of **A** and **B** is a vector **C**, which is perpendicular to both **A** and **B** and is de-

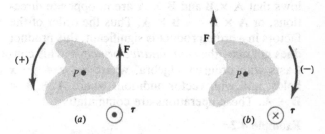

(a)

(b)

Figure 4.6. (a) Counterclockwise torques are taken to be positive. The torque vector is out of the page and is symbolized by a dot representing the tip of an arrow. (b) Clockwise torques are taken to be negative, or into the page. The cross represents the tail of an arrow.

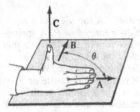

Figure 4.7. $C = A \times B$ has a magnitude $AB \sin \theta$. Its direction is given by the right-hand rule.

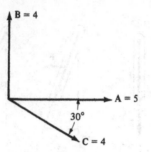

Figure 4.8.   Example 4.2. **A**, **B**, and **C** are all in the plane of the page. **A** $\times$ **B** is directed out of the page, and **A** $\times$ **C** points into the page.

noted by

$$C = A \times B \qquad (4.4)$$

The magnitude of **C** is (see Fig. 4.7)

$$C = AB \sin \theta \qquad (4.5)$$

where θ is the angle between **A** and **B**.

Since **C** is perpendicular to both **A** and **B**, it points along the direction perpendicular to the plane defined by **A** and **B**. You can determine whether **C** points toward or away from this plane with the aid of the *right-hand rule* as follows:

1   Place the two vectors tail to tail, and put your right hand at their intersection.
2   Point the fingers of your right hand along the first vector (**A** in Fig. 4.7).
3   Orient your arm so that you can bend your hand at the wrist and rotate your palm forward, through an angle of less than 180°, until your fingers point toward **B**.
4   Your thumb now points in the same direction as $C = A \times B$.

From the definition of the cross product, it follows that **A** $\times$ **B** and **B** $\times$ **A** are in opposite directions, or $A \times B = -B \times A$. Thus the order of the factors in a cross product is significant; this product does not obey the *commutative principle*. This contrasts with ordinary algebra, where $x \cdot y = y \cdot x$ holds, and with vector addition, where $A + B = B + A$. These operations are commutative.

Example 4.2

The vectors in Fig. 4.8 are all in the plane of the page. Find the magnitude and direction of (a) **A** $\times$ **A**; (b) **A** $\times$ **B**; (c) **A** $\times$ **C**.

(a) Since **A** is parallel to itself, the magnitude of **A** $\times$ **A** is

$$|A \times A| = A \cdot A \sin \theta = (5)^2 \sin 0° = (25)(0) = 0$$

The cross product of any vector and a parallel vector is zero.

(b) The magnitude of **A** $\times$ **B** is

$$|A \times B| = A \cdot B \sin \theta = (5)(4) \sin 90° = (20)(1) = 20$$

To find the direction of the product, we use the right-hand rule. We rotate our right palm from **A** toward **B**. Our right thumb then points out of the page. (See Fig. 4.7.)

(c) The magnitude is

$$|A \times C| = A \cdot C \sin \theta = (5)(4) \sin 30°$$
$$= (20)(0.5) = 10$$

Now when we rotate our right palm through 30° from **A** toward **C**, our thumb points into the page. Note that if we hold our right hand with its thumb out of the page, we have to rotate our palm almost around a full circle to go from **A** to **C**. According to the definition, we must rotate less than 180°, or a half-circle.

In terms of this notation, the torque τ can be written as

$$\tau = r \times F \qquad (4.6)$$

We note that the magnitude of τ is $\tau = rF \sin \theta$ as before. The direction of τ is given by the right-hand rule and indicates the axis about which rotation will tend to occur.

To further illustrate the right-hand rule, suppose **r** is in the $+x$ direction and **F** is in the $+y$ direction (Fig. 4.9a). Using the right-hand rule, we point the

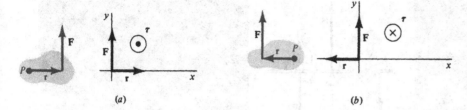

Figure 4.9. (*a*) When torques are computed about point P, $\tau = \mathbf{r} \times \mathbf{F}$ is out of the page. (*b*) τ is into the page.

fingers of our right hand in the $+x$ direction. When our palm faces the $+y$ direction, and our thumb is out of the page, we can rotate our fingers 90° toward the $+y$ direction. Thus $\tau = \mathbf{r} \times \mathbf{F}$ is *out* of the page.

Suppose instead that $\mathbf{r}$ is in the $-x$ direction and $\mathbf{F}$ is in the $+y$ direction (Fig. 4.9*b*). Pointing our fingers toward $-x$ with the palm toward $+y$, we can rotate 90° from $\mathbf{r}$ to $\mathbf{F}$. In this case our thumbs and $\tau = \mathbf{r} \times \mathbf{F}$ are into the page. Note that these results are equivalent to those in Fig. 4.6.

Couples

A pair of forces with equal magnitudes but opposite directions acting along different lines of action is called a *couple*. The pair of forces applied to the lunch counter seat in Fig. 4.1 is an example of a couple. Couples do not exert a net force on an object even though they do exert a net torque. They have the interesting property that the net torque is independent of the choice of the point P from which distances are measured. This is seen explicitly in the following example.

Example 4.3

Two forces with equal magnitudes but opposite directions act on an object with different lines of action (Fig. 4.10). Find the net torque on the object resulting from these forces.

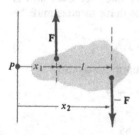

Figure 4.10. The torque due to a couple is the same about every point.

If we compute the torque about the point P in the figure, the torque resulting from the force at x_2 is $\tau_2 = -x_2 F$. (The minus sign indicates a clockwise torque.) The torque resulting from the force at x_1 is $\tau_1 = x_1 F$. The net torque is

$$\tau = \tau_1 + \tau_2 = x_1 F - x_2 F$$
$$= (x_1 - x_2)F = -lF$$

The minus sign means that the net torque tends to cause clockwise rotation and is directed into the page. Note that only the distance l between the lines of action of the forces appears in the result, so that the torque is independent of the location of the point P.

In the next section, we see how torques are used to determine whether a system is in rotational equilibrium.

4.2 | EQUILIBRIUM OF RIGID BODIES

From the discussion in the preceding section, we see that there are two conditions for the equilibrium of a rigid body:

1 *The net force on the object must be zero,*

$$\mathbf{F} = 0 \tag{4.7}$$

2 *The net torque on the object computed about any convenient point must be zero,*

$$\tau = 0 \tag{4.8}$$

These two conditions ensure that a rigid body will be in both translational and rotational equilibrium. They have been motivated earlier by qualitative or intuitive arguments, but they can be derived by applying Newton's laws of motion to the forces acting on a rigid body and to the forces among its constituent particles.

A familiar application of these conditions is provided by two children balancing on a seesaw

(a)

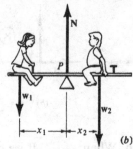
(b)

(c)

Figure 4.11. (a), (b) When two children balance on a seesaw, the heavier child must be closer to the pivot. (c) Another equilibrium configuration. [(a) M. Sternheim, (b) M. Sternheim]

(Fig. 4.11). If their weights are unequal, they soon find that the heavier child must be closer to the pivot. For example, if one child is twice as heavy as the other, he or she must sit half as far from the pivot. Let us see how this comes about from the equilibrium conditions.

Example 4.4

Two children of weights w_1 and w_2 are balanced on a board pivoted about its center (Fig. 4.11). (a) What is the ratio of their distances x_2/x_1 from the pivot? (b) If $w_1 = 200$ N, $w_2 = 400$ N, and $x_1 = 1$ m, what is x_2? (For simplicity, we assume the board to be weightless; this will not affect the result.)

(a) According to the first equilibrium condition, the force N exerted by the support must balance their weights so that the net force is zero:

$$N - w_1 - w_2 = 0, \qquad N = w_1 + w_2$$

This gives us no information about their positions. However, we have not yet used the condition that the net torque is zero. We will compute torques about the pivot point, P. Then the lever arm is zero for N, since its line of action passes through the pivot, and it has no torque. The torques resulting from the weights are $\tau_1 = x_1 w_1$ and $\tau_2 = -x_2 w_2$. Thus, $\tau = \tau_1 + \tau_2 = 0$ requires

$$x_1 w_1 - x_2 w_2 = 0$$

or

$$\frac{x_2}{x_1} = \frac{w_1}{w_2}$$

This is the condition relating the positions x_1 and x_2 when the seesaw is balanced. Either position may be chosen arbitrarily; the other is then determined by this condition.

(b) If $w_1 = 200$ N, $w_2 = 400$ N, and $x_1 = 1$ m, then we must have

$$x_2 = x_1 \frac{w_1}{w_2} = (1 \text{ m})\left(\frac{200 \text{ N}}{400 \text{ N}}\right) = 0.5 \text{ m}$$

This is consistent with our initial statement that if one child is twice as heavy as the other, he or she must sit half as far from the pivot.

In this example, we chose to compute the torques about the pivot point. However, the equilibrium condition says that the torques calculated about *any* point must add up to zero. In the next example we will solve the same problem, computing torques about a different point. We will find that the result is the same.

Example 4.5

Again find x_2/x_1 for the seesaw of the preceding example, calculating torques about the point P_1, where the child of weight w_1 is seated.

To proceed, we redraw the force diagram of Fig. 4.11 as in Fig. 4.12. Computing torques about P_1, N and w_2 produce torques $x_1 N$ and $-(x_1 + x_2)w_2$, respectively; w_1 produces no torque, since its lever arm is zero. In equilibrium the sum of these torques must be zero, so

$$-(x_1 + x_2)w_2 + x_1 N = 0 \qquad \text{(i)}$$

But the forces must also add up to zero, so

$$N - w_1 - w_2 = 0$$

or

$$N = w_1 + w_2$$

Substituting for N in Eq. i, we find

$$-(x_1 + x_2)w_2 + x_1(w_1 + w_2) = 0$$

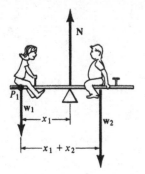

Figure 4.12. Calculation of the torques about P_1.

Canceling some terms, we obtain our earlier result

$$x_2 w_2 = x_1 w_1 \quad \text{or} \quad \frac{x_2}{x_1} = \frac{w_1}{w_2}$$

This example illustrates that we can often simplify our calculations with a clever choice of the point about which we compute the torques. For example, using the pivot eliminated the unknown normal force **N** from the torque equation. The same final results are always obtained no matter what point is used to calculate torques.

We now use the equilibrium conditions to find the forces on a human forearm.

Example 4.6

A model for the forearm in the position shown in Fig. 4.13 is a pivoted bar supported by a cable. The weight w of the forearm is 12 N and can be treated as concentrated at the point shown. Find the tension **T** exerted by the biceps muscle and the force **E** exerted by the elbow joint.

The tension **T** and the weight **w** have no horizontal components. Since the net horizontal force must be zero, the force **E** exerted by the joint cannot have a horizontal component. We assume tentatively that **E** is

directed downward; a negative result will indicate it points the opposite way.

Applying the condition **F** = 0,

$$T - E - w = 0$$

This contains both unknowns, T and E. Calculating torques about the pivot, **E** produces no torque, **w** produces a torque $-(0.15 \text{ m})w$, and **T** produces a torque $(0.05 \text{ m})T$. Thus $\tau = 0$ becomes

$$-0.15w + 0.05T = 0$$

or

$$T = 3w = 3(12 \text{ N}) = 36 \text{ N}$$

The first equation then gives

$$E = T - w = 36 \text{ N} - 12 \text{ N} = 24 \text{ N}$$

E is positive, so it is directed downward as initially assumed.

Note that both the tension **T** exerted by the muscle and the force **E** exerted by the elbow are considerably larger than the weight they are supporting. This is because, relative to the joint, the lever arm for the weight is larger than that for the muscle. When a weight is held in the hand, it is even farther from the joint, and the additional forces the muscle and joint must provide are correspondingly larger.

When the forces do not all act in the same direction, the condition **F** = 0 gives us more than one equation.

Example 4.7

An advertising sign is hung from a hinged beam that is supported by a cable (Fig. 4.14). The sign has a weight $w = 1000$ N, and the weights of the beam and cable are negligible. Find the tension in the cable and the force exerted by the hinge.

The forces that act on the beam are the downward force due to the weight of the sign, a tension force **T** along the cable, and a force **H** due to the hinge. The

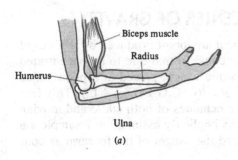

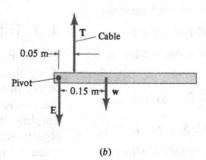

Figure 4.13. (a) The forearm is supported by the biceps muscle and pivoted at the elbow. (b) The forearm can be considered as a pivoted bar supported by a cable. The pivot represents the elbow joint, and the cable represents the biceps. (Adapted from Williams and Lissner.)

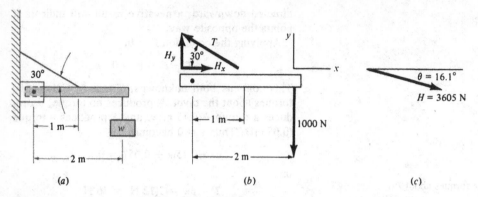

Figure 4.14. The tension force T and the hinge force H are larger than the weight of the sign because the lever arm of its weight about the hinge is much larger than is that of the cable.

magnitude of **H** and the angle θ it makes with the x axis are related to its components H_x and H_y by

$$H = [H_x^2 + H_y^2]^{1/2}$$

$$\tan \theta = \frac{H_y}{H_x}$$

In drawing the diagram, we assume the components H_x and H_y are in the indicated directions; if they turn out to be negative, this will mean they are in the opposite directions.

We need three equations to determine T, H_x, and H_y; the equations above will then give us H and θ. With the x and y axes chosen as shown, the conditions $F_x = 0$ and $F_y = 0$ provide two equations. Setting the torque about some axis equal to zero yields the third.

Taking components along the x and y directions, $F_x = 0$ and $F_y = 0$ become

$$H_x - T \cos 30° \qquad\qquad = 0 \qquad (i)$$
$$H_y + T \sin 30° - 1000 \text{ N} = 0 \qquad (ii)$$

The condition $\tau = 0$ can be applied to any axis, but a good choice simplifies the algebra. If we take torques about the hinge, H_x and H_y have no lever arm and do not contribute. Then we get for our third equation

$$T(1 \text{ m})(\sin 30°) - (1000 \text{ N})(2 \text{ m}) = 0 \qquad (iii)$$

Equation iii immediately gives the tension in the cable,

$$T = \frac{2(1000 \text{ N})}{\sin 30°} = \frac{2000 \text{ N}}{0.5} = 4000 \text{ N}$$

Having found T, we now find H_x from Eq. i:

$$H_x = T \cos 30° = (4000 \text{ N})(0.866) = 3464 \text{ N}$$

The horizontal force on the beam due to the hinge is toward the right, balancing the horizontal component of the force due to the cable. Then with Eq. ii,

$$H_y = 1000 \text{ N} - T \sin 30°$$
$$= (1000 \text{ N}) - (4000 \text{ N})(0.5) = -1000 \text{ N}$$

H_y is negative, or opposite to the direction assumed in Fig. 4.14b.

H and θ can now be found:

$$H = [H_x^2 + H_y^2]^{1/2} = [(3464 \text{ N})^2 + (1000 \text{ N})^2]^{1/2}$$
$$= 3605 \text{ N}$$

$$\tan \theta = \frac{H_y}{H_x} = \frac{-1000}{3464} = -0.2887$$

$$\theta = -16.1°$$

The minus sign indicates that θ is below the horizontal direction (Fig. 4.14c). Note that both T and H are much larger than the 1000-N weight of the sign. This happens because the lever arm associated with its weight is much larger than that of the cable. If the cable were attached closer to the right end of the beam, or at a larger angle to it, these forces would be reduced.

4.3 | THE CENTER OF GRAVITY

The torque about any point produced by the weight of an object is equal to that due to a concentrated object of the same weight placed at a point called the *center of gravity* (C.G.) (Fig. 4.15). This fact simplifies the mechanics of both static and moving objects and was implicitly assumed in Example 4.6 when we treated the weight of the forearm as con-

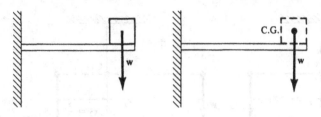

Figure 4.15.   The torque produced by the weight of a rigid body is equal to that due to a concentrated object of the same weight placed at the center of gravity.

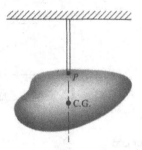

Figure 4.17.   An object will hang so that its center of gravity is below the point of suspension, P.

centrated at a point. The centers of gravity of uniformly dense symmetric objects are at their geometric centers (Fig. 4.16). For less symmetric objects, the C.G. can be calculated mathematically or located experimentally.

A suspended object always hangs so that its center of gravity is directly below the point of suspension, since in this position the torque resulting from the weight about that point is zero (Fig. 4.17). This observation provides a way of locating the C.G. experimentally. If an object is suspended from a point P_1, it comes to rest with the C.G. on the vertical line through P_1. Suspending the object from a second point P_2, the C.G. lies on the vertical line through P_2. The C.G. is then at the intersection of the two lines (Fig. 4.18).

We now show how to find the center of gravity mathematically, starting with the simplest possible system: two point weights on a weightless rod (Fig. 4.19). We take the C.G. to be a distance x_1 from w_1 and x_2 from w_2. Then the net torque about the C.G. due to the two weights must be equal but opposite. This is similar to the seesaw of Example 4.4, and we can use the balance condition obtained there,

$x_2/x_1 = w_1/w_2$. For example, if $w_1 = w_2$, then $x_1 = x_2$; the C.G. is at the midpoint, as is always true for a symmetric object. If $w_2 = 2w_1$, then $x_2 = x_1/2$; the C.G. is closer to the heavier weight, as we might have expected.

Another way of finding the C.G. of two weights leads to a formula that can immediately be adapted to any number of weights. Figure 4.20 shows the same two weights on a weightless rod located on an x axis. The C.G. is at an unknown point X. From the definition, a weight $w = w_1 + w_2$ concentrated at X will produce a torque equal to the sum of the torques due to w_1 and w_2. The individual torques about the origin are $\tau_1 = -x_1 w_1$ and $\tau_2 = -x_2 w_2$. Thus the total torque is

$$\tau = \tau_1 + \tau_2 = -x_1 w_1 - x_2 w_2$$

A single weight w at X gives a torque $\tau = -Xw$. Equating the two expressions for τ, we find the cen-

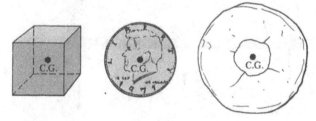

Figure 4.16.   The center of gravity of a uniformly dense symmetric object is at its geometric center. Note that the C.G. of the doughnut is at the center of the hole and hence not in the object itself.

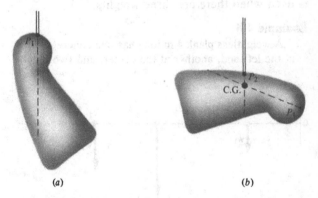

(a)   (b)

Figure 4.18.   (a) The center of gravity lies on the vertical line through P_1. (b) The C.G. also lies on the vertical line through P_2, so it is located at the intersection of the two lines.

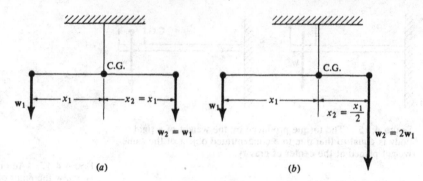

Figure 4.19. The center of gravity of two point weights. (*a*) Equal weights. (*b*) Unequal weights.

(*a*)

(*b*)

ter of gravity is at

$$X = \frac{x_1 w_1 + x_2 w_2}{w}$$

Suppose, for example, that $w_1 = w_2$. Then $w = w_1 + w_2 = 2w_1$, and

$$X = \frac{x_1 w_1 + x_2 w_1}{2w_1} = \frac{x_1 + x_2}{2}$$

Thus the center of gravity X is midway between the two weights, as was found before.

If there are more than two weights, the center of gravity is found in the same way. The result is

$$X = \frac{x_1 w_1 + x_2 w_2 + x_3 w_3 + \cdots}{w} \qquad (4.9)$$

where

$$w = w_1 + w_2 + w_3 + \cdots \qquad (4.10)$$

The following example illustrates how this result is used when there are three weights.

Example 4.8

A weightless plank 4 m long has one concrete block at the left end, another at the center, and two blocks

at the right end (Fig. 4.21). Where is the center of gravity?

Let us call the weight of a block w_0; the numerical value is not needed since it will cancel out. We can choose our origin arbitrarily, so we will take it at the left end. Then the total weight is $w = w_1 + w_2 + w_3 = 4w_0$, and Eq. 4.9 becomes

$$X = \frac{x_1 w_1 + x_2 w_2 + x_3 w_3}{w}$$

$$= \frac{0 + (2 \text{ m})w_0 + (4 \text{ m})(2w_0)}{4w_0} = 2.5 \text{ m}$$

Thus the C.G. is between the center of the plank and the heavier end.

The equation for the center of gravity, Eq. 4.9, contains weights in both the numerator and denominator. If we substitute $w = mg$ for each weight, the factors of g cancel out. Then X involves the masses instead of the weights, and it is called the *center of mass* (C.M.). There is no difference between the C.G. and C.M. as long as **g** has the same direction and magnitude for each weight.

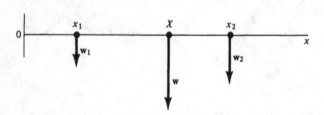

Figure 4.20. The center of gravity of two point weights on a weightless rod is at X.

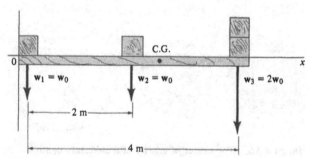

Figure 4.21. The center of gravity is between the center of the plank and the heavier end.

Although we have only discussed weights placed at several points on a straight line, the procedure for finding the center of gravity for more complicated arrangements is basically the same. If weights are at several points in a plane, then the C.G. is at a point (X, Y) in the plane. Equation 4.9 is then used to find X, and an analogous equation involving the y coordinates of the weights is used to find Y.

When the weight is distribution continuously, rather than being concentrated at several discrete points, the sum in Eq. 4.9 must be replaced by an integral:

$$X = \frac{1}{w} \int x \, dw \qquad (4.11)$$

Here w is the total weight:

$$w = \int dw \qquad (4.12)$$

These equations are used in the next example.

Example 4.9

(a) Find the center of gravity X of a thin metal rod of length L with a uniform weight per unit length λ_0 (Fig. 4.22a). (b) Find the center of gravity for the rod in Fig. 4.22b that is shaped so that its weight per unit length λ varies according to the formula $\lambda = \lambda_0(1 - x/L)$.

(a) Since this rod is symmetric about the point $x = L/2$, its C.G. is clearly located there. Nevertheless, we will use Eqs. 4.11 and 4.12 to derive this result to illustrate the procedure in the simplest type of situation.

We imagine cutting the rod into small segments of

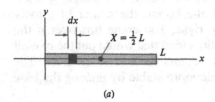

(a)

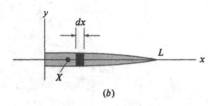

(b)

Figure 4.22. (a) The weight of a segment of width dx is $\lambda_0 dx$. The center of gravity of a uniformly dense rod is at its midpoint. (b) The center of gravity is nearer the heavier end.

length dx. The product of dx and the weight per unit length λ_0 is the weight of the segment,

$$dw = \lambda_0 \, dx$$

Thus the total weight of the rod is the integral

$$w = \int_0^L \lambda_0 \, dx = \lambda_0 x \, \Big|_0^L = \lambda_0 L$$

The total weight is just the weight per unit length times the length.

Now each small segment contributes $x \, dw$ to the numerator of Eq. 4.11. Thus the center of gravity is located at

$$X = \frac{1}{w} \int_0^L x \, dw = \frac{1}{\lambda_0 L} \int_0^L \lambda_0 x \, dx$$

$$= \frac{1}{L} \int_0^L x \, dx = \frac{1}{2L} x^2 \, \Big|_0^L$$

$$= \frac{L^2}{2L} = \frac{L}{2}$$

The C.G. is at the midpoint, as anticipated.

(b) Again we imagine cutting the rod into small segments of length dx. The weight of a segment is $dw = \lambda \, dx = \lambda_0(1 - x/L)dx$, and the total weight of the rod is

$$x = \int_0^L \lambda_0 \left(1 - \frac{x}{L}\right) dx = \lambda_0 \left[x - \frac{x^2}{2L}\right]_0^L$$

$$= \lambda_0 \left((L - \frac{L^2}{2L}\right) = \lambda_0 \frac{L}{2}$$

Then the center of gravity is located at

$$X = \frac{1}{w} \int_0^L x \, dw = \frac{1}{\lambda_0 L/2} \int_0^L x \lambda_0 \left(1 - \frac{x}{L}\right) dx$$

$$= \frac{1}{L/2} \int_0^L \left(x - \frac{x^2}{L}\right) dx$$

$$= \frac{(x^2/2 - x^3/3L)}{L/2} \, \Big|_0^L = \frac{L}{3}$$

The center of gravity is at $X = L/3$. It is to the left of the midpoint $L/2$ of the rod because the left side is heavier.

The following example illustrates how to find the center of gravity in two dimensions.

Example 4.10

Figure 4.23 shows a crane used in building construction. The mass of the movable boom is 1000 kg, and the

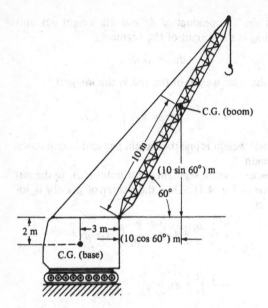

Figure 4.23. A construction crane. It will tip if the overall C.G. is not over the base.

mass of the base is 10,000 kg. Where is the center of gravity of the crane?

Since we have the masses rather than the weights, we use the masses in Eq. 4.9. The horizontal distance x_2 from the C.G. of the base to the C.G. of the boom is

$$x_2 = 3 \text{ m} + (10 \text{ m})(\cos 60°) = 3 \text{ m} + 5 \text{ m} = 8 \text{ m}$$

Taking the origin at the C.G. of the base, we have

$$X = \frac{x_1 m_1 + x_2 m_2}{m_1 + m_2}$$

$$= \frac{0 + (1000 \text{ kg})(8 \text{ m})}{10,000 \text{ kg} + 1000 \text{ kg}} = 0.727 \text{ m}$$

The vertical distance from the C.G. of the base to the C.G. of the boom is

$$y_2 = 2 \text{ m} + (10 \text{ m})(\sin 60°) = 10.66 \text{ m}$$

Replacing the x's by y's, we have

$$Y = \frac{y_1 m_1 + y_2 m_2}{m_1 + m_2}$$

$$= \frac{0 + (1000 \text{ kg})(10.66 \text{ m})}{10,000 \text{ kg} + 1000 \text{ kg}} = 0.969 \text{ m}$$

The C.G. of the crane is located 0.727 m to the right and 0.969 m above the C.G. of the base, or within the base itself.

Note, however, that attaching an object to the end of the boom moves the overall C.G. of the system toward the right. The overall C.G. must be over the base of the crane to avoid tipping. We explore this further in the next section.

4.4 | STABILITY AND BALANCE

The number and position of an animal's legs have apparently been partially determined by its requirements for stability and balance. The basic idea is illustrated by the beam in Fig. 4.24. If its center of gravity is between the two supports, the torques about the C.G. due to N_1 and N_2 are opposite and cancel, so the beam is in equilibrium. However, when the center of gravity is to the left of the supports, the torques about the C.G. due to N_1 and N_2 are both positive. Since the net torque is not zero, the beam topples over. Thus, an object is balanced only when its *center of gravity lies above the base area* defined by its supports.

The construction crane in Fig. 4.23 provides a good illustration of this point. If a weight is hung from the end of the boom, the center of gravity shifts toward the right. The crane tips over if the operator tries to lift a load that would put the overall center of gravity beyond the end of the base. The crane can be made more stable by making the base

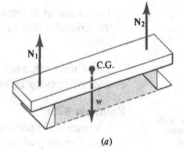

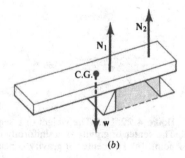

Figure 4.24. The beam is (a) in equilibrium; (b) not in equilibrium. The base area defined by the supports is shown in color.

(a)

(b)

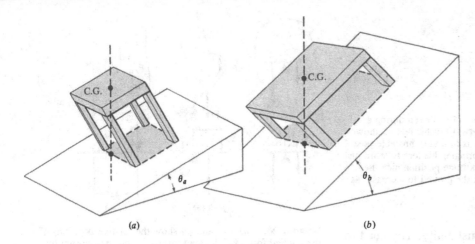

Figure 4.25. A four-legged table will tip when a vertical line from the center of mass passes just outside the base area formed by the legs. Since $\theta_a < \theta_b$, a long-legged table (a) is less stable than a short-legged one (b).

heavier or longer. Sometimes extensions are attached to the ends of such cranes to extend their bases.

Stability is also important for animals. An animal standing on four legs is analogous to a table. A table placed on a surface that is gradually tilted will topple over when the center of gravity is no longer over the portion of the surface defined by the tips of the four legs (Fig. 4.25). The shorter the legs for a given tabletop, the larger the angle θ at which this occurs and the greater its stability; a low table is more stable than a high one. Similarly, the centers of gravity of automobiles, ships, and even vases must be kept low for good stability to be achieved. Thus, we can see that rats and squirrels, which have relatively short legs, are adapted well for living on steep slopes or on tree branches. The long-legged horse and antelope are proportioned for efficient running on nearly flat terrain.

If a quadruped lifts one leg, it will remain balanced if its center of gravity is over the triangular base area formed by its remaining three legs. By moving its legs in the correct sequence, it also can walk slowly while always keeping three feet on the ground and the center of mass over the triangle they define (Fig. 4.26). This sequence is right front, left rear, left front, right rear, and it is used by all four-legged animals and by human infants. Of course, humans, birds, and some animals can balance on one or two feet, but their large feet make it relatively easy to do this.

When a quadruped runs rapidly, it can happen

that only one or two legs are on the ground at one time. The tendency to tip diagonally forward or to roll sideways is quickly countered when the other feet are set down. Thus brief periods of instability are required for fast motion of quadrupeds and bipeds (Fig. 4.27).

Three feet on the ground is the minimum for stability for animals with small feet, so insects that have six legs can move three at a time and still be stable at all times. Since they have very small masses, even a slight gust of wind would tip them

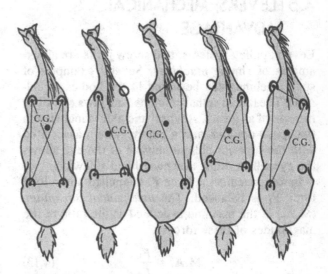

Figure 4.26. The diagram of a quadruped walking as seen from above. The open circle represents the foot that is off the ground. Note that the center of gravity is always within the triangle formed by the three feet on the ground.

Figure 4.27. A sprinter, at the start of and even during a race, has his center of mass well forward of his feet as shown in this drawing. This means that he is in a very unstable position. He maintains his balance by bringing his legs forward just in time to keep from falling. This extreme position aids the athlete in exerting a larger force on the ground to increase his acceleration.

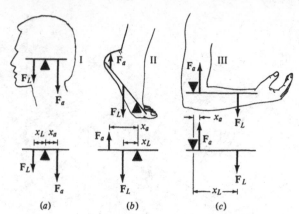

Figure 4.28. (a), (b), and (c) show the relative positions of the applied force $\mathbf{F}_a$, the load force $\mathbf{F}_L$, and the fulcrum for class I, II, and III levers, respectively, with examples of such levers in the human body. The load force $\mathbf{F}_L$ shown here is equal and opposite to the force produced by the lever on the load, $-\mathbf{F}_L$.

over if they had periods of instability. The need to be stable in a moderate wind also explains why their legs do not point nearly vertically as in mammals, but are instead splayed outward.

The fact that animals usually have the minimum number of legs consistent with stability is apparently related to considerations of strength and weight. A single leg weighing as much as two thinner legs is better able to withstand torques tending to bend the leg. Accordingly, the portion of the body weight composing the legs is minimized by keeping the number of legs as small as possible.

4.5 | LEVERS; MECHANICAL ADVANTAGE

Levers, pulley systems, and screw jacks are all examples of simple *machines*. Several examples of such machines can be found in the bodies of animals. The limbs, spinal columns, and jaws can all be thought of as levers. A wheel and axle is included in the spinal column, and a pulley system associated with the superior oblique muscle of the eye allows the eyeball to rotate downward and sideways.

In any machine, a force $\mathbf{F}_a$ is applied and a load force $\mathbf{F}_L$ is balanced. The *mechanical advantage* (M.A.) of the machine is defined as the ratio of the magnitudes of these forces,

$$\text{M.A.} = \frac{F_L}{F_a} \qquad (4.13)$$

Levers | A lever in its simplest form is a rigid bar used with a fulcrum (Fig. 4.28). Three classes of

levers are defined according to the relative positions of F_L, $\mathbf{F}_a$, and the fulcrum. The following example illustrates the effects of a lever.

Example 4.11

Suppose the load $\mathbf{F}_L$ on a class I lever (Fig. 4.28a) has a magnitude of 2000 N. A person exerts a force $F_a = 500$ N to balance the load. (a) What is the ratio of the distances x_a and x_L? (b) What is the mechanical advantage of this lever?

(a) To find x_a/x_L, we compute the torques about the fulcrum. The torque due to $\mathbf{F}_a$ is $\tau_a = -x_a F_a$, and the torque due to $\mathbf{F}_L$ is $\tau_L = x_L F_L$. For balance, these must sum to zero, so

$$x_L F_L - x_a F_a = 0$$

and

$$\frac{x_a}{x_L} = \frac{F_L}{F_a} = \frac{2000 \text{ N}}{500 \text{ N}} = 4$$

(b) The mechanical advantage of the lever used in this way is then

$$\text{M.A.} = \frac{F_L}{F_a} = \frac{x_a}{x_L} = 4$$

For all classes of levers the mechanical advantage can be expressed as a ratio of distances from the fulcrum, as in the preceding example. If the forces are at right angles to the lever, in equilibrium the ratio of the magnitudes of the load force to the applied force is

$$\frac{F_L}{F_a} = \frac{x_a}{x_L}$$

Hence for all classes of levers,

$$\text{M.A.} = \frac{x_a}{x_L} \quad \text{(forces} \perp \text{lever)} \quad (4.14)$$

With the forces at right angles to the lever, the M.A. of class III levers is always less than 1, and the M.A. of class II levers is always greater than 1. Class I levers can have an M.A. larger or smaller than 1.

For all levers, the M.A. given in Eq. 4.14 is an ideal value. Real machines always have frictional forces present that reduce the actual mechanical advantage below the ideal value.

4.6 | MUSCLES

Many examples of levers are found in the bodies of animals. Muscles provide the forces for using these levers.

A muscle is composed of thousands of long, thin fibers. When a muscle is stimulated by an electrical pulse from the nervous system, it contracts briefly or *twitches*, thereby exerting a force. A series of pulses sent to a muscle causes a series of twitches in the fibers. The twitches are close together in time but occur at different times in different parts of the muscle, so the apparent result is a smooth contraction of the muscle. If the frequency of the twitches is increased, the tension in the muscle increases up to a state of maximum tension. Further nerve impulse rate increases cause no further increase in tension.

The maximum tension of a muscle is proportional to its cross-sectional area at the widest point. This maximum tension also depends on the length of the muscle, which can be varied. The greatest tension can be achieved when the muscle is only slightly elongated relative to its resting or undisturbed state and is about 30 to 40 newtons per square centimetre of cross-sectional area. The maximum tension possible drops rapidly if the muscle is substantially elongated or shortened. To see an example of this, bend your wrist forward as far as you can and try to make a tight fist. Most people either fail to close their fingers completely or else do so with a rather weak grip.

4.7 | LEVERS IN THE BODY

The evolutionary development of the limbs and other skeletal structures in animals has been strongly affected by the animals' needs. We recall that when the forces are perpendicular to a lever, its mechanical advantage is $F_L/F_a = x_a/x_L$. Thus short limbs with small values of x_L will have relatively large mechanical advantages and be able to exert large forces (Fig. 4.29). However, the distance that the end of a limb moves is proportional to its length X_L, so rapid motion requires a long limb. Consequently, a compromise must be made between strength and speed of movement. For example, the foreleg of a fast-moving horse has a mechanical advantage of 0.08. The armadillo, which is a burrowing animal, has a foreleg with an M.A. of about 0.25. Hence it cannot move as quickly, but it has the strength needed for burrowing.

The Spinal Column | The human spinal column is made up of 24 *vertebrae* separated by *disks* filled with a gelatinous material. When a person bends, the spine is effectively a lever with a very small M.A. Hence, bending over to pick up even a light object produces a very large force on the *lumbrosacral* disk, which separates the last vertebra from the *sacrum*, the bone supporting the spine (Fig. 4.30). If weakened, this disk can rupture or be deformed, causing pressure on nearby nerves and severe pain.

To understand why this force is so large, we can use a model that treats the spine as a pivoted rod.

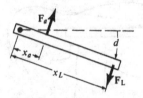

Figure 4.29. A limb being flexed may be represented by a pivoted bar supported by a cable. The cable represents a muscle and the pivot represents a joint. The M.A. of the limb is x_a/x_L, while the distance d that the end of the limb moves is proportional to x_L.

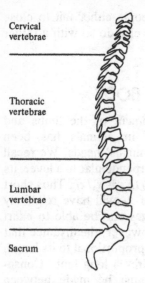

Cervical
vertebrae

Thoracic
vertebrae

Lumbar
vertebrae

Sacrum

Figure 4.30.   The anatomy of the spinal column.

The pivot corresponds to the sacrum and exerts a force **R** (Fig. 4.31). The various muscles of the back are equivalent to a single muscle producing a force **T** as shown. When the back is horizontal, the angle α is 12°; **w** is the weight of the torso, head, and arms, about 65 percent of the total body weight.

Note that because α is small, the line of action of **T** passes close to the pivot, so its lever arm $r_\perp$ is small. However, the weight **w** acts at right angles to the spine, and its lever arm is much longer. Hence for their torques to balance, the muscle force **T** must be much greater than the weight. Because **T** is large, its horizontal component is also large. In equilibrium, the force **R** due to the sacrum must have an equal but opposite horizontal component,

so this force due to the sacrum is also much larger than the weight.

If this calculation is carried out in detail, the numbers obtained are impressively large. For a man weighing 750 N (a mass of 77 kg), **T** and **R** are each close to 2200 N! If the man is also lifting a 175-N (18-kg) child, so that there is an extra 175-N weight at the right end of the bar in Fig. 4.31, **T** and **R** are each about 3300 N! Such forces in the muscles and on the disk are potentially quite hazardous.

Since even bending over without lifting a load puts great stress on the spine, it should be avoided. If, instead, one flexes the knees but keeps the back vertical, then the centers of gravity of all the weights lie almost directly above the sacrum. Consequently their torques about the sacrum are small, and the muscles need not exert any appreciable force. The force on the disk is then approximately the total weight supported. For the 750-N man, this weight is about 490 N for the body alone and 665 N with a 175-N load. This is a far safer way to lift even a light object (Fig. 4.32).

SUMMARY

The quantity that indicates the ability of a force to cause rotation is the torque τ. If a force **F** acts at a distance **r** from a point P, the torque about that point has a magnitude $rF \sin \theta$, where θ is the angle between **r** and **F**. The torque is a vector quantity and is directed perpendicular to the plane of **r** and **F**. In the vector or cross-product notation, $\tau = \mathbf{r} \times \mathbf{F}$, the direction of τ is then given by a right-hand rule. Alternatively, if the motion is in a specific plane, counterclockwise torques are conventionally taken as positive and clockwise torques as negative.

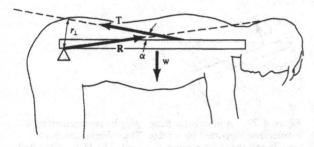

Figure 4.31.   Force diagram for the spine of a person bending over with the back horizontal.

Figure 4.32.   (a) Incorrect and (b) correct ways to lift a weight.

For a rigid body to be in equilibrium, two vector equations must be satisfied:

$$\mathbf{F} = 0$$

$$\tau = 0$$

The first of these is the condition that the net force is zero and ensures that there is no change in the translational motion. The second is the condition that the net torque about some convenient point is zero; it ensures that the rotational motion remains the same.

For objects at rest or in motion, the entire weight and mass of the object can be considered to be located at a point called the center of gravity or center of mass. This fact facilitates the understanding of stability and balance.

The mechanical advantage (M.A.) of a lever or other simple machine is defined as the ratio F_L/F_a of the load force $\mathbf{F}_L$ balanced by an applied force $\mathbf{F}_a$. In the bodies of animals, limbs with small mechanical advantages are suited to fast motion, while those with large mechanical advantages are able to exert large forces.

Checklist

Define or explain:

rigid body	center of gravity
torque	center of mass
vector product or cross product	base area
	machines
couple	mechanical advantage
equilibrium conditions	

REVIEW QUESTIONS

Q4-1 A rigid body does not change its _____ or _____ when subjected to a force.

Q4-2 The quantity that indicates the ability of a force to cause rotation is called the _____.

Q4-3 The perpendicular distance from the axis of rotation to the line of action of a force is the _____.

Q4-4 The greatest torque is obtained when a force is applied _____ to a wrench.

Q4-5 The vector product of two vectors points _____ to the plane of those vectors.

Q4-6 According to our sign convention, clockwise torques are _____ and counterclockwise torques are _____.

Q4-7 A pair of forces with equal magnitudes but opposite directions is called a _____.

Q4-8 For a rigid body to be in translational equilibrium, the _____ on it must be zero.

Q4-9 For a rigid body to be in rotational equilibrium, the _____ on it must be zero.

Q4-10 The rotational equilibrium condition may be applied about _____.

Q4-11 The weight of an object is effectively concentrated at its _____.

Q4-12 An object is balanced when its C.G. lies above its _____.

Q4-13 The M.A. is the ratio of the _____ to the _____.

Q4-14 When forces are applied perpendicular to a lever, its M.A. is the distance from the fulcrum to the _____ divided by the distance to the _____.

EXERCISES

Section 4.1 | Torques

4-1 Find the magnitude and sign of the torque due to each of the weights in Fig. 4.33 relative to point P.

4-2 Find the magnitude and sign of the torque due to each of the weights in Fig. 4.33 relative to point Q.

4-3 In Fig. 4.34, consider the vector products $\mathbf{A} \times \mathbf{A}$, $\mathbf{A} \times \mathbf{B}$, $\mathbf{A} \times \mathbf{C}$, $\mathbf{A} \times \mathbf{D}$, and $\mathbf{A} \times \mathbf{E}$. (a) Which of these vector products are zero? (b) Which are directed into the page? (c) Which are directed out of the page? (d) Which are equal to each other in magnitude and direction?

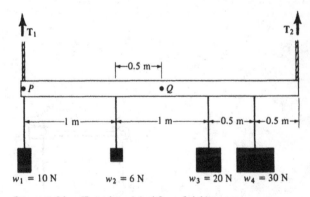

Figure 4.33. Exercises 4-1, 4-2, and 4-11.

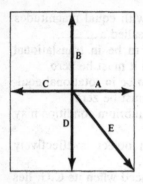

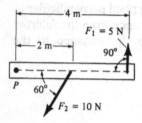

Figure 4.34. The vectors are drawn from the center of a rectangle. Exercises 4-3, 4-4, and 4-5.

Figure 4.35. Exercises 4-7, 4-8, and 4-10.

4-4 In Fig. 4.34, what are the directions of (a) **B** × **C**; (b) **C** × **B**; (c) **B** × **E**?

4-5 In Fig. 4.34, how is **D** × **A** related to **A** × **E**? Explain.

4-6 Using a wrench 0.4 m long, a force of at least 100 N is needed to turn a nut. (a) How large a torque is required? (b) How large a force is needed to turn the nut using a wrench 0.15 m long?

4-7 In Fig. 4.35, how large are the lever arms for the torques about point P due to F_1 and F_2?

4-8 In Fig. 4.35, find the torques due to F_1 and F_2 relative to point P.

4-9 A cyclist applies a downward force **F** of magnitude 100 N to the pedal of her bicycle (Fig. 4.36). (a) Find the magnitude and direction of the torques in each position shown. (b) In which position is the torque a maximum?

Section 4.2 | Equilibrium of Rigid Bodies

4-10 The bar in Fig. 4.35 is pivoted at point P. Will it tend to start rotating if it is initially at rest? Explain, and indicate in which direction it would rotate if your answer is yes.

4-11 A weightless bar supported by two vertical ropes has four weights hung from it (Fig. 4.33). Find the tensions T_1 and T_2 in the ropes.

4-12 Two children balance on a weightless see-saw. One weighs 160 N and is seated 1.5 m from the fulcrum. The second is seated 2 m on the other side of the fulcrum. What is the weight of the second child?

4-13 Find the forces F_1 and F_2 on the tooth in Fig. 4.37. (In orthodonture, forces applied to the teeth lead to forces on the supporting bones. Gradually the bone tissue breaks down and permits the tooth to rotate or translate. New bone tissue grows in the space left behind. The forces must be small enough to avoid damaging the root of the tooth.)

4-14 Figure 4.38 shows the forearm considered in Example 4.6 when the person is holding a 12-N weight w_1 in the hand (w is the weight of the fore-

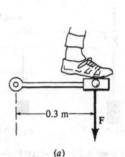

Figure 4.36. Exercise 4-9.   (a)

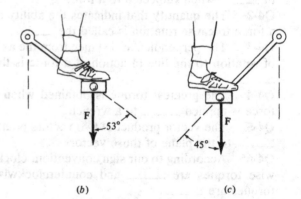

(b)   (c)

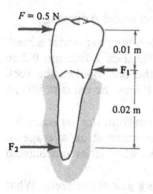

Figure 4.37.   Exercise 4-13.

arm). (a) Find the force **T** exerted by the biceps muscle and the force **E** exerted by the elbow joint. (b) In Example 4.6, with $w_1 = 0$, we found $T = 36$ N and $E = 24$ N. Why are these forces more than twice as large here?

4-15   Children with weights w_1 and w_2 balance on a seesaw. The weight w of the seesaw can be considered to act at its center of gravity, which is directly over the pivot. In terms of w, w_1, and w_2, find (a) the force exerted by the pivot; and (b) the ratio x_2/x_1 of the children's distances from the pivot.

4-16   A heavy load of wet laundry is hung from a clothesline. Is the line more likely to break if it is stretched tightly or allowed to sag considerably? Explain.

Section 4.3 | The Center of Gravity

4-17   Three weights are positioned on a weightless rod, as shown in Fig. 4.39. Where is their center of gravity?

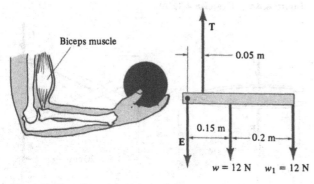

Figure 4.38.   Exercises 4-14 and 4-36.

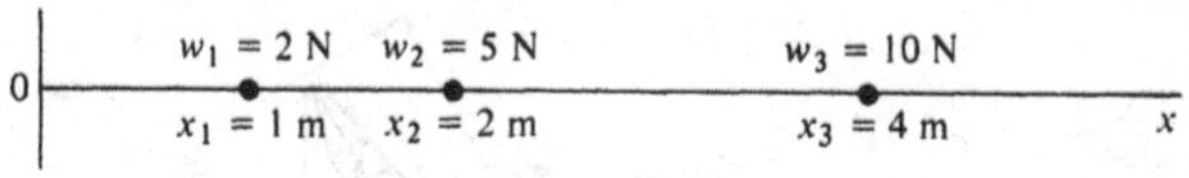

Figure 4.39.   Exercise 4-17.

4-18   Two weights are hung from the ends of a horizontal metre stick. If the weight at $x = 0$ is 10 N and the center of gravity is at $x = 0.8$ m, what is the weight at $x = 1$ m? (Neglect the weight of the stick.)

4-19   A woman's forearm has a mass of 1.1 kg and her upper arm has a mass of 1.3 kg. When her arm is held straight out, the C.G. of the forearm is 0.3 m from the shoulder joint, and the C.G. of the upper arm is 0.07 m from the shoulder joint. What is the position of the center of gravity of the entire arm with respect to the shoulder joint?

4-20   An 80-kg hiker carries a 20-kg pack. The center of gravity of the hiker is 1.1 m above the ground when he is not wearing the pack. The C.G. of the pack is 1.3 m from the ground when it is worn. How far above the ground is the C.G. of the hiker and the pack?

4-21   The axles of a car are 3 m apart. The front wheels support a total weight of 9000 N and the rear wheels support 7000 N. How far is the center of gravity from the front axle?

4-22   Using the data on the inside rear cover, find the position of the center of mass of the earth–moon system.

4-23   Two metre sticks are glued together at their ends. One extends from $x = 0$ to $x = 1$ m and the other from $y = 0$ to $y = 1$ m. (a) Where is their center of gravity? (b) How far is the C.G. from the origin?

4-24   A sheet of plywood is 2 m by 3 m. (a) Where is its center of gravity? (b) A 1-m square is removed from one of its corners. Where is the C.G. now, relative to the corner opposite the one where the square was removed?

4-25   A table consists of a thin top plus four legs of constant thickness and of length 0.7 m. If the C.G. of the table is 0.05 m below the top, find the ratio of the mass of the top to the total mass of the legs.

4-26   How large a mass m can be hung from the end of the boom in Fig. 4.40 before it will tip

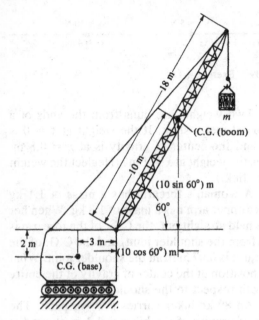

Figure 4.40. Exercise 4-26.

over? (The mass of the movable boom is 1000 kg, and the mass of the base is 10,000 kg.)

4-27   At what angle θ will the table in Fig. 4.41 tip over?

4-28   Ships returning to their home ports without a cargo are sometimes loaded with rocks in their holds or water in their tanks. Why is this done?

4-29   An amusing toy consists of a figure holding a curved pole with weights at either end (Fig. 4.42). It is stable in the position shown and will not fall when pushed gently. Explain why. (*Hint*: Where is the center of gravity?)

4-30   A steel girder with a mass of 1000 kg and a length of 10 m rests on a concrete slab, with 4 m overhanging the edge. How far can a 100-kg man walk on the girder?

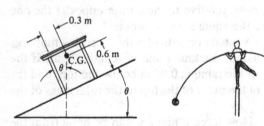

Figure 4.41. Exercise 4-27.   **Figure 4.42.** Exercise 4-29.

Section 4.5 | Levers; Mechanical Advantage

4-31   A man places a 2-m-long bar under a boulder weighing 4500 N. He uses a fulcrum 0.2 m from the point where the bar touches the rock (Fig. 4.43). What force **F** must he exert to lift the rock?

4-32   An oar is held 0.4 m from the oarlock (Fig. 4.44). If it contacts the water at an average of 1.4 m from the oarlock, what is its mechanical advantage?

4-33   Figure 4.45 shows a pair of tweezers. What is its mechanical advantage?

4-34   Figure 4.46 shows a pair of pliers. (a) What is its mechanical advantage? (b) If a force $F =$

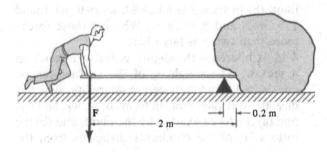

Figure 4.43. Exercise 4-31.

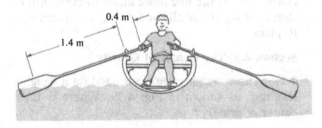

Figure 4.44. Exercise 4-32.

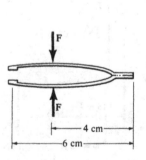   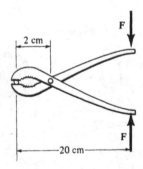

Figure 4.45. Exercise 4-33.   **Figure 4.46.** Exercise 4-34.

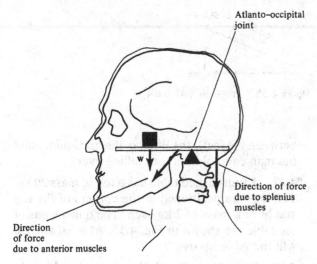

Figure 4.47. Muscles moving and supporting the head. Exercise 4-37.

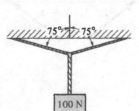

Figure 4.48. Problem 4-39.

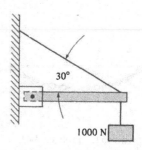

Figure 4.49. Problems 4-40 and 4-41.

10 N is applied, what force is exerted on the object?

4-35 Give examples of class I levers with M.A.s equal to 1, less than 1, and greater than 1.

Section 4.7 | Levers in the Body

4-36 Figure 4.38 shows the forearm represented as a pivoted bar; T is the force exerted by the biceps muscle. (a) What class of lever does this represent? (b) What is the mechanical advantage of the forearm for supporting its own weight, w? (c) What is its M.A. for supporting a load w_1 held in the hand? (d) If the muscle contracts 1 cm, how far will the load in the hand move?

4-37 The head pivots about the atlanto-occipital joint (Fig. 4.47). The splenius muscles attached behind the joint support the head. (a) What class of lever does this represent? (b) The anterior muscles produce forward motions of the head. What class of levers does their action represent? (c) Which muscles have the larger mechanical advantage? Speculate on the reasons for this.

PROBLEMS

4-38 Vector **A** points north, and vector **C** = **A** × **B** points straight up. What can you say about (a) the vertical component of **B**; (b) the compo-

nent of **B** toward the east; (c) the component of **B** toward the north?

4-39 Find the tension in the ropes in Fig. 4.48.

4-40 In Fig. 4.49, an object is supported by a hinged, weightless rod and a cable. Find the tension in the cable and the force exerted by the hinge.

4-41 Repeat the preceding problem if the weight of the rod is 1000 N.

4-42 In Fig. 4.50, the hinged rod and cable are weightless. The cable will break when the tension exceeds 2000 N. What is the maximum weight w that can be supported?

***4-43** The tension T at each end of the chain in Fig. 4.51 is 20 N. What is the weight of the chain?

4-44 A horse stands with its left forefoot off the ground (Fig. 4.52). The left rear and right front legs each support 1500 N of its weight, which is 5000 N. (a) What force is exerted by the right hind

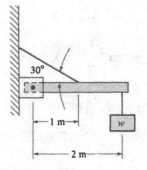

Figure 4.50. Problem 4-42.

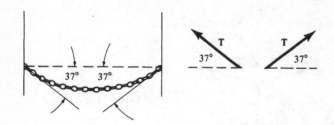

Figure 4.51. Problem 4-43.

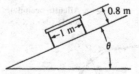

Figure 4.55. Problems 4-47 and 4-48.

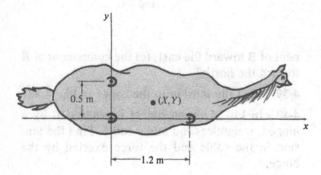

Figure 4.52. A horse viewed from above standing on three legs. Problem 4-44.

leg? (b) Find the position (X, Y) of the center of gravity.

4-45 What is the position of the center of mass of the three masses of Fig. 4.53?

4-46 The man in Fig. 4.54 has a mass of 100 kg. His arms are held straight out to the side, and in one hand he holds a mass M. (a) Find the horizontal and vertical positions of the C.G. of the man plus the mass M. (Choose the origin to be midway

between his feet). (b) What is the maximum mass the man can hold without falling over?

*4-47 A four-legged table has a top of mass 20 kg. The legs are positioned at the corners of the top and have a mass of 2 kg each. The dimensions of the table are shown in Fig. 4.55. At what angle θ will the table tip over?

4-48 The table in Fig. 4.55 has massless legs. At what angle θ will it tip over?

4-49 A uniform wooden board has a mass of 20 kg and a length of 2 m. A circular hole is cut out with its center 0.5 m from one end. If the C.G. is now 0.9 m from the opposite end, what is the mass of the wood removed?

*4-50 The ammonia (NH_3) molecule is a pyramid, with the three hydrogen (H) atoms forming the base and the nitrogen (N) atom at the apex. The centers of the hydrogen atoms are separated by 16.3 nm (1 nm = 10^{-9} m), and the nitrogen atom is 3.8 nm above the center of the base. Where is the center of mass of the molecule relative to the nitrogen atom? (The mass of a nitrogen atom is 14 times that of a hydrogen atom.)

*4-51 The deltoid muscle raises the upper arm to a horizontal position (Fig. 4.56). (a) Find the tension T exerted by the muscle and the components R_x and R_y of the force exerted by the shoulder joint. (b) What is the mechanical advantage of the muscle for lifting the arm?

*4-52 A vase 0.4 m tall has its center of gravity 0.15 m from the bottom, which is a circle of radius 0.05 m (Fig. 4.57). How far can the top of the vase be pushed to the side without toppling it?

4-53 Show that the M.A. of a class III lever is always less than 1, assuming the forces are perpendicular to the lever.

4-54 Show that the M.A. of a class II lever is

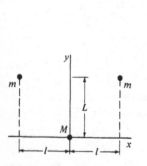

Figure 4.53. Problem 4-45.

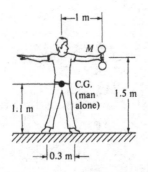

Figure 4.54. Problem 4-46.

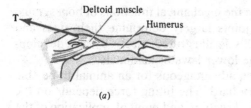

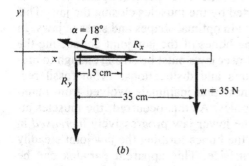

Figure 4.56. Problem 4-51. (Adapted from Williams and Lissner.)

always greater than 1, assuming the forces are perpendicular to the lever.

*4-55 In Fig. 4.58, the weight of the upper body is $w = 490$ N. Find the force T exerted by the spinal muscles and the components R_x and R_y of the force R exerted by the pivot (sacrum) if the weight w_1 is (a) zero; (b) 175 N.

4-56 Show that 1 N m = 1 kg m^2 s^{-2}.

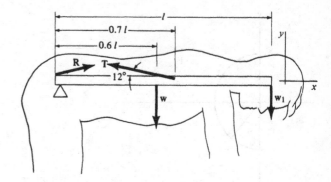

Figure 4.58. Problem 4-55.

ᶜ4-57 A rod is shaped so that its weight per unit length λ is $\lambda_0(1 - x/2L)$ for $0 \le x \le L$. Find its center of gravity.

ᶜ4-58 Find the center of gravity of the triangular metal plate in Fig. 4.59.

ᶜ4-59 A solid cone of uniform density has a height h (Fig. 4.60). (a) Show that its weight per

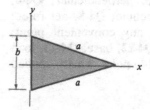

Figure 4.59. Problem 4-58.

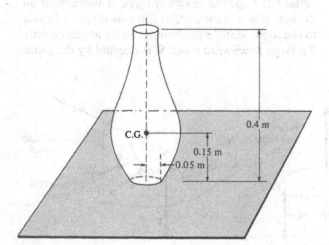

Figure 4.57. Problem 4-52.

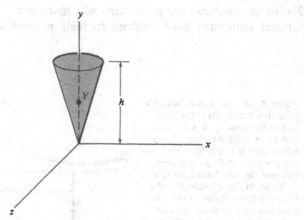

Figure 4.60. Problem 4-59.

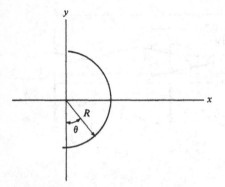

Figure 4.61. Problem 4-60.

unit length alone the y direction varies as y^2. (b) Find its center of gravity, Y.

ᶜ**4-60** A wire is bent into a semicircle of radius R (Fig. 4.61). Find its center of gravity. [*Hint:* Write $\int x\,dw$ in terms of the angle θ.

ANSWERS TO REVIEW QUESTIONS

Q4-1, size or shape; **Q4-2**, torque; **Q4-3**, lever arm; **Q4-4**, perpendicular; **Q4-5**, perpendicular; **Q4-6**, negative, positive; **Q4-7**, couple; **Q4-8**, net force; **Q4-9**, net torque; **Q4-10**, any convenient point; **Q4-11**, center of gravity; **Q4-12**, base; **Q4-13**, load force, applied force; **Q4-14**, point where applied force acts, load.

SUPPLEMENTARY TOPICS

4.8 | THE JAWS OF ANIMALS

Mechanics enables us to understand why many anatomical structures have evolved to their present state, since the mechanical functions of bones, muscles, and joints largely determine their sizes and shapes. This is illustrated nicely by the development of the lower jaws of mammals.

It is often advantageous for an animal to be able to bite very hard. The biting force depends on the magnitude, direction, and point of application of the forces exerted by the muscles closing the jaw. This leads to certain optimal shapes and sizes of jaws. In addition, the bones of the jaw joint connecting the upper and lower jaws must be strong enough to prevent fractures and dislocations. From fossil records, we know that mammals evolved from mammal-like reptiles. As this occurred, the muscles attached to the lower jaw progressively *increased* in size, while the bones forming the jaw joint steadily *decreased* in size. This apparent paradox can be explained in terms of the changes in the direction and point of application of the muscular forces.

Figure 4.62 shows the basic differences between the lower jaws of a primitive reptile and a typical present-day mammal. The first is a simple bar, with the muscles pulling upward at a point close to the joint. The mammalian jaw has a large bump or projection called the *coronoid process*. Attached to this is the *temporalis* muscle, which pulls *backward* as well as upward (force **T** in Fig. 4.62). The *masseter* and *pterygoideus* muscles pull *forward* as well as upward (force **M**).

A primitive reptile biting with an upward force −**B** on food between its back teeth experiences an equal but opposite reaction force **B** downward on the jaw. Since the muscular force **M** is applied close to the joint, static equilibrium can be achieved only if a large downward force **R** is exerted by the joint.

Figure 4.62. (*a*) Lower jaw of a primitive reptile. **M** is the force due to the muscle, **B** is the reaction force from the object being bitten, and **R** is the force due to the jaw joint at *J*. (*b*) A mammalian jaw. Muscle forces are shown as **T** and **M**. As explained in the text, the force **R** due to the jaw joint can be zero if the lines of action of the three forces **T**, **B**, and **M** intersect as shown here.

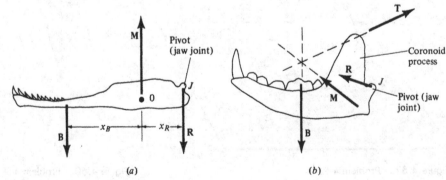

Calculating torques about the point 0, the net torque is zero if

$$x_B B - x_R R = 0 \quad \text{or} \quad R = \frac{x_B}{x_R} B$$

Since the net force on the jaw must be zero, $M - B - R = 0$, and the required muscle force is

$$M = B + R = B \left(1 + \frac{x_B}{x_R} \right)$$

For example, if $x_B = 2x_R$ and $B = 1$ N, then $R = 2$ N, and $M = 3$ N. Thus the force B on the food is smaller than the forces M and R exerted by the muscle and the joint, respectively. Clearly the strength of the joint is a limiting factor in how hard the reptile can bite and in how large a muscle it can safely employ.

In the mammalian jaw, the force **M** is applied further from the joint and another muscular force, **T**, is also present (Fig. 4.63). If the lines of action of **T**, **M**, and **B** all cross at a point, their torques about this point are zero. Then the second equilibrium condition, $\tau = 0$, requires that the line of action of **R** pass through this point as well. Furthermore, when the forces also satisfy **T** + **M** + **B** = 0, *no force R need be supplied by the joint to satisfy the requirement* **F** = 0. If **T** + **M** + **B** is not zero, or if their lines of action do not exactly meet at one point, a force **R** will have to be supplied by the joint, but **R** will still be much smaller than in the reptile. Thus a smaller joint structure is adequate, and the strength of the joint does not limit the size of the muscle the animal can have.

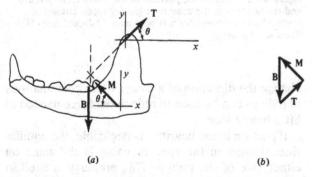

Figure 4.63. Forces on the mammalian jaw when no force is supplied by the jaw joint.

Example 4.12

To illustrate the superiority of the mammalian jaw, suppose that the muscle forces **T** and **M** of Fig. 4.63 are both at $\theta = 45°$ to the horizontal. If there is to be no force **R** supplied by the joint, how is **M** related to **T**, and how large a force **B** is exerted on the food? (Assume the lines of action of **B**, **T**, and **M** all cross at a point, so the second equilibrium condition $\tau = 0$ is satisfied.)

Since the forces have both x and y components, **F** = 0 can be used in component form as $F_x = 0$ and $F_y = 0$. With $F_x = 0$, we obtain

$$T \cos \theta - M \cos \theta = 0$$

so $M = T$. With $F_y = 0$,

$$T \sin \theta + M \sin \theta - B = 0$$

Using $M = T$ and $\sin \theta = \sin 45° = \sqrt{2}/2$,

$$B = (T + M) \sin \theta = 2T \sin \theta = \sqrt{2} T$$

Thus the force B exerted by the jaw on the food is greater than either of the muscular forces T and M, and the force due to the joint is zero. (This conclusion is also evident from the lengths of the vectors in Fig. 4.63b.) By contrast, we found that in the reptile, B is smaller than the muscular force or the joint force.

Just as we have compared mammalian and more primitive jaws, one can also compare different mammals. Carnivores use their powerful front teeth to seize or tear their prey, while herbivores grind their food sideways between their molars. The weight of a carnivore's temporalis muscle is one half to two thirds of the total weight of the jaw-closing muscles. However, in herbivores, this muscle weighs only about one tenth of the total. It is left as an exercise to show why this is the proper adaptation for the needs of these two types of animals.

4.9 | CENTER OF GRAVITY OF HUMANS

Information about the center of gravity of humans is useful in many applications. The center of gravity of a freely falling object follows the same trajectory as a simple particle, even though the object may be rotating or changing its shape. This simplifies the analysis of jumping, gymnastics, and other athletic activities. In physical therapy, an amputee fitted with an artificial limb that is lighter than the natural

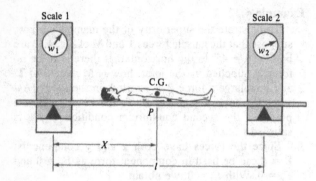

Figure 4.64. A method for finding the center of gravity of a human.

limb has his or her center of gravity shifted. This must be taken into account in planning the person's rehabilitation.

In Section 4.3, we described how the center of gravity can be located by suspending an object from two different points. Another technique is better suited for live humans and animals (Fig. 4.64). A board of length l is supported at its ends by knife edges resting on scales adjusted to read zero with the board alone. When the person lies on the board, the scales read w_1 and w_2, respectively.

The condition $\tau = 0$ for the net torque on the board can be used to find X. Calculating torques about point P,

$$-Xw_1 + (l - X)w_2 = 0$$

or

$$X = \frac{lw_2}{w_1 + w_2} \qquad (4.15)$$

The measurement is repeated twice more with the subject first standing up and then turning 90°. In this way all three coordinates of the center of gravity are determined.

The detailed measurement of the masses, sizes, and centers of gravity of body segments is difficult, and the results vary from individual to individual. Data for a typical man are given in Figs. 4.65 and 4.66 and Table 4.1 and are used in some of the exercises.

4.10 | PULLEY SYSTEMS

Pulleys, like levers, are simple machines that are used in many situations. A single pulley is used to

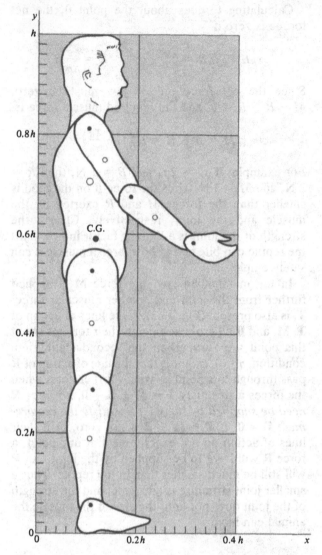

Figure 4.65. The limbs, position of the joints (solid circles), and the position of the centers of gravity (open circles) of several body segments for a typical man. (Adapted from Williams and Lissner.)

change the direction of a force, while combinations of pulleys can be used to reduce the force needed to lift a heavy load.

If friction in the bearings is negligible, the equilibrium tension in the rope or cable is the same on either side of the pulley. This property is used in discussing some typical pulley arrangements in the following examples. We assume in these examples

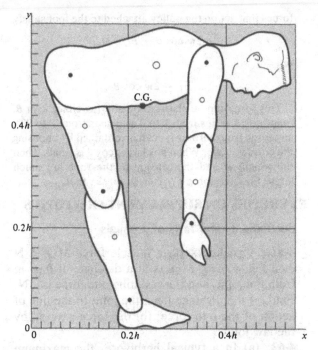

Figure 4.66. The man shown in Fig. 4.65 is now bending over so that his back is nearly horizontal. Note that his center of gravity is still over his feet. (Adapted from Williams and Lissner.)

that the friction is negligible and that the pulleys and ropes are massless.

Example 4.13

What applied force F_a is necessary to lift the weight w in Fig. 4.67?

The forces on pulley 1 are shown in Fig. 4.67b. The rope is continuous, and the tension on both sides of the

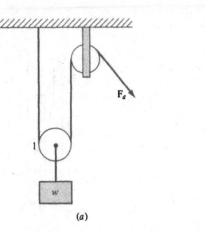

Figure 4.67. The tension in the rope is the same throughout the system, so the two forces on either side of pulley 1 are equal. Example 4.13.

pulleys is the same. If the weight is being raised at constant speed, the system is in equilibrium. Hence $2F_a - w = 0$, and $F_a = w/2$. The force required is only half the weight, and the mechanical advantage is

$$\text{M.A.} = \frac{w}{F_a} = 2$$

Example 4.14

What applied force F_a is necessary to raise the weight w with the pulley system of Fig. 4.68? What is the mechanical advantage of this system?

Again the tension in each vertical segment of rope is the same, so $4F_a - w = 0$, and $F_a = w/4$. The mechanical advantage for this system is

$$\text{M.A.} = \frac{w}{F_a} = 4$$

TABLE 4.1

Masses and centers of gravity of body segments of the man in Figs. 4.65 and 4.66. His total mass is m and his height is h. For example, if his mass is 70 kg, then the mass of his trunk and head is $0.593m = 0.593(70 \text{ kg}) = 41.5$ kg.

| | | Center of Gravity Position for Segment | | | |
| | | Figure 4.65 | | Figure 4.66 | |
Segment	Mass	x	y	x	y
Trunk and head	$0.593m$	$0.10\,h$	$0.70\,h$	$0.26\,h$	$0.52\,h$
Upper arms	$0.053m$	$0.14\,h$	$0.75\,h$	$0.35\,h$	$0.45\,h$
Forearms and hands	$0.043m$	$0.24\,h$	$0.64\,h$	$0.34\,h$	$0.29\,h$
Upper legs	$0.193m$	$0.12\,h$	$0.42\,h$	$0.11\,h$	$0.40\,h$
Lower legs and feet	$0.118m$	$0.10\,h$	$0.19\,h$	$0.17\,h$	$0.18\,h$

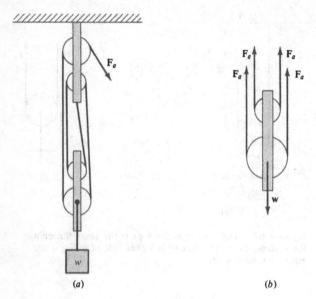

Figure 4.68.   Example 4.14.

From the preceding two examples, we can infer a rule for the mechanical advantage of pulley systems used to lift weights. *The mechanical advantage of the system is equal to the number of parallel ropes supporting the pulley to which the load is attached:* 2 in Fig. 4.67 and 4 in Fig. 4.68. Note that this rule does *not* apply when, as in the next example, the forces applied to the load are not all parallel.

Example 4.15

Leg traction is applied to a patient's leg as shown in Fig. 4.69. What horizontal force is exerted on the leg?

The sum of the forces on each pulley is zero, since the pulleys are at rest. From Fig. 4.69b, the horizontal

forces that act on the pulley attached to the foot satisfy

$$2w \cos \theta - F_L = 0$$

or

$$F_L = 2w \cos \theta$$

This force can be changed by altering either w or θ. Since $\cos \theta$ varies from 1 to 0 as θ goes from 0° to 90°, any force from zero to $2w$ can be obtained by choosing the correct angle. When θ is large, $\cos \theta$ is small. Then the weight w and the tension in the rope are much larger than the force F_L exerted on the foot.

EXERCISES ON SUPPLEMENTARY TOPICS

Section 4.8 | The Jaws of Animals

4-61   A snake exerts a muscle force $M = 5$ N (see Fig. 4.62a). M acts at a distance of 0.03 m from the joint, and the resulting bite force is 2 N. Find (a) the distance from the joint to the line of action of the bite force; (b) the force exerted by the jaw joint.

4-62   (a) In a typical herbivore, the maximum magnitude of the force T is one tenth the maximum magnitude of the force M in Fig. 4.70. Assuming that there is no force at the joint, would you expect the animal to exert the largest biting force near the front or back of the jaw? (b) In a carnivore the maximum value of T is about twice that of M. Would you expect the maximum biting force to be exerted further from or closer to the jaw joint than in the herbivore? Explain.

Section 4.9 | Center of Gravity of Humans

4-63   A board 4 m long is used to find the C.G. as in Fig. 4.64. When a person is on the board, the

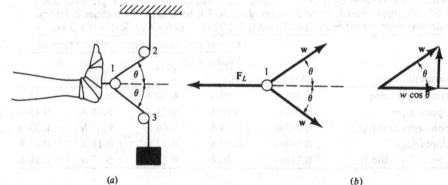

Figure 4.69.   (a) A system of pulleys used to apply a force in leg traction. The magnitude of this force can be adjusted by changing the angle θ. Pulley 1 is attached to the foot, and pulleys 2 and 3 are mounted on a rigid frame that is not shown. (b) The forces on pulley 1.

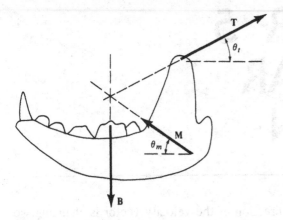

Figure 4.70. Exercise 4-62; Problems 4-69 and 4-70.

scale readings are $w_1 = 200$ N and $w_2 = 600$ N. What is the position of the C.G. of the person?

4-64 Using the data of Table 4.1, find the C.G. of the man in Fig. 4.65.

4-65 Using the data of Table 4.1, find the C.G. of the man in Fig. 4.66.

Section 4.10 | Pulley Systems

4-66 What force F must be applied in Fig. 4.71 to lift the load?

4-67 In Fig. 4.69, a 50-N force is to be applied to the leg. If a 10-kg mass is hung from the cable, what angle θ should be used?

4-68 Suppose the rope in Fig. 4.68 is pulled at 0.25 m s^{-1}. How fast will the load rise?

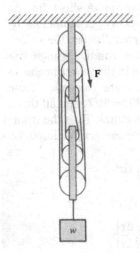

Figure 4.71. Exercise 4-66.

PROBLEMS ON SUPPLEMENTARY TOPICS

4-69 A mammal bites so that the muscle force **M** of Fig. 4.70 has a magnitude of 30 N. What is the force **B** of the bite? (Assume $\theta_t = \theta_m = 45°$.)

*4-70 In a particular carnivore the magnitude of the force T is 1.3 times the magnitude of M (Fig. 4.70). There is no force at the jaw joint. If $\theta_m = 60°$, find (a) θ_t; (b) the ratio B/M.

Additional Reading

John M. Cooper and Ruth B. Glassow, *Kinesiology*, 4th ed., The C. V. Mosby Co., St. Louis, 1976. Balance and body levers in humans.

Signi Brunnstrom, *Clinical Kinesiology*, 3rd ed., F. A. Davis Co., Philadelphia, 1972. Balance and body levers in humans.

Katherine F. Wells and Janet Wessel, *Kinesiology*, 5th ed., W. B. Saunders Co., Philadelphia, 1971. Balance and body levers in humans.

Marian Williams and Herbert R. Lissner, *Biomechanics of Human Motion*, W. B. Saunders Co., Philadelphia, 1962. Physical therapy applications.

John J. Hay, *The Biomechanics of Sports Techniques*, Prentice-Hall, Inc., Englewood Cliffs, N.J., 1973.

Sir James Gray, *How Animals Move*, Cambridge University Press, Cambridge, 1953. Chapter 3 discusses balance and stability.

R. A. R. Tricker and B. J. K. Tricker, *The Science of Movement*, Mills and Boon Ltd., London, 1967. Chapters 3, 4, 15, and 16 discuss balance and stability.

R. C. Thurow, *Edgewise Orthodontics*, 3rd ed., The C. V. Mosby Co., St. Louis, 1972. Applications of statics.

R. McNeill Alexander, *Animal Mechanics*, University of Washington Press, Seattle, 1968. Pages 5–13 discuss the jaws of animals.

A. W. Crompton, On the Lower Jaw of Diarthrognathus and the Origin of the Mammalian Lower Jaw, *Proceedings of the Zoological Society of London*, vol. 140, 1963, pp. 697–753.

Scientific American articles:

Milton Hildebrand, How Animals Run, May 1960, p. 148.

Jearl Walker, In Judo and Aikido Application of the Physics of Forces Makes the Weak Equal to the Strong. *The Amateur Scientist*, July 1980, p. 1950.

Marc H. Raibert and Ivan E. Sutherland, Machines That Walk, January 1983, p. 44.

CHAPTER 5
CIRCULAR MOTION

Newton's laws of motion permit us to find the motion of any object if we know the forces acting upon the object and its initial position and velocity. In the preceding chapter, we considered objects that are in equilibrium and remain at rest. Earlier, we discussed the uniformly accelerated motion that occurs when the net force is constant in magnitude and direction. In this chapter, we consider another kind of motion frequently encountered, motion in a circular path.

When an object moves in a circular path at a constant speed, its acceleration is directed toward the center of the circle. The force required to produce this acceleration can be provided in various ways. Friction provides the required force for a car on a flat, circular track; gravity for an artificial satellite orbiting the earth; and electric forces for an electron orbiting an atomic nucleus. In this chapter, we discuss these and other examples of circular motion.

Closely related to the motion of an object in a circular path is the rotation of a rigid body about an axis. Examples are easy to find: lawn mower blades, automobile wheels, the earth spinning on its axis. *Each point* in such an object is undergoing circular motion. Again, we will see that Newton's laws permit us to predict and analyze such motions.

5.1 | CENTRIPETAL ACCELERATION

Consider a car going around a circular track at a constant speed (Fig. 5.1a). The car is said to be undergoing *uniform circular motion*. Because the magnitude of the velocity is constant, the car has no acceleration component along the direction of motion; its *tangential acceleration* is zero. However,

the direction of the velocity vector is changing, so there is an acceleration component along the direction at right angles to the velocity. We now develop a formula for this *centripetal acceleration*. We shall see examples of its use in this and later sections.

In Fig. 5.1b, $\mathbf{v}$ is the velocity at some instant, and $\mathbf{v} + \Delta\mathbf{v}$ is the velocity a short time interval Δt later. The velocity change $\Delta\mathbf{v}$ that occurs in the short interval Δt points toward the center of the circle. The instantaneous acceleration is the ratio $\Delta\mathbf{v}/\Delta t$ evaluated in the limit as Δt approaches zero. Thus the acceleration $\mathbf{a}_r$ points along $\Delta\mathbf{v}$ or toward the center of the circle. The subscript r reminds us that the acceleration is *radially inward*. $\mathbf{a}_r$ is also called the *centripetal acceleration* because it is directed toward the *center*.

The magnitude of $\mathbf{a}_r$ can be found with the aid of the triangles in Fig. 5.1b. The motion is along the circumference of the circle, so the velocity is always tangential to the circle or perpendicular to the radius. Thus $\mathbf{v}$ is perpendicular to $\mathbf{r}$. A short time Δt later, the velocity vector $\mathbf{v} + \Delta\mathbf{v}$ is perpendicular to $\mathbf{r} + \Delta\mathbf{r}$. Since they remain perpendicular, the velocity vector and position vector rotate through the same angle. Hence the angle θ in the two triangles is the same. Since the triangles are isosceles, their other two angles are each $(180° - \theta)/2$, and all three angles in the two triangles are equal. Thus the triangles are similar, and their sides are proportional, or

$$\frac{1}{v}|\Delta\mathbf{v}| = \frac{1}{r}|\Delta\mathbf{r}|$$

Now if we divide by Δt, we have

$$\frac{1}{v}\left|\frac{\Delta\mathbf{v}}{\Delta t}\right| = \frac{1}{r}\left|\frac{\Delta\mathbf{r}}{\Delta t}\right|$$

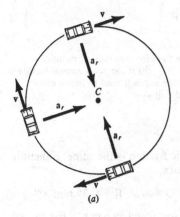

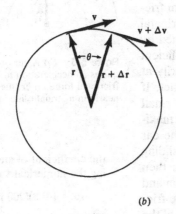

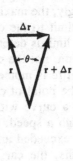

(a)

(b)

Figure 5.1. (a) A car going around a circular track at a constant speed has an acceleration directed toward the center C of the circle. Its tangential acceleration component is zero since the speed is constant. (b) The velocity vector $\mathbf{v}$ and the position vector r rotate at the same rate, so the angle θ is the same in both triangles. Thus the triangles are similar, and $|\Delta\mathbf{v}|/v = |\Delta\mathbf{r}|/r$.

Taking the limit $\Delta t \to 0$ gives

$$\frac{a_r}{v} = \frac{v}{r}$$

Hence the centripetal acceleration has a magnitude

$$a_r = \frac{v^2}{r} \qquad (5.1)$$

The acceleration varies inversely with the radius; the smaller the circle, the greater the acceleration. It also varies as v^2; the centripetal acceleration needed to negotiate a curve increases rapidly with the speed.

The following example illustrates the use of this radial acceleration formula.

Example 5.1

A car goes around a flat, circular track of radius 200 m at a constant speed of 30 m s^{-1}. What is its acceleration?

Since the speed is constant, there is no tangential acceleration. However, because the velocity vector is changing direction, there is an acceleration toward the center of the circle. This acceleration has a magnitude of

$$a_r = \frac{v^2}{r} = \frac{(30 \text{ m s}^{-1})^2}{200 \text{ m}} = 4.5 \text{ m s}^{-2}$$

In the absence of any net force, an object moves in a straight line at a constant speed in accordance with Newton's first law. If the object moves in a circular path, it has a radial acceleration $a_r = v^2/r$, so some force must be producing this acceleration. From the second law, the force must be equal to the mass times the acceleration. *Thus the net force* F *needed to produce an acceleration* a_r *is*

$$F = ma_r = \frac{mv^2}{r} \qquad (5.2)$$

In the case of a car on a flat truck, the centripetal acceleration results from a frictional force exerted on the tires by the road (Fig. 5.2). Other forces also act on the car: its weight, directed downward; an equal but opposite upward normal force due to the

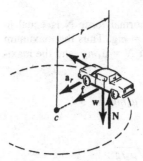

Figure 5.2. Forces on a car on a flat circular track. Not shown are the forces due to the air and the road along the direction of motion. A frictional force $\mathbf{f}$ is directed toward the center of the circle.

road; a backward force due to air resistance; and a forward force exerted by the road on the tires. However, the only force that can produce a radial acceleration is the frictional force acting perpendicular to the motion. Accordingly, the maximum frictional force possible sets a limit to the centripetal acceleration of the car. This limit is determined by the coefficient of *static* friction, not the coefficient of kinetic friction, since the tire is momentarily at rest relative to the road at the point of contact. If the driver tries to negotiate a curve with a small radius of curvature at too high a speed, the maximum frictional force will be exceeded and the car will skid. Once a skid begins, the car is sliding rather than rolling, so the frictional force is then determined by the coefficient of kinetic friction and is reduced in magnitude. This reduction in the frictional force makes it difficult to regain control of the vehicle and can lead to an accident. The force needed to produce a centripetal acceleration is found in the next example.

Example 5.2

The car in the preceding example travels on a flat, circular track of radius 200 m at 30 m s^{-1} and has a centripetal acceleration $a_r = 4.5$ m s^{-2}. (a) If the mass of the car is 1000 kg, what frictional force is required to provide the acceleration? (b) If the coefficient of static friction μ_s is 0.8, what is the maximum speed at which the car can circle the track?

(a) Since the mass is 1000 kg and the acceleration is 4.5 m s^{-2}, Newton's second law gives

$$F = ma_r = (1000 \text{ kg})(4.5 \text{ m s}^{-2}) = 4500 \text{ N}$$

This is the frictional force required to circle the track at 30 m s^{-1}.

(b) From Fig. 5.2, the normal force **N** is equal in magnitude to the weight **w** = mg. Thus the maximum frictional force possible is $\mu_s N = \mu_s mg$, and the maximum velocity satisfies

$$\frac{mv^2}{r} = \mu_s mg$$

or

$$v = \sqrt{\mu_s r g}$$

Note that the mass has canceled, so the maximum velocity on this track is the same for any car as long as

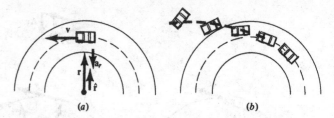

Figure 5.3. (*a*) A car on a flat circular track of radius *r* requires an acceleration $a_r = v^2/r$. (b) If the road cannot supply a frictional force mv^2/r, then the car will tend to move more nearly in a straight line and will skid.

the coefficient of static friction is the same. Substituting the numerical values,

$$v = [(0.8)(200 \text{ m})(9.8 \text{ m s}^{-2})]^{1/2} = 39.6 \text{ m s}^{-1}$$

If the driver attempts to exceed 39.6 m s^{-1}, the car will not be able to continue on the circular course, and it will skid as in Fig. 5.3.

Vector Notation

It is useful to write the expression for the centripetal acceleration in vector form. In Fig. 5.4, **r** is a vector directed from the center of the circle, and $\hat{\mathbf{r}} = \mathbf{r}/r$ is a unit vector in that direction. The acceleration $\mathbf{a}_r$ is directed opposite to **r**, so

$$\mathbf{a}_r = -\frac{v^2}{r}\hat{\mathbf{r}} \qquad (5.3)$$

Similarly the net force $\mathbf{F} = m\mathbf{a}_r$ producing the acceleration can be written in vector form as

$$\mathbf{F} = -\frac{mv^2}{r}\hat{\mathbf{r}} \qquad (5.4)$$

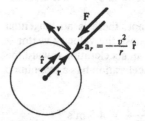

Figure 5.4. The vector $\hat{\mathbf{r}} = \mathbf{r}/r$ is parallel to **r** and has unit magnitude. $\mathbf{a}_r$ and $\mathbf{F} = m\mathbf{a}_r$ are directed opposite to **r** and $\hat{\mathbf{r}}$.

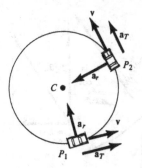

Figure 5.5. A car going around a circular track with an increasing speed. It has a centripetal acceleration $a_r = v^2/r$ and a tangential acceleration a_T equal to the rate of change of the speed. (Note that both v and a_T are larger at P_2 than at P_1.)

The equation $\mathbf{a}_r = -(v^2/r)\hat{\mathbf{r}}$ is also applicable in some cases other than uniform circular motion. For example, when a car moves on a circular track with a variable speed, its acceleration can be resolved into two components. One is parallel or tangential to the track, and the other is perpendicular to the track. The tangential component $\mathbf{a}_T$ is equal in magnitude to the rate of change of the speed, dv/dt (Fig. 5.5). However, its acceleration component perpendicular to the motion is still v^2/r. Thus

$$a_T = \frac{dv}{dt}, \qquad a_r = \frac{v^2}{r} \qquad (5.5)$$

Also, if the car travels on a road that is not circular, any small segment of the road can be considered as part of a circle. The radius of that circle is called the *radius of curvature* at the point P (Fig. 5.6). Again v^2/r is the acceleration component perpendicular to the motion.

5.2 | EXAMPLES OF CIRCULAR MOTION

In the preceding section, we considered in some detail the example of a car on a flat, circular track. We now discuss some other examples of circular motion.

Banked Turns | Good highways usually have banked or slanted curves, so that the normal force exerted by the road on the car has a horizontal component. This horizontal component can provide part of or all the force needed to produce the centripetal acceleration, reducing the role of the frictional force. The road is then much safer, especially under slippery conditions.

To examine this idea in detail, we consider a car on a banked curve. We suppose that the driver wants to drive at the correct speed v, so that no frictional force is required to provide the centripetal acceleration. The problem, then, is to find what that speed should be.

Figure 5.7 shows the relevant forces acting on the car: its weight $\mathbf{w} = m\mathbf{g}$ and the normal force $\mathbf{N}$. (The forces along the direction of motion play no role here.) Since the horizontal component of $\mathbf{N}$ must

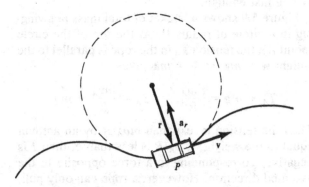

Figure 5.6. At P the road has a radius of curvature r. The centripetal acceleration at P is $a_r = v^2/r$.

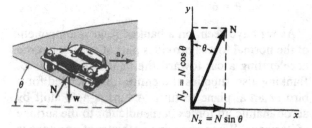

Figure 5.7. A car on a banked curve is moving at the correct speed v so that the horizontal component N_x of the normal force provides the centripetal acceleration and no frictional force is required.

provide all the centripetal acceleration,

$$N \sin \theta = \frac{mv^2}{r}$$

There is no vertical acceleration component, so the net vertical force is zero, and

$$N \cos \theta = mg$$

Dividing the first equation by the second, the masses cancel out, leaving

$$\frac{\sin \theta}{\cos \theta} = \frac{v^2}{rg}$$

Since $\sin \theta / \cos \theta = \tan \theta$, this gives

$$v^2 = rg \tan \theta \qquad (5.6)$$

This equation gives the speed v at which the car can negotiate a curve banked at an angle θ without any assistance from frictional forces. At any other speed, a frictional force will be needed to supplement the horizontal component of the normal force. On a very slippery day, a car going faster will tend to slide out of the curve and a slow car will tend to slide toward the inside of the curve. The use of this result is illustrated by the following example.

Example 5.3

A curve of radius 900 m is banked, so no friction is required at a speed of 30 m s^{-1}. What is the banking angle θ?

Solving Eq. 5.6 for $\tan \theta$,

$$\tan \theta = \frac{v^2}{rg} = \frac{(30 \text{ m s}^{-1})^2}{(900 \text{ m})(9.8 \text{ m s}^{-2})} = 0.102$$

$$\theta = 6°$$

As we have seen, on a banked road a component of the normal forces provides part of or all the force accelerating a car toward the center of the curve. Banking also supplies the entire force needed for a bird or an airplane to turn. A bird is held aloft by aerodynamic lift forces perpendicular to the surface of its wings. When one wing or the tip of one wing is rotated about its long axis, the lift forces become unbalanced, and the bird tilts or banks. In airplanes, banking is accomplished with ailerons, which are

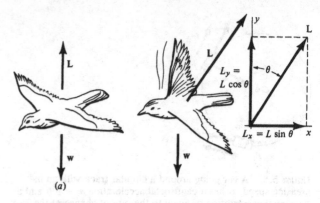

Figure 5.8. (a) Forces on a bird include its weight w and a lift force **L**. (The forward thrust and backward drag forces are not shown.) (b) When the bird banks, the lift force **L** has a horizontal component.

movable surfaces on the trailing edges of the wings. Banking causes the aerodynamic lift force to have a horizontal component and to make the bird or airplane turn (Fig. 5.8).

This is exactly the same situation as in the banked curve, and Eq. 5.6 can therefore be used to relate the banking angle, the speed, and the radius of the turn. For example, birds such as swallows, which can maneuver very rapidly, experience accelerations of a few g's.

Motion in a Vertical Circle | Swinging a water-filled bucket in a vertical circle provides a simple but dramatic example of circular motion. Now we see why spilling can be avoided if the pail is swung fast enough.

Figure 5.9 shows a bucket of total mass m swinging in a circle of radius R. At the top of the circle (point A), the tension $\mathbf{T}_A$ in the rope is parallel to the weight $w = mg$, so $\mathbf{F} = m\mathbf{a}_r$ gives

$$T_A + mg = \frac{mv_A^2}{R}, \qquad T_A = \frac{mv_A^2}{R} - mg$$

Thus the tension is less than mv_A^2/R by an amount equal to the weight. If v_A^2/R is less than g, then T is negative, corresponding to a force opposite to the assumed direction. However, a rope can only pull, not push, so this cannot happen. Consequently, if the pail is swung too slowly, the pail and its con-

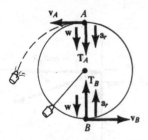

Figure 5.9. Forces acting on a pail swung in a vertical circle. If the rope breaks at the top of the circle, the pail follows the dashed path.

tents will drop below the circular path; to avoid wet clothing, we must have $T_A \geq 0$ at the top of the circle, or

$$\frac{v_A^2}{R} \geq g$$

For example, if $R = 1$ m, v_A must satisfy

$$v_A \geq \sqrt{gR} = \sqrt{(9.8 \text{ m s}^{-2})(1.0 \text{ m})} = 3.13 \text{ m s}^{-1}$$

It is natural to ask why the pail and the water do not fall when they reach the top of the circle. The answer is *that they do fall, but not fast enough.* One way to see this is to consider what would happen if the rope broke as the pail reached the top of the circle. It would then follow the dashed curve in Fig. 5.9 and fall less rapidly than when the rope is intact. Thus the rope forces the pail and its contents to fall even faster than they do under the influence of gravity alone.

At the bottom of the circle (point B), the tension in the rope $\mathbf{T}_B$ and the acceleration are opposite to the weight, so

$$T_B - mg = \frac{mv_B^2}{R}, \qquad T_B = \frac{mv_B^2}{R} + mg$$

Thus the tension here is mv_B^2/R *plus* the weight. Even though we discussed what would happen if the rope broke at the top of the circle, it is more likely to break at the bottom. This is true because the tension is *less* than mv_A^2/R at the top and *more* than mv_B^2/R at the bottom. Also, the gravitational force accelerates the pail as it falls, so the speed is greater at the bottom than at the top, which further increases the tension at the bottom.

Effective Weight | We noted in Chapter Three that our perceived or effective weight is determined by the forces exerted by the floor or chair supporting us. The effective weight is zero for a person in free fall, and more generally is given by

$$\mathbf{w}^e = m\mathbf{g} - m\mathbf{a} \qquad (5.7)$$

Rather large accelerations are encountered in some carnival rides (Fig. 5.10), and the effective weight may be quite different from mg.

Figure 5.10. Amusement park rides can have large centripetal accelerations. Riders experience large effective weights. (M. Sternheim.)

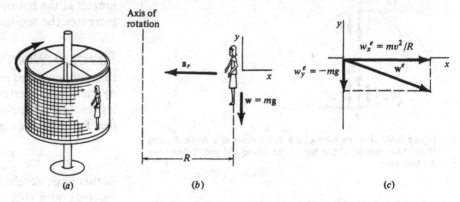

Figure 5.11.   Forces on a girl in a spinning cage.

(a)   (b)   (c)

Example 5.4

On a carnival ride, a girl of mass m stands in a cylindrical cage of radius R. The cage is spun about its cylindrical axis so that her speed is v (Fig. 5.11). What is her effective weight?

From Eq. 5.6, $\mathbf{w}^e = m\mathbf{g} - m\mathbf{a}$. Taking horizontal and vertical components,

$$w_x^e = \frac{mv^2}{R}, \qquad w_y^e = -mg$$

Using the Pythagorean relation (Fig. 5.11c),

$$w^e = m\sqrt{g^2 + \left(\frac{v^2}{R}\right)^2}$$

Thus the girl's effective weight is greater than mg.

The sedimentation of material in a liquid occurs because the weight of the material exceeds that of an equal volume of liquid. The sedimentation rate is proportional to the acceleration of gravity g, which can in effect be increased by spinning the material rapidly in a centrifuge. Ultracentrifuges used in research laboratories achieve accelerations of up to $500,000g$.

5.3 | ANGULAR VARIABLES

Suppose a runner has gone 100 m along a circular track of circumference 400 m. If we say that she has gone one fourth of the way, or 90° around the track, we are describing her motion in terms of the change in her *angular position*. The rate at which the angular position changes is the *angular velocity*, and its rate of change is the *angular acceleration*. These angular variables are especially useful in discussing the rotation of a rigid body about a fixed axis. For example, on the colored spoke of the wheel in Fig. 5.12, every point moves through 360° in one full rotation, even though points near the rim have traveled farther than points near the axis.

Angles can be measured either in degrees or in *radians* (rad). Referring to Fig. 5.12, we define the *angular position* θ in radians by

$$\theta = \frac{s}{r} \tag{5.8}$$

This result for θ is the same for any point on the colored spoke of the wheel. The value of s for a point a distance r from the rotation axis is $r\theta$. For a complete rotation of the wheel, s is equal to the circumference $2\pi r$, and $\theta = 2\pi$ rad. Since a full circle is 360°, 2π rad = 360°. Thus

$$1 \text{ rad} = \frac{360°}{2\pi} = 57.3°$$

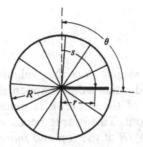

Figure 5.12.   A wheel of radius R rotates about its axle. The spoke shown in color was initially vertical and the wheel has rotated through an angle θ. The point at a distance r from the center has moved a distance $s = r\theta$ along a circular path.

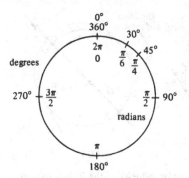

Figure 5.13. Typical angles in degrees and radians. An object that rotates through one and one-half revolutions is said to have rotated through $2\pi + \pi = 3\pi$ radians. 1 radian = 57.3°.

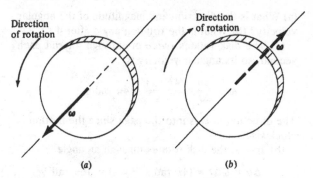

Figure 5.14. (a) For counterclockwise rotations, $\boldsymbol{\omega}$ is directed out of the page. (b) $\boldsymbol{\omega}$ is directed into the page for clockwise rotations.

A convenient way to state the relationship is

$$\pi \text{ rad} = 180° \qquad (5.9)$$

The degree–radian conversion is illustrated in Fig. 5.13 and in the following example.

Example 5.5

Convert (a) 30° to radians; (b) 0.5 rad to degrees.
(a) Multiplying by 1,

$$(30°)\left(\frac{\pi \text{ rad}}{180°}\right) = \frac{\pi}{6} \text{ rad} = 0.524 \text{ rad}$$

(b) Again multiplying by 1,

$$(0.5 \text{ rad})\left(\frac{180°}{\pi \text{ rad}}\right) = \frac{90°}{\pi} = 28.6°$$

The definition $\theta = s/r$ implies that θ is dimensionless; it is the ratio of two lengths. Thus the radian is not a unit in quite the same sense as the metre or kilogram. We use radians as a reminder of how the angle is defined.

Angular Velocity
The magnitude of the angular velocity ω (Greek letter "omega") is equal to the rate of change of the angle. The average regular speed is defined by $\overline{\omega} = \Delta\theta/\Delta t$, where $\Delta\theta$ is the change in angle in the time Δt. As Δt becomes arbitrarily small, the angular speed at a given instant in radians per second is

$$\omega = \frac{d\theta}{dt} \qquad (5.10)$$

If θ is in radians and t is in seconds, then the units of ω are radians per second. For example, if a run-

ner goes once around a circular track in 50 s, her average angular velocity is $(2\pi \text{ rad})/(50 \text{ s}) = 0.126$ rad s^{-1}.

The vector $\boldsymbol{\omega}$ is conventionally taken to be directed *along the axis of rotation.* It is directed out of the page, parallel to the rotation axis, if the rotation is counterclockwise (Fig. 5.14a). If the rotation is clockwise, as in Fig. 5.14b, $\boldsymbol{\omega}$ is directed into the page. (These conventions are similar to those given for the directions of torques in Chapter Four.) One way of identifying the direction of $\boldsymbol{\omega}$ is to curl the fingers of the right hand around the rotation axis in the direction of rotation. The right thumb then points in the direction of $\boldsymbol{\omega}$ (Fig. 5.15). The following example illustrates these ideas.

Example 5.6

A disk rotates clockwise with a constant angular velocity at two revolutions per second (Fig. 5.14b).

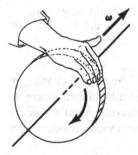

Figure 5.15. Curling the fingers of the right hand in the direction of rotation, the thumb points perpendicular to the disk in the direction of $\boldsymbol{\omega}$.

(a) What is the direction and magnitude of the angular velocity? (b) What is the rotation angle after 4 s?

(a) The disk rotates twice or through 4π rad each second, so its angular velocity is

$$\omega = \frac{\Delta\theta}{\Delta t} = \frac{4\pi \text{ rad}}{1 \text{ s}} = 4\pi \text{ rad s}^{-1}$$

The direction of ω is into the page since the motion is clockwise.

(b) In 4 s, the disk rotates through an angle

$$\Delta\theta = \omega\Delta t = (4\pi \text{ rad s}^{-1})(4 \text{ s}) = 16\pi \text{ rad}$$

The speed $v = ds/dt$ of a point on a rotating object can be related to ω. By definition, $\theta = s/r$, so $\omega = d\theta/dt = (ds/dt)(1/r) = v/r$, and

$$v = r\omega \qquad (5.11)$$

In S.I. units, r has units of metres (m) and ω is in radians per second (rad s^{-1}), but the product $r\omega$ has units of rad m s^{-1} = m s^{-1}; the radians are dropped in the final result.

The speed of points on a rotating object is proportional to the distance r from the rotation axis. The high speeds sometimes encountered when objects rotate are illustrated in the following example.

Example 5.7

The maximum speed of the blades on rotary lawn mowers is limited to reduce the hazard from flying stones and other debris. A currently available model has a rotation rate of 3700 revolutions per minute and a blade 0.25 m in radius. What is the speed at the tip of the blade?

To use $v = r\omega$, we need to find ω. Converting 3700 rev min^{-1} to rad s^{-1},

$$\omega = 3700 \frac{\text{rev}}{\text{min}} \left(\frac{2\pi \text{ rad}}{\text{rev}}\right)\left(\frac{1 \text{ min}}{60 \text{ s}}\right) = 387 \text{ rad s}^{-1}$$

Then the velocity at the blade tip is $v = r\omega = (0.25 \text{ m})(387 \text{ rad s}^{-1}) = 97 \text{ m s}^{-1}$, which is nearly 350 km h^{-1}.

Angular Acceleration

The rate of change of the angular velocity is the angular acceleration α (Greek letter "alpha"). The average angular acceleration is $\Delta\omega/\Delta t$, and the instantaneous acceleration is

$$\alpha = \frac{d\omega}{dt} \qquad (5.12)$$

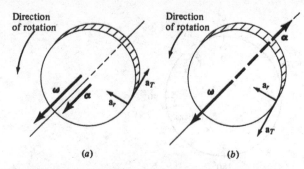

Figure 5.16. In (a) the angular velocity of the disk is increasing, so α and ω are parallel. In (b) the angular velocity is decreasing, so α and ω are antiparallel. The tangential and radial accelerations $\mathbf{a}_T$ and $\mathbf{a}_r$ of a point on the disk are also shown.

The S.I. units of α are radians per second per second. If the orientation of the rotation axis does not change, α points along the axis and is either parallel or opposite to ω. For example, if the disk of Fig. 5.16 is increasing its rotation rate, α and ω are parallel. If the disk is slowing down, α is opposite to ω.

If the angular velocity of the object is changing so that it has an angular acceleration, then points on the object will experience tangential accelerations (Fig. 5.16). The magnitude of the tangential acceleration of a point is $a_T = dv/dt$, so from $v = r\omega$, we have $dv/dt = r \, d\omega/dt$, and

$$a_T = r\alpha \qquad (5.13)$$

These ideas are illustrated by the next example.

Example 5.8

In Example 5.7, the lawn mower blade has an angular velocity of 387 rad s^{-1} and a radius of 0.25 m. If it accelerates to this velocity uniformly from rest over a 10-s interval, find (a) the angular acceleration; (b) the tangential acceleration at the tip of the blade.

(a) Since the acceleration is uniform,

$$\alpha = \frac{\Delta\omega}{\Delta t} = \frac{387 \text{ rad s}^{-1}}{10 \text{ s}} = 38.7 \text{ rad s}^{-2}$$

(b) The tangential acceleration component is

$$a_T = \alpha r = (38.7 \text{ rad s}^{-2})(0.25 \text{ m}) = 9.68 \text{ m s}^{-2}$$

We could have found the same result using $a = \Delta v/\Delta t$ and the final linear velocity.

Points on a rotating object also experience a radial or centripetal acceleration of magnitude v^2/r.

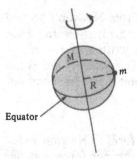

Figure 5.17. A star spinning on its axis. Particles at the equator move the fastest and have the greatest centripetal acceleration.

Since $v = \omega r$, the centripetal acceleration can be written in angular variables as

$$\mathbf{a}_r = -\omega^2 r \hat{\mathbf{r}} \qquad (5.14)$$

If the forces among the particles of a rapidly spinning object such as a centrifuge or a star are not large enough to provide this centripetal acceleration, it will break up when a critical angular velocity ω_c is reached. For example, consider the rotating star in Fig. 5.17 that has a mass M and radius R. A particle of mass m on its equator has an acceleration $\omega^2 R$. The gravitational force GmM/R^2 due to the star must be at least equal to ma_r. Hence, the star is just barely able to hold together for an angular velocity ω_c satisfying $m\omega_c^2 R = GmM/R^2$, or

$$\omega_c^2 = \frac{GM}{R^3}$$

The density of the star is its mass-to-volume ratio, $\rho = M/(\frac{4}{3}\pi R^3)$. Hence we find

$$\omega_c^2 = \frac{4}{3}\pi G\rho \qquad (5.15)$$

This result implies that the maximum angular velocity of a star is determined by its average density. A star with the density of the sun cannot rotate faster than about once every 3 hours; the sun actually rotates about once in 27 days. *Pulsars*, however, are stars that rotate as fast as roughly every 0.001 second. According to Eq. 5.15, they must have enormous densities. Pulsars are believed to be neutron stars, with densities comparable to those of atomic nuclei and greater than that of the sun by a factor of 10^{12}.

TABLE 5.1

Translational and rotational motion comparisons

Quantity	Translation	Rotation	Relationship
Position, displacement	x, s	θ	$s = r\theta$
Velocity	$\mathbf{v}$	ω	$v = r\omega$
Acceleration	$\mathbf{a} = \mathbf{a}_r + \mathbf{a}_T$	α	$a_T = r\alpha$
			$a_r = \omega^2 r$

Finding the Motion | The description of rigid body rotation can be rather complicated if the angular acceleration and velocity are not parallel. This situation arises, for example, in Chapter Seven when we discuss the motion of a gyroscope or the precession of the equinoxes of the Earth. However, when an object is constrained to rotate about an axis fixed in space, the angular variables θ, ω, and α are related to each other in exactly the same way as are the variables x, v, and a for motion along a straight line (see Table 5.1). Consequently, given the angular acceleration and the initial angular position and velocity, we can find the subsequent motion, just as in Chapter One. For example, if the angular acceleration is constant, the derivation of the equations of motion will proceed precisely as before, with obvious changes in notation. The results are listed in Table 5.2 for convenient reference, and are illustrated by the next example.

Example 5.9

In Example 5.7, a lawn mower blade rotates at 387 rad s^{-1}. If the blade comes to a stop with a constant

TABLE 5.2

Equations for constant angular acceleration α along the axis of rotation and their translational motion analogs. In using these equations, one direction along the rotation axis is defined as positive and the other as negative; θ, ω, and α can each be positive or negative.

Constant Linear Acceleration α	Constant Angular Acceleration α
$v = v_0 + a\,\Delta t$	$\omega = \omega_0 + \alpha\,\Delta t$
$\Delta x = v_0\,\Delta t + \frac{1}{2}a\,(\Delta t)^2$	$\Delta\theta = \omega_0\,\Delta t + \frac{1}{2}\alpha\,(\Delta t)^2$
$\bar{v} = \frac{1}{2}(v_0 + v)$	$\bar{\omega} = \frac{1}{2}(\omega_0 + \omega)$
$\Delta x = \frac{1}{2}(v_0 + v)\,\Delta t$	$\Delta\theta = \frac{1}{2}(\omega_0 + \omega)\,\Delta t$
$v^2 = v_0^2 + 2a\,\Delta x$	$\omega^2 = \omega_0^2 + 2\alpha\,\Delta\theta$

acceleration in 3 s, find the number of turns it makes as it slows down.

The angle it moves through is

$$\Delta\theta = \tfrac{1}{2}(\omega_0 + \omega)\Delta t = \tfrac{1}{2}(387 \text{ rad s}^{-1} + 0)(3 \text{ s})$$
$$= 581 \text{ rad}$$

The number of turns is $581/2\pi = 92.4$.

5.4 | TORQUE, ANGULAR ACCELERATION, AND THE MOMENT OF INERTIA

We saw in Chapter Four that when the net torque is zero on a rigid body constrained to move about a fixed axis, the rotational motion of that body remains constant. When there is a net torque, the object experiences an angular acceleration proportional to that torque. We can identify the proportionality factor by applying Newton's second law of motion to a simple object.

Figure 5.18 shows a point mass m at the end of a string swinging on a frictionless plane in a horizontal circle. The vertical forces on the mass are its weight $\mathbf{w}$ and a normal force $\mathbf{N}$. These forces are equal in magnitude, and their torques about the center C cancel. The tension in the string, which produces the centripetal acceleration $\mathbf{a}_r$, is directed toward the center; since its line of action passes through C, its torque about that point is zero. Only the force $\mathbf{F}_a$ applied at right angles to the string

produces a torque about C. From Newton's second law, $\mathbf{F}_a = m\mathbf{a}_T$, and by Eq. 5.13, $a_T = r\alpha$. Thus the torque due to $\mathbf{F}_a$ can be written as $\tau = rF_a = r(ma_T) = rm(r\alpha) = (mr^2)\alpha$. The quantity mr^2 is the *moment of inertia I* of the point mass. In vector notation, our result is

$$\tau = I\alpha \qquad (5.16)$$

This equation is similar in form to Newton's second law, $\mathbf{F} = m\mathbf{a}$, relating the net force and the acceleration; Eq. 5.16 relates the net torque and the angular acceleration. The moment of inertia is analogous to the mass and indicates the inertia of the object to changes in its rotational motion. Although we have obtained Eq. 5.16 for a particularly simple object, it applies quite generally to the motion of a rigid body about a fixed axis if the moment of inertia is calculated as described in the following subsection.

Moment of Inertia | Despite the fact that $\tau = I\alpha$ is similar in form to $\mathbf{F} = m\mathbf{a}$, it is important to realize that both the torque τ and the moment of inertia I depend on the position of the axis of rotation. We will also find that I depends on the shape and mass of the rotating object.

To calculate the moment of inertia of a complex object, we must mentally separate the object into N small pieces of mass $m_1, m_2, \ldots, m_N$. Then each piece is a distance $r_1, r_2, \ldots, r_N$ from the axis of rotation. The moment of inertia of the first piece is $m_1r_1^2$, that of the second is $m_2r_2^2$, and so on. The net moment of inertia is the sum of all such terms:

$$I = m_1r_1^2 + m_2r_2^2 + \cdots + m_Nr_N^2$$
$$= \sum_{i=1}^{N} m_i r_i^2 \qquad (5.17)$$

From this we see that the moment of inertia is large when the pieces are far from the rotation axis. In the limit where the masses are arbitrarily small, the sum becomes an integral, and the moment of inertia is given by

$$I = \int r^2 \, dm \qquad (5.18)$$

The following examples illustrate the calculation of the moment of inertia, and Table 5.3 gives the moments of inertia for several shapes.

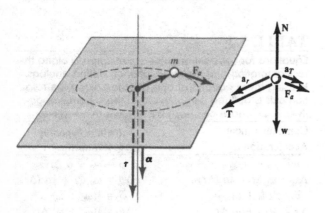

Figure 5.18. The force $\mathbf{F}_a$ exerts a torque on m about the point C, resulting in a tangential acceleration $\mathbf{a}_T$.

TABLE 5.3

Moments of inertia. The mass of each object is taken to be m. The dashed line is the rotation axis.

$I = \frac{1}{2}mR^2$	Uniform disk or cylinder of radius R
$I = \frac{1}{12}ml^2$	Thin rod of length l with the rotation axis through its center
$I = \frac{1}{3}ml^2$	Thin rod of length l with the rotation axis through one end
$I = mR^2$	Thin ring or cylindrical shell of radius R
$I = \frac{2}{5}mR^2$	Sphere of radius R
$I = \frac{2}{3}mR^2$	Spherical shell of radius R

Example 5.10

Two equal point masses m are at the ends of a massless thin bar of length l (Fig. 5.19). Find the moment of inertia for an axis perpendicular to the bar through (a) the center; (b) an end.

(a) For an axis through the center, each mass is a distance $l/2$ from the axis. Summing the mr^2 terms for each of the two masses,

$$I = m\left(\frac{l}{2}\right)^2 + m\left(\frac{l}{2}\right)^2 = \frac{ml^2}{2}$$

(b) For an axis through an end, the mass at that end has $r = 0$, while the other mass is at a distance l, so

$$I = 0 + ml^2 = ml^2$$

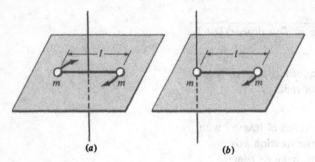

Figure 5.19. Two point masses on a massless bar with axis of rotation (a) through the center; (b) through an end.

Thus we see that the moment of inertia depends on the position of the rotation axis.

Example 5.11

Find the moment of inertia of a bicycle wheel of radius R if the mass m is concentrated in the rim and tire. (The spokes are considered massless.)

If we break up the tire into small pieces, each one is the same distance R from the axle. Thus the moment of inertia is just the total mass m times R^2:

$$I = mR^2$$

This arrangement yields the maximum moment of inertia for a wheel of a given mass and radius. It is this large moment of inertia that gives a bicycle some of its stability. Any torques caused, for example, by a rough road will only produce small angular accelerations, since $\alpha = \tau/I$ and I is large.

Example 5.12

Find the moment of inertia of a thin rod of length l and mass m about an axis through its center (Fig. 5.20).

The moment of inertia is found by breaking the rod into many small masses and integrating their contributions to Eq. 5.18. The mass per unit length of the rod is m/l, and the mass of a small segment of length dx is $dm = m\,dx/l$. Its contribution to I is then $x^2\,dm = x^2\,m\,dx/l$. Integrating over the length of the rod, we find the moment of inertia

$$I = \frac{m}{l}\int_{-l/2}^{l/2} x^2 dx = \frac{m}{l}\left[\frac{x^3}{3}\right]_{-l/2}^{l/2}$$

$$= \frac{m}{3l}\left[\left(\frac{l}{2}\right)^3 - \left(\frac{-l}{2}\right)^3\right] = \frac{ml^2}{12}$$

Parallel Axis Theorem | Given the moment of

inertia about an axis passing through the center of mass, we can immediately write down the moment of inertia about any axis parallel to that axis. To see this, consider the point masses in Fig. 5.21. The center of mass is at a distance X from the y axis, which is the axis of rotation. Mass m_i is located at a distance x_i from the axis of rotation or at a distance $r_i = x_1 - X$ from the C.M. The contribution of mass m_i to the moment of inertia is then

$$m_i x_i^2 = m_i(r_i + X)^2$$

$$= m_i(X^2 + r_i^2 + 2r_i X)$$

Summing over the masses, the first term is $(\Sigma m_i)X^2 = mX^2$, where m is the total mass of the system. The second term is $\Sigma m_i r_i^2 = I_{C.M.}$, the moment of inertia relative to the C.M. The last term, $2(\Sigma m_i r_i)X$, is proportional to the net torque $\Sigma w_i r_i = \Sigma(m_i g)r_i$ about the C.M. due to the weights of the

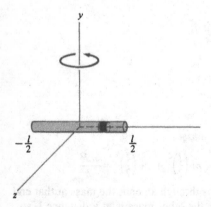

Figure 5.20. The segment of length dx has a mass $dm = m\,dx/l$, and contributes $x^2 dm = x^2\,m\,dx/l$ to the moment of inertia.

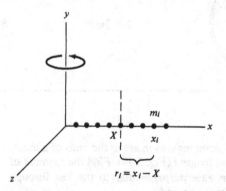

Figure 5.21. The dashed axis passes through the C.M. (point X), and the moment of inertia about this axis is $I_{C.M.}$. The moment of inertia about a parallel axis (the y axis) is related to $I_{C.M.}$ by the parallel axis theorem.

particles. Since the C.M. (or C.G.) was defined in Chapter Four as the point where the weight is effectively concentrated, the net torque about the C.M. is zero, and the last term vanishes. Thus the moment of inertia about the y axis is given by the *parallel axis theorem*,

$$I = I_{C.M.} + mX^2 \quad \text{(parallel axis theorem)} \quad (5.19)$$

The moment of inertia about any axis is determined by the moment of inertia about the C.M., $I_{C.M.}$, the total mass of the system, m, and the distance from the axis to the C.M., X.

A simple illustration of this theorem is provided by Example 5.10. This example showed that two point masses m_0 at the ends of the massless rod of length l have a moment of inertia $I_{C.M.} = m_0 l^2/2$ about the center, which is the C.M. The ends of the rod are at a distance $X = l/2$ from the C.M. The total mass of the system is $m = 2m_0$, so by the parallel axis theorem, the moment of inertia about an axis perpendicular to the rod through an end is

$$I = \frac{m_0 l^2}{2} + (2m_0)\left(\frac{l}{2}\right)^2 = m_0 l^2$$

This is the result found in Example 5.10 by directly summing the $m_i r_i^2$ terms.

Now let us apply the parallel axis theorem to a more complex situation. Consider the third object in Table 5.3, a thin rod of length l rotating about an axis through its end. Its C.M. is the center of the rod. We found in Example 5.12 that $I_{C.M.} = ml^2/12$. With $X = l/2$, the parallel axis theorem gives the moment of inertia about an axis through the end of the rod,

$$I = \frac{ml^2}{12} + m\left(\frac{l}{2}\right)^2 = \frac{ml^2}{3}$$

In this case, I can also be obtained readily by integration, but this is not always true.

Radius of Gyration
For irregular objects such as a bone or forearm, it is usually necessary to determine the moment of inertia experimentally. Such experimental results are often expressed by giving the mass m of the object and *radius of gyration k* defined by

$$I = mk^2 \quad \text{or} \quad k = \sqrt{\frac{I}{m}} \quad (5.20)$$

A point mass m at a distance k from the rotation axis would have the same moment of inertia as the actual object. For example, the radius of gyration of the sphere in Table 5.3 is found from

$$k = \sqrt{\frac{I}{m}} = \sqrt{\frac{\frac{2}{5}mR^2}{m}} = R\sqrt{\frac{2}{5}} = 0.63R$$

The following example shows how $\tau = I\alpha$ can be used in a problem involving both rotation and translation.

Example 5.13
A wheel is on a horizontal axis of radius $r = 0.01$ m supported by frictionless bearings (Fig. 5.22). A 5-kg block attached to a string is wrapped around the axle and released from rest. It falls with an acceleration of 0.02 m s^{-2}. (a) What is the tension in the string? (b) What is the moment of inertia of the wheel and axle?

(a) Using Newton's second law for the falling mass, $mg - T = ma$. Solving for T,

$$T = m(g - a) = (5 \text{ kg})(9.8 - 0.02) \text{ m s}^{-2} = 48.9 \text{ N}$$

(b) The lines of action of the bearing force **N** and weight Mg pass through the rotation axis, so they give zero torque; the magnitude of the torque due to **T** is rT. The acceleration a of the block is also the tangential acceleration of a point on the edge of the axle. With $a = r\alpha$, $\tau = I\alpha$ becomes $rT = Ia/r$. Solving for I,

$$I = \frac{r^2 T}{a} = \frac{(0.01 \text{ m})^2(48.9 \text{ N})}{0.02 \text{ m s}^{-2}} = 0.245 \text{ kg m}^2$$

This example illustrates one method of determining I experimentally. By measuring the time for the

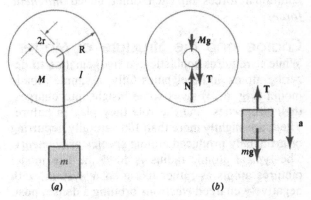

Figure 5.22. (a) A wheel and axle mounted on frictionless bearings have a block of mass m hanging from a string wrapped around the axle. (b) The forces on the axle and on the falling mass. **T** is the tension on the string, and **N** is the force exerted by the bearings.

mass to fall, we can find the acceleration and obtain I. The procedure is often used in the introductory physics laboratory.

5.5 | ELECTRIC CHARGES; FUNDAMENTAL FORCES

We have seen that gravitational forces are responsible for keeping the planets in their nearly circular orbits around the sun. *Electric* forces, which are in some ways very similar to gravitational forces and in other ways quite different, are responsible for keeping electrons in their orbits in atoms. Although we will defer a full discussion of electric forces until Chapter Sixteen, we introduce them here and discuss a simple model of an atom.

The gravitational force is a fundamental force of nature. Related to this force is the concept of mass, which plays a basic role in the description of the physical world. An equally basic concept is that of *charge*. Just as two masses produce forces on each other, so also do two charges produce forces on one another. However, an important difference is that there are two kinds of charges, described in mathematical terms as positive and negative. Although two masses always attract each other, like charges (both positive or both negative) repel each other, while unlike charges attract each other. A further complication is that charges may produce two types of forces. Charges at rest exert forces on each other called *electric forces*, but charges in motion exert additional forces on each other called *magnetic forces*.

Charge and the Structure of Matter |

While it requires sophisticated mathematics to describe atoms and molecules fully, a simple atomic model (Fig. 5.23) gives some insight into charges, their properties, and the role they play in nature. There are slightly more than 100 naturally occurring or artificially produced atomic species or *elements*. The typical atomic radius is 10^{-10} m. The model pictures atoms as rather like a solar system, with negatively charged *electrons* orbiting a dense, positively charged *nucleus*. The attractive electric force between the negative electrons and the positive nucleus holds the atom together, just as the gravitational attraction holds the solar system together.

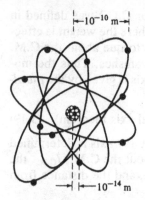

Figure 5.23. A simple model of an atom. Negatively charged electrons orbit a small, massive nucleus under the influence of electric forces. The nucleus, which is not shown to scale, contains two kinds of nucleons: positively charged protons and neutral neutrons.

When an atom has its full complement of electrons, it is electrically neutral; that is, its total charge is zero. If one or more electrons are added or taken away, the atom is said to be *ionized*.

The constituents of the massive nucleus were not completely identified until the 1930s. These constituents, collectively called *nucleons*, are *neutrons* that are uncharged and *protons* that have a positive charge. The proton charge is denoted by e and is exactly equal in magnitude to the electron charge, $-e$. A neutron or proton is approximately 1800 times as massive as an electron.

A typical nuclear radius is 10^{-14} m, some 10,000 times smaller than that of the atom. One may well ask how a nucleus can have many positively charged protons so close together if they repel each other. The explanation depends on the existence of still another fundamental force of nature that does not depend upon charge. If two protons approach each other, they electrically repel each other more and more strongly until they are close enough for the *strong* nuclear force to take effect. This force overwhelms the electric repulsion and holds the protons together.

Atoms combine in various ways, all of which depend on the electric forces produced by charges, to form molecules and macroscopic objects that, in their normal state, are electrically neutral. Thus common objects are not ordinarily charged, but their existence and solidity depend on charges being present in their microscopic structure.

Two remarkable facts concerning charges have emerged from physics research up to the present. Using particle accelerators, complex nuclear reactions have been produced in which particles are created or destroyed. In this way, many short-lived particles have been discovered that are not ordinarily present in matter. Every one of these particles has an electric charge that is an exact integer multiple of the electronic charge: 0, ±e, ±2e, ... In recent years, evidence has accumulated that nucleons are not the most elementary objects, and that they too are composite structures made up of particles called *quarks*. Quarks appear to have charges that are a fraction of the electronic charge. However, no particles having such fractional charges have ever been observed directly. Thus it currently seems that isolated charges cannot exist in units other than that found on the electron.

The second observation is that when particles are created or destroyed, the net charge remains constant. This is referred to as *conservation of charge*. For example, if a positive charge is destroyed, a negative charge is also destroyed, leaving the net charge unchanged. The reasons for these characteristics of charge are not known.

The Four Fundamental Forces

In addition to electric forces, charges exert magnetic forces on each other if they are in motion. Since objects at rest in one reference frame are in motion in another, it is clear that electric and magnetic forces are intimately related, and may be regarded as types of *electromagnetic forces*. Electromagnetic and gravitational forces are two of the fundamental forces in nature, and Newton's laws are applied to both in the same way.

There are a total of four known fundamental forces, the other two being the strong nuclear force just mentioned and the so-called *weak force*, which is responsible for the fact that some nuclei are radioactive and decay or change into other nuclear species. It is now thought that the weak and electromagnetic forces may be intrinsically related, so there are at most three truly fundamental forces. In order of decreasing strength, the fundamental forces among subatomic particles are the strong, electromagnetic, weak, and gravitational.

Unlike electromagnetic and gravitational forces, the strong and weak forces act only at distances comparable to nuclear dimensions. At these very short distances, Newton's laws cannot be applied without modifications. Nevertheless, many of the concepts developed in our discussions of Newton's laws are still applicable.

5.6 | COULOMB'S LAW

The earliest published studies of the detailed properties of the forces between charges were made in 1784 by Charles Augustin de Coulomb (1736–1806). He found that the electric force, like the gravitational force, is inversely proportional to the distance squared. However, because there are two kinds of charge, the force can be either attractive or repulsive.

Two point charges, q_1 and q_2, exert equal and opposite electric forces on each other. If the distance to q_1 from q_2 is r, then the *force experienced by q_1 due to q_2 is given by Coulomb's law*,

$$\mathbf{F}_{12} = \frac{kq_1q_2}{r^2}\,\hat{\mathbf{r}} \qquad (5.21)$$

Here $\hat{\mathbf{r}}$ is a unit vector pointing from q_2 to q_1, and k is an experimentally determined constant. Note that in the form given, Coulomb's law holds in the vacuum and, to a very good approximation, in air, the only cases we consider. It must be modified if the charges are in a denser medium such as water or body fluids.

The S.I. unit of charge is the *coulomb* (C). In S.I. units, it is found that

$$k = 9.0 \times 10^9 \text{ N m}^2 \text{ C}^{-2} \qquad (5.22)$$

and that the magnitude of the charge on a proton or electron is

$$e = 1.60 \times 10^{-19} \text{ C}$$

The coulomb is a large unit of charge. For example, according to Coulomb's law, the force between a pair of 1-C charges 1 m apart is

$$F = (9 \times 10^9 \text{ N m}^2 \text{ C}^{-2}) \frac{(1 \text{ C})(1 \text{ C})}{(1 \text{ m})^2} = 9 \times 10^9 \text{ N}$$

This is about 1 million tons! Consequently isolated charges as large as a coulomb are rarely encountered.

Although we know it today as Coulomb's law, the expression for the electrostatic force between two charges was first discovered by Henry Cavendish. This fact is not surprising when one learns about Cavendish's bizarre personality.

Charles Augustin de Coulomb was a French nobleman who began a career as a military engineer and gradually became interested in scientific research. At the beginning of the French Revolution, he wisely retired to the safety of a provincial town to concentrate on his experiments. In 1777, he competed for a prize offered by the French Academy of Sciences for the improvement of magnetic compasses. He found that if he suspended a compass needle from a fine hair or thread, the torque exerted on the needle was proportional to the angle through which it had rotated. This *torsion balance* principle made it possible for him to measure electrostatic forces accurately and to obtain the force law. His results were published in the normal fashion, and he received the credit for this important discovery.

Unknown to Coulomb, his English contemporary, Cavendish, had already done the same kinds of electrostatic experiments with a torsion balance. Cavendish was an extraordinarily eccentric person: shy, absentminded, and reclusive to the point of insisting on dying alone. He never completed his studies at Cambridge because he could not bear to face his professors at the required examinations. He avoided all people, especially women, as much as possible.

Cavendish came from a wealthy family and never cared for nor needed to worry about money. Devoting himself to scientific research for his entire life, he made many major discoveries. However, he published very few of them and had no concern about receiving credit for his advances. In particular, his electrical researches anticipated many discoveries of the following decades but remained unknown until James Clark Maxwell examined Cavendish's notes decades after his death. Cavendish did publish some of his early work on the properties of hydrogen gas, but his experiments in which he discovered the inert gas now called argon were ignored until they were repeated a century later.

The most important experiment performed by Cavendish was, in effect, a measurement of the mass of the earth. From Newton's law of universal gravitation, it follows that the gravitational acceleration at the surface of the earth is $g = GM_E/R_E^2$, where G is the gravitational constant and M_E and R_E are the earth's mass and radius, respectively. Since g and R_E are easily measured, a determination of either G or M_E determines the other quantity. Cavendish used a torsion balance to measure the small gravitational force exerted on two small spheres at the ends of a pivoted rod by two other large spheres. This gave him a value for G and therefore for the mass of the earth.

The direction of the electric force depends on the relative signs of the charges q_1 and q_2 (Fig. 5.24). If the two charges have the same sign (both positive or both negative), then q_1q_2 is positive, so that $\mathbf{F}_{12}$ is directed along $\hat{\mathbf{r}}$, and the charges repel each other. If the charges have opposite signs, with one positive and the other negative, then q_1q_2 is negative; $\mathbf{F}_{12}$ is then directed along $-\hat{\mathbf{r}}$, and the charges attract. In each case, Newton's third law holds true: the force $\mathbf{F}_{21}$ on q_2 due to q_1 equals $-\mathbf{F}_{12}$.

The gravitational force law (see Chapter Three) can be written in a vector form similar to Eq. 5.21 for the electric force. The gravitational force on a particle of mass m_1 due to a particle of mass m_2 is

$$\mathbf{F}_{12} = -\frac{Gm_1m_2}{r^2}\hat{\mathbf{r}} \qquad (5.23)$$

Again $\hat{\mathbf{r}}$ is a unit vector pointing from particle 2 toward particle 1; the minus sign indicates the force is toward particle 2, or attractive. Since both the gravitational and electric forces vary as $1/r^2$, their ratio for a pair of particles of given mass and charge is independent of the separation.

The next two examples illustrate some features of the simplest atom, hydrogen, which has a single electron orbiting a proton.

Example 5.14

In a simple model of the hydrogen atom, an electron moves around a proton in a circular orbit of radius 5.29×10^{-11} m. The proton mass is $M = 1.67 \times 10^{-27}$ kg and the electron mass is $m = 9.11 \times 10^{-31}$ kg (Fig. 5.25). What are the electric and gravitational forces exerted on the electron by the proton?

Since the proton and electron have opposite charges, $+e$ and $-e$, the electric force is attractive, and its magnitude is

$$F = \frac{ke^2}{r^2}$$

$$= (9 \times 10^9 \text{ N m}^2 \text{ C}^{-2})\frac{(1.6 \times 10^{-19} \text{ C})^2}{(5.29 \times 10^{-11} \text{ m})^2}$$

$$= 8.23 \times 10^{-8} \text{ N}$$

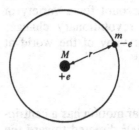

Figure 5.25. A simple model of the hydrogen atom. A negative electron moves in a circular orbit around a massive positive proton.

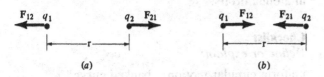

Figure 5.24. (a) Like charges, both positive or both negative, repel each other. (b) Unlike charges, one positive and one negative, attract each other.

The gravitational force is also attractive; from Eq. 5.23, its magnitude is

$$F_G = \frac{GmM}{r^2}$$

$$= (6.67 \times 10^{-11} \text{ N m}^2 \text{ kg}^{-2})$$

$$\times \frac{(1.67 \times 10^{-27} \text{ kg})(9.11 \times 10^{-31} \text{ kg})}{(5.29 \times 10^{-11} \text{ m})^2}$$

$$= 3.63 \times 10^{-47} \text{ N}$$

Comparison of these two forces shows that in this situation the electric force is about 10^{39} times stronger than the gravitational force. Thus in atomic physics the gravitational force can be completely ignored.

Example 5.15

Using the numbers given in the preceding example, find the speed of the electron in the hydrogen atom.

The centripetal acceleration of the electron results from the electric force, so the speed v satisfies

$$\frac{mv^2}{r} = \frac{ke^2}{r^2}$$

or

$$v = \sqrt{\frac{ke^2}{mr}}$$

Substituting the numerical values from the preceding example,

$$v = \left[\frac{(9 \times 10^9 \text{ N m}^2 \text{ C}^{-2})(1.6 \times 10^{-19} \text{ C})^2}{(9.11 \times 10^{-31} \text{ kg})(5.29 \times 10^{-11} \text{ m})} \right]^{1/2}$$

$$= 2.19 \times 10^6 \text{ m s}^{-1}$$

This is a large velocity; it is about 1 percent of the speed of light, 3×10^8 m s^{-1}.

We shall see later that this simple model of the hydrogen atom and its generalization for atoms with many electrons correctly predicts some, but not all, of the observed properties of atoms. The failure of Newtonian mechanics to account for a variety of atomic phenomena led to revolutionary changes early in this century in our view of the world at atomic and subatomic levels.

SUMMARY

An object undergoing circular motion has a centripetal acceleration $\mathbf{a}_r = -(v^2/r)\hat{\mathbf{r}}$ directed toward the center of the circle. If its speed is changing, it also has a tangential acceleration $\mathbf{a}_T$ along its direction of motion.

The centripetal acceleration is produced by a net force equal to $m\mathbf{a}_r$ acting on the object. On a flat curve in a road, the net force is provided entirely by friction, but part of all of the required force can be provided by the normal force in a banked road. When an object swings rapidly in a vertical circle, a downward force in addition to its weight is necessary to keep the object in its path.

The angular position, velocity, and acceleration conveniently describe the rotational motion of a rigid body about a fixed axis. The definitions and relationships are analogous to those for translational motion along a straight line, and are summarized in Tables 5.1 and 5.2.

When a rigid body constrained to move about a fixed axis has a net torque about a point on that axis, it has an angular acceleration found from

$$\tau = I\alpha$$

The moment of inertia I is mr^2 for a point mass, so it is large when the mass is far from the axis of rotation. For a complex object, we divided the object into many small parts and sum or integrate the individual mr^2 contributions.

Atoms consist of negatively charged electrons orbiting around a dense, positively charged nucleus. Charges at rest exert electric forces on each other, while moving charges also exert magnetic forces. The known fundamental forces are the strong, electromagnetic, weak, and gravitational forces, in order of decreasing strength.

Coulomb's law states that the electric force between two charges is proportional to the product of the charges and inversely proportional to their separation squared:

$$F_{12} = \frac{kq_1q_2}{r^2}$$

The force is attractive for unlike charges and repulsive for like charges. Electric forces keep electrons in atomic orbits.

Checklist

Define or explain:

uniform circular motion	banked curve
centripetal acceleration	radian
tangential acceleration	angular position,
radius of curvature	velocity, acceleration

torque
moment of inertia
parallel axis theorem
radius of gyration
electric charge
electric force
nucleus
atomic model
nucleons, protons,

neutrons
electronic charge
quarks
conservation of charge
magnetic force
electromagnetic forces
strong, weak forces
Coulomb's law

REVIEW QUESTIONS

Q5-1 Motion in a circular path with a constant speed is _____.

Q5-2 When an object moves along a circular path with a constant speed, it has an acceleration directed toward the _____.

Q5-3 An object undergoing uniform circular motion must have a net force on it directed toward _____.

Q5-4 Skids occur when the maximum frictional force of a flat road on a car is less than _____.

Q5-5 If an object moving along a circular path has its speed changing, it has a _____ equal to the rate of change of the speed.

Q5-6 A complete circle is _____ radians.

Q5-7 The angular velocity is the rate of change of the _____, and points along the _____.

Q5-8 The angular acceleration is the rate of change of the _____.

Q5-9 The angular acceleration of a rigid body about a fixed axis is proportional to the _____.

Q5-10 The moment of inertia of a point mass depends on its mass and on the _____.

Q5-11 For a given object, the moment of inertia depends on the location of the _____.

Q5-12 Atoms and molecules are held together by _____.

Q5-13 Nuclei are held together by _____.

Q5-14 Like charges _____, unlike charges _____.

Q5-15 A nucleus is made up of two types of _____, _____ and _____.

Q5-16 A nucleus is about _____ times smaller than an atom.

Q5-17 Nucleons are thought to be made up of _____.

Q5-18 The four fundamental forces are the _____.

Q5-19 The electric force between two charges is inversely proportional to the _____.

EXERCISES

Section 5.1 | Centripetal Acceleration

5-1 If the speed with which a car rounds a curve is doubled, by what factor does its centripetal acceleration change?

5-2 Cars moving at 100 km h^{-1} require a 0.5 m s^{-2} acceleration to go around a curve. (a) What is the radius of the curve? (b) How long will it take a car to go around the curve if the road direction changes from due north to due east?

5-3 A woman runs on a circular track of radius 100 m at a speed of 8 m s^{-1}. What is her acceleration?

5-4 A boy rides a bicycle at 10 m s^{-1} on a flat curve of radius 200 m. (a) What is his acceleration? (b) If the boy and the bike have a total mass of 70 kg, how large a force is needed to provide this acceleration?

5-5 A racing car rounds a turn at 60 m s^{-1}. If the force needed to provide the centripetal acceleration is equal to the weight of the car, what is the radius of the turn?

5-6 A man sits without a seat belt in a car. He tends to slide to the left as the car makes a right turn. Is there a force pushing the man to the left? Explain.

5-7 The speeds of centrifuges are limited in part by the strength of the materials used in their construction. A centrifuge spins a 10 g = 10^{-2} kg sample at a radius of 0.05 m at 60,000 revolutions per minute. (a) What force must the centrifuge exert on the sample? (b) What is the mass of a sample at rest with a weight equal to this force?

5-8 A child sits 4 m from the center of a merry-go-round, which turns completely each 10 s. What is the child's acceleration?

5-9 A jet fighter plane flying at 500 m s^{-1} pulls out of a dive on a circular path. What is the radius of the path if the pilot is subjected to an upward acceleration of 5g?

5-10 The radius of the earth's orbit about the sun is 1.5 × 10^8 km, and its period is 365 days. what is the centripetal acceleration of the earth?

5-11 A trained pilot can pull out of a dive on a circular path with an upward acceleration of 5.5g at the bottom of the path. An untrained pilot can perform the same maneuver at the same speed but only with an acceleration of 3g. What is the ratio of the minimum radii of the paths in which the two pilots can fly?

5-12   A centrifuge used for testing human tolerance to acceleration has a gondola at a distance of 16 m from the vertical axis of rotation. What speed is required to produce a horizontal acceleration of 11g?

5-13   A car is traveling around a flat curve of radius 0.25 km. The coefficient of static friction between the tires and the road is 0.4. At what speed will the car begin to skid?

5-14   A woman of mass 60 kg runs around a flat, circular track of radius 200 m at 6 m s^{-1}. (a) What is her acceleration? (b) What force produces this acceleration? (c) How large is this force?

5-15   Show that v^2/r has the dimensions of an acceleration.

Section 5.2 | Examples of Circular Motion

5-16   At what angle should the track of Exercise 5-14 be banked so that there is no frictional force required?

5-17   A racing car travels around a curve of radius 1000 m. If the frictional force is zero and the speed is 50 m s^{-1}, at what angle is the curve banked?

5-18   A curved track has a radius of 336 m and is banked at 35°. At what speed is the frictional force zero?

5-19   Why might it be unsafe to drive on steeply banked curves at low speeds under very slippery conditions?

5-20   A swallow flies in a horizontal arc of radius 15 m at 18 m s^{-1}. (a) What is its acceleration? (b) What is the banking angle?

5-21   A curve is banked so that no friction is required at 60 km h^{-1}. If a car is moving at 40 km h^{-1} on the curve, in which direction is a frictional force exerted by the road?

5-22   An airplane climbs and then turns downward in a circular arc of radius R. If its speed is 400 m s^{-1}, at what radius will the pilot experience weightlessness at the top of the arc?

5-23   An ultracentrifuge spins samples so that their effective weight is 10^5 times their normal

weight. If the sample is at a radius of 0.05 m, how many revolutions per minute does the machine make?

5-24   A bird of weight w flies at 15 m s^{-1} in a horizontal circle of radius 15 m. What is the bird's effective weight?

5-25   A Ferris wheel of radius 16 m rotates in a vertical circle uniformly once every 20 s. (a) What is the centripetal acceleration? (b) What is the effective weight of a 45-kg rider at the highest point of the ride? (c) What is the rider's effective weight at the lowest point of the ride?

Section 5.3 | Angular Variables

5-26   Convert to radians (a) 1°; (b) 53°; (c) 120°.

5-27   Convert to degrees (a) 0.1 rad; (b) $\pi/4$ rad; (c) 4π rad.

5-28   A point on a bicycle wheel moves a distance $s = 1$ m. If this point is 0.4 m from the wheel axis, through what angle has the wheel rotated in (a) radians; (b) degrees?

5-29   The following angles are given in radians. Find the corresponding angles in degrees, and sketch these angular coordinates on circles as in Fig. 5.13. (a) $\theta = \pi/3$ rad; (b) $\theta = 3\pi/4$ rad; (c) $\theta = 9\pi/4$ rad.

5-30   Figure 5.26 shows a right triangle with two of the angles given. (a) Find these two angles in radians. (b) The sum of the internal angles of any triangle is 180°; find the third angle in Fig. 5.26 in radians.

5-31   Figure 5.27 shows a sphere rotating about a vertical axis. What is the direction of the angular velocity in (a); in (b)?

5-32   If the sphere in Fig. 5.27a rotates at a constant rate, what is the direction and magnitude of ω if the angular displacement is (a) π rad in 0.4 s; (b) 270° in 0.6 s?

5-33   A bicycle rider moves past us from left to right. If her speed is 5 m s^{-1}, (a) what is the direc-

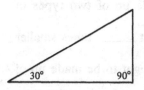

Figure 5.26.   Exercise 5-30.

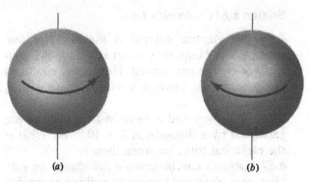

Figure 5.27. The colored arrows indicate the direction of rotation of the sphere about a vertical axis. Exercises 5-31 and 5-32.

tion and magnitude of the angular velocity of one of the wheels, which is 0.4 m in radius? (b) The rider is increasing her speed as she passes, and her acceleration is 1 m s^{-2}. What is the angular acceleration of a wheel?

5-34 (a) Find the radial acceleration at the edge of a phonograph record of radius 0.15 m rotating at 78 rev min^{-1}. (b) The record comes to a stop with a uniform angular acceleration in 2 s. Find the tangential acceleration at the edge and the angular acceleration.

5-35 An ultracentrifuge produces a radial acceleration of 300,000 times the acceleration of gravity at a distance of 0.05 m from the rotation axis. What is the angular velocity in radians per second and revolutions per minute?

5-36 A Ferris wheel at an amusement park rotates in a vertical circle once every 20 s. Its radius is 10 m. (a) What is its angular velocity in radians per second? (b) What is the radial acceleration of a passenger?

5-37 Pulsars are astronomical objects that rotate as fast as once every 0.03 s. Using the data in Table 3.2, determine whether they are (a) ordinary stars like our sun; (b) white dwarf stars; (c) neutron stars.

5-38 Assume a wheel has an initial angular velocity of $\omega_0 = 10$ rad s^{-1}. The angular acceleration is 2.5 rad s^{-2} directed opposite to ω_0. (a) How long does it take for the wheel to stop turning? (b) Through what angle has the wheel turned in this time?

5-39 A car accelerates uniformly from rest to

20 m s^{-1} in 15 s. The wheels have a radius of 0.3 m. (a) What is the final angular velocity of the wheels? (b) What is the angular acceleration of the wheels? (c) What is their angular displacement during the 15-s interval?

5-40 The flywheel of an automobile engine is turning at 700 revolutions per minute. The accelerator is depressed, and in 6 s the speed is 3500 rev min^{-1}. (a) Find the initial and final angular velocities in rad s^{-1}. (b) Find the average angular acceleration. (c) Assuming constant angular acceleration, find the angular displacement during the 6-s acceleration period. (d) Find the tangential acceleration of a point on the flywheel of the engine that is 0.2 m from the axis.

Section 5.4 | Torque, Angular Motion, and the Moment of Inertia

5-41 A bicycle wheel has a mass of 2 kg and a radius of 0.35 m. What is its moment of inertia?

5-42 Two wheels of mass m each have a radius R. Wheel A is a uniform disk, while wheel B has nearly all its mass at the rim. Find the ratio of the moments of inertia, I_B/I_A.

5-43 Is it easier to spin a bucket filled with water before or after it is frozen? Explain.

5-44 Compare a solid sphere and a solid cylinder with the same mass and radius. Which has the larger moment of inertia about the axes shown in Table 5.3? Give a qualitative explanation for your answer.

5-45 Find the radius of gyration of a rod of length l pivoted about an axis through its center.

5-46 What is the radius of gyration of a spherical shell of radius R rotating about an axis through its center?

5-47 A grinding wheel, a disk of uniform thickness, has a radius of 0.08 m and a mass of 2 kg. (a) What is its moment of inertia? (b) How large a torque is needed to accelerate it from rest to 120 rad s^{-1} in 8 s?

5-48 Assuming that the earth is a uniform sphere, find its moment of inertia about an axis through its center. (The mean radius of the earth is 6.38×10^6 m. Its total mass is 5.98×10^{24} kg.)

5-49 Two masses m_1 and m_2 hang on a pulley of mass M (Fig. 5.28). The pulley is a solid cylinder of radius R and rotates without friction. What is

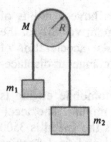

Figure 5.28. Exercises 5-49 and 5-50.

the tangential acceleration of the wheel if $M = m_2$ and $m_1 = \frac{1}{2}m_2$?

5-50 Two masses m_1 and m_2 hang on a frictionless pulley of mass M (Fig. 5.28). If all the mass of the pulley can be considered to be at its rim, and $M = 2m_2 = 3m_1$, find the acceleration of the masses m_1 and m_2.

5-51 Using the parallel axis theorem, find the moment of inertia of a rod of mass m and length l about an axis perpendicular to the rod at a distance $l/4$ from an end.

c5-52 Solve the preceding exercise using integration rather than the parallel axis theorem.

5-53 A thin ring of radius R and mass m lies on a horizontal plane. Find its moment of inertia for rotation about a vertical axis passing through the edge of the ring.

c5-54 (a) Show that a cone of mass m and length l (Fig. 5.29) has a mass per unit length which is proportional to $(l - x)^2$. (b) Find its moment of inertia for rotation about the y axis.

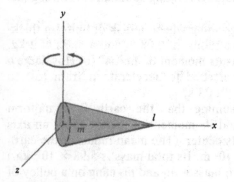

Figure 5.29. Exercise 5-56.

Section 5.6 | Coulomb's Law

5-55 An electric current is measured in amperes; a 1-A (ampere) current is a flow of 1 coulomb of charge per second. How many electrons per second pass through a wire carrying a 10-A current?

5-56 A proton and a neutron in a nucleus are separated by a distance of 2×10^{-15} m. What is the electrical force between them?

5-57 Objects can be given a net charge by rubbing, as is observed by people walking on woolen rugs in dry weather. How many electrons must be transferred to give an object a net charge of $+10^{-6}$ C? Must electrons be added or taken away?

5-58 A gram of hydrogen contains about 6×10^{23} atomic electrons. What fraction of the electrons must be removed to give the sample a net charge of 10^{-3} C?

5-59 Two identical charges 0.1 m apart exert electrical forces of 10 N on each other. (a) What is the magnitude of one of the charges? (b) Find the ratio of this charge to that on an electron.

5-60 Cosmic ray protons strike the upper atmosphere at an average rate of 1500 protons per square metre each second. How much charge is received by the earth in a 24-hour day? (The radius of the earth is 6.38×10^6 m.)

5-61 A kilogram of molecular hydrogen contains 3.01×10^{26} molecules, each consisting of two hydrogen atoms. (a) What is the total charge on the electrons in 1 kg of hydrogen? (b) What is the total charge on the protons? (c) If all the electrons were removed and placed 1 m away from the protons, what would be the electric force between them?

5-62 In a nucleus the minimum separation between two protons is about 10^{-15} m. (a) Find the electrical force between two protons at this distance. (b) Find the ratio of this force to the force between a proton and an electron separated by 10^{-10} m.

5-63 A salt crystal is made up of Na$^+$ ions, which are lacking one electron, and Cl$^-$ ions, which have one extra electron. What is the force between a Na$^+$ ion and a Cl$^-$ ion separated by 5×10^{-10} m?

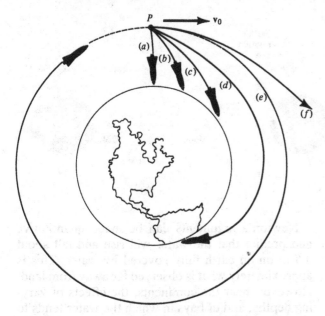

Figure 5.31. Rockets placed at P with their engines off experience a gravitational acceleration toward the earth. Trajectory (a) corresponds to a rocket with no initial velocity; it falls straight down. As the rocket is given an increasingly large initial velocity v_0 in the direction shown, the trajectory changes as indicated by paths (b), (c), and so on. Trajectory (e) is a closed circular orbit, corresponding to an artificial earth satellite. If the initial velocity is slightly larger than in (e), the rocket will move in a closed elliptical orbit. If the initial velocity is sufficiently large, the rocket will escape from the earth (f). Note that the rocket is always falling, just as a thrown rock falls. In a circular orbit, it moves parallel to the surface just fast enough so that its fall carries it around the earth.

can be rewritten as

$$\frac{GmM_E}{r^2} = \frac{m}{r}\left(\frac{2\pi r}{T}\right)^2$$

Solving for T^2, we find the relation between T and r,

$$T^2 = Cr^3 \qquad (5.24)$$

The constant C is

$$C = \frac{4\pi^2}{M_E G} \qquad (5.25)$$

Notice that C is independent of the satellite mass m. Hence the motion of the moon and of all artificial earth satellites will satisfy $T^2 = Cr^3$ with the *same* value of C.

The relation $T^2 = Cr^3$ also holds true for the planets in their nearly circular orbits about the sun. (In this case, M_E in the constant C must be replaced by the solar mass, and r must be replaced by the average orbital radius.) This was one of the three laws of planetary motion discovered by Kepler in the early part of the seventeenth century from the careful analysis of observations made by earlier workers. Newton showed that all three laws could be derived using the gravitational force law and the equations of motion.

In the next example, we calculate the orbital radius of a communications satellite that has a period of exactly 1 day and consequently is always above the same point on the earth.

Example 5.16

The moon has a period $T_m = 27.3$ days and an orbital radius $r_m = 3.84 \times 10^5$ km. What is the orbital radius r_s of a satellite that has a period $T_s = 1$ day?

We can apply $T^2 = Cr^3$ to both the artificial satellite and the moon:

$$T_s^2 = Cr_s^3$$
$$T_m^2 = Cr_m^3$$

If we take the ratio of these equations, C cancels, leaving

$$\frac{T_s^2}{T_m^2} = \frac{r_s^3}{r_m^3}$$

or

$$r_s = r_m\left[\frac{T_s}{T_m}\right]^{2/3} = (3.84 \times 10^5 \text{ km})\left[\frac{1 \text{ day}}{27.3 \text{ days}}\right]^{2/3}$$
$$= 4.24 \times 10^4 \text{ km}$$

The motion of the earth's natural satellite, the moon, provided another test of Newton's ideas. Its acceleration $a_m = v^2/r$ can be calculated from its period and its distance from the earth. Using the $1/r^2$ dependence of the gravitational force and the value of g at the earth's surface, one can also predict the gravitational acceleration g' at the radius of the moon's orbit. Newton found that a_m and g' agreed well. (See Problem 5-95.)

Tides | Newton gave the first explanation of the intervals between successive high tides, and he also accounted for their typical height. His explanation

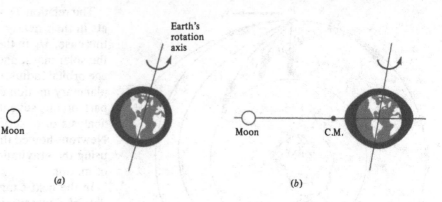

Figure 5.32. (*a*) The moon and the earth, not to scale. If both were at rest except for the daily rotation of the earth, water would be pulled toward the side of the earth facing the moon. (*b*) The moon and earth move in nearly circular orbits (perpendicular to the page) around their common center of mass. C.M. Water farthest from the C.M. has the greatest centripetal acceleration but the weakest attraction to the moon. The effective weight of that water is reduced.

involves a rather subtle interplay between gravitational forces and circular motion.

Initially, let us imagine that the earth and the moon are isolated from the sun, and are at rest, except for the earth's daily rotation. The gravitational force exerted by the moon on the water covering most of the earth pulls it toward the side facing the moon, producing a bulge (Fig. 5.32a). As the earth turns, a land mass will encounter the bulge once a day, producing a daily high tide and a low tide 12 hours later.

However, high and low tides occur approximately *twice* each day. Newton realized that this happens because the moon and the earth are *both* moving in nearly circular paths about their common center of mass under the influence of their gravitational attractions. (This effect is not too obvious, since the earth is about 80 times as massive as the moon and, therefore, moves in a much smaller circle.) The water farthest from the center of mass has the greatest centripetal acceleration $\omega^2 r$, but the pull of the moon is weakest there. Therefore the effective weight of the water on that side is reduced, and a second bulge develops (Fig. 5.32b).

This reasoning suggests high tides every 12 hours. Actually, they occur every 12 hours and 25 minutes, because the moon changes its position as the earth rotates. The gravitational pull of the sun also contributes to the tides, but this effect is less than half that due to the moon. When the moon and the sun are in line at full moon or new moon, larger than average *spring* tides occur. When their directions appear to be at right angles (quarter or three-quarter moon), smaller than average *neap* tides occur.

Newton's arguments can be made quantitative and predict that the water will rise and fall about 0.5 m on an earth fully covered by water. This is approximately what is observed far away from land. However, near the continents, the effects of varying depths, and of bays in which the water tends to resonate much like water sloshing in a bathtub, can lead to much larger tides. Quantitative understanding of the tides remains a difficult and not fully solved problem.

5.8 | PHYSIOLOGICAL EFFECTS OF ACCELERATION

The advent of high-speed aviation and, more recently, of space travel has spurred considerable research into the physiological reactions of humans to acceleration. Some representative accelerations and their time durations are given in Table 5.4.

Most of us have experienced moderate vertical accelerations in high-speed elevators. The effects we feel are related to the fact that most, but not all, of the body is fairly rigid. The blood flows in distensible vessels, so when the body is accelerated upward, the blood accumulates in the lower body. When the acceleration is downward, the blood volume increases in the upper body. Also, the internal organs of the body are not rigidly held in place, and there may be unpleasant feelings produced by the displacement of these organs during acceleration.

The ability of a person to withstand an acceleration depends on both the magnitude and the duration of the acceleration. Because of the inertia of the blood and distensible organs, the effects on them of moderate accelerations (a few *g*'s) are un-

TABLE 5.4

The approximate duration and magnitude of some brief accelerations in multiples of the gravitational acceleration, $g = 9.8$ m s^{-2}

Type of Acceleration	Acceleration in Multiples of g	Duration (seconds)
Elevators		
Fast service	0.1–0.2	1–5
Comfort limit	0.3	
Emergency stop	2.5	
Automobiles		
Comfortable stop	0.25	5–8
Very unpleasant	0.45	3–5
Maximum possible	0.70	3
Crash (possibly survivable)	20–100	0.1
Aircraft		
Normal takeoff	0.5	10–20
Catapult takeoff	2.5–6	1.5
Crash landing (possibly survivable)	20–100	
Seat ejection	10–15	0.25
Humans		
Parachute opening	8–33	0.2–0.5
Parachute landing	3–4	0.1–0.2
Fall into firefighters' net	20	0.1

Adapted from D. E. Goldman and H. E. von Gierke in Harris & Crede (eds.), *Shock and Vibration Handbook*, McGraw-Hill, New York, 1961, Chapter 44.

important if the acceleration lasts for only a small fraction of a second. The limit of tolerance is then some tens of g's and is set by the structural strength of the vertebrae. As the time duration increases, so also do the dangers.

Extensive studies have been made of the circulatory disturbances of pilots subjected to accelerations lasting a few seconds or longer. Pilots in an airplane pulling out of a dive for several seconds may experience two successive types of *blackouts*. A visual blackout occurs first at about $3g$ as a result of reduced blood pressure in the retina, which is very sensitive to oxygen deprivation. The blood pressure drops because the heart has difficulties in pumping the blood with its increased effective weight. By modifying the pilot's position, training him to tense his abdominal muscles, and equipping him with a flight suit that reduces blood pooling in the lower body, the visual blackout threshold can be increased to about $5g$. In addition, the reduced sup-

ply of blood to the brain leads to a complete blackout or unconsciousness at about $6g$. Since many high-performance planes can sustain about $9g$ when pulling out of a dive, the limits of human tolerance may easily be exceeded.

When a plane climbs and then circles downward, the plane and pilot are both more susceptible than they are at the bottom of a dive. An engorgement of the vessels in the head causes a reduction of heart activity and hence a reduction of the oxygen supplied to the retina and brain. Planes are usually not designed to withstand as large a stress in this maneuver as in a dive, so they also will be structurally sound only under lower g stresses. An illustration of the upward effective weight attained during some maneuvers is provided by the next example.

Example 5.17

An airplane of mass m is flown at a speed of 300 m s^{-1} in a vertical circle (Fig. 5.33). What is the

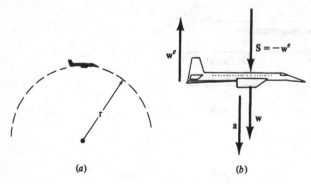

Figure 5.33. S is the downward force exerted by the air on the airplane.

minimum radius r of the circle so that the upward effective weight does not exceed $3mg$?

Since the effective weight w^e is now upward and equal to $3mg$ in magnitude, $w^e = 3mg$. According to Eq. 5.7, $w^e = mg - ma$, so

$$-3mg = mg - ma$$

or $a = 4g$. The acceleration here is the centripetal acceleration, so we have

$$\frac{v^2}{r} = 4g$$

Thus the radius that will lead to an upward effective weight of $3mg$ is

$$r = \frac{v^2}{4g} = \frac{(300 \text{ m s}^{-1})^2}{4(9.8 \text{ m s}^{-2})} = 2300 \text{ m}$$

A smaller radius will lead to a larger effective weight.

5.9 | SENSORY PERCEPTION OF ANGULAR MOTION

If a person is blindfolded and put on a chair that can rotate smoothly, the following results are observed.

1 If the chair is turned 90° clockwise and stopped, the person can identify the direction of rotation and the fact that it has stopped. Reversal of the process yields the same results.

2 If the chair is rapidly accelerated and the rotation is continued, the person can correctly identify the direction of rotation for about 20 s. After 20 s the answers are uncertain.

3 If after about 30 s the chair is slowed to a lower angular velocity, the person will generally indicate that motion has stopped.

4 If the chair is then stopped, the person usually perceives rotation in the opposite direction.

To interpret these results we must examine the structure of the inner ear. The inner ear is composed of two portions (Fig. 5.34). One portion, the *cochlea*, contains the auditory response elements. The other portion is comprised of three *semicircular canals*, which primarily detect motion of the head and have little auditory function.

The structure of one of the semicircular canals is shown in Fig. 5.35. The canal contains a watery fluid called the *endolymph* and has a projection somewhat like a swinging door, called the *cupola*, which senses relative motion of the fluid. To understand the operation of the canal, consider what happens to a bucket of water suspended from a rope when it is set into rotation (Fig. 5.36). The water is initially at rest, and it remains at rest when the bucket starts spinning, since the frictional force between the wall of the bucket and the water is small. However, the torque resulting from this force gradually increases the angular velocity of the water, and after some seconds, the water is rotating with the same angular velocity as the bucket. If the bucket is now stopped, the water continues to rotate for some time. The *relative* motion of the water

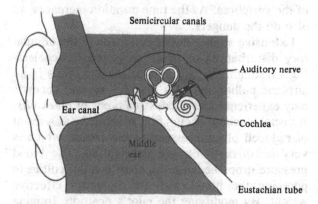

Figure 5.34. A schematic view of the right ear of a human. The three mutually perpendicular semicircular canals function as indicators of rotations about three perpendicular axes in space.

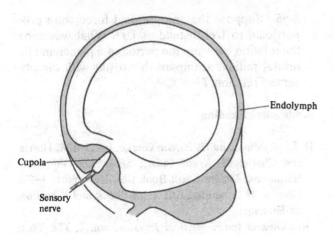

Figure 5.35. A semicircular canal of a human ear. The endolymph is a fluid that can flow around the canal. The ampulla is a swelling into which the cupola projects. The cupola can block the entire canal, but it is elastic and will bend when the fluid moves. When the cupola is pushed aside by the flowing fluid, the sensory nerve detects this motion and the information is transmitted to the brain.

and bucket is now opposite to that when the bucket was first set into motion.

In the inner ear, it takes a second for the endolymph to start moving at about the speed of the canal, so initially the cupola is deflected by its motion relative to the fluid. This deflection is sensed by the nerve, and information is transmitted to the brain. Once the canal, fluid, and cupola are all rotating at the same rate, the cupola starts to return to its normal position. However, the elastic or spring force on the cupola is so weak that it takes about 20 s for this return to be completed. The perception of rotation persists during this 20-s period, but afterward the ear can no longer detect rotation.

If the rotation rate is now reduced, the canal slows while the fluid continues to move briefly at the higher speed. Thus the cupola is deflected in the opposite direction, and the subject perceives a change in the direction of rotation. If this slower rotation continues for about 20 s, the cupola once more returns to its normal position, and the subject again perceives no rotation. Finally, if the rotation is stopped, the cupola is again deflected, and the subject perceives a rotation opposite to the original direction.

When a subject is put through the same sequence but is not blindfolded, the eyes do not normally stare directly outward at passing objects. Instead, the eyes focus briefly on a given object, then fix on another object, and so on. This is called the *nystagmus reflex*. The flicking of the eyes will continue as long as the sensory nerve detects a bending of the cupola. When the cupola resumes its normal position, the reflex action of the eyes stops and the subject, if untrained, sees objects streaking by. Then balance is lost.

When the rotation is stopped, the cupola is again deflected and the nystagmus reflex acts, this time in the opposite direction. Objects at rest appear to be moving steadily and then moving back again. The postural muscles are then trying to respond to nonexistent motion, resulting in staggering.

EXERCISES ON SUPPLEMENTARY TOPICS

Section 5.7 | Satellites; Tides

5-88 An artificial earth satellite moves in a circular orbit with a radius one-fourth that of the moon's orbit. What is its period?

5-89 An artificial satellite is to be placed in an orbit around the sun so that its period is 8 earth years. By definition, the radius of the earth's orbit is 1 astronomical unit (A.U.). What is the radius of the satellite's orbit in A.U.?

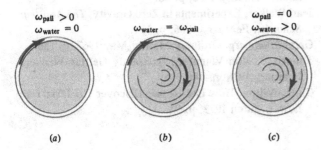

Figure 5.36. (a) A bucket of water is spun, with the water initially at rest. (Small scraps of paper on the surface make its motion more readily visible.) The water remains nearly at rest for a few seconds, and the pail is moving *clockwise* relative to the water. (b) After a while the frictional torques have increased the angular velocity of the water, and it has the same angular velocity as the bucket. (c) When the bucket is stopped, the water continues to move for some time until slowed by the frictional torques. Relative to the water, the pail is now moving *counterclockwise*.

5-90 The distance from the sun to the earth is 1 A.U. What is the length of a "year" on a planet 9 A.U. from the sun?

5-91 The average distance from Mars to the sun is 1.524 times the distance from the earth to the sun. How long does it take for Mars to go around the sun?

5-92 Using the data on the inside back cover, find the time an artificial satellite would need to go once around the sun in an orbit whose radius is twice that of the sun.

5-93 The period of the moon's orbit around the earth is 27.3 days, and its mean distance is 3.84×10^8 m. From these data, determine the mass of the earth.

5-94 Newton's theory of the tides predicts that the difference in the height of the oceans at high and low tides should be $h = 3GMR_E^2/2gr^3$, where G is the gravitational constant, M is the mass of the moon, R_E is the average radius of the earth, g is the acceleration due to gravity at the surface of the earth, and r is the earth–moon distance. Using the numerical values listed on the inside back cover evaluate h.

PROBLEMS ON SUPPLEMENTARY TOPICS

5-95 The orbital radius of the moon is 3.84×10^5 km and its period is 27.3 days. (a) Find its acceleration a_m. (b) The gravitational acceleration at the earth's surface, which is 6380 km from its center, is $g = 9.81$ m s^{-2}. Using the $1/r^2$ dependence of the gravitational force law, what gravitational acceleration g' would one expect at the radius of the moon's orbit? (c) Compare g' and a_m. (This was one of Newton's original tests of the universal law of gravitation.)

5-96 Suppose the gravitational force were proportional to $1/r^3$ instead of $1/r^2$. What would be the relation between the period of a planet and its orbital radius? Compare this result with the observed relation $T^2 = Cr^3$.

Additional Reading

D. E. Goldman and H. E. von Gierke, in Cyril M. Harris and Charles E. Crede (eds.), *Shock and Vibration Handbook*, McGraw-Hill Book Co., New York, 1961. Chapter 44 is entitled Effects of Shock and Vibration on Humans.

Otto Glasser (ed.), *Medical Physics*, vol. I, The Year Book Publishers, Inc., Chicago, 1944. Page 22 discusses the effects of acceleration.

J. L. E. Dreyer, *Tycho Brahe: A Picture of Scientific Life and Work in the Sixteenth Century*, Dover Publications Inc., New York, 1963. Brahe and his observations of planetary motions.

Judah Levine, The Earth Tides, *The Physics Teacher*, vol. 20, 1982, p. 588.

Scientific American articles:

J. W. Beams, Ultrahigh-Speed Rotation, April 1961, p. 134.

Richard P. Post and Stephen F. Post, Flywheels, December 1973, p. 17.

Terence A. Rogers, The Physiological Effects of Acceleration, February 1962, p. 60.

Jearl Walker, Experiments in Zero Gravity, *The Amateur Scientist*, February 1986, p. 114.

Gerald Feinberg, Ordinary Matter, May 1967, p. 126.

Thomas C. Van Vlandern, Is Gravity Getting Weaker? February 1976, p. 44.

Curtis Wilson, How Did Kepler Discover His First Two Laws? March 1972, p. 92.

UNIT TWO

UNIT TWO

ADDITIONAL TOPICS IN MECHANICS

The principles described in Unit One form the basis for analyzing all mechanics problems. In particular, Newton's laws of motion tell us how to use the forces on objects to predict their motion. There are, however, large classes of problems for which it is either difficult or inconvenient to use Newton's laws directly. For example, it is difficult to determine all the forces when a skier descends an uneven slope, or two objects collide, or a skater begins a rapid spin. Nevertheless, there are convenient ways based on *conservation laws* to handle many such problems.

In the first chapter of this unit, we define *work* and *energy* and show that the work done on an object equals the change in its energy. When no work is done, the energy remains constant, and it is said to be *conserved*. In such a situation, if we know the initial energy of an object—or a system of objects—we can immediately make some statements about its state of motion at a later time, even though we may lack detailed information about the forces that are present.

In Chapter Seven, we discuss *linear* and *angular momentum*. When no net force acts on a system, its linear momentum is conserved, and when no net torque acts, its angular momentum is conserved. These conservation laws make it possible to partially or fully analyze some rather difficult-looking problems. For example, linear momentum is conserved in collisions between two objects—two cars, a bat and a ball, two astronomical bodies—where the external forces due to other objects are either absent or negligible in comparison to the very large forces the colliding objects exert on each other. Similarly, the fact that the angular momentum of a skater, a diver, or a gymnast remains constant during certain maneuvers helps to explain what they can and cannot accomplish.

Unlike the idealized rigid bodies used to illustrate the principles of mechanics, real objects may deform significantly or break if they are subjected to large forces or torques. In Chapter Eight, we see how the strength of an object depends on its size, shape, and composition. Construction materials, bones, and trees provide obvious examples of the importance of these questions.

The final chapter of this unit applies Newton's laws of motion to mechanical oscillations and vibrations. From a knowledge of the forces, we can tell whether vibrational motion may occur and predict its frequency. The general features of this kind of motion are usually similar, whether we are dealing with molecules in a solid oscillating about their equilibrium positions, human vocal cords vibrating to produce sound, or a spider web vibrating as an insect struggles.

This unit concludes our formal development of mechanics, but it is by no means the end of its usefulness to us. Throughout this text, we make explicit or implicit use of the principles of mechanics. Since these first two units are based almost entirely on Newton's laws, the general range of application of mechanics is as broad as the various forces that appear in nature. Even in our discussion of atoms and molecules, where Newton's laws break down, many of the principles we have discussed will survive. In particular, the conservation laws will remain as universally valid concepts.

CHAPTER 6
WORK, ENERGY, AND POWER

Work, *energy*, and *power* are words that have a variety of meanings in everyday usage. However, to the scientist these terms have very specific definitions. In this chapter, we consider these definitions and the relationships between work and various kinds of energy for mechanical systems. Although these relationships are obtained from Newton's laws, they can often be readily used when the forces are unknown or when the systems are so complex as to make the direct use of Newton's laws impracticably difficult.

This chapter also provides us with our first look at a *conservation law*. We find that under certain conditions the mechanical energy of a system is *constant* and is then said to be *conserved*. This fact provides a very powerful tool for understanding and solving certain mechanical problems.

However, it is now known that a much broader energy conservation law is valid in nature. If we calculate or measure the *total energy*—mechanical, electrical, thermal, and so on—then this total energy is constant, even though any one type need not be conserved. What is observed in nature is an interchange of energy from one form to another, with the *sum* remaining constant. This total energy conservation law became fully understood when Einstein showed that matter and energy are two forms of the same quantity. He saw that not only may energy be converted from one form to another, but it may also be converted to matter, and vice versa.

Energy is a concept that plays a key role in an enormous range of applications. Biological processes, the weather, the evolution of astronomical systems, chemical reactions—these are all constrained by the fact of energy conservation and the limitations on how energy may be used and trans-

formed. Some of these limitations are considered in Chapter Eleven, when we study thermal energy, the energy associated with the motions of the molecules in an object. Also, we have become increasingly aware of the importance of energy in our technological society. We will see that the basic principles developed in this chapter can help us to understand the possibilities and difficulties associated with alternatives to our dwindling fossil fuel resources.

6.1 | WORK

In this section, we define the work done on an object by a force and show how it is calculated. It becomes clear in the following sections that the concept of work plays a fundamental role in the analysis of many mechanical problems.

Suppose that an object is displaced a distance s, and that a force **F** acting on the object has a constant component F_s along **s** (Fig. 6.1). Then the *work done by the force* is defined as the product of the force component and the displacement,

$$W = F_s s \qquad (6.1)$$

If **F** is at an angle θ to **s**, as in Fig. 6.2, then $F_s = F \cos \theta$, and the work can be written as

$$W = Fs \cos \theta \qquad (6.2)$$

The S.I. unit of work is the *joule* (J). Since work has dimensions of force times distance, a joule is a newton metre.

The definition of work can be stated conveniently in terms of a product of two vectors called the *scalar*, or *dot*, product. Suppose we have two vectors **A** and **B**, with an angle θ between them. The scalar

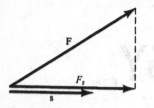
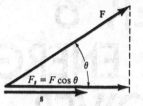

Figure 6.1. The work done by the force **F** during a displacement **s** is $W = F_s s$.

Figure 6.2. The component of **F** along **s** is $F_s = F \cos \theta$. The work is then $W = Fs \cos \theta$.

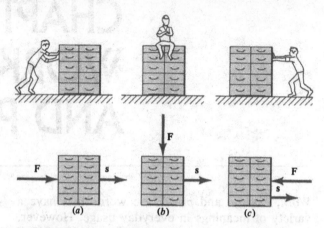

Figure 6.3. A force is applied (a) parallel to the motion; (b) perpendicular to the motion; (c) opposite to the motion. In each case the work done by the force **F** is different. In part (c) we may imagine that the dresser is being slowed and brought to rest. In (a) the man does work on the dresser; in (b) he does no work; in (c) the dresser does work on the man.

product **A · B** is the product of their magnitudes and of $\cos \theta$,

$$\mathbf{A} \cdot \mathbf{B} = AB \cos \theta \quad \text{scalar product} \quad (6.3)$$

Note that **A · B** is an ordinary number or scalar, unlike the cross product **A × B**, which is a vector. Thus $W = F_s s$ can be rewritten as

$$W = \mathbf{F} \cdot \mathbf{s} \quad (6.4)$$

Note that our definition of work differs in some ways from the nontechnical meaning of the word. According to Eq. 6.2, we do twice as much work in pushing an object along the floor if we double its weight or the distance it moves. This is consistent with the everyday notion of work. However, this is not so if we stand in one spot supporting a heavy weight. We would consider that we are working rather hard, but since there is no displacement, we conclude that no work is done on the weight.

However, work is being done in the body as nerve impulses repeatedly trigger muscle fiber contractions. Unlike a bone or a steel post, a muscle fiber cannot sustain a static load. Instead, it must repeatedly relax and contract, doing work in each contraction. We are unaware of this process because of the large number of fibers and the rapidity of the contractions.

In the following examples, we show how the work done by a force acting on an object is computed.

Example 6.1

A 600-N force is applied by a man to a dresser that moves 2 m. Find the work done if the force and displacement are (a) parallel; (b) at right angles; (c) oppositely directed (Fig. 6.3).

(a) When **F** and **s** are parallel, $\cos \theta = \cos 0° = 1$, and Eq. 6.2 gives

$$W = \mathbf{F} \cdot \mathbf{s} = Fs \cos \theta = (600 \text{ N})(2 \text{ m})(1) = 1200 \text{ J}$$

The man does 1200 J of work on the dresser. Since **F** is parallel to **s**, $F_s = F$, and we obtain the same result using $W = F_s s$.

(b) When **F** is perpendicular to **s**, $\cos \theta = \cos 90° = 0$, and $W = 0$. No work is done when the force is at right angles to the displacement, since $F_s = 0$.

(c) When **F** and **s** are opposite, $\cos \theta = \cos 180° = -1$, and

$$W = Fs \cos \theta = (600 \text{ N})(2 \text{ m})(-1) = -1200 \text{ J}$$

In this case, the work done by the force is negative, so *the object is doing work on the man*. Note that here **F** is opposite to **s**, so $F_s = -F$.

Example 6.2

A horse pulls a barge along a canal with a rope in which the tension is 1000 N (Fig. 6.4). The rope is at an angle of 10° with the towpath and the direction of the barge. (a) How much work is done by the horse in pulling the barge 100 m upstream at a constant velocity? (b) What is the net force on the barge?

(a) The work done by the constant force **T** in moving the barge a distance **s** is given by $W = \mathbf{T} \cdot \mathbf{s} = Ts \cos \theta$, where θ is the angle between **T** and **s**. Using $\cos 10° = 0.985$,

$$W = (1000 \text{ N})(100 \text{ m})(0.985) = 9.85 \times 10^4 \text{ J}$$

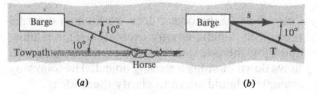

Figure 6.4. (a) A horse pulling a barge at constant velocity. (b) The tension in the rope is **T**.

(b) Since the barge moves at a constant velocity, the sum of all the forces on it must be zero. There must be another force acting that is not shown in Fig. 6.4, a force exerted on the barge by the water that is equal in magnitude and opposite to **T**.

In this example the net work done by all the forces acting on the barge is zero because the net force is zero. The work done by the force due to the water is -9.85×10^4 J. In other words, the barge does 9.85×10^4 J of work on the water.

In our equation defining work, $W = F_s s = \mathbf{F} \cdot \mathbf{s}$, we assumed that the force component F_s was constant over the displacement. In many situations, this is, at best, only approximately true. If the force varies in magnitude or direction relative to the displacement, we must consider many small displacements. In each of these F_s is approximately constant. Then $\Delta W_i = \mathbf{F} \cdot \Delta \mathbf{s}_i$ is the work done in one small displacement, and the total work done is the sum $\Sigma \, \Delta W_i$. In the limit as the displacements approach zero, the sum becomes an integral. Thus the work done when the object is moved from point a to point b is the integral

$$W = \int_a^b \mathbf{F} \cdot \mathbf{ds} = \int_a^b F_s \, ds \qquad (6.5)$$

This integral has a direct interpretation in terms of a graph of F_s versus s. The work $\Delta W_i = F_s \, \Delta s_i$ done in a small displacement Δs_i is approximately equal to the area of the colored rectangular strip (Fig. 6.5a). The work done when the object is moved from a to b is the area under the curve between these two points (Fig. 6.5b).

Equation 6.5 can be used to calculate the work W even if as in Fig. 6.5c the path is not a straight line. The dot product $\mathbf{F} \cdot \mathbf{ds} = F_s \, ds = F \, ds \cos \theta$ must be calculated everywhere along the path in order to evaluate the integral. Technically, the integral in Eq. 6.5 is then a *line integral*.

One other point should be made about computing the total or net work done on an object. If several forces act on the object, we can find their vector sum as usual to find the net force, and then calculate the work done by this net force. Alternatively, we can calculate the work done by each of the forces and sum these scalar quantities. Either procedure gives the same result.

6.2 | KINETIC ENERGY

The *kinetic energy* of an object is a measure of the work an object can do by virtue of its motion. As we show in the following, the translational kinetic energy of an object of mass m and velocity $\mathbf{v}$ is $\frac{1}{2}mv^2$.

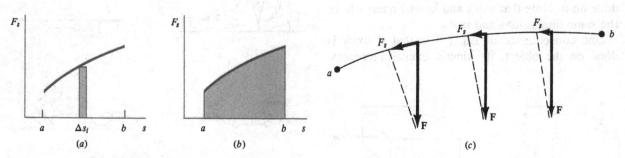

Figure 6.5. (a) The work $\Delta W_i = F_s \, \Delta s_i$ in a small displacement Δs_i is approximately equal to the area of the rectangle. (b) The work done when the object is moved from a to b is the area under the curve. (c) The curved path followed by a projectile. The force **F** due to gravity is constant, but the component F_s varies because the displacements change direction.

The work done on an object and its kinetic energy obey the following fundamental principle:

The final kinetic energy of an object is equal to its initial kinetic energy plus the total work done on it by all the forces acting upon it.

Note the emphasis here on *all* the forces; later, we categorize forces into several types, and we restate this principle in a modified form.

This work–energy principle is derived at the end of this section quite generally from Newton's laws of motion. However, it is instructive to see how it comes about in a simple situation.

Consider an object of mass m subjected to a constant force $\mathbf{F}$ (Fig. 6.6). The object moves a distance s parallel to $\mathbf{F}$. Since its acceleration $\mathbf{a} = \mathbf{F}/m$ is constant, the initial velocity $\mathbf{v}_0$ and final velocity $\mathbf{v}$ satisfy the constant acceleration formulas of Chapter One. From the table on the front endpapers we have $v^2 = v_0^2 + 2as$. Multiplying by $m/2$, this becomes

$$\tfrac{1}{2}mv^2 = \tfrac{1}{2}mv_0^2 + mas \qquad (6.6)$$

Using Newton's second law $F = ma$, the work done by the force $\mathbf{F}$ is $W = Fs = mas$, which is the last term in Eq. 6.6. The final kinetic energy K and the initial kinetic energy K_0 are defined by

$$K = \tfrac{1}{2}mv^2 \quad \text{and} \quad K_0 = \tfrac{1}{2}mv_0^2 \qquad (6.7)$$

Hence we can rewrite Eq. 6.6 as

$$K = K_0 + W \qquad (6.8)$$

Therefore, the final kinetic energy is equal to the initial kinetic energy of the object plus the work done on it. Note that work and kinetic energy have the same dimensions and units.

One consequence of Eq. 6.8 is that if work is done on the object, its kinetic energy increases.

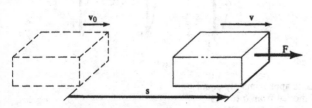

Figure 6.6. A force $\mathbf{F}$ does work on an object as it moves a distance s. The velocity changes from $\mathbf{v}_0$ to $\mathbf{v}$.

Conversely, if the object does work on an external agency, its kinetic energy decreases. This is illustrated by the work that is done on a person who slows down or stops a moving object. The following examples should serve to clarify these ideas.

Example 6.3

A woman pushes a toy car, initially at rest, toward a child by exerting a constant horizontal force $\mathbf{F}$ of magnitude 5 N through a distance of 1 m (Fig. 6.7a). (a) How much work is done on the car? (b) What is its final kinetic energy? (c) If the car has a mass of 0.1 kg, what is its final speed? (Assume no work is done by frictional forces.)

(a) The force the woman exerts on the car is parallel to the displacement, so the work she does on the car is

$$W = Fs = (5 \text{ N})(1 \text{ m}) = 5 \text{ J}$$

(b) The initial kinetic energy K_0 is zero, so the final kinetic energy of the car is

$$K = K_0 + W = 0 + 5 \text{ J} = 5 \text{ J}$$

(c) The final kinetic energy is $K = \tfrac{1}{2}mv^2$, so

$$v = \sqrt{\frac{2K}{m}} = \sqrt{\frac{(2)(5 \text{ J})}{0.1 \text{ kg}}} = 10 \text{ m s}^{-1}$$

Example 6.4

In the preceding example the woman releases the toy car with a kinetic energy of 5 J. It moves across the floor and reaches the child who stops the car by exerting a constant force $\mathbf{F}'$ opposite to its motion. The car

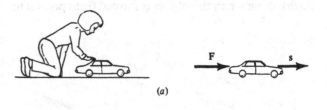

(a)

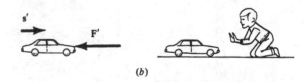

(b)

Figure 6.7. (a) A woman pushes a toy car to the right. She exerts a horizontal force $\mathbf{F}$ on the car, which is parallel to its displacement s. (b) A child stopping the car exerts a force $\mathbf{F}'$ on the car. $\mathbf{F}'$ is opposite to the displacement s' of the car as it is brought to rest.

stops in 0.25 m. Find $\mathbf{F}'$ (Fig. 6.7*b*) if no work is done on the car by frictional forces.

While the car is moving toward the child, no work is done on the car, and its kinetic energy remains 5 J until it reaches the child. The initial kinetic energy K_0 is 5 J, and the final kinetic energy K is zero, since the car comes to rest, so

$$W = K - K_0 = 0 - 5\,\text{J} = -5\,\text{J}$$

Since $\mathbf{F}'$ is opposite to $\mathbf{s}'$, the work done is $W = -F's'$. Thus

$$F' = -\frac{W}{s'} = -\frac{-5\,\text{J}}{0.25\,\text{m}} = 20\,\text{N}$$

The negative sign for the work done, $W = -5$ J, indicates that *the car does work on the child*. These two examples show that positive work done on an object gives it kinetic energy, which is then available to do work, in this case on the child.

We now derive the work–energy principle without making the constant force assumption. Suppose a small displacement $d\mathbf{s}$ of an object is parallel to the force $\mathbf{F}$ acting on it, so $\mathbf{F} \cdot d\mathbf{s} = F\,ds$. According to the second law of motion, $F = ma$. Using the chain rule for differentiation, we can rewrite the acceleration a as

$$a = \frac{dv}{dt} = \frac{dv}{ds}\frac{ds}{dt} = \frac{dv}{ds}\,v = \frac{1}{2}\frac{d}{ds}(v^2)$$

Then the work can be written as

$$W = \int_a^b F\,ds = \int_a^b ma\,ds = \int_a^b \frac{m}{2}\frac{d}{ds}(v^2)ds$$
$$= \frac{m}{2}v_b^2 - \frac{m}{2}v_a^2$$

Thus the work done equals the change in kinetic energy when $\mathbf{F}$ is parallel to the displacement but variable in magnitude.

If the force is not parallel to the displacement, only its component F_s along the motion affects the speed. The component perpendicular to v changes its direction, but not its magnitude. Hence the derivation still applies if F is replaced by F_s.

6.3 | POTENTIAL ENERGY AND CONSERVATIVE FORCES

The work–energy relationship of the preceding section includes the work done by *all* the forces acting on the object. However, it is useful when gravitational forces do work to treat them separately, and to refer to the other forces acting on the object as *applied forces*, for want of a better name. The work done by gravity on the object can be taken care of very conveniently if we introduce another form of energy called *potential energy*. Forces that can be dealt with in this way are called *conservative forces*. The condition a force must satisfy to be conservative is discussed at the end of this section.

To motivate the introduction of the gravitational potential energy, consider a ball thrown straight up. Its velocity decreases steadily as it rises. From the point of view of this chapter, the gravitational force $m\mathbf{g}$ is doing negative work, since it is opposite to the displacement, and the kinetic energy is diminishing correspondingly. Once the ball starts to come down, the gravitational force does an equally large amount of positive work, and the kinetic energy returns to its initial value once the ball returns to its starting point.

Alternatively, we can think of the rising ball losing kinetic energy and gaining *potential energy*. This potential energy is converted back into kinetic energy when the ball falls. In general, potential energy is energy associated with the position or configuration of a mechanical system. The potential energy can, at least in principle, be converted into kinetic energy or used to do work.

We now put these ideas into quantitative form. In Fig. 6.8*a*, a ball rises from an initial height h_0 to a height h. The gravitational force $m\mathbf{g}$ is opposite in direction to the displacement $s = h - h_0$, so the work done is *negative*:

$$W(\text{grav}) = -mg(h - h_0)$$

However, according to our discussion the potential energy increases in this situation, and the change in potential energy $\Delta\mathcal{U} = \mathcal{U} - \mathcal{U}_0$ is *positive*. The magnitude of $\Delta\mathcal{U}$ is defined to be equal to the magnitude of $W(\text{grav})$, so we write

$$\mathcal{U} - \mathcal{U}_0 = -W(\text{grav}) \qquad (6.9)$$

The minus sign takes care of the differences in sign. Using our expression for $W(\text{grav})$, Eq. (6.9) becomes

$$\mathcal{U} - \mathcal{U}_0 = mg(h - h_0) \qquad (6.10)$$

Figure 6.8. (a) A ball rises a distance $s = h - h_0$. The gravitational force does work $W(\text{grav}) = -mg(h - h_0)$. (b) A block slides up an inclined plane. The component of **w** along **s** is $w_s = -mg \cos \theta$, so $W(\text{grav}) = -mgs \cos \theta$. Since $s \cos \theta = h - h_0$, we again find $W(\text{grav}) = -mg(h - h_0)$.

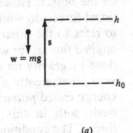

(a)

(b)

This result for the *potential energy change* involves a difference of two terms on each side, and suggests that we define the *potential energies themselves* at h and h_0, respectively, by

$$\mathcal{U} = mgh \quad \text{and} \quad \mathcal{U}_0 = mgh_0 \qquad (6.11)$$

As we see shortly, these definitions do not uniquely specify the potential energies, but they are nevertheless very useful.

By the work–energy principle, $K = K_0 + W(\text{grav}) = K_0 - (\mathcal{U} - \mathcal{U}_0)$, so we have the important result

$$K + \mathcal{U} = K_0 + \mathcal{U}_0 \qquad (W_a = 0) \qquad (6.12)$$

The notation $W_a = 0$ reminds us that the work done by applied forces is zero; only the gravitational force is doing work here. The sum of the kinetic energy and the potential energy is called the *total mechanical energy*,

$$E = K + \mathcal{U} \qquad (6.13)$$

Thus Eq. 6.12 means that *when there is no work done by applied forces, the total mechanical energy is constant or conserved.*

If applied forces also do work, Eq. 6.12 must be generalized to include this work W_a. Then we have

$$K + \mathcal{U} = K_0 + \mathcal{U}_0 + W_a \qquad (6.14)$$

or

$$E = E_0 + W_a \qquad (6.15)$$

The final mechanical energy $E = K + \mathcal{U}$ is equal to the initial mechanical energy $E_0 = K_0 + \mathcal{U}_0$ plus the work done by the applied forces.

Several points should be noted in interpreting these results. First, we considered a ball moving straight upward. However, even when an object follows a more complex path, the work done by the

gravitational force is still $-mg(h - h_0)$, so the potential energy change $\Delta \mathcal{U} = \mathcal{U} - \mathcal{U}_0$ depends only on the difference in heights. This is verified, for example, in Fig. 6.8b for an object moving up an inclined plane.

Second, suppose we measure our heights from a different level so that h and h_0 change by the same amount. Then $\Delta \mathcal{U} = mg(h - h_0)$ remains the same, even though $\mathcal{U}$ and $\mathcal{U}_0$ are changed. Accordingly, we can measure heights from any convenient reference level: the ground, the top of a building, and so on.

Third, if an object goes high enough, the gravitational force is not constant, and mgh is no longer the appropriate form for the potential energy. Nevertheless, the potential energy change is still defined as the negative of the work done by the gravitational force, as in Eq. 6.9. A similar definition of $\Delta \mathcal{U}$ also applies for other conservative forces. These points are considered later in this chapter.

Finally, we must remember that $E = E_0 + W_a$ is just another form of our original work–energy principle $K = K_0 + W$, which involves the work done by *all* the forces. In $E = E_0 + W_a$, the work done by the gravitational forces is still present, but it is now separated from the work W_a done by the other "applied" forces and taken into account through the potential energy.

The following example shows how energy conservation can be used to solve an otherwise complex problem.

Example 6.5

A woman skis from rest down a hill 20 m high (Fig. 6.9). If friction is negligible, what is her speed at the bottom of the slope?

The forces acting on the skier are her weight and a normal force due to the ground. The effects of the

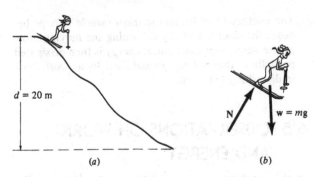

$d = 20$ m

(a)   (b)

Figure 6.9. The forces on the skier are a normal force **N** and the weight **w** = m**g**.

weight (the gravitational force) are contained in the potential energy, and the normal force does no work because it is perpendicular to the displacement. Thus no work is done by applied forces, and the total energy $E = K + \mathcal{U}$ is constant.

Since we can choose the reference level for measuring potential energy as we wish, we choose the bottom of the slope as the level at which $\mathcal{U} = 0$. The kinetic energy at the top is $K_0 = 0$, since she starts from rest; her potential energy there is $\mathcal{U}_0 = mgd$. Her final kinetic energy at the bottom of the hill is $K = \frac{1}{2}mv^2$, and her final potential energy is $\mathcal{U} = 0$. Thus $K + \mathcal{U} = K_0 + \mathcal{U}_0$ becomes

$$\tfrac{1}{2}mv^2 + 0 = 0 + mgd$$

Her speed v at the bottom of the slope is then

$$v = \sqrt{2gd} = \sqrt{2(9.8 \text{ m s}^{-2})(20 \text{ m})}$$
$$= 19.8 \text{ m s}^{-1}$$

This example shows the advantage of the energy conservation approach to solving mechanics problems. We cannot use $\mathbf{F} = m\mathbf{a}$ directly unless we know the exact shape of the slope so that we can compute the force. Even with this information the calculation would be difficult. Energy conservation immediately tells us the velocity at any height.

Conservative Forces | The gravitational force

has the interesting property that when an object moves from one point to another, the work done by the force does not depend on the choice of path. For example, in Fig. 6.10 the work done by gravity when an object moves from B to C is $-mg(h - h_0)$. No work is done by gravity when the object moves horizontally from A to B, so the total work done by

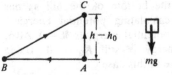

Figure 6.10. The work done by gravity is the same for the paths ABC and AC. Whenever the work done by a force is the same for all paths, the force is said to be conservative, and its effects can be included in the potential energy.

gravity along the path ABC is $-mg(h - h_0)$. When the block is moved vertically from A to C, the work done by gravity again is $-mg(h - h_0)$. Therefore the work is the same for both paths.

Any force that has the property that the work it does is the same for all paths between any two given points is said to be a *conservative* force. This property makes it meaningful to associate a potential energy with a position. Gravitational, electrical, and spring forces are examples of conservative forces; friction and many other forces are not conservative. The effects of *any* conservative force can always be taken into account by introducing a suitable potential energy term.

6.4 | DISSIPATIVE FORCES

We have seen that the work done by conservative forces can be handled conveniently by the introduction of the potential energy concept. This is not true for frictional forces, and they must be treated as applied forces.

Frictional forces are not conservative, since the work done by friction depends on the path. Also, friction always opposes the motion of an object, so it always does negative work. The energy expended by an object against the frictional forces is usually converted into thermal energy and hence is lost as mechanical energy. For this reason, friction is referred to as a *dissipative force*. This reduction in mechanical energy is seen in the next example.

Example 6.6

Suppose that as in the preceding example, a woman skis down a 20-m-high hill. However, this time frictional forces are not negligible, so her speed at the bottom of the hill is only 10 m s^{-1}. How much work is done by frictional forces if her mass is 50 kg?

Again we choose the bottom of the hill as our reference level for calculating potential energies, which means her final potential energy is $\mathcal{U} = 0$. Also, her initial kinetic energy is still $K_0 = 0$. Using $E = E_0 + W_a$, we have in this case

$$\tfrac{1}{2}mv^2 + 0 = 0 + mgd + W_a$$
$$W_a = \tfrac{1}{2}mv^2 - mgd$$
$$= \tfrac{1}{2}(50\text{ kg})(10\text{ m s}^{-1})^2$$
$$- (50\text{ kg})(9.8\text{ m s}^{-2})(20\text{ m})$$
$$= -7300\text{ J}$$

As anticipated, the work done by the applied force is negative, since frictional forces always oppose the motion. The skier has done 7300 J of work against friction, and this mechanical energy has been converted into thermal energy.

The frictional force on a moving object was written earlier as the coefficient of kinetic friction times the normal force. (Since work is done only on moving objects, it is the coefficient of kinetic friction that must always be used. When an object rolls, the point of contact between the object and the supporting surface is instantaneously at rest. In this special case the frictional force does no work.) The frictional force is always directed opposite to the motion, so if an object moves a distance s against a frictional force $\mu_k N$, the mechanical energy dissipated is

$$W_a = -\mu_k N s \qquad (6.16)$$

We illustrate this in the following example.

Example 6.7

A skier reaches the flat ground at the bottom of the slope with a speed of 19.8 m s^{-1} and then, by turning her skis sideways, quickly comes to a stop. If the coefficient of kinetic friction is 2.5, how far will she skid before coming to a halt?

Since the ground is level, there is no potential energy change and all her kinetic energy $\tfrac{1}{2}mv^2$ must be dissipated. The normal force is equal and opposite to her weight, so the work done by the frictional force over a distance s is $W_a = -\mu_k mgs$. Thus $E = E_0 + W_a$ becomes

$$0 = \tfrac{1}{2}mv^2 - \mu_k mgs$$

and solving for s,

$$s = \frac{v^2}{2g\mu_k} = \frac{(19.8\text{ m s}^{-1})^2}{2(9.8\text{ m s}^{-2})(2.5)} = 8\text{ m}$$

The coefficient of friction in this example is large because the skier is actually deforming and moving snow as she stops. Her mechanical energy is then dissipated partially as thermal energy and partially as work done in disturbing the snow.

6.5 | OBSERVATIONS ON WORK AND ENERGY

In this section we discuss the implications of the work–energy relationship. With all the forces categorized as conservative or applied, this relationship assumes its most useful form,

$$K + \mathcal{U} = K_0 + \mathcal{U}_0 + W_a$$

or

$$E = E_0 + W_a$$

The total mechanical energy of an object was defined as $E = K + \mathcal{U}$, where the kinetic energy is $K = \tfrac{1}{2}mv^2$, and the potential energy $\mathcal{U}$ may be characterized as the energy by virtue of position.

As we saw, *if no work is done by applied forces, the total mechanical energy E is constant*. Then

$$K + \mathcal{U} = K_0 + \mathcal{U}_0 \qquad (W_a = 0)$$

This result is referred to as *mechanical energy conservation*. Under these circumstances, the total mechanical energy or the sum of potential and kinetic energies remains constant, although either may change at the expense of the other.

In many situations, dissipative forces that convert mechanical energy into other forms of energy are present. The heat and noise generated by a saw or drill are examples of this. *Heat* represents energy transferred to the random motion of the molecules of a substance, increasing their average velocity or their thermal energy. As we see in Chapter Ten, increasing the average molecular energy is equivalent to raising the temperature.

Thermal energy can also be converted to mechanical energy, as in a steam engine, where hot steam expands and does work. The limitations inherent in such processes are discussed in Chapter Eleven.

Forms of Energy | Energy exists in many forms in addition to mechanical and thermal energy. A hot

TABLE 6.1

Approximate energy in joules associated with various events and phenomena

Description	Energy
Big bang	10^{68}
Radio energy emitted by the galaxy during its lifetime	10^{55}
Rotational energy of the Milky Way	10^{52}
Energy released in a supernova explosion	10^{44}
Oceans' hydrogen in fusion	10^{34}
Rotational energy of the earth	10^{29}
Annual solar energy incident on the earth	5×10^{24}
Annual wind energy dissipated near earth's surface	10^{22}
Annual global energy usage by humans	3×10^{20}
Annual energy dissipated by the tides	10^{20}
Annual U.S. energy usage	8×10^{19}
Energy release during Krakatoan eruption of 1883	10^{18}
Energy release of 15-megaton fusion bomb	10^{17}
Annual electrical output of large generating plant	10^{16}
Thunderstorm	10^{15}
Energy released in burning 1000 kg coal	3×10^{10}
Kinetic energy of a large jet aircraft	10^{9}
Energy released in burning 1 litre gasoline	3×10^{7}
Daily food intake of a human adult	10^{7}
Kinetic energy of a home run in baseball	10^{3}
Work done by a human heart per beat	0.5
Turning this page	10^{-3}
Flea hop	10^{-7}
Discharge of a single neuron	10^{-10}
Typical energy of a proton in a nucleus	10^{-13}
Typical energy of an electron in an atom	10^{-18}
Energy to break one bond in DNA	10^{-20}

object transmits energy to its surroundings not only by direct contact but also by the emission of electromagnetic waves that travel with the speed of light. The chemical bonds in molecules arise from electric forces. These chemical bonds can be broken or altered, causing the chemical energy to be released. For example, when a fossil fuel and oxygen are brought together at an elevated temperature, chemical changes occur that release energy. Similarly, the body uses food to synthesize molecules that later break down to provide energy as needed.

The energy associated with the forces that bind atomic nuclei together is very large. Some of this is released in a nuclear weapon or power reactor when uranium nuclei *fission* into smaller nuclei. Energy is also released when hydrogen nuclei combine or *fuse* to form a larger nucleus. Fusion supplies the energy in stars and in hydrogen bombs. In a more controlled form, fusion may supply much of our future energy if present research programs are successful. Table 6.1 lists the energies associated with various phenomena.

Conservation of Total Energy | We see that energy occurs in many forms. It has been found experimentally that energy can be changed into different forms, but it is never created or destroyed. *This is the principle of conservation of total energy.* Historically, failures of energy conservation have led to the identification of new forms of energy. Since energy occurs in so many forms, energy conservation is an underlying concept that unifies all of science. Although mechanical energy conservation occurs only under special circumstances, the total energy is always conserved. In this chapter, our discussion is mainly limited to mechanical energy, but the concepts developed here will appear often in the remainder of the book.

6.6 | SOLVING PROBLEMS USING WORK AND ENERGY

We have used simple examples to infer a general result

$$E = E_0 + W_a.$$

In this section we present examples that illustrate the great variety of situations in which work and energy are useful concepts.

A systematic procedure is used in solving problems using work and energy. The procedure includes the following steps:

1 We draw a force diagram showing all the forces acting on the object of interest. This step may be done mentally in simple cases, but it is very helpful in complex situations to actually draw the diagram.

2 We identify the conservative forces—such as the gravitational force—that may be included in the potential energy, as well as the applied forces that do work.

3 We calculate the work done by the applied forces and the mechanical energy at two points in the motion. These quantities are then related by $E = E_0 + W_a$.

The following examples make use of this procedure.

Example 6.8

Two identical balls of mass m are thrown from a window a height h above the ground. The initial speed of each ball is v_0, but they are thrown in different directions (Fig. 6.11). What is the speed of each ball as it strikes the ground? (Neglect air resistance.)

Each ball is subject only to the gravitational force mg after it is released, so its total mechanical energy is constant. For either ball, choosing the ground as the reference level, the initial potential energy is $\mathcal{U}_0 = mgh$ and the final potential energy is $\mathcal{U} = 0$. Also, both balls have the same initial kinetic energy, $K_0 = \frac{1}{2}mv_0^2$. Thus $K + \mathcal{U} = K_0 + \mathcal{U}_0$ tells us that both final kinetic energies are the same, and the balls land with the same speed! With $K = \frac{1}{2}mv^2$, that speed satisfies

$$\tfrac{1}{2}mv^2 = \tfrac{1}{2}mv_0^2 + mgh$$

or

$$v = \sqrt{v_0^2 + 2gh}$$

Thus while the two balls do not strike the ground at the same time, they do have the same speed when they hit.

Example 6.9

In the pole vault, an athlete uses a pole to convert the kinetic energy of running into potential energy

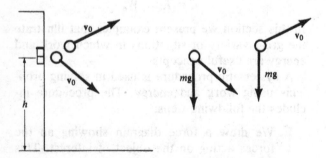

Figure 6.11. Two identical balls thrown in different directions with the same initial speed. The force on each is mg and is directed downward.

Figure 6.12. Photo of a pole vaulter at equally spaced time intervals. Note that the vaulter is nearly at rest at the top of the jump where all his kinetic energy has been converted to potential energy. (© Harold Edgerton/Palm Press)

when the pole is vertical (Fig. 6.12). A good sprinter runs at a speed of 10 m s^{-1}. Disregarding the additional height the athlete gains by using his arms to raise his center of gravity well above the position of his hands on the pole, how high can the athlete raise his center of gravity?

Initially, his C.G. is about 1 m above the ground. Just before the athlete begins to use the pole, $\mathcal{U}_0 = 0$ and $K_0 = \frac{1}{2}mv^2$, where $v = 10$ m s^{-1}. At the top of an ideal jump, $v = 0$, so $K = 0$ and $\mathcal{U} = mgh$, where h is the height of his center of gravity above its initial position. Since only the force of gravity acts on the airborne jumper, $E = E_0$ and

$$0 + mgh = \tfrac{1}{2}mv^2 + 0$$

Then

$$h = \frac{v^2}{2g} = \frac{(10 \text{ m s}^{-1})^2}{2(9.8 \text{ m s}^{-2})} = 5.1 \text{ m}$$

His center of gravity is then about 6.1 m above the ground. The present world pole vault record is near 5.8 m.

Example 6.10

The tides are used to generate electrical energy at a dam across the mouth of the Rance River in France. At this location the tidal rise—the difference in height between high and low tides—averages 8.5 m. The river basin is closed off after it fills at high tide, and at low tide approximately 6 hours later the water is allowed to fall through turbines that drive the electric generators (Fig. 6.13). The area of the basin is 23 km² = 23 × 10⁶ m². How much work does the falling water do, as-

suming that its initial and final kinetic energies are negligible?

Since the kinetic energies are both zero, we have $\mathcal{U} = \mathcal{U}_0 + W_a$ or $W_a = \mathcal{U} - \mathcal{U}_0$. To calculate this potential energy difference, we need the mass of the water and the distance it falls. The mass is the product of the density ($\rho = 10^3$ kg m⁻³) and the volume, which is the area A times the depth d. Hence the mass is $m = \rho A d$. The water at the top of the basin falls the full 8.5 m, but as the level drops, the water falls a shorter

Figure 6.13. The tidal power plant at the mouth of the Rance River in France. Water enters the river basin through the turbines at high tide and leaves the basin through the turbines at low tide. The turbines can also use electricity from other installations to pump extra water in each direction to increase the subsequent "head," the distance the water will fall. (Marcel Mochet / AFP / Getty Images, Inc.)

distance; on the average, the drop is half the full depth. Thus the work done by the applied forces is

$$W_a = \mathcal{U} - \mathcal{U}_0 = -mgh = -(\rho A d)g\left(\frac{d}{2}\right) = -\tfrac{1}{2}\rho A g d^2$$

$$= -\tfrac{1}{2}(1000 \text{ kg m}^{-3})(23 \times 10^6 \text{ m}^2)(9.8 \text{ m s}^{-2})(8.5 \text{ m})^2$$

$$= -8.14 \times 10^{12} \text{ J}$$

The work is negative because the water does work *on* the turbines. Some of this work is lost as thermal energy, but most of it is converted into electrical energy. This facility can supply enough electricity for a few hundred thousand people. On the Bay of Fundy in Canada, a small demonstration tidal power plant was completed in 1984 at Annapolis Royal, Nova Scotia. Much larger plants have also been considered. The most promising is a project at a site in the Minas Basin. It would involve an 8-km-long causeway with 128 turbines and a total water flow of 184,000 m^3 s^{-1}. Construction would take an estimated 12 years and would cost up to 22 billion Canadian dollars. The annual electrical energy output would be 5×10^{16} J, equivalent to that of about three very large nuclear or fossil fuel plants, and would supply a large part of the electrical energy needed in eastern Canada and the New England region of the United States. As other energy sources become more expensive, projects of this kind are increasingly attractive despite their high capital costs.

6.7 | GRAVITATIONAL POTENTIAL ENERGY

We saw in Section 6.3 that the gravitational force on an object near the earth's surface can be taken into account by defining its potential energy to be *mgh*. We assumed that the gravitational force *mg* was constant, and used the property that the work it did depended only on the change in height and not on the path taken. Once we move a distance that is a significant fraction of the earth's radius R_E, it is no longer correct to treat the gravitational force as constant. Nevertheless, it can be shown that the work it does still depends only on the initial and final heights. In more formal terms, the gravitational force is still a conservative force. Thus the potential energy concept can still be used to take account of the gravitational force, although the formula for $\mathcal{U}$ must be modified.

We saw in Chapter Five that the attractive gravitational force between two points or spherical

masses *M* and *m* can be written in vector form as

$$\mathbf{F} = -\frac{GMm}{r^2}\hat{\mathbf{r}} \qquad (6.17)$$

When the separation *r* becomes very large, this force becomes negligibly small, which suggests defining the potential energy of the two masses to be zero when *r* is infinite. With this choice of the reference level, two very distant objects—which exert no forces on each other—also have no potential energy. As the objects approach, the gravitational force does work on them, increasing the kinetic energy and decreasing the potential energy. (Recall $\mathcal{U}$ *increases* when we raise an object and *decreases* when we lower it.) Since $\mathcal{U}$ is zero at $r = \infty$, it becomes negative as *r* decreases.

To find the magnitude of $\mathcal{U}$, we must apply the definition, $\mathcal{U} - \mathcal{U}_0 = -W(\text{grav})$; the change in potential energy equals the negative of the work done by gravity. Suppose *M* is stationary at the origin. We move *m* so that its displacement *d*r is parallel to the vector **r** from *M* to *m* (Fig. 6.14). Then using Eq. 6.17 for **F**,

$$-dW(\text{grav}) = -\mathbf{F} \cdot d\mathbf{r} = \frac{-(-GMm\hat{\mathbf{r}})}{r^2} \cdot d\mathbf{r}$$

$$= \frac{GMm\,dr}{r^2}$$

Integrating from r_0 to r_1, we obtain $-W(\text{grav})$, and the potential energy change is

$$\mathcal{U} - \mathcal{U}_0 = \int_{r_0}^{r_1} GMm\,\frac{dr}{r^2} = GMm\left[-\frac{1}{r}\right]_{r_0}^{r_1}$$

$$= \frac{-GMm}{r_1} + \frac{GMm}{r_0}$$

This is the difference between the potential energies at separations of r_1 and r_0. Although we assumed a

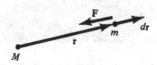

Figure 6.14. Since the gravitational force **F** is opposite to *d*r, **F** · *d*r is negative. When *m* moves away from *M*, the gravitational force does negative work, and the potential energy increases.

displacement along **r**, the result is quite general, since no additional work is needed to move m along a circular path centered at M.

With the choice of reference level $\mathcal{U}_0 = 0$ at $r_0 = \infty$, the potential energy at a distance $r = r_1$ is

$$\mathcal{U} = \frac{-GMm}{r} \qquad (6.18)$$

Note that this result can be obtained quickly but incorrectly by arguing "the work equals the force GMm/r^2 times the distance r." Since the masses move from a separation of infinity to one of r, which is quite different from moving a distance r, this approach is not correct.

At the end of this section we show that Eq. 6.18 is equivalent to the simpler expression $\mathcal{U} = mgh$ when an object remains near the surface of the earth. However, it must be used whenever the height changes by a significant fraction of the earth's radius, as in the following applications to satellites.

Energy of a Satellite

The total mechanical energy of a satellite in a circular orbit can be calculated with the aid of Eq. 6.18. Applying Newton's second law $\mathbf{F} = m\mathbf{a}$ to the circular motion of a mass m under the gravitational attraction of the earth, we have

$$\frac{GM_Em}{r^2} = \frac{mv^2}{r}$$

or

$$mv^2 = \frac{GM_Em}{r}$$

Thus the kinetic energy can be written as

$$K = \frac{1}{2}mv^2 = \frac{GM_Em}{2r} = -\frac{1}{2}\mathcal{U}$$

Since $\mathcal{U}$ is negative, K is positive and half as large as $\mathcal{U}$ in magnitude. The total energy is

$$E = K + \mathcal{U} = -\tfrac{1}{2}\mathcal{U} + \mathcal{U} = \tfrac{1}{2}\mathcal{U}$$

or

$$E = -\frac{GM_Em}{2r} \qquad (6.19)$$

Example 6.11

How much work must be done to lift an artificial satellite of mass m from the surface of the earth and put it in a circular orbit with a radius equal to twice the earth's radius?

Initially, $K_0 = 0$ and $\mathcal{U}_0 = -GM_Em/R_E$. When the satellite is in orbit, according to Eq. 6.19, its total mechanical energy is $E = -GM_Em/4R_E$. Since $E = E_0 + W_a$, we have

$$W_a = E - E_0 = -\frac{GM_Em}{4R_E} - \frac{(-GM_Em)}{R_E} = \frac{3GM_Em}{4R_E}$$

Escape Velocity

The escape velocity is the minimum initial velocity v_0 required for a projectile fired vertically at the earth's surface to escape its gravitational force (Fig. 6.15). At the surface of the earth the velocity is v_0, so

$$E_0 = K_0 + \mathcal{U}_0 = \frac{1}{2}mv_0^2 - \frac{GM_Em}{R_E}$$

If the projectile is to escape permanently from the earth, it will eventually reach a very large value of r, so that $\mathcal{U} = 0$. If it has the minimum energy needed to do this, its velocity and kinetic energy will also be zero at this distance. Thus the minimum total energy needed to escape the earth is $E = K + \mathcal{U} = 0$. Since the mechanical energy is conserved,

$$\frac{1}{2}mv_0^2 - \frac{GM_Em}{R_E} = 0$$

Then

$$v_0 = \sqrt{\frac{2GM_E}{R_E}}$$

The weight of an object of mass m at the surface of the earth is $mg = GM_Em/R_E^2$. Using this, we have

$$v_0 = \sqrt{\frac{2GM_E}{R_E}} = \sqrt{2gR_E} \qquad (6.20)$$

This is the minimum velocity necessary at the earth's surface to escape from the earth.

The escape velocity for any planet can be found from its gravitational acceleration and radius. For the earth, $g = 9.8 \text{ m s}^{-2}$ and $R_E = 6.4 \times 10^6$ m, so the escape velocity is

$$v_0 = \sqrt{2(9.8 \text{ m s}^{-2})(6.38 \times 10^6 \text{ m})}$$
$$= 1.12 \times 10^4 \text{ m s}^{-1}$$

ing Eq. 6.20 to the case where the escape velocity equals the speed of light c. According to the theory of relativity, this is the maximum speed any object can have. For a star of mass M and radius R, if $v_0 = c$, then $c = (2GM/R)^{1/2}$. Squaring and solving for R, we find

$$R = \frac{2GM}{c^2} \qquad (6.21)$$

This is called the *Schwarzschild* radius, and it is proportional to the mass of the black hole. Any particle approaching the black hole closer than this radius will never be able to leave.

The Schwarzschild radii predicted for typical stellar masses are incredibly small, as we see in this next example.

Example 6.12

The mass of our sun is 1.99×10^{30} kg. Find the Schwarzschild radius for a black hole with the same mass.

Substituting the solar mass into Eq. 6.21, we find that the Schwarzschild radius is

$$\begin{aligned} R &= \frac{2GM}{c^2} \\ &= \frac{2(6.67 \times 10^{-11} \text{ N m}^2 \text{ kg}^2)(1.99 \times 10^{30} \text{ kg})}{(3.00 \times 10^8 \text{ m s}^{-1})^2} \\ &= 3000 \text{ m} = 3 \text{ km} \end{aligned}$$

Any particle approaching within 3 km is trapped by the black hole and can never escape!

Objects Near the Surface of the Earth

Earlier in this chapter, we used $\mathcal{U} = mgh$ for the gravitational potential energy, whereas we have used $\mathcal{U} = -GM_E m/r$ here. It is left as a problem to show that if an object is at a small height $h \ll R_E$ above the earth's surface, the potential energy is

$$\mathcal{U} = -\frac{GM_E m}{R_E + h} \simeq -\frac{GM_E m}{R_E}\left(1 - \frac{h}{R_E}\right)$$

(The symbol $\simeq$ means approximately equal.)

Using $g = GM_E/R_E^2$, this becomes

$$\mathcal{U} = -mgR_E + mgh$$

Since we always discuss potential energy differences, the constant term $-mgR_E$ drops out of all calculations. Thus as long as we are near the earth's surface, we can use $\mathcal{U} = mgh$.

Black Holes | Black holes are astronomical objects that exert forces so large that nothing—not even light—can ever escape from them. They form late in the evolution of a star, as it collapses under the influence of its internal gravitational forces—its own weight—after all its nuclear fuel is exhausted.

Newton's laws of motion and the gravitational force law must both be modified to apply to such extreme situations. However, we can discover what turns out to be the correct relationship between the mass of a black hole and a critical radius by apply-

6.8 | ELECTRICAL POTENTIAL ENERGY

The gravitational force is not the only conservative force that we encounter. The electric force is also conservative. In Chapter Five, we saw that the force on a charge q due to a second charge Q a distance r away in air or vacuum is

$$\mathbf{F} = k\frac{qQ}{r^2}\hat{\mathbf{r}} \qquad (6.22)$$

where $k = 9 \times 10^9$ N m^2 C^{-2}. Except for a minus sign and the fact that qQ can be positive or negative, this is identical in mathematical form to the gravitational force law. Thus we can immediately say that the *electric force is conservative*. If we replace $-GMm$ by kqQ in the gravitational potential energy formula, $\mathcal{U} = -GMm/r$, we obtain an expression for the potential energy of the two charges q and Q,

$$\mathcal{U} = \frac{kqQ}{r} \qquad (6.23)$$

Because the electric force is conservative, the change in potential energy if the charge q is moved from r_1 to r_2 is the same, *no matter what path is taken*.

Since the electrical and gravitational potential energies are identical in mathematical form, the results obtained in the preceding section can be immediately applied to electric forces, as we do in the next example.

Example 6.13

In a hydrogen atom, the electron orbits about a proton under the influence of the electric force. If the orbit is a circle with radius $a_0 = 5.3 \times 10^{-11}$ m, what is the energy of the electron? (The electron and proton charges are $-e = -1.60 \times 10^{-19}$ C and $+e = +1.60 \times 10^{-19}$ C, respectively.)

In the preceding section, the energy of a satellite orbiting under gravitational forces was calculated to be $E = -GM_Em/2r$. The result holds true for this problem also if we replace GM_Em by $(-kqQ)$. Then $E = +kqQ/2r$. With $q = -e$, $Q = e$, and $r = a_0$, the energy of the electron is

$$E = -\frac{1}{2}\frac{ke^2}{a_0}$$

$$= -\frac{1}{2}\frac{(9 \times 10^9 \text{ N m}^2 \text{ C}^{-2})(1.6 \times 10^{-19} \text{ C})^2}{5.3 \times 10^{-11} \text{ m}}$$

$$= -2.17 \times 10^{-18} \text{ J}$$

To remove the electron from the atom, we must supply 2.17×10^{-18} J in some way.

In atomic physics, a joule is a very large energy unit. A more convenient unit is the *electron volt* (eV), where

$$1 \text{ eV} = 1.60 \times 10^{-19} \text{ J}$$

To illustrate, in the previous example the hydrogen atom has an energy of magnitude 2.17×10^{-18} J, or

$$(2.17 \times 10^{-18} \text{ J})\left(\frac{1 \text{ eV}}{1.6 \times 10^{-19} \text{ J}}\right) = 13.6 \text{ eV}$$

6.9 | POWER

We are often less concerned with the net amount of work done or energy transferred than with the rate at which this occurs. For example, we may remove snow from a driveway either with a hand shovel or with a snowplow. The same work is done, but the plow does it much faster. We say that the plow is more powerful. In this section, we describe the relationship between work and power.

When an amount of work ΔW is done in a time Δt, the *average power* is defined as the average rate of doing work,

$$\overline{\mathcal{P}} = \frac{\Delta W}{\Delta t} \qquad (6.24)$$

The instantaneous power $\mathcal{P}$ is found by considering smaller and smaller time intervals, so

$$\mathcal{P} = \frac{dW}{dt} \qquad (6.25)$$

From this definition, we see that the S.I. power unit is a joule per second, which is called a *watt* (W). A watt is rather a small unit for many purposes. It takes about 9 kilowatts (1 kW = 10^3 W) to overcome the dissipative forces acting on a 2000-kg car moving at a constant 65 km h^{-1}. A medium-sized electric power plant might generate 200 megawatts (1 MW = 10^6 W), and a rather large one might generate 1 gigawatt (1 GW = 10^9 W).

Energy is often sold by electrical utilities by the kilowatt hour (kW h). This is 1 kilowatt of power for 1 hour. In terms of S.I. units,

$$1 \text{ kW h} = (10^3 \text{ W})(3600 \text{ s}) = 3.6 \times 10^6 \text{ J}$$

The following examples illustrate the concept of power in various situations.

Example 6.14

A 70-kg man runs up a flight of stairs 3 m high in 2 s. (a) How much work does he do against gravitational forces? (b) What is his average power output?

(a) The work done ΔW is equal to his change in potential energy mgh. Thus

$$\Delta W = mgh = (70 \text{ kg})(9.8 \text{ m s}^{-2})(3 \text{ m})$$
$$= 2060 \text{ J}$$

(b) His average power is the work done divided by the time,

$$\overline{\mathcal{P}} = \frac{\Delta W}{\Delta t} = \frac{2060 \text{ J}}{2 \text{ s}} = 1030 \text{ W}$$

This is a high power output for a human.

Example 6.15

Since the early 1970s, the efficiencies of homes, autos, and appliances have been increased greatly to conserve nonrenewable energy sources. Between 1973 and 1993, the average electrical energy use of a new refrigerator or freezer will drop from 5.2 to 1.9 kW h per day. The additional cost of the more efficient unit will be about $100. (a) At 8 cents per kW h, how long will it take to recover the extra $100 cost of the more efficient appliance? (b) A typical large electric power plant produces 10^6 kW and operates about 60 percent of the time, allowing for maintenance, and so on. There are 125 million refrigerators and freezers in the United States. How many fewer power plants are needed if they all consume 1.9 kW h daily instead of 5.2?

(a) The difference in daily energy usage is

$$(5.2 - 1.9) \text{ kW h} = 3.3 \text{ kW h}$$

This energy costs

$$(3.3 \text{ kW h})(8 \text{ cents/kW h}) = 26.4 \text{ cents}$$

or $0.264 per day. Thus the $100 cost will be recovered in

$$\frac{\$100}{\$0.264 \text{ day}^{-1}} = 378 \text{ days}$$

The payback period is just about one year.

(b) The reduction in the average power used by the newer appliances is $\Delta W/\Delta t = (3.3 \text{ kW h})/(24 \text{ h}) = 0.14 \text{ kW}$. Multiplying by the 125 million units in use, the total power saved is

$$(0.14 \text{ kW})(1.25 \times 10^8) = 1.8 \times 10^7 \text{ kW}$$

One power plant, operating 60 percent of the time at 10^6 kW, produces an average of 0.6×10^6 kW. Hence the number of power plants "saved" is

$$(1.8 \times 10^7 \text{ kW})/(0.6 \times 10^6 \text{ kW}) = 30$$

Example 6.16

The blades of a wind-powered electrical generator sweep out a circle of area A. (a) If the wind moves at a velocity v perpendicular to the circle, what is the mass of the air passing through it in time t? (b) What is the kinetic energy of that air? (c) Suppose the machine converts 30 percent of the wind's energy into electrical energy, and that $A = 30 \text{ m}^2$ and $v = 10 \text{ m s}^{-1}$ (36 km h^{-1}). What is the electrical power output? (The density of air at 20° C is 1.2 kg m^{-3}.)

(a) In time t, the wind moves a distance vt. Hence all the air in a cylinder of cross-sectional area A, length vt, and volume $V = Avt$ will cross the circle. Multiplying V by the density of the air ρ, the mass is

$$m = \rho A v t$$

(b) The kinetic energy of the air crossing in time t is

$$K = \tfrac{1}{2}mv^2 = \tfrac{1}{2}(\rho A v t)v^2 = \tfrac{1}{2}\rho A v^3 t$$

(c) The power available from the wind is its kinetic energy divided by the time it takes to cross the circle defined by the blades. Thirty percent is converted to electrical power, so

$$\mathcal{P} = \frac{(0.30)K}{t} = \frac{(0.30)(\tfrac{1}{2}\rho A v^3 t)}{t} = 0.15\rho A v^3$$
$$= (0.15)(1.2 \text{ kg m}^{-3})(30 \text{ m}^2)(10 \text{ m s}^{-1})^3$$
$$= 5400 \text{ W} = 5.4 \text{ kW}$$

This is enough electrical power for about five typical American homes. Note, however, we need a fairly high wind speed of 36 km h^{-1}. $\mathcal{P}$ varies as v^3, so if the wind speed were to decrease 50 percent, the power output would become only $(5.4/2^3)$ kW = 0.675 kW.

Another expression for the power is often useful. The work done by a force $\mathbf{F}$ acting through a small displacement Δs in a short time Δt is $\Delta W = F_s \Delta s$. Dividing by Δt gives the power,

$$\overline{\mathcal{P}} = F_s \frac{\Delta s}{\Delta t}$$

Since $\Delta s/\Delta t$ is the velocity, the power is also given by,

$$\mathcal{P} = F_s v = \mathbf{F} \cdot \mathbf{v} \qquad (6.26)$$

Thus the power is the force component F_s times the velocity. This result is used in the next example.

Example 6.17

A 250-kg piano is raised by a hoist at a constant velocity of 0.1 m s⁻¹. What is the power expended by the hoist?

Since the force mg is parallel to the velocity,

$$\mathcal{P} = Fv = (250 \text{ kg})(9.8 \text{ m s}^{-1})(0.1 \text{ m s}^{-1})$$
$$= 245 \text{ W}$$

6.10 | WORK AND ENERGY FOR ROTATIONAL MOTION

Objects can have kinetic energy associated with rotational motion as well as with translation. We now obtain expressions for the work, power, and kinetic energy appropriate for objects rotating about a fixed axis.

Consider a wheel of radius r rotating about its axis. When it rotates through an angle θ, a point on the rim moves a distance $s = r\theta$. A force F acting tangential to the wheel during this displacement will do work $Fs = Fr\theta$. Since Fr is the torque τ due to this force, the work done can be written as

$$W = \tau\theta \qquad (6.27)$$

The power is defined as $\Delta W/\Delta t$. With this result for W, $\mathcal{P} = \tau\,\Delta\theta/\Delta t$. Since $\Delta\theta/\Delta t = \omega$, we have

$$\mathcal{P} = \tau\omega \qquad (6.28)$$

When an object moves in a circular path, $v = \omega r$, and the kinetic energy $\frac{1}{2}mv^2$ can be rewritten as $\frac{1}{2}mr^2\omega^2$. If a rigid body rotates about a fixed axis, each of its constituent particles moves in a circle with the same angular velocity. Adding up the individual kinetic energies therefore amounts to summing up the mr^2 factors, or to finding the moment of inertia. Hence the kinetic energy is

$$K = \frac{1}{2}I\omega^2 \qquad (6.29)$$

All of these results are analogs of the corresponding formulas for translation, with the natural replacements $s \to \theta$, $v \to \omega$, $F \to \tau$, and $m \to I$. If rotating objects are present, the work and energy terms in $E = E_0 + W_a$ must take this into account, as in the next example.

Example 6.18

A 20-kg bucket is held above a well by a massless rope wound about a windlass (Fig. 6.16). The windlass is a cylinder with a radius of 0.2 m and a moment of inertia of 0.2 kg m². If the bucket is released from rest, what is its speed just before it hits the water 10 m below? (Assume there is no friction or air resistance.)

With the reference height for the potential energy at the water, $\mathcal{U}_0 = mgh$ and $\mathcal{U} = 0$. The kinetic energy K_0 at the top is zero. When the bucket hits the water, if its speed is v, the angular velocity of the windlass is $\omega = v/r$, and their combined kinetic energy is $K = \frac{1}{2}mv^2 + \frac{1}{2}I\omega^2 = \frac{1}{2}mv^2 + \frac{1}{2}Iv^2/r^2$. Since the mechanical energy is conserved, $E = E_0$, and

$$\tfrac{1}{2}mv^2 + \tfrac{1}{2}I\frac{v^2}{r^2} = mgh$$

Solving for v, we find

$$v = \left(\frac{2mgh}{m + I/r^2}\right)^{1/2}$$

$$= \left[\frac{(2)(20 \text{ kg})(9.8 \text{ m s}^{-2})(10 \text{ m})}{(20 \text{ kg}) + (0.2 \text{ kg m}^2)/(0.2 \text{ m})^2}\right]^{1/2}$$

$$= 12.5 \text{ m s}^{-1}$$

In the previous example, if the bucket were not attached to the windlass, it would have acquired a greater speed. Some of its potential energy was converted into kinetic energy of the windlass. Similarly, if an object rolls down a hill, some of the potential energy is converted into rotational kinetic energy, and it reaches the bottom of the hill with a

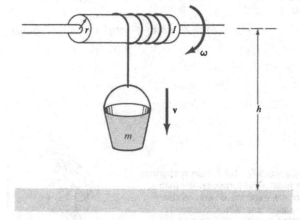

Figure 6.16.   When the bucket falls, gravitational potential energy is converted into kinetic energy of the bucket and windlass.

lower speed than an object sliding frictionlessly down the hill.

6.11 | JUMPING; SCALING LAWS IN PHYSIOLOGY

In Chapter One, we related the heights reached by jumping animals to the velocities and accelerations involved. Here we describe a procedure invented by Galileo called *scaling*, which we use in this section to draw some general conclusions about jumping. We begin by reanalyzing the vertical jump of a human in terms of work and energy.

Figure 6.17 shows a man jumping. Initially he crouches, lowering his center of gravity a distance d called the acceleration distance. We shall measure potential energy from this reference level. As he accelerates and straightens, he does work to raise his potential and kinetic energies. At the instant of takeoff, his potential energy is $\mathcal{U}_0 = mgd$. If his upward velocity at this instant is v_0, his kinetic energy is $\frac{1}{2}mv_0^2$. Thus in reaching the erect takeoff position, he has done work W_a where

$$W_a = mgd + \tfrac{1}{2}mv_0^2$$

From takeoff to the top of the jump, the only force acting on the man is his weight. Thus during the airborne part of the jump, his mechanical energy is constant. At the top of the jump, $K = 0$ and $\mathcal{U} = mg(h + d)$. This must equal the energy at takeoff, so

$$W_a = mgd + \tfrac{1}{2}mv_0^2 = mg(h + d) \quad (6.30)$$

Thus the total energy that the human must supply to make the jump is $W_a = mg(h + d)$. In our subsequent discussion, we neglect d compared to h and use

$$W_a \simeq mgh$$

This is only a fair assumption for humans, since $d/h \simeq \frac{1}{2}$, but it is a good approximation for smaller animals. Note that Eq. 6.30 also gives us the takeoff velocity

$$v_0 = \sqrt{2gh}$$

Having found the total energy in terms of the height reached in the jump, we might hope to determine the energy expended by various muscles and compare these numbers for various animals. Unfortunately, the large number of bones and muscles involved makes such an analysis very complicated, a difficulty characteristic of many biological problems. However, we can make some progress in comparing the jumping abilities of different animals with the aid of a procedure called *scaling*. Scaling assumes that the basic characteristics of a biological system change or *scale* with its overall size in a simple but plausible way. This procedure, which can be used in many physiological problems, leads to predicted *scaling laws* for the jumping ability versus the size of an animal, which can be compared to the data.

The simplest scaling model assumes that the mass m of an animal is proportional to its volume and that this volume is proportional to the cube of some characteristic length l. Thus the scaling assumption

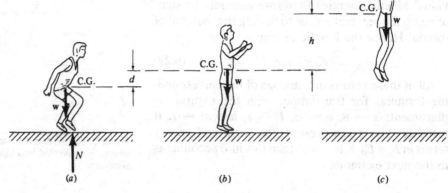

Figure 6.17. (*a*) A man preparing to jump. The forces on the man are his weight **w** down and the normal force **N** of the ground acting upward. (*b*) The man at takeoff. (*c*) During the airborne phase the only force on the man is **w**. The total change in the position of his center of gravity during the jump is $d + h$.

is $m = cl^3$, where c is a constant. For example, the ratio of the characteristic lengths of a 0.02-kg mouse and a 700-kg cow would be

$$\frac{l_{\text{cow}}}{l_{\text{mouse}}} = \left(\frac{m_{\text{cow}}}{m_{\text{mouse}}}\right)^{1/3} = \left(\frac{700 \text{ kg}}{0.02 \text{ kg}}\right)^{1/3} = 32.7$$

This may, for example, represent the relative lengths of the legs.

Using this length, we note that the volume of an animal or any of its organs is proportional to l^3, the surface area of the body and the cross-sectional areas of the muscles are proportional to l^2, and the length of the limbs is proportional to l.

Comparing the jumping ability of animals we note the interesting fact that the heights of the jumps are not so very different for animals that are extremely different in size. Thus the rat kangaroo, about the size of a rabbit, jumps nearly as high as a large kangaroo. Locusts and the much smaller flea jump to roughly the same height. We may ask, what characteristics do they share that would explain this result?

Two possibilities come immediately to mind.

1   The energy supplied per unit mass of muscle is the same for all animals.
2   The power supplied per unit mass of muscle is the same for all animals.

We examine the first assumption here, leaving the second as a problem (Problem 6-124). The first assumption says that an animal should be able to do an amount of work proportional to its mass m. But we saw that the work done during a jump of height h is mgh. Thus $mgh \propto m$, and h does not depend on m or l.

This prediction, that the height reached is independent of the size of an animal, is roughly correct experimentally. By contrast, the predictions obtained with the second hypothesis disagree with the data. Thus we may tentatively conclude that the *energy expended per unit mass is about the same for all animals of the same general type.*

Another conclusion follows by noting that the takeoff velocity $v_0 = \sqrt{2gh}$ is roughly independent of size. The acceleration distance d is proportional to the characteristic length l, so the takeoff time $t = d/\bar{v} = d/(\frac{1}{2}v_0)$ also scales as l. The power expended per unit mass is the energy expended per unit mass

divided by this time. Since the energy expended per unit mass is independent of l, the power must vary as $1/l$. *This predicts that larger animals will expend their energy at a slower rate..*

Comparisons between mammals and insects are complicated by the different ways they use their leg muscles. Mammals use muscle contractions directly, but insects employ a catapult arrangement. For example, a flea has an elastic material called *resilin* in its knee joint. The flea gradually bends its leg, stretching the resilin, and locks the knee in position. In a jump, the knee is unlocked, and the resilin contracts rapidly, straightening the leg. Thus insects employ stored *elastic* potential energy and use their muscles somewhat indirectly.

The discussion of scaling laws as applied to jumping shows how interesting qualitative insights can sometimes be obtained in complex biological systems. The model we have used assumed that all body dimensions scale in exactly the same way with the mass of the animal. However, it is possible to make other scaling assumptions. Another approach to scaling is described in Chapter Eight.

SUMMARY

Many problems can be most easily solved using the concepts of work and energy. The relationship between these quantities is contained in the two most important statements of this chapter.

1   The final kinetic energy of an object is equal to its initial kinetic energy plus the work W done by all the forces acting on it:

$$K = K_0 + W$$

In this equation, $W = F_s s$, where s is the displacement of the object, and F_s is the component of the net force along the direction of the displacement. $K_0 = \frac{1}{2}mv_0^2$ and $K = \frac{1}{2}mv^2$ are the kinetic energies of the object before and after the displacement, respectively.

2   If conservative forces act on an object, their effects can be taken into account by including appropriate terms in the potential energy $\mathcal{U}$. The other forces acting on the object are called applied forces, and they do work W_a. Then the general work–energy relationship just given is rewritten in the more useful form

$$K + \mathcal{U} = K_0 + \mathcal{U}_0 + W_a$$

A force is conservative if the work it does as an object moves from one location to another is independent of the path. Gravitational and electric forces are conservative.

When there is no work done by applied forces, the total mechanical energy $E = K + \mathcal{U}$ is conserved. The kinetic and potential energies may each change, but their sum must remain constant. When dissipative forces are present, mechanical energy is converted into thermal energy. Energy is never destroyed or created—it is only transformed from one form to another.

Near the earth's surface, the gravitational force is approximately constant, and the potential energy is $\mathcal{U} = mgh$. The more general form for the gravitational potential energy is $\mathcal{U} = -GMm/r$. The electrical potential energy of two point charges is $\mathcal{U} = kqQ/r$.

The rate $\Delta W/\Delta t$ at which work is done or energy is transferred is the power. An equivalent expression is $\mathcal{P} = F_s v = \mathbf{F} \cdot \mathbf{v}$.

For an object rotating about a fixed axis, the formulas for the work, power, and kinetic energy are obtained by replacing s, v, F, and m by their analogs θ, ω, τ, and I, respectively.

Checklist
Define or explain:

work	gravitational potential
joule	energy
scalar product	electrical potential
kinetic energy	energy
potential energy	electron volt
conservative force	power
total mechanical energy	watt
dissipative force	kilowatt hour
applied force	rotational kinetic
mechanical energy	energy
conservation	scaling
escape velocity	

REVIEW QUESTIONS

Q6-1 The work done by a force is positive when **F** is _____ to s, negative when **F** is _____ to s, and zero when **F** is _____ to s.

Q6-2 The S.I. unit for work is the _____.

Q6-3 The kinetic energy of an object is a measure of its ability to _____.

Q6-4 The translational kinetic energy of an object of mass m and velocity v is _____.

Q6-5 The final kinetic energy of an object equals its _____ plus the total work done by _____.

Q6-6 Forces that can be included in the potential energy are said to be _____.

Q6-7 The total mechanical energy is the _____ plus the _____.

Q6-8 Mechanical energy is conserved when _____.

Q6-9 Potential energy is energy associated with the _____.

Q6-10 The place where the potential energy is zero is _____.

Q6-11 In general, the increase in the potential energy is equal to the negative of the _____.

Q6-12 Dissipative forces usually convert mechanical energy into _____.

Q6-13 The work done by frictional forces is always _____.

Q6-14 The gravitational potential energy formula $\mathcal{U} = mgh$ holds for objects _____.

Q6-15 The minimum velocity for an object fired upward at the earth's surface to permanently leave the earth is called the _____.

Q6-16 Power is the rate at which _____.

Q6-17 The S.I. power unit is the _____.

Q6-18 A kilowatt hour is a unit of _____.

Q6-19 _____ assumes that the basic characteristics of a biological system change with its overall size in a direct way.

EXERCISES

Section 6.1 | Work

6-1 A child pulls a toy car with a 10-N force at a 20° angle to the horizontal (Fig. 6.18). If the car moves a distance of 6 m, how much work does the child do?

6-2 A woman pushes horizontally on a chair with a force of 300 N. Compute the work she does on the chair if (a) it moves 2 m parallel to the force; (b) it moves 1 m opposite to the force; (c) it does not move.

6-3 A woman exerts a constant horizontal force of 200 N on a child and a tricycle. The tricycle moves 2 m, and the work done by the woman

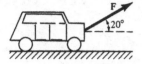

Figure 6.18. Exercise 6-1.

is 100 J. What is the angle between the force and the displacement of the tricycle?

6-4 A motorcycle comes to a skidding stop in 5 m. During stopping, the force on the cycle due to the road is 200 N and is directly opposed to the motion. (a) How much work does the road do on the cycle? (b) How much work does the cycle do on the road?

6-5 A girl pulls a box weighing 40 N a distance of 10 m across the floor at constant speed. How much work does she do if the coefficient of sliding friction is 0.2?

6-6 A box of mass 10 kg falls straight down a distance of 2 m. How much work is done by gravitational forces?

6-7 A car of mass 1300 kg rolls down a hill a distance of 100 m. The road is at an angle of 10° to the horizontal direction. How much work is done on the car by gravitational forces?

ᶜ6-8 The force on an object is $F = C/x^2$, where C is a constant. (a) What are the units of C? (b) How much work is done by this force when the object is moved from $x = a$ to $x = 3a$? (c) How much work is done by F when the object is moved from $x = 3a$ to $x = \infty$?

ᶜ6-9 The force of an object is $F = -kx$, where k is a positive constant. (a) At what location is the object in equilibrium? (b) Using integration, find how much work is done by F when the object moves from $x = -a$ to $x = 0$. (c) How much work is done by F when the object moves from $x = -a$ to $x = +a$?

Section 6.2 | Kinetic Energy

6-10 A 1000-kg automobile has a velocity of 40 km h⁻¹. What is its kinetic energy?

6-11 What is the kinetic energy of a 0.25-kg stone moving at 10 m s⁻¹?

6-12 A baseball of mass 0.15 kg is thrown at 30 m s⁻¹. (a) What is its kinetic energy? (b) If it is thrown by a man who exerts a constant force

over a distance of 1.5 m, what force does he exert?

6-13 A 100-kg man is in a car traveling at 20 m s⁻¹. (a) Find his kinetic energy. (b) The car strikes a concrete wall and comes to rest after the front of the car has collapsed 1 m. The man is wearing a seat belt and harness. What is the average force exerted by the belt and harness during the crash?

6-14 Show that kinetic energy has dimensions of force times distance.

6-15 A 200-kg swordfish swimming at 5 m s⁻¹ rams a wooden yacht that is at rest. Its sword penetrates the yacht, and the fish is stopped in 1 m. (a) What is the initial kinetic energy of the fish? (b) How much work is done by the fish?

6-16 Fishing line is usually sold as being capable of withstanding a certain force. What strength line is necessary to handle a 10-kg salmon swimming at 3 m s⁻¹ if it is stopped in 0.2 m?

6-17 A baseball is thrown from center field to second base, and its velocity diminishes from 20 m s⁻¹ to 15 m s⁻¹. If its mass is 0.15 kg, how much energy was lost due to air resistance? (Assume the initial and final heights are the same.)

6-18 A ball of mass 0.2 kg falls straight down a distance of 10 m. (a) How much work is done by gravitational forces on the ball? (b) If it was initially at rest, what is its speed after falling the 10 m?

6-19 A golf club strikes a ball lying on the grass. It remains in contact for a distance of 2 cm. If the ball acquires a speed of 60 m s⁻¹ and its mass is 0.047 kg, what is the average force exerted by the club?

Section 6.3 | Potential Energy and Conservative Forces

6-20 A girl of mass 30 kg on a swing rises 1.5 m as she goes from the lowest to the highest point in her motion. Find how much work gravity does on her (a) during the time she is moving upward; (b) as she moves downward.

6-21 A 4-kg brick is on a table 1 m above the floor. The ceiling is 4 m above the floor. Find the potential energy of the brick if its height is measured relative to (a) the floor; (b) the table; (c) the ceiling.

166

yes

6-22 (a) If the speed of a ball is doubled, what happens to its kinetic energy? (b) If the distance a ball is lifted is doubled, what happens to its potential energy change? (c) If a ball is thrown straight up, how does the distance it rises vary with its initial speed?

6-23 A ball is thrown straight up with an initial velocity v_0. (a) How high will it go? (b) What is its velocity when it has reached half its maximum height?

6-24 A child on a swing reaches a maximum height of 2 m above her lowest position. What is the speed of the swing at the lowest point? (Neglect frictional forces.)

6-25 A beer can is dropped from a window 30 m above the ground. How fast will it be moving just before it lands? (Neglect air resistance.)

6-26 A car moving at 40 m s^{-1} hits a concrete wall. From what height would a car have to be dropped onto concrete to achieve the same result?

6-27 A boy sits on a Ferris wheel. How much work is done on him by gravitational forces when the wheel makes one complete turn?

6-28 A 6-kg salmon swims a distance of 5 m up a fish ladder at constant velocity. It experiences a 1.3-N dissipative force from the water. The fish rises a distance of 0.5 m while swimming up the ladder (Fig. 6.19). (a) How much work must the fish do to overcome the dissipative force? (b) What is the change in the fish's potential energy? (c) How much total work does the fish do in swimming up the ladder?

6-29 A baseball thrown straight up reaches a height of 50 m. What was its initial velocity? (Neglect air resistance.)

6-30 Water flows over a dam and falls a distance h in a smooth stream, as shown in Fig. 6.20. Assume that the water has zero velocity at the top of the falls. What is the velocity at the base of the falls?

6-31 A car goes off a cliff with a speed of 30 m s^{-1}. How fast will it be moving after falling 20 m?

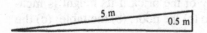

Figure 6.19. Exercise 6-28.

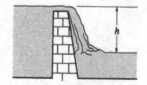

Figure 6.20. Water going over a dam. It has zero velocity at the top and drops a distance h. Exercise 6-30.

6-32 A 0.5-m length of rope is held at rest on a frictionless table so that half of it is hanging freely over the side and half is on the table. The rope is then released. How fast is it moving when the end of the rope has just left the table?

6-33 An elevator and its contents have a mass of 2000 kg. It is counterweighted by a piece of metal of mass 1700 kg that falls as the elevator rises. How much work must the motor do against gravitational forces to raise the elevator 30 m?

Section 6.4 | Dissipative Forces

6-34 A boy on a sled slides down a hill of height 30 m and up another, coming to a stop 10 m above his lowest point. If his mass is 50 kg, how much mechanical energy has been lost?

6-35 A 1200-kg car moving at 30 m s^{-1} coasts to a stop in 400 m on flat ground. What is the average frictional force?

6-36 A hockey puck with an initial velocity of 4 m s^{-1} slides on ice. The coefficient of kinetic friction is 0.1. How far will the puck slide before stopping?

6-37 A box with an initial speed of 2 m s^{-1} slides to rest on a horizontal floor in 3 m. What is the coefficient of kinetic friction?

6-38 At some amusement parks, one can slide down a ramp, as shown in Fig. 6.21. (a) What is the velocity at the bottom? (Assume the ramp is frictionless.) (b) What distance l is necessary to stop if the coefficient of friction at the bottom is 0.5?

6-39 A sled slides 100 m down a hill that slopes at an angle of 30° with the horizontal direction. The sled attains a final velocity of 20 m s^{-1} at the base of the slope. What fraction of the energy was lost due to friction?

6-40 A 70-kg skier is moving at 15 m s^{-1} when she is at a point 50 m higher than the bottom of a hill. She reaches the bottom and coasts up the

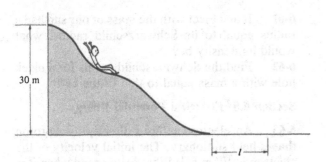

Figure 6.21. Profile of the amusement park slide. l is the stopping distance. Exercise 6-38.

next hill until she comes to a stop. (a) If there are no dissipative forces acting, how high will she go? (b) She actually comes to a stop at a point 30 m above the bottom of the hill. How much work was done against dissipative forces?

6-41 A roller coaster reaches the top of a grade at 10 m s^{-1}. It then goes downhill and uphill once more. If the second peak is 15 m lower than the first, how fast will the roller coaster be moving at that peak? (Assume that no dissipative forces act.)

6-42 A car plus its driver has a mass of 1400 kg. When the driver takes his foot off the accelerator, the car slows from 30 m s^{-1} to 20 m s^{-1} in 20 s. (a) How much work was done by dissipative forces? (b) Assuming a uniform deceleration, find the average dissipative force.

6-43 A military aircraft is flying at 2000 km h^{-1} at an altitude of 15,000 m. (a) If it dives to an altitude of 13,000 m, what will be its resulting speed if dissipative forces are neglected? (b) Find the resulting speed if only half the potential energy released is converted into kinetic energy and the remainder is converted into heat.

Section 6.5 | Observations on Work and Energy; Section 6.6 | Solving Problems Using Work and Energy

6-44 A 50-kg woman climbs a mountain 3000 m high. (a) How much work does she do against gravitational forces? (b) A kilogram of fat supplies about 3.8×10^7 J of energy. If she converts fat into mechanical energy with a 20 percent efficiency rate, how much fat will she consume in the climb?

6-45 A dieter lifts a 10-kg mass a distance of 0.5 m 1000 times. (a) How much work does he do against gravitational force? (Assume the potential energy lost each time he lowers the mass is dissipated.) (b) Fat supplies 3.8×10^7 J of energy per kilogram, which is converted to mechanical energy with a 20 percent efficiency rate. How much fat will the dieter use up?

6-46 A man lifts a 20-kg mass 0.5 m vertically. (a) How much work does he do against gravitational forces? (b) When he lowers the mass to its original height, how much work is done on the man? (c) What happens to this energy?

6-47 A reservoir has a volume of 10^7 m^3. If the water in the reservoir falls an average distance of 30 m, and 80 percent of the potential energy lost is actually converted into electrical energy by turbines, how much electrical energy is generated? (The density of water is 1000 kg m^{-3}.)

6-48 Water passing through a rapids has a speed of 3 m s^{-1} as it enters the rapids and a speed of 15 m s^{-1} as it leaves. The elevation of the river changes along the rapids from 200 m above sea level to 180 m. What fraction of the potential energy lost by the water is dissipated?

6-49 As it leaves Lake Ontario, the St. Lawrence River has a flow of 6800 m^3 s^{-1}. Lake Ontario is 75 m above sea level. Ignoring any water entering the river further downstream, what is the maximum energy that could, in principle, be extracted by electric generating plants every 24 hours? (The density of water is 1000 kg m^{-3}.)

6-50 In Fig. 6.22, the pulley and strings are massless and there is no friction. If the system is released from rest, what is its speed after the masses have moved a distance d?

6-51 In Fig. 6.22, the pulley and strings are massless. The coefficient of kinetic friction between the block and the plane is 0.2, and

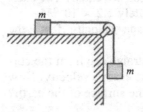

Figure 6.22. Exercises 6-50, 6-51, and 6-91.

$m = 5$ kg. (a) How much work is done against friction as the system moves 3 m? (b) If it is initially at rest, what is its speed after it has moved 3 m?

Section 6.7 | Gravitational Potential Energy
(Use the solar and terrestrial data on the inside back cover.)

6-52 A spaceship of mass m is in circular orbit around the earth. Its distance from the earth's surface is equal to the radius of the earth. How much energy is required to double its distance from the surface of the earth?

6-53 Suppose a spaceship of mass m is in a circular orbit around the sun at the same distance as the earth. (a) In terms of the solar mass M_S and the earth–sun distance R, how much energy E_S is required for the spaceship to escape from the solar system? (b) How much energy E_E was needed for this spaceship to escape the earth? (c) Find the numerical value of the ratio E_S/E_E.

6-54 Two identical space stations collide head on and come to rest at a distance above the earth equal to twice its radius. At what speed will the fragments reach the earth's surface, neglecting the dissipative forces?

6-55 What is the change in their gravitational potential energy when two balls of mass 10 kg with their centers initially 10 m apart are moved so that they are only 0.1 m apart?

6-56 How much energy would be required for the moon to "escape" from the earth?

6-57 On planet X, the acceleration due to gravity is four times that on earth, and the radius of the planet is twice that of the earth. What is the escape velocity?

6-58 The average center-to-center distance from the earth to the moon is 3.84×10^5 km. What is the smallest distance from the center of the earth at which the gravitational potential energies of the earth and moon are equal? The mass of the moon is approximately $1.2 \times 10^{-2} M_E$.

6-59 What is the escape velocity from the moon?

6-60 A rocket is fired straight up from the surface of the earth at half the escape velocity. How high will it go relative to the surface of the earth? (Neglect dissipative forces.)

6-61 If an object with the mass of our sun had a radius equal to its Schwarzschild radius, what would its density be?

6-62 Find the Schwarzschild radius for a black hole with a mass equal to that of the earth.

Section 6.8 | Electrical Potential Energy

6-63 An electron is fired directly at a proton that is held stationary. The initial velocity of the electron is 10^7 m s^{-1}. What is its speed when it is 10^{-11} m from the proton?

6-64 According to Bohr's theory of the hydrogen atom, the only possible radii for the electron are $a_0, 2^2 a_0, 3^2 a_0, \ldots$, where $a_0 = 5.3 \times 10^{-11}$ m. How much energy in electron volts must be supplied to make the transition from the orbit of radius a_0 to the orbit with radius $n^2 a_0, n = 2, 3, \ldots$? (This energy can be supplied by electromagnetic radiation.)

6-65 In a uranium atom, the nucleus contains 92 protons. The electrons move in orbits with varying radii, but the closest electrons have a radius $\frac{1}{92}$ times that of the radius of the electron in the hydrogen atom. Find the ratio of the energy needed to remove one of these closest electrons from a uranium atom to that needed to remove the electron from the hydrogen atom.

6-66 Find the ratio of the electrical and gravitational potential energies of the electron and proton in a hydrogen atom.

6-67 An electron in a cathode-ray tube in a television set is accelerated by electric forces from rest to 8×10^7 m s^{-1}. What is the change in its electrical potential energy in (a) joules; (b) electron volts?

6-68 In an X-ray machine, electrons are accelerated by electric forces. If they are initially at rest and they lose 50,000 eV of electrical potential energy, what is their speed?

Section 6.9 | Power

6-69 A car must do work at a rate of 10 kW to maintain a constant speed of 25 m s^{-1} on flat ground. How large are the forces opposing its motion?

6-70 A 1500-kg car moves at 30 m s^{-1} on a hill that makes an angle of 5° with the horizontal direction. If it takes 15 kW to maintain this speed on flat ground, how much power is required on the hill?

6-71 An electric hair dryer uses 1200 W of electrical power. (a) A student uses the dryer 5 minutes each day. At 10 cents per kW h, what is the annual cost of using the dryer? (b) An average power plant supplies 10^6 kW and operates 60 percent of the time. If 50 million people use their dryers at this rate, how many power plants are required?

6-72 An electric clothes dryer uses 4200 watts of electrical power. If it takes 50 minutes to dry a load and electricity costs 10 cents per kW h, how much does drying one load of laundry cost?

6-73 Two teams of students pull a rope in a tug of war. Team A is gaining over B, since the rope is moving in its direction at a constant rate of 0.01 m s^{-1}. The tension in the rope is 4000 N. How much power is expended by team A?

6-74 If a man can do mechanical work at a rate of 8 W kg^{-1} of body mass during sustained activity, how fast can he run up stairs?

6-75 A girl of mass 40 kg climbs a rope 8 m long at constant speed in 15 s. What power does she expend against gravitational forces during the climb?

6-76 An elevator motor produces 2000 W of power. How fast can it lift a 1000-kg load?

6-77 Cruising speeds for fish 0.3 m long are about 0.35 m s^{-1}. The average power expended is about 4.5 W kg^{-1} of body mass. Assume the fish has a mass of 0.4 kg. (a) What is the average power expended by the cruising fish? (b) What is the average force exerted by the fish on the water? (c) How much work does the fish do on the water in 10 minutes?

6-78 A motor operating a water pump can produce 1000 W of power. If the kinetic energy change is negligible, how many kilograms of water per second can it pump from a well 20 m deep?

6-79 A bicyclist moving on flat ground at a constant speed of 5 m s^{-1} expends 100 W against dissipative forces. (a) If the dissipative forces are independent of the velocity, what power will she expend at a constant speed of 10 m s^{-1}? (b) The portion of the dissipative forces arising from air resistance actually increases rapidly with the speed. If we suppose the dissipative forces are

proportional to the square of the speed, what power will she have to expend at a constant 10 m s^{-1}?

6-80 A 2000-kg car accelerates from rest to 30 m s^{-1} in 10 s. What average power is required?

6-81 A chair lift delivers two skiers to the top of a 500-m tall hill every 12 s. The average mass of a skier plus equipment is 80 kg. Assuming dissipative forces are negligible, find the power expended by the chair lift motor.

6-82 Direct sunlight reaches a horizontal surface at an average rate of 200 watts per square metre of surface area, averaging over day and night, times of the year, and cloudy and clear weather. Suppose 10 percent of this solar energy could be converted into electrical power. How large an area in square kilometres would be required to replace a large nuclear power plant that supplies 10^9 W?

6-83 An average American family of four persons uses about 8 kW of power in all forms in its home. (a) Direct solar energy is incident on a horizontal surface at an average rate of 200 W per square metre. If 20 percent of this energy is collected and used, how large an area is needed to supply the 8 kW? (b) Compare this area to that of the roof on a typical single-family home.

6-84 Solar energy is received at a rate of 350 W per square metre of the earth's surface, averaging over latitude and time of day and year. (The energy is received no matter what the weather.) About 2 percent of that energy is converted into wind energy. (a) Find the ratio of the wind power generated by the sun over the globe to the total power used by humans, about 10^{13} W. (The radius of the earth is 6.38×10^6 m.) (b) It has been suggested that a maximum of about 3 percent of the wind power could in principle be extracted for human activities. Would this be adequate to supply our global energy needs?

Section 6.10 | Work and Energy for Rotational Motion (See Table 5.3 for moments of inertia.)

6-85 A tricycle wheel of moment of inertia 0.04 kg m^2 is rotating once per second. What is its kinetic energy?

6-86 Using the astronomical data on the inside back cover, find the kinetic energy associated with the earth's daily rotation. (Assume the earth is a uniform sphere.)

6-87   A 3-kg cylinder of radius 0.2 m is rotating about its axis at 40 rad s^{-1}. (a) Find the kinetic energy if the cylinder is solid. (b) Find the kinetic energy if the cylinder is a thin shell.

6-88   Refinements in materials technology have opened the possibility of using the energy stored in flywheels to operate vehicles. (a) If a flywheel is a solid cylinder of mass 1000 kg and radius 1 m, what is its kinetic energy when it rotates at 1000 rad s^{-1}? (b) How long can it supply energy to a vehicle at an average power of 20 kW?

6-89   A lawn mower blade has a mass of 3 kg and a radius of gyration of 0.1 m. It is rotating at 300 rad s^{-1}. (a) What is its kinetic energy? (b) When the engine is stopped, the blade comes to rest after 100 full rotations. What is the average torque acting on the blade? (c) What has happened to the kinetic energy?

6-90   An electric drill is rotating at 200 rad s^{-1} as the bit bores through a block of wood. If the drill motor is expending 400 W of power, what torque is the wood exerting on the drill bit?

6-91   In Fig. 6-22, the pulley is a uniform cylindrical disk of mass m and radius r. The strings are massless and there is no friction. If the system is initially at rest, find the speed of the blocks after they have moved a distance d.

6-92   A bicycle wheel has a mass of 4 kg and a radius of 0.35 m. All its mass may be considered to be concentrated at the edge. When the bicycle is lifted off the ground and the wheel is spun at 5 rev s^{-1}, it comes to rest after 20 full revolutions. (a) What is the average torque acting on the wheel? (b) If this torque is due entirely to friction in the bearings, and this force acts opposite to the motion at a distance of 1 cm from the axis, how large is it?

Section 6.11 | Jumping; Scaling Laws in Physiology

6-93   Using the data in Table 1.4, calculate the work and power per unit mass in jumping for (a) a kangaroo; (b) a locust.

6-94   Which of the animals listed in Table 1.4 does the most work per unit mass in jumping vertically? Which does the least?

6-95   Show that if the rate at which oxygen is absorbed by an animal and supplied to its tissues varies as the surface area of the arteries, then its power output per unit mass should vary as l^{-1}. What does this suggest about the pulse rate?

6-96   How does the rate of heat loss per unit body mass in a cold environment vary with the characteristic length l of an animal? (The rate of heat loss is proportional to the surface area.)

PROBLEMS

6-97   A block is released from rest and slides down a plane which makes a 30° angle with the horizontal direction. If the coefficient of kinetic friction is 0.1, how fast is the block moving after it has slid 1 m along the plane?

6-98   Record distances for the javelin, discus, and shotput are approximately 89 m, 69 m, and 21 m, respectively. The corresponding masses are 0.8 kg, 2.0 kg, and 7.2 kg. (a) Find the minimum initial kinetic energies for each of the three throws. (b) For which events does air resistance apparently play the largest and smallest roles? Explain.

6-99   A horizontal force **F** applied to a block of mass m pushes it at constant speed a distance l along a plane at an angle θ to the horizontal (Fig. 6.23). If the plane is frictionless, how much work is done by the force **F**?

6-100   The force needed to compress a certain spring a distance s from its normal length when undisturbed is $F = ks$, where $k = 300$ N m^{-1}. (a) Draw a graph of F versus s. (b) How much work must be done to compress the spring from its normal length to 0.2 m less? (c) How much more work must be done to compress it an additional 0.2 m?

*6-101   If a salmon encounters a falls when swim-

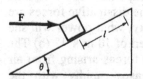

Figure 6.23.   Problem 6-99.

ming upstream, it will attempt to ascend the falls in one of two ways. If it can swim fast enough, it will swim up the falls. If it cannot, it will jump from the base of the falls into the falls at a height where the water is moving slowly enough so that it can swim up to the top.

Assume that the salmon has a maximum swimming speed of 5 m s^{-1} in still water and that the water at the top of the falls and in the pool at the base of the falls is at rest. (a) What is the maximum height of a falls that the salmon can swim up without jumping? (b) If the falls is 1 m high, what is the velocity of the fish with respect to the ground when it begins to swim upward at the bottom of the falling stream? (c) If the falls is 2 m high, what is the minimum height in the stream to which the fish must jump in order to swim up the rest of the way? (d) In order to jump the distance necessary in part (c), what must the fish's initial velocity be when it leaves the water?

*6-102 On a certain river, a falls 6 m high is encountered by the salmon of Problem 6-101. To facilitate the progress of the salmon upstream, a fish ladder is constructed. It is a series of sloping flow passages with connecting resting pools where the water velocity is virtually zero. If we refer to each pool with its flow passage as a step, what is the minimum number of steps necessary to allow the salmon to ascend the falls without jumping?

6-103 An upper limit for the amount of energy that can be extracted from water power in the United States can readily be calculated. The average depth of the annual rainfall is about 0.75 m, and the area of the United States is 8×10^6 km^2. (a) What is the mass of the annual rainfall? (b) Averaging over mountains, plains, and coastal areas, the average elevation is about 500 m. If all the rainwater eventually reached the oceans, how much potential energy would be dissipated? (c) Actually, two thirds of the water evaporates and returns to the atmosphere. Suppose all the remaining water were used to generate electric power. What would be the average power produced, assuming no energy was dissipated as heat? (The installed hydroelectric capacity in the United States is about 65 GW.)

6-104 Large fossil fuel or nuclear electrical power plants operate most economically when run at full capacity 24 hours a day. Excess electrical energy can be "stored" and recovered by pumping water into a reservoir on top of a mountain and letting it fall through turbines during periods of peak demand. At such a facility at Northfield Mountain in Massachusetts, the water falls an average distance of 250 m. The reservoir has a surface area of 1.3 km^2 and a depth averaging 10 m. (a) How much energy is available each time the reservoir is emptied? (b) If it is emptied over a period of 10 hours, and 80 percent of the energy is converted into electrical energy, what is the power generated?

6-105 In parts of the Bay of Fundy, the height difference between high and low tide can reach the huge value of 17 m. The average height difference in the bay is about 4 m. The bay is about 300 km long and 65 km wide. (a) How much gravitational potential energy is lost when the bay empties? (b) Suppose half this energy could be transformed into electrical power each time the bay emptied and also each time it filled. There are approximately two high and two low tides daily. What would be the average electrical power generated? (c) Find the ratio of this power to the electrical power currently used in Canada, about 2×10^{10} W.

6-106 Water on the sides of the earth facing and opposite the moon is higher than the water in between. The rotation of the earth under these bulges causes high and low tides approximately twice each day. (a) Show that when water in an area A of the ocean falls a distance d from high to low tide, the decrease in gravitational potential energy is $\rho g A d^2/2$, where ρ is the density of the water. (b) Assuming the earth is fully covered with water, show that the global total of the daily decreases in potential energy is $4\pi R_E^2 \rho g d^2$, where R_E is the radius of the earth. (Some of this energy is dissipated as thermal energy each day and is replaced by kinetic energy from the rotational motion of the earth. In the process, the rotation slows slightly, so that the day lengthens by 1.5×10^{-3} seconds per century.)

6-107 In the preceding problem, a formula is

given for the daily potential energy changes associated with the tides. (a) Calculate this energy if the average height change d from high to low tide is 0.5 m. (The density of water is 1000 kg m^{-3}, and the radius of the earth is 6.38×10^6 m.) (b) What is the average power corresponding to this energy? (c) What is the ratio of this power to the total power used by people worldwide, about 10^{13} W?

6-108   The Horseshoe Falls on the Niagara River in Canada is about 50 m high and 800 m wide. The water is moving at 10 m s^{-1} and has a depth of 1 m as it goes over the falls. (a) What volume of water goes over the falls every second? (b) What is the change in potential energy of this volume of water? (One cubic metre of water has a mass of 10^3 kg.) (c) If this potential energy could be converted directly into electrical energy, how much electrical power would be produced? (d) The total electrical power-generating capacity in the United States is about 5×10^{11} W. What percentage of this power could be produced by harnessing the Horseshoe Falls with 80 percent efficiency?

6-109   For a 2000-kg car to maintain a constant speed of 65 km h^{-1}, work must be done against dissipative forces at a rate of 9 kW. (a) How large are the dissipative forces? (b) The efficiency of a gasoline engine is only 20 percent, some power is lost in the transmission and drive train, and additional power is required to operate the lights, generator, water pump, and other accessories. Hence only 12.5 percent of the energy obtained by burning the gasoline is actually used to keep the car in motion. How far can the car travel at this speed on a litre of gasoline, which contains 3.4×10^7 J of chemical energy?

6-110   (a) What is the kinetic energy of a 2000-kg car traveling at 65 km h^{-1}? (b) If this speed is reached in 10 s, what average power is required? (c) Find the ratio of this power to the 9 kW required to maintain a steady 65 km h^{-1}. (d) Using the data in the preceding problem, calculate the amount of gasoline in litres needed to bring a car from rest to 65 km h^{-1}.

6-111   When a car goes uphill, extra power must be supplied in addition to that needed to maintain a constant speed on flat ground. For the car moving at 65 km h^{-1} in Problem 6-109, at what angle is the road to the horizontal if the power requirements are double that on flat ground?

6-112   Some of the power required to keep a car moving is dissipated by air resistance, and some by the work done in deforming the tires as they roll along the road (road resistance). At 65 km h^{-1}, these are about equal. (a) The air resistance varies approximately as the square of the velocity, while the road resistance forces are nearly independent of the velocity. By what factor will the power expenditure increase if the speed of the car is doubled? (b) By what factor will the number of kilometres driven per litre be reduced?

*6-113   The potential energy of an object of mass m at a height h above the earth's surface is $\mathcal{U} = -GM_Em/(R_E + h)$. R_E is the earth's radius and M_E its mass. Using Eq. B.15 in Appendix B, show for $h \ll R_E$ that

$$\mathcal{U} \simeq -\frac{GM_Em}{R_E}\left(1 - \frac{h}{R_E}\right)$$

*6-114   Show that for a rocket fired in the vicinity of the earth, the minimum velocity to escape the solar system is $v_s = \sqrt{2}C/T$, where C is the circumference of the earth's orbit and T is 1 year, the period of the earth's rotation about the sun. (Neglect the energy needed to escape the earth.)

6-115   Using the formula in the preceding problem, compare the escape velocities needed to escape the earth and to escape the solar system.

6-116   Assuming all planets have the same density or mass-to-volume ratio, show how the escape velocity varies with the radius of the planet.

6-117   At one time it was thought that the sun's energy came from gravitational sources. If the sun were originally larger and it had contracted to its present size, gravitational potential energy would have been transformed into heat. To estimate the energy involved, suppose the sun originally had two distant parts, each of mass $M_S/2$, where M_S is the mass of the sun. (a) If the pieces were brought from infinity to an average separation of R_S, show that the energy released would be $GM_S^2/4R_S$. (R_S is the radius of the sun.) (b) Calculate that energy using the data on the inside rear cover of this textbook. (c) The sun is believed to have radiated energy at its present rate, 3.8×10^{26} W, for 5×10^9 years. How long could it radiate at that rate, based on the estimate calculated in part (b)? (The short time the energy would last was once used to set a limit on the age of the solar system. This limit served as an argument against Darwin's theory of evolution, since it required a much longer time scale. The sun's main source of energy is nuclear fusion.)

6-118 An orbiting space station at a distance above the earth's surface equal to its radius ejects an instrument package with an initial velocity of 5000 m s^{-1} relative to the earth. What is its velocity when it reaches the atmosphere just a few kilometres above the earth?

6-119 The energy dissipated in the oceans by the tides is replenished via frictional forces from the earth's rotational kinetic energy. Suppose we could somehow extract the present global needs of 10^{13} W from the tides. (This is 100 times as much power as could realistically be obtained from the tides.) If this were an additional drain on the earth's kinetic energy, by how much would the day lengthen after a century? (Assume the earth is a uniform sphere and use the solar and terrestrial data on the inside rear cover.)

*6-120 The day lengthens by 1.5×10^{-3} s each century due to tidal friction. At what rate is power being dissipated by the tides? (Assume the earth is a uniform sphere and use the solar and terrestrial data on the inside rear cover.)

6-121 The muscle force is proportional to the cross-sectional area of the muscle. Show that if the speed of contraction is constant, the power per kilogram is proportional to l^{-1}.

*6-122 Show that if the power output of an animal of length l varies as l^2, the speed with which it can run uphill varies as l^{-1}.

6-123 Show that if the consumption of oxygen for a mammal of characteristic length l varies as l^2, the time it can remain under water without breathing varies as l.

6-124 Show that if the power expended per unit mass of muscle were the same for all animals of the same type, the height jumped would vary as $l^{2/3}$, where l is the characteristic size of the animal.

*6-125 A car starts from rest with a constant acceleration a. (a) After a time t has elapsed, how much work has been done on the car? (b) At time t, what is the instantaneous power delivered to the car?

*6-126 A car of mass m starts from rest and accelerates so that the instantaneous power delivered to the car has the constant magnitude $\mathcal{P}_0$. (a) After a time t has elapsed, how much work has been done on the car? (b) At time t, what is the instantaneous velocity of the car?

ANSWERS TO REVIEW QUESTIONS

Q6-1, parallel, opposite, perpendicular; **Q6-2**, joule; **Q6-3**, do work; **Q6-4**, $\frac{1}{2}mv^2$; **Q6-5**, initial kinetic energy, all the forces acting on it; **Q6-6**, conservative; **Q6-7**, kinetic energy, potential energy; **Q6-8**, applied forces do no work; **Q6-9**, position or configuration; **Q6-10**, arbitrary; **Q6-11**, work done by conservative forces; **Q6-12**, thermal energy; **Q6-13**, negative; **Q6-14**, near the surface of the earth; **Q6-15**, escape velocity; **Q6-16**, work is done; **Q6-17**, watt; **Q6-18**, energy; **Q6-19**, scaling.

SUPPLEMENTARY TOPICS

6.12 | RUNNING

In our discussion of jumping, we assumed that all the work done by the muscles is converted into mechanical energy and that no energy is dissipated. This cannot be true for an animal running at constant speed on flat ground. In this case the mechanical energy remains constant. However, in each stride, energy is expended by the muscles in accelerating the legs and in lifting the center of gravity of the body. This energy is dissipated as the legs slow down and the center of gravity falls. A variety of dissipative forces are involved, making any model that relies on a direct analysis based on Newton's laws very difficult to use for running.

Another kind of model proposed by a mathematician, J. B. Keller, sidesteps the details of the forces. The runner is assumed to exert a net force f that varies with the time but never exceeds a maximum force, F_{max}. The power expended by the runner is the force times the velocity, fv. A dissipative force, D, opposes the motion and is assumed to be proportional to the velocity, so $D = cv$. The runner is able to draw on an initial reserve of stored energy E_0, but once that is exhausted the speed is limited by the rate σ (assumed constant) at which additional energy is supplied by metabolic processes.

Given these assumptions, the mathematical problem is to find the force f that the runner must exert to run a given race as fast as possible. The four physiological parameters of this model—the quantities F_{max}, c, E_0, and σ—are chosen by comparing the calculated times with the men's world records for several distances. If the model then predicts many other records correctly, it can be considered successful and its physiological parameters may be of use in studying other activities.

Keller's solution to this problem states that for races shorter than 291 m, a runner should exert the maximum force F_{max} throughout the race. In longer events, he should accelerate as fast as possible for a second or two and then run at constant speed until he slows slightly in the last few steps. These results are consistent with the usual advice to maintain a steady pace. However, runners often finish long races with a burst of speed rather than by slowing down. The competitive aspects of racing may be the reason for this.

Table 6.2 gives the four physiological parameters found by comparison with the men's world records. Figure 6.24 shows that the predicted average speed-versus-distance curve agrees very well with the

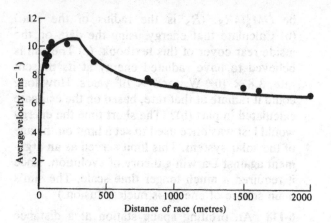

Figure 6.24. The average velocity for running races of various lengths. The dots represent average speeds for men's world records. The curve is the theoretical prediction using the values of the four parameters in Keller's model that give the best overall fit to the world records. (From Joseph B. Keller, *Physics Today*. © American Institute of Physics.)

data at all distances up to about 10,000 m. The striking initial rise and later decrease in this speed as the distance increases is correctly predicted.

The use of the physiological parameters is illustrated by the following example.

Example 6.19

The world record for the 5000-m run is 796.6 s, corresponding to an average velocity of 6.28 m s^{-1}. Find the power dissipated at this speed by a runner with a mass of 80 kg, and compare this with the rate at which additional energy is supplied by metabolic processes.

The power dissipated is $\mathcal{P}_d = Dv = (cv)v$. From Table 6.2, $c = 89.7$ N s m^{-1}, and

$$\mathcal{P}_d = cv^2 = (89.7 \text{ N s m}^{-1})(6.28 \text{ m s}^{-1})^2$$
$$= 3538 \text{ W}$$

Energy is supplied at a rate of $\sigma = 3330$ W, so the runner is expending stored energy. The difference between the power dissipated and the power supplied is 208 W. In 797 s, this corresponds to an energy expenditure of $E = (208 \text{ W})(797 \text{ s}) = 166,000$ J. This is close to the total stored energy $E_0 = 193,000$ J, indicating as expected that the runner has used nearly all his stored energy.

It remains to be seen whether this particular model correctly describes the most important features of running. In any event, it shows how a simple model incorporating energy considerations can illuminate a very complex problem.

TABLE 6.2

Physiological parameters in S.I. units for the Keller model of running for a man of mass 80 kg. These constants are all proportional to the body mass. For example, for a runner of mass 100 kg, the parameters should be multiplied by 100/80 = 1.25.

Maximum force	$F_{max} = 976$ N
Coefficient of the dissipative force	$c = 89.7$ N s m^{-1}
Stored metabolic energy	$E_0 = 193,000$ J
Rate of metabolic energy conversion	$\sigma = 3330$ W

EXERCISES ON SUPPLEMENTARY TOPICS

Section 6.12 | Running

6-127 (a) According to Keller's model, how large is the dissipative force on an 80-kg man running at 8 m s^{-1}? (b) What is his power expenditure?

6-128 Metabolizing a gram of fat yields about 8000 J of mechanical energy. If all his energy is supplied from metabolizing fat, how much does an 80-kg runner consume at 7 m s^{-1} according to Keller's model?

PROBLEMS ON SUPPLEMENTARY TOPICS

6-129 In Keller's model, the power expenditure of a runner equals the power input when $v^2 = \sigma/c$. Calculate the velocity at which this occurs, and compare it to the world record average velocity for a 5000-m race, which is 6.28 m s^{-1}.

6-130 (a) Calculate the maximum force a 60-kg runner can exert. (b) In a 2000-m race, the world record average speed is 6.64 m s^{-1}. What is the dissipative force? (c) Explain the difference.

6-131 (a) Suppose a runner exerted the maximum possible force and did not have any additional energy supply. How far could he run using his stored energy? (b) What period of time is needed for the metabolic processes to supply an amount of energy equal to the stored reserves?

Additional Reading

Donald E. Hall, The Hazards of Encountering a Black Hole, *The Physics Teacher*, vol. 23, 1985, p. 540.

Hans C. Ohanian, *Physics*, W. W. Norton & Company, New York, 1985. Interlude E, Gravity and Geometry, discusses gravitation, black holes, and related topics.

A. Z. Hendel, Solar Escape, *The American Journal of Physics*, vol. 51, 1983, p. 746. Velocity for a rocket fired from the earth to escape the solar system. A problem treated incorrectly in many textbooks.

Elmer L. Offenbacher, Physics and the Vertical Jump, *American Journal of Physics*, vol. 38, 1970, p. 829.

Sir James Gray, *How Animals Move*, Cambridge University Press, Cambridge, 1953. Pages 69–80 discuss jumping.

R. McNeill Alexander, *Animal Mechanics*, University of Washington Press, Seattle, 1968. Pages 28–33 discuss jumping.

E. F. Adolph, Quantitative Relations in the Physiological Constitutions of Mammals, *Science*, vol. 109, 1949, p. 579. Scaling in biology.

Walter R. Stahl, Similarity and Dimensional Methods in Biology, *Science*, vol. 137, 1962, p. 205.

A. Gold, Energy Expenditure in Animal Locomotion, *Science*, vol. 181, 1973, p. 275.

John Maynard Smith, *Mathematical Ideas in Biology*, Cambridge University Press, Cambridge, 1968. Scaling, running.

Joseph B. Keller, A Theory of Competitive Running, *Physics Today*, vol. 26, September 1973, p. 42.

Knut Schmidt-Nielsen, Locomotion: Energy Cost of Swimming, Flying, and Running, *Science*, vol. 177, 1972, p. 222.

Knut Schmidt-Nielsen, *How Animals Work*, Cambridge University Press, London, 1972. Applications of physical principles to physiology, scaling.

Galileo Galilei, *Dialogues Concerning Two New Sciences*, translated by Henry Crew and Alfonso de Salvio. Macmillan Publishing Company, New York, 1914; Dover Publications Inc., New York, 1954. The first discussion of scaling in biology.

David Pilbeam and Stephen Jay Gould, Size and Scaling in Human Evolution, *Science*, vol. 186, 1974, p. 892.

V. A. Tucker, The Energetic Cost of Moving About, *American Scientist*, vol. 63, 1975, p. 413. Advantages of flying, swimming, bicycling compared to walking and running.

The additional reading in Chapter Eleven includes many references to energy-related topics. *Science* and *Scientific American* print many up-to-date articles on alternative energy sources and related topics. Some articles relating to the topics mentioned in this chapter are:

George F. D. Duff, Tidal Power in the Bay of Fundy, *Technology Review*, November 1978, p. 34.

M. R. Gustavson, Limits to Wind Power Utilization, *Science*, vol. 204, April 6, 1979, p. 13.

John D. Isaacs and Walter R. Schmitt, Ocean Energy: Forms and Prospects, *Science*, vol. 207, January 18, 1980, p. 265.

G. Waring, Energy and the Automobile, *The Physics Teacher*, vol. 18, 1980, p. 494.

J. Kelly Beatty, Solar Satellites, *Science 80*, December 1980, p. 28.

Bernard L. Cohen, Cost per Million BTU of Solar Heat, Insulation, and Conventional Fuels, *The American Journal of Physics*, vol. 52, 1984, p. 614.

The following books present detailed discussions of the consequences of finite energy resources, environmental effects, and the science and technology of alternative energy sources.

Robert H. Romer, *Energy, An Introduction to Physics*, W. H. Freeman and Co., San Francisco, 1976. A basic physics text with many energy applications.

Joseph Priest, *Energy for a Technological Society*, 2nd ed., Addison-Wesley Publishing Co., Reading, Mass., 1979. Paperback.

John M. Fowler, *Energy and the Environment*, McGraw-Hill Book Co., New York, 1975. Paperback.

Energy, Readings from Scientific American, W. H. Freeman and Co., San Francisco, 1979. Paperback.

Delbert W. Devins, *Energy: Its Physical Impact on the Environment*, John Wiley & Sons, New York, 1982.

Scientific American articles:

Milton Hildebrand, How Animals Run, May 1960, p. 149.

Henry W. Ryder, Harry J. Carr, and Paul Herget, Future Performances in Footracing, June 1976, p. 109.

T. J. Dawson, Kangaroos, August 1977, p. 78. Energetics of hopping.

Charles L. Gray, Jr., and Frank von Hippel, The Fuel Economy of Light Vehicles, May 1981, p. 48.

Peter M. Moretti and Louis V. Divone, Modern Windmills, June 1986, p. 110.

David A. Greenberg, Modeling Tidal Power, November 1987, p. 128

John H. Gibbons, Peter D. Blair, and Holly L. Gwin, Strategies for Energy Use, September 1989, p. 136.

Howard G. Wilson, Paul B. MacReady, and Chester R. Kyle, Lessons of Sunraycer, March 1989, p. 90. Solar powered race car.

Jearl Walker, Thinking About Physics While Being Scared to Death (on a Falling Roller Coaster), *The Amateur Scientist*, October 1983, p. 162.

CHAPTER 7
LINEAR AND ANGULAR MOMENTUM

We have seen how energy conservation can be used in many situations to analyze the motion of both simple and complex systems. In this chapter, we introduce two other quantities that are conserved under certain conditions: *linear momentum* and *angular momentum*. Like energy conservation, the conservation of linear and of angular momentum are concepts of widespread applicability, and they are useful even in the subatomic world where Newton's laws do not hold.

Many common events can be regarded as collisions even though we may not think of them as such. A baseball player hitting or catching a ball, a blow struck in a boxing match, and the action of seat belts on passengers during an automobile accident are all examples of collisions. Although collisions are not unusual in our experience, they are difficult to analyze using the methods we have described so far in this textbook. In particular, since the forces acting during a collision are often difficult to determine, Newton's second law is hard to use directly. Furthermore, in many collisions, mechanical energy is not conserved, and the methods of energy conservation described in the previous chapter are also frustrated.

Linear momentum, which is often referred to more concisely as *momentum* when there is no chance of confusion with the angular momentum, is especially useful in dealing with collisions. The momentum of an object is the product of its mass and velocity. When two objects collide for a brief time, the momentum of each changes, but the *total* momentum of the system often remains constant, either exactly or to a very good approximation.

The change in the linear momentum of an object is very closely related to the forces on the object.

Because of this, we can sometimes find the average forces acting during a very complex event by measuring the momentum changes. The forces acting when momentum changes occur are contained in a quantity called the *impulse*.

The angular momentum of a rigid body rotating about a fixed axis is its moment of inertia times its angular velocity. Just as linear momentum conservation can be used to analyze translational motion, angular momentum conservation provides insight into complex rotational motion problems. For example, spinning figure skaters, tumbling gymnasts, and falling cats all have a constant angular momentum. This fact is important in understanding their motion.

7.1 | IMPULSE AND LINEAR MOMENTUM

With the aid of an example, we now define *impulse* and *linear momentum* and find the relationship between them. Figure 7.1 shows a man pushing a

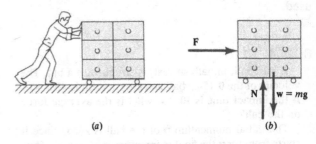

Figure 7.1. (a) A man pushes a dresser, which moves frictionlessly on casters. (b) The forces on the dresser are **F**, the weight $w = mg$, and the normal force **N**. The net force is equal to **F**.

(a)   (b)

177

dresser with casters. We will suppose that the frictional forces on the dresser are negligible. With Newton's laws, we can find a relation between the forces acting on the dresser, its velocity change, and the time the force acts.

The force **F** acts on the dresser for a time Δt. During this period the velocity of the dresser changes from **v** to **v**'. By definition, the average acceleration $\bar{a}$ is the velocity change divided by the time, $\bar{a} = (\mathbf{v}' - \mathbf{v})/\Delta t$. However, from Newton's second law, the average acceleration and net force are related by $\bar{\mathbf{F}} = m\bar{a}$, so

$$\bar{\mathbf{F}} = m\left(\frac{\mathbf{v}' - \mathbf{v}}{\Delta t}\right)$$

or

$$\bar{\mathbf{F}} \, \Delta t = m\mathbf{v}' - m\mathbf{v} \qquad (7.1)$$

The product of the average force and the time $\bar{\mathbf{F}} \, \Delta t$ is called the *impulse*. An equivalent expression is $\int \mathbf{F} \, dt$, where the integral is over the time interval Δt that the force acts. The product $m\mathbf{v}$ is the *linear momentum*,

$$\mathbf{p} = m\mathbf{v} \qquad (7.2)$$

We will refer to **p** more simply as the *momentum* only when there is no angular motion and hence no chance of confusion with the angular momentum. From its definition, the S.I. momentum unit is the kilogram metre per second (kg m s^{-1}). Equation 7.1 means that *the impulse equals the change in momentum*,

$$\bar{\mathbf{F}} \, \Delta t = \mathbf{p}' - \mathbf{p} \qquad (7.3)$$

The following example illustrates how this result is used.

Example 7.1

A baseball, initially at rest, is struck with a bat. The velocity of the 0.15-kg ball just after it is hit is 40 m s^{-1}. If the impact time is 10^{-3} s, what is the average force on the ball?

The initial momentum **p** of the ball is zero, since it starts from rest; the final momentum is $\mathbf{p}' = m\mathbf{v}'$. Thus from $\bar{\mathbf{F}} \, \Delta t = \mathbf{p}' - \mathbf{p}$, the average force $\bar{F}$ on the ball is

$$\bar{F} = \frac{mv'}{\Delta t} = \frac{(0.15 \text{ kg})(40 \text{ m s}^{-1})}{(10^{-3} \text{ s})} = 6000 \text{ N}$$

Highway Safety | Automobile accidents are complex events involving many variables. However, many questions about the safety of passengers involved in such accidents can be explored using the concepts of impulse and momentum.

To visualize what happens in an accident, suppose that a car hits a stone wall or a tree head on at an appreciable speed. The front end of the car will collapse, and the passenger compartment will come to rest in a metre or so. The time required for this to occur is typically a few tenths of a second. A passenger who is wearing a seat belt or shoulder harness will therefore come to rest in a few tenths of a second. However, an unrestrained passenger will slide forward at roughly the original speed of the car, striking the windshield or dashboard (Fig. 7.2). Such a passenger will come to rest in a very short time and experience much larger forces during the impact. The force may also be applied over a very small area, increasing the severity of the injuries. The following example illustrates the difference between the two situations.

Example 7.2

A car traveling at 10 m s^{-1} (36 km h^{-1}) collides with a tree. (a) An unrestrained passenger strikes the windshield headfirst and comes to rest in 0.002 s. The contact area between the head and windshield is 6×10^{-4} m^2, and the mass of the head is 5 kg. Find the average force and the force per unit area exerted on the head. (b) A passenger of mass 70 kg wearing a shoulder harness comes to rest in 0.2 s. The area of the harness in contact with the passenger is 0.1 m^2. Find the average force and the average force per unit area.

(a) Again we use $\bar{\mathbf{F}} \, \Delta t = \mathbf{p}' - \mathbf{p}$. The final momentum is zero, since the windshield is stationary, and the initial momentum is the head mass times the velocity.

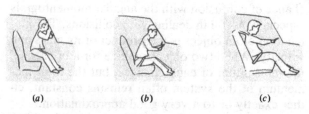

(a) (b) (c)

Figure 7.2. A passenger in a vehicle during a collision: (a) without seat belts; (b) with a lap belt only; (c) with a lap belt and shoulder harness.

Thus the magnitude of the average force is

$$\overline{F} = \frac{p}{\Delta t} = \frac{(5 \text{ kg})(10 \text{ m s}^{-1})}{0.002 \text{ s}} = 25,000 \text{ N}$$

The average force per unit area is

$$\frac{\overline{F}}{A} = \frac{25,000 \text{ N}}{6 \times 10^{-4} \text{ m}} = 4.17 \times 10^7 \text{ N m}^{-2}$$

This is a very large force per unit area and is certain to cause serious injury.

(b) The average force is found from the change in momentum of the entire body as the speed of the car changes from 10 m s^{-1} to zero. Thus the magnitude of $\overline{F}$ is

$$\overline{F} = \frac{p}{\Delta t} = \frac{(70 \text{ kg})(10 \text{ m s}^{-1})}{0.2 \text{ s}} = 3500 \text{ N}$$

This is much smaller than the force exerted on the head of the unrestrained passenger in part (a). The average force per unit area is

$$\frac{\overline{F}}{A} = \frac{3500 \text{ N}}{0.1 \text{ m}^2} = 3.5 \times 10^4 \text{ N m}^{-2}$$

Since this is smaller than the force per unit area on the unrestrained passenger by a factor 1200, the chance of serious injury is much smaller for this passenger.

Improving the safety of passengers in automobile collisions involves increasing the time over which the momentum changes or increasing the area over which the decelerating forces are applied. In the first category are improved passenger restraints and front-end designs that permit more gradual slowing of the passenger compartment. The removal of sharp objects and the use of inflatable air bags are examples of attempts to increase the contact area.

7.2 | MOMENTUM CONSERVATION

The concept of momentum is most useful when two or more objects act on one another. For example, in Fig. 7.3, we show two objects that collide. Friction is negligible, and each object experiences a gravitational force and a normal force. During the collision, they also exert forces on each other. These forces, $\mathbf{F}_{12}$ and $\mathbf{F}_{21}$, are an action–reaction pair, so they are equal and opposite and $\mathbf{F}_{12} + \mathbf{F}_{21} = 0$.

If the collision time is Δt, the change in momentum of each object can be computed from the average forces $\overline{\mathbf{F}}_{12}$ and $\overline{\mathbf{F}}_{21}$. For m_1, $\overline{\mathbf{F}}_{12} \Delta t = \mathbf{p}_1' - \mathbf{p}_1$; and for m_2, $\overline{\mathbf{F}}_{21} \Delta t = \mathbf{p}_2' - \mathbf{p}_2$. But $\overline{\mathbf{F}}_{12} + \overline{\mathbf{F}}_{21} = 0$, so if we

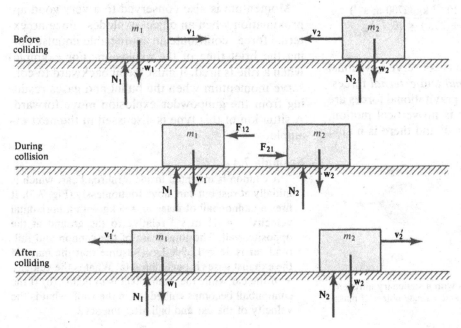

Figure 7.3. Two objects slide frictionlessly toward each other. Their initial momenta are $\mathbf{p}_1 = m_1\mathbf{v}_1$ and $\mathbf{p}_2 = m\mathbf{v}_2$. During the collision the objects exert equal and opposite forces on each other. After the collision the momenta of the two objects are $\mathbf{p}_1' = m_1\mathbf{v}_1'$ and $\mathbf{p}_2' = m_2\mathbf{v}_2'$.

add these two equations, we find

$$\mathbf{p}_1' - \mathbf{p}_1 + \mathbf{p}_2' - \mathbf{p}_2 = 0$$

or

$$\mathbf{p}_1 + \mathbf{p}_2 = \mathbf{p}_1' + \mathbf{p}_2' \qquad (7.4)$$

This equation means that the net momentum of the two objects before and after the collision is the same, or the total momentum of the system is conserved.

This is important because it means that we can relate the velocities of the objects before and after the collision *without knowing anything about the forces between them during the collision*. The fact that these forces are always equal and opposite is sufficient to obtain the result. The following example illustrates this idea.

Example 7.3

A neutron moving at 2700 m s^{-1} collides head-on with a nitrogen nucleus at rest and is absorbed. The neutron and nitrogen masses are $m = 1.67 \times 10^{-27}$ kg and $M = 23.0 \times 10^{-27}$ kg, respectively. What is the final velocity of the combined object? (Fig. 7.4).

The only forces affecting the motion during the collision are those between the neutron and nucleus. Thus the net momentum is constant. Before the collision, $p = mv$ and afterward, $p' = (m + M)v'$, where v' is the final velocity. Then $mv = (m + M)v'$, so

$$v' = \frac{mv}{m + M} = \frac{(1.67 \times 10^{-27} \text{ kg})(2700 \text{ m s}^{-1})}{(1.67 + 23.0) \times 10^{-27} \text{ kg}}$$
$$= 183 \text{ m s}^{-1}$$

To know when momentum is conserved, we must understand the role of *internal* and *external* forces. In Fig. 7.3b, the normal and gravitational forces are external forces. Since there is no vertical motion, $\mathbf{N}_1 + \mathbf{w}_1 = 0$ and $\mathbf{N}_2 + \mathbf{w}_2 = 0$, and there is no net

impulse as a result of these forces. The force $\mathbf{F}_{12}$ is an external force on m_1, and $\mathbf{F}_{21}$ is an external force on m_2. However, if m_1 and m_2 are considered as *one system*, we can say that $\mathbf{F}_{12}$ and $\mathbf{F}_{21}$ are internal forces of the system. Thus in Fig. 7.3, there is *no net external force acting on the system*. The momentum of m_1 alone is not conserved nor is that of m_2. However, the net momentum of the system is conserved.

Whenever there is no net external force acting on a system, its momentum is conserved. Momentum is therefore always conserved for an isolated system, one subjected only to internal forces.

In many situations of interest to us, the momentum is only approximately conserved because there are net external forces acting. However, the impulses resulting from these external forces are often small enough to be neglected. For example, when two cars collide, they exert huge forces on each other for a very short time, and the impulse on each is substantial. An external force such as a frictional force exerted by the road may also be present, but its magnitude is not large enough to contribute any appreciable impulse in the brief time of the collision. Hence only the internal forces between the cars are really important, and momentum conservation can be used to analyze the collision.

Momentum is also conserved to a very good approximation when an object explodes, since no external forces contribute an appreciable impulse during the brief time of the explosion. For example, when a rifle is fired, it must recoil backward to conserve momentum when the bullet and gases resulting from the gunpowder explosion move forward. A situation of this type is discussed in the next example.

Example 7.4

A cannon is mounted inside a railroad car, which is initially at rest but can move frictionlessly (Fig. 7.5). It fires a cannonball of mass $m = 5$ kg with a horizontal velocity $v = 15$ m s^{-1} relative to the ground at the opposite wall. The total mass of the cannon and railroad car is $M = 15,000$ kg. (Assume that the mass of the exhaust gases is negligible.) (a) What is the velocity V of the car while the cannonball is in flight? (b) If the cannonball becomes embedded in the wall, what is the velocity of the car and ball after impact?

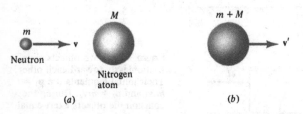

Figure 7.4. (a) A neutron collides with a stationary nitrogen atom. (b) The neutron is absorbed and a single object of mass $m + M$ is formed.

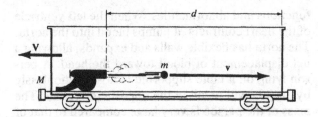

Figure 7.5. The cannon fires a ball toward the right. The cannon is mounted firmly to the floor of the railroad car.

(a) When fired, the cannon exerts a force to the right on the ball. The ball exerts an equal and opposite force on the cannon, so the car and cannon recoil to the left. The net momentum is conserved because there is no external frictional force. The momentum before firing is zero, so after firing the momentum of the ball to the right must be equal in magnitude to that of the car and cannon to the left. Thus $mv = MV$ and

$$V = \frac{mv}{M} = \frac{(5 \text{ kg})15 \text{ m s}^{-1}}{(15,000 \text{ kg})}$$
$$= 5 \times 10^{-3} \text{ m s}^{-1}$$

The recoil speed of the car and cannon is very small because of their large mass.

(b) As the ball becomes embedded in the wall, it exerts a force on the wall to the right in Fig. 7.5. The wall, in turn, exerts a force to the left on the ball. The ball and car both stop moving when this happens, since the net momentum is still zero. Meanwhile the car will have rolled to the left as the ball traveled to the right.

Often employed as an introductory physics lab experiment, the *ballistic pendulum* uses conservation laws to find the velocity of a bullet (Fig. 7.6).

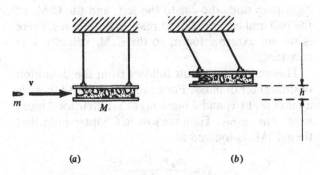

Figure 7.6. A ballistic pendulum. (*a*) A bullet stops in a block. Momentum, but not energy, is conserved. (*b*) The block plus bullet rises a distance h. Their energy, but not their momentum, is conserved.

Example 7.5

A gun is fired horizontally into a wooden block suspended by strings (Fig. 7.6). The bullet stops in the block, which rises 0.2 m. The mass of the bullet is 0.03 kg, and the mass of the block is 2 kg. (a) What was the velocity of the block just after the bullet stopped in it? (b) What was the velocity of the bullet before it struck the block?

(a) It is convenient to divide this experiment mentally into two stages. The first is the rapid "collision" of the bullet and the block; the second is the subsequent rise of the block plus the embedded bullet. The only forces acting after the collision are gravity and the tension in the string. The tension is at right angles to the motion, so it does no work. Thus the mechanical energy, the gravitational potential energy plus the kinetic energy, is conserved in the second stage as the system rises. This permits us to relate the height h reached and the velocity V just after the bullet stopped in the block.

Immediately after the bullet is imbedded in the block, their common velocity is V, and their kinetic energy is $K = \frac{1}{2}(m + M)V^2$. At the highest point reached, the kinetic energy is zero. The increase in potential energy is $(m + M)gh$. Thus

$$\tfrac{1}{2}(m + M)V^2 = (m + M)gh$$

Solving for V,

$$V = (2gh)^{1/2} = [2(9.8 \text{ m s}^{-2})(0.2 \text{ m})]^{1/2} = 1.98 \text{ m s}^{-1}$$

(b) Before the bullet strikes the block, its momentum is mv. After it comes to rest in the block, the momentum of the system is $(m + M)V$. Since momentum is conserved in the collision,

$$mv = (m + M)V$$

Hence

$$v = \frac{(m + M)V}{m}$$
$$= \frac{(0.03 \text{ kg} + 2 \text{ kg})(1.98 \text{ m s}^{-1})}{0.03 \text{ kg}}$$
$$= 134 \text{ m s}^{-1}$$

It is important to realize that momentum is a *vector quantity*, and that if the total momentum of a system is constant, each *component* must be constant. This is illustrated by the next example.

Example 7.6

A car of mass $m = 1000$ kg moving at 30 m s^{-1} collides with a car of mass $M = 2000$ kg traveling at

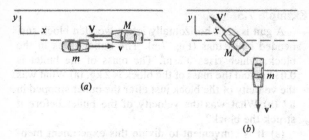

Figure 7.7. The x and y components of the total momentum of the two cars are each conserved in the collision.

20 m s^{-1} in the opposite direction. Immediately after the collision, the 1000-kg car moves at right angles to its original direction at 15 m s^{-1}. Find the velocity of the 2000-kg car right after the collision (Fig. 7.7).

Let us take the x and y axes as in Fig. 7.7. Then the x component of the total momentum of the two cars is conserved, so

$$mv_x + MV_x = mv'_x + MV'_x$$

Since $v'_x = 0$, we can solve for V'_x and substitute

$$V'_x = \frac{mv_x + MV_x}{M} = \frac{mv_x}{M} + V_x$$

$$= \frac{1000 \text{ kg}}{2000 \text{ kg}} (30 \text{ m s}^{-1}) + (-20 \text{ m s}^{-1}) = -5 \text{ m s}^{-1}$$

The initial momentum components along the y direction were zero, so $mv'_y + MV'_y = 0$, and

$$V'_y = -\frac{mv'_y}{M} = -\frac{1000 \text{ kg}}{2000 \text{ kg}} (-15 \text{ m s}^{-1}) = 7.5 \text{ m s}^{-1}$$

We see from these examples that momentum conservation is a very powerful tool for analyzing many kinds of problems. However, like energy conservation, it does have limits to what it can tell us, and we must usually have some additional information about the final state of the system. Thus in Example 7.3, we know that the neutron and nucleus move together as a single object, and in Example 7.4, we know the velocity of the cannonball. Momentum conservation by itself tells us only that the total momentum of a system is conserved in the absence of a net external force, and not how this momentum is shared among the objects in a system.

Ballistocardiography | Ballistocardiography is an application of the principle of momentum conservation to a medical problem, the study of heart functions and abnormalities. When the left ventricle of the heart contracts, it pumps blood into the aorta. The aorta has flexible walls and expands, allowing a net displacement of blood toward the head. A person lying on a table supported almost frictionlessly by air jets will recoil in the opposite direction. The mass of the person is very large compared to that of the displaced blood, so the recoil velocity is small, typically 1 millimetre per second or less. The recoil velocities change steadily, averaging out to zero over a full heart cycle. A record of these motions is called a *ballistocardiogram*. Attempts to use such measurements for diagnostic purposes have had only limited success.

7.3 MOTION OF THE CENTER OF MASS

The motion of two colliding objects or of the pieces of an exploding artillery shell may be quite complicated and hard to predict. Nevertheless, the motion of the center of mass (C.M.) of such a system is unaffected by the internal forces and is determined entirely by the external forces acting on the system. For example, when the neutron in Example 7.3 is absorbed by the nucleus, the velocity of the center of mass of the two objects is the same before and after the collision. Similarly, when the cannonball is fired in Example 7.4, the ball moves farther to the right than does the car to the left, and the C.M. of the ball and car remains at rest. In both cases, there is no net external force, so the C.M. velocity V is constant.

This important result follows from the definition of the center of mass. For example, suppose there is a mass m_1 at x_1 and a mass m_2 at x_2; their total mass is $M = m_1 + m_2$. Then we saw in Chapter Four that their C.M. is located at

$$X = \frac{m_1 x_1 + m_2 x_2}{M}$$

In a time interval Δt, x_1 changes by $v_1 \Delta t$, x_2 by $v_2 \Delta t$, and X by $V \Delta t$. These changes are related by

$$V \, \Delta t = \frac{m_1 v_1 \, \Delta t + m_2 v_2 \, \Delta t}{M}$$

Dividing by Δt and using the definition of the momentum, we have in vector notation an expression for the C.M. velocity:

$$\mathbf{V} = \frac{\mathbf{p}_1 + \mathbf{p}_2}{M} \qquad (7.5)$$

From this result, we see that when there is no net external force and the total momentum $\mathbf{p}_1 + \mathbf{p}_2$ is constant, the velocity of the center of mass remains constant. When a net external force $\mathbf{F}_{ext}$ does act on a system, the center of mass has an acceleration equal to $\mathbf{F}_{ext}/M$. Thus the center of mass moves under the influence of $\mathbf{F}_{ext}$ in exactly the same fashion as a single particle of mass M. This principle is illustrated by the following example.

Example 7.7

An artillery shell explodes in the air. Neglecting air resistance, what can be said about the subsequent motion of its fragments?

Before the explosion, the shell moves in the trajectory described in our discussion of projectiles in Chapter Two. After the explosion the fragments fly off in many directions, and we cannot determine anything about their individual paths without more information. However, their center of mass is unaffected by the internal forces of the explosion, so it continues to follow the original trajectory (Fig. 7.8). Similarly, divers or gymnasts may execute complicated maneuvers, but their centers of mass follow simple trajectories (Fig. 7.9).

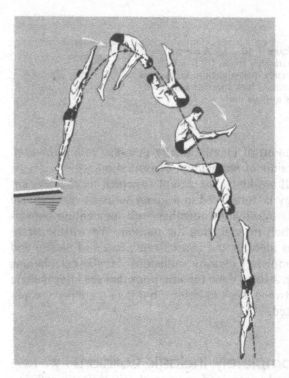

Figure 7.9. The diver's center of mass moves in a projectile trajectory after he leaves the board.

7.4 | ELASTIC AND INELASTIC COLLISIONS

In a brief collision, the total momentum is conserved, either exactly or to a very good approximation. However, mechanical energy may or may not be conserved in such situations. For example, when we drop a lively rubber ball onto a concrete floor, it rises again to nearly its original height; little mechanical energy is lost as it strikes the floor. By contrast, if we drop a ball of putty, it remains where it lands. All its kinetic energy is lost as heat or as work done in deforming the putty.

A collision that conserves mechanical energy is said to be *elastic*. If mechanical energy is not conserved, the collision is called *inelastic*. In a *completely inelastic* collision, *relative* motion ceases; the objects join and move as a single object, as when the bumpers of two vehicles lock (Fig. 7.10a). This type of collision dissipates the maximum

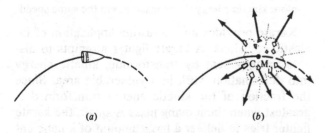

Figure 7.8. (a) The trajectory of an artillery shell. (b) The motion of the center of mass of a system is determined solely by the external forces. Therefore, the center of mass of the shell continues to follow the original trajectory after the shell explodes. None of the fragments need follow this path.

Figure 7.10. (*a*) A car strikes a stationary truck. (*b*) In a completely inelastic collision, the two vehicles lock together and move as a single unit.

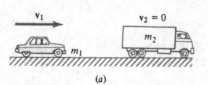

(*a*)

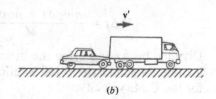

(*b*)

amount of kinetic energy possible within the constraints of momentum conservation.

If we know the extent to which mechanical energy is conserved in a given collision, we can use this information together with momentum conservation in analyzing the motion. We will illustrate this idea for the two extreme cases of elastic and completely inelastic collisions. Similar calculations can also be done for situations that are intermediate between these extremes, but they are more complicated.

Completely Inelastic Collisions | We have

already examined one completely inelastic collision in Example 7.3, where a neutron was captured by a nitrogen nucleus. We now study such collisions in more detail.

In a completely inelastic collision, the amount of mechanical energy lost to heat and deformation work depends on the relative masses of the two objects. For example, suppose a car of mass m_1 and velocity v_1 strikes a stationary truck of mass m_2 and they move together afterward (Fig. 7.10). The ratio of the final and initial kinetic energies is

$$\frac{K'}{K_1} = \frac{\frac{1}{2}(m_1 + m_2)v'^2}{\frac{1}{2}m_1 v_1^2}$$

Momentum conservation requires $m_1 v_1 = (m_1 + m_2)v'$, or $v' = m_1 v_1/(m_1 + m_2)$. With this expression for v', we find

$$K' = \left(\frac{m_1}{m_1 + m_2}\right) K_1 \qquad \text{(totally inelastic (7.6) collision)}$$

This result implies that the final kinetic energy is small when the moving mass m_1 is small compared to the stationary mass m_2; most of the kinetic energy is lost in the collision. This result is illustrated by the next example.

Example 7.8

(a) A 1000-kg car traveling at 10 m s^{-1} hits a stopped truck of mass 9000 kg, and the vehicles lock together (Fig. 7.10). How much kinetic energy is lost? (b) If instead the truck is initially moving at 10 m s^{-1} and the car is stationary, how much kinetic energy is dissipated?

(a) The kinetic energy of the car before the collision is $K_1 = \frac{1}{2}m_1 v_1^2 = \frac{1}{2}(1000 \text{ kg})(10 \text{ m s}^{-1})^2 = 5 \times 10^4$ J. After the collision, the total kinetic energy of the vehicles is

$$K' = \left(\frac{m_1}{m_1 + m_2}\right)K_1$$

$$= \frac{(1000 \text{ kg})(5 \times 10^4 \text{ J})}{(1000 + 9000) \text{ kg}} = 5 \times 10^3 \text{ J}$$

Thus the kinetic energy dissipated is

$$K_1 - K' = (5 \times 10^4 \text{ J}) - (5 \times 10^3 \text{ J}) = 4.5 \times 10^4 \text{ J}$$

Ninety percent of the kinetic energy is dissipated.

(b) Now $K_1 = \frac{1}{2}(9000 \text{ kg})(10 \text{ m s}^{-1})^2 = 4.5 \times 10^5$ J, and

$$K' = \frac{(9000 \text{ kg})(4.5 \times 10^5 \text{ J})}{(9000 + 1000) \text{ kg}} = 4.05 \times 10^5 \text{ J}$$

Hence $K_1 - K' = (4.5 \times 10^5 \text{ J}) - (4.05 \times 10^5 \text{ J}) = 4.5 \times 10^4$ J. Since this equals the kinetic energy dissipated in part (a), the collisions are equally destructive. However, here only 10 percent of the kinetic energy is dissipated because the more massive truck has much more kinetic energy than the car has at the same speed.

Karate provides an interesting application of inelastic collisions. A karate fighter attempts to disable an opponent by transforming kinetic energy into deformation work in a vulnerable area. Since the fraction of the kinetic energy transformed is greatest when the moving mass is small, the karate fighter tries to deliver a large amount of kinetic energy with a relatively small part of his or her body, such as an arm. An arm strike (Fig. 7.11) is aimed so that the fist makes contact at the instant of most rapid motion, which occurs when the arm is about

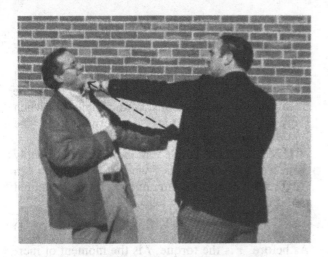

Figure 7.11. A forward punch in karate. The dashed line shows the path of the fist. (Courtesy of M. Sternheim)

70 percent extended (Fig. 7.12). Stepping forward increases the velocity and hence the kinetic energy at impact. Karate experts seldom follow through after a blow. Contact made during the follow-through of a wide swing involves lower speeds and larger body masses; there is less deformation work and a risk of a loss of balance.

Elastic Collisions | After two objects collide elastically, they may move in various directions. If we know the direction of either object, we can use energy and momentum conservation to calculate both

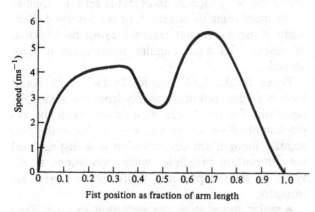

Figure 7.12. The speed of the fist versus the fractional arm extension in a forward karate punch. The data are taken from the study of high-speed motion pictures. (From J. D. Walker, *American Journal of Physics*, vol. 43, October 1975, p. 845.)

final velocity vectors. The procedure is straightforward in principle, but the results are complicated in appearance and are not very easy to interpret, except in special cases.

Fortunately, a number of general features can be seen in one such case: a head-on elastic collision of a moving object and a stationary object, with both objects moving afterward either parallel or opposite to the original direction of motion (Fig. 7.13). Applying the momentum conservation to this situation,

$$m_1 v_1 = m_1 v_1' + m_2 v_2' \tag{7.7}$$

Since the collision is elastic, $K_1 = K_1' + K_2'$, or

$$\tfrac{1}{2} m_1 v_1^2 = \tfrac{1}{2} m_1 v_1'^2 + \tfrac{1}{2} m_2 v_2'^2 \tag{7.8}$$

If we solve Eq. 7.7 for v_1' and substitute this result in Eq. 7.8, we can find v_2' after several lines of algebra. We then obtain for the kinetic energies

$$K_1' = \frac{(m_1 - m_2)^2}{(m_1 + m_2)^2} K_1 \tag{7.9}$$

$$K_2' = \frac{4 m_1 m_2}{(m_1 + m_2)^2} K_1 \tag{7.10}$$

These results hold for any masses m_1 and m_2. When $m_1 = m_2$, we get $K_1' = 0$ and $K_2' = K_1$. This result is familiar to billiard players: a cue ball comes to rest when it hits a stationary ball head on, and all the kinetic energy is transferred to the struck ball. By contrast, when the masses are very different, little energy is transferred no matter which of the objects is initially in motion. This is true for any elastic collision, not just the special head-on case considered here. The next example illustrates one elastic head-on collision.

Example 7.9

A neutron of mass m and velocity v_1 has an elastic head-on collision with a carbon nucleus of mass $12m$. (a) What fraction of the neutron's kinetic energy is transferred to the carbon nucleus? (b) What are the

Figure 7.13. (a) Before an elastic head-on collision of a moving and a stationary object. (b) Motion after the collision.

velocities of the neutron and the carbon nucleus after the collision?

(a) Using Eq. 7.10 with $m_1 = m$ and $m_2 = 12m$,

$$K_2' = \frac{4m_1m_2}{(m_1 + m_2)^2} K_1 = \frac{4m(12m)}{(m + 12m)^2} K_1$$

$$\frac{K_2'}{K_1} = \frac{48}{13^2} = 0.284$$

The carbon nucleus has acquired 28.4 percent of the kinetic energy, so the neutron still retains 71.6 percent of its initial energy.

(b) From part (a),

$$\frac{K_2'}{K_1} = \frac{\frac{1}{2}m_2v_2'^2}{\frac{1}{2}m_1v_1^2} = \frac{48}{13^2}$$

Substituting $m_1 = m$ and $m_2 = 12m$, we find

$$v_2'^2 = \frac{4v_1^2}{13^2}$$

and

$$v_2' = \frac{2}{13} v_1$$

We choose the positive square root for v_2', since the nucleus moves forward when struck by the neutron, not backward or opposite to v_1. Then using $m_1v_1 = m_1v_1' + m_2v_2'$, we find

$$v_1' = v_1 - \frac{m_2}{m_1} v_2'$$

$$= v_1 - \frac{12m}{m} \left(\frac{2v_1}{13}\right) = -\frac{11}{13} v_1$$

The neutron has reversed its direction, and its speed is $(11/13)v_1$. This reversal always happens in a head-on collision when the moving object is less massive than the stationary target.

In nuclear reactors, a neutron from the fission of a uranium nucleus must be slowed by a *moderator* before it can be captured by another uranium nucleus and cause this nucleus to fission as the next step in a *chain reaction*. Carbon in the form of graphite is sometimes used as a moderator, but water is much more common. Each water molecule contains two hydrogen nuclei (protons) plus an oxygen nucleus. Since the proton mass differs from the neutron mass by only 0.1 percent, protons are ideal for slowing neutrons.

7.5 | ANGULAR MOMENTUM OF A RIGID BODY

We have seen that when there is no net external force acting on an object or a system of objects, the linear momentum is conserved. Similarly, when there is no net torque due to external forces, the *angular momentum* is conserved.

This important result can be obtained readily from Newton's second law when it is written, as in Chapter Five, in the form convenient for rotational motion,

$$\tau = I\alpha \tag{7.11}$$

As before, τ is the torque, I is the moment of inertia, and α is the angular acceleration. If the angular velocity of an object rotating about a fixed axis changes from ω to ω' in a time Δt, the angular acceleration is $\alpha = (\omega' - \omega)/\Delta t$. Substituting this expression for α in Eq. 7.11 and multiplying by Δt, we have

$$\tau \Delta t = I\omega' - I\omega \tag{7.12}$$

We define the *angular momentum* by

$$L = I\omega \tag{7.13}$$

Then Eq. 7.12 becomes

$$\tau \Delta t = L' - L \tag{7.14}$$

This result states that the *angular impulse* $\tau \Delta t$ equals the change in the angular momentum $L' - L$. When the net torque on an object is zero, its angular momentum remains constant, or is conserved. Similarly, if there is no net external torque on a system of objects, its total angular momentum is conserved.

These results look simple. In fact, they could have been guessed immediately from the analogous equations for the linear momentum, with the replacements $F \rightarrow \tau$, $m \rightarrow I$, $v \rightarrow \omega$. Nevertheless, angular momentum conservation is a distinct and very important principle, with applications as diverse as atomic physics, figure skating, and astronomy.

Angular momentum conservation can be illustrated quite readily. Suppose you spin on a stool that has well-lubricated bearings. The friction is small, as is the torque tending to change the angular momentum. If you spin with your arms and legs folded and then extend them, your moment of inertia increases. Since the angular momentum $L = I\omega$ is nearly constant, the angular velocity ω decreases. Conversely, if you initially spin with your limbs extended and then bring them closer to the rotation axis, your angular velocity increases. This is precisely what a figure skater does: she starts a spin with her limbs extended and then increases her angular velocity by pulling her limbs closer to her body (Fig. 7.14).

In both these examples the angular momentum is conserved, but there is a change in the rotational kinetic energy. When the limbs are extended or retracted, there are equal and opposite forces acting on the body and limbs. These two forces produce no net torque, but they each do work. Thus, when we retract our limbs to spin faster, we do work, increasing our kinetic energy. This energy change is calculated in the following example.

Example 7.10

A figure skater begins to spin at 3π rad s^{-1} with her arms extended. (a) If her moment of inertia with arms folded is 60 percent of that with arms extended, what is her angular velocity when she folds her arms? (b) What is the fractional change in her kinetic energy?

(a) If we assume that the ice is nearly frictionless, angular momentum is conserved: $I'\omega' = I\omega$. With $I' = 0.6I$ and $\omega = 3\pi$ rad s^{-1}, we have

$$\omega' = \frac{I\omega}{I'} = \frac{3\pi \text{ rad s}^{-1}}{0.6} = 5\pi \text{ rad s}^{-1}$$

(b) Her initial and final kinetic energies are $K = \frac{1}{2}I\omega^2$ and $K' = \frac{1}{2}I'\omega'^2$. To find the fractional change, we compute

$$\frac{\Delta K}{K} = \frac{K' - K}{K}$$

$$= \frac{\frac{1}{2}(0.6I)(5\pi \text{ rad s}^{-1})^2 - \frac{1}{2}I(3\pi \text{ rad s}^{-1})^2}{\frac{1}{2}I(3\pi \text{ rad s}^{-1})^2}$$

$$= \frac{2}{3}$$

Figure 7.14. A figure skater can increase her angular speed by folding her arms. (Peter Kramer / NBC / NBCU Photo Bank / Getty Images, Inc.)

The skater increases her kinetic energy by 67 percent when she folds her arms. This is equal to the work she has to do to bring her arms in.

Conservation of angular momentum does *not* mean that the angular position of an object must remain the same in the absence of external torques. One example of this is given in Fig. 7.15, where a man rotates his swivel chair by executing a suitable sequence of moments.

A more interesting example of this principle is provided by a falling cat, which can always land on its feet if the fall is long enough. Looking at Fig. 7.16, in (b) the cat prepares to turn about a horizontal axis by drawing the front paws close to this axis, diminishing the moment of inertia of the fore part. The hind legs are left extended, so the rear part has a larger moment of inertia. In (c) the cat rotates the fore part in one direction and the rear part in the opposite direction as required by angular momentum conservation. In (d) the fore legs are extended and the hind legs drawn in, so the rear portion has the smaller moment of inertia. Thus in (e) the cat rotates the hind portion with relatively little counterrotation of the fore part.

Like figure skaters, divers—as well as astronauts floating in spaceships and gymnasts—can twist or spin. This is a rotation about an axis passing through their centers of mass and extending from

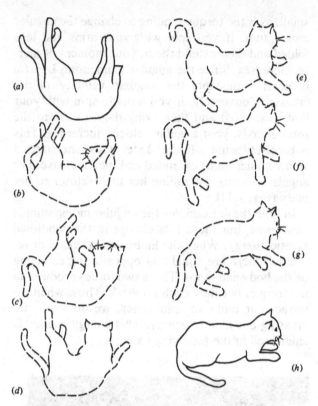

Figure 7.16. The sequence of motions performed by a cat falling from rest when initially upside down. The sketches are from photos at $\frac{1}{20}$-s intervals. The motions are described in the text. (Adapted from Tricker and Tricker.)

the head to the toes. In addition, they can somersault or rotate about an axis through their C.M. from one side to the other, and they can change their moments of inertia about *either* axis. Once in the air, a diver is not subjected to any torques about the C.M., so his or her *total* angular momentum is constant. However, there can be an interchange between the angular momenta associated with twisting and somersaulting. An understanding of angular momentum conservation has aided athletes and coaches in developing increasingly complex maneuvers.

7.6 | ANGULAR MOMENTUM OF A PARTICLE

The angular momentum of a particle (Fig. 7.17a) is defined to be the vector cross product of its distance

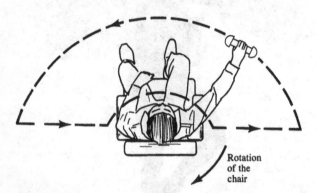

Figure 7.15. Top view of a person sitting in a swivel chair that turns easily. If an arm is moved repeatedly along the dashed path, the swivel chair gradually rotates clockwise. The chair is in motion only when the hand is moving along the circular parts of the path, since the hand's angular momentum is zero when moving along a line through the axis of rotation. Holding a heavy weight in the hand makes the chair rotate faster.

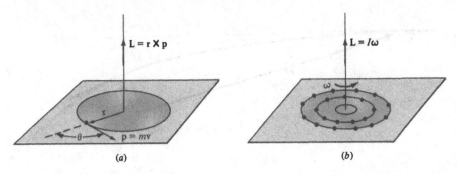

Figure 7.17. (a) The angular momentum of a particle is **L = r × p**. (b) The total angular momentum of a system of particles rotating about a common center is the sum of the individual angular momenta. This sum is equivalent to **L = Iω**.

r from a specified point and its linear momentum **p** = *m***v**:

$$\mathbf{L} = \mathbf{r} \times \mathbf{p} \qquad (7.15)$$

The magnitude of **L** is $rp \sin \theta$. When **r** and **p** are perpendicular, $\sin \theta = 1$, and $L = rp = rmv$. Its direction is given by the right-hand rule and is perpendicular to **r** and **p**.

This definition of **L** is equivalent to that given earlier, **L** = *I*ω, if we consider a system of particles rotating about a common center (Fig. 7.17b). If a particle of mass *m* moves in a circle of radius *r* with a velocity $v = r\omega$, then its angular momentum has a magnitude $rmv = rm(r\omega) = (mr^2)\omega$ and is directed along ω. Summing over all the particles, ω is the same for each and we get the total of the mr^2 terms. Since this total is the moment of inertia *I*, the total angular momentum is *I*ω, as expected.

The basic result of the preceding section, $\tau \, \Delta t = \mathbf{L}' - \mathbf{L}$, applies not only to a rigid body but to a single particle as well. Hence when there is no net torque on a particle about a given point, its angular momentum relative to that point is conserved.

For example, from the discussion in Section 7.3, the motion of the earth about the sun can be found by considering the earth as a single particle located at its C.M. The line of action of the gravitational force exerted by the sun passes through the center of the sun, so there is no torque about that point. Consequently, the angular momentum of the earth relative to the center of the sun is constant. The earth's orbit is almost circular, but not quite; it is actually an ellipse, with the earth–sun distance varying by about 3 percent between its extremes. We see that although *r*, *v*, and *θ* may change, the product $L = mrv \sin \theta$ must remain constant throughout the motion (Fig. 7.18).

The gravitational force the sun exerts on the earth is a *central force*, a force that points toward or away from a fixed central point. Other central forces are the gravitational force a planet exerts on a satellite or a meteor and the electric force an atomic nucleus exerts on a proton or electron. In all these situations, the line of action of the force passes through a central point. No torque is exerted about this point, and the angular momentum about it is conserved.

In general, finding the detailed motion of an object subjected to a central force is complicated. However, using angular momentum and energy conservation simplifies the analysis. For example, suppose an object of mass *m* approaches a planet, and we ignore the effects of other planets and the sun (Fig. 7.19). Its speed far from the planet is v_0, and its *impact parameter* is *b*: it would miss the planet by a distance *b* if it were not deflected.

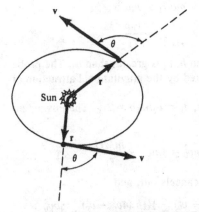

Figure 7.18. The angular momentum of the earth, $mvr \sin \theta$, is constant as it moves about the sun. The orbit is an ellipse, with the sun at one focal point. The earth–sun distance varies by 3 percent between its extremes.

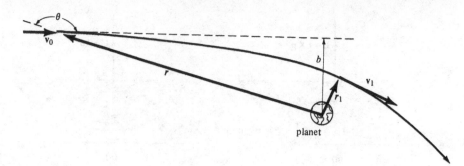

Figure 7.19. A spaceship approaches a planet. If the gravitational force were somehow turned off, it would follow the dashed trajectory. Its shortest distance from the center of the planet would then be the impact parameter b.

The initial angular momentum is $L = rp \sin \theta = mv_0(r \sin \theta)$. Since $r \sin \theta = b$, the angular momentum is

$$L = mv_0b \qquad (7.16)$$

The angular momentum has this value throughout the motion. The sum of the kinetic and potential energies is also constant. These conservation laws are used in the next example.

Example 7.11

A space probe has a speed v_0 far from a planet and an impact parameter b. Neglect the effects of other astronomical bodies. (a) If the probe's shortest distance from the planet is r_1, what is its speed at that point? (b) If $r_1 = \frac{1}{2}b$, what is the mass of the planet?

(a) The initial angular momentum is $L = mv_0b$. At the point of closest approach, the velocity $\mathbf{v}_1$ is perpendicular to $\mathbf{r}_1$, so the angular momentum is $mvr \sin \theta = mv_1r_1$. Angular momentum is conserved by the central gravitational pull of the planet on the probe. Thus

$$mv_1r_1 = mv_0b$$

$$v_1 = \frac{v_0b}{r_1}$$

Since r_1 is less than b, v_1 is greater than v_0. The probe has been accelerated by the gravitational attraction of the planet.

(b) With $r = \frac{1}{2}b$, $v_1 = v_0b/\frac{1}{2}b = 2v_0$. Then using energy conservation,

$$\tfrac{1}{2}mv_0^2 = \tfrac{1}{2}mv_1^2 - \frac{mMG}{r_1}$$

Solving for M, m cancels out, and

$$M = \frac{\frac{1}{2}r_1(v_1^2 - v_0^2)}{G} = \frac{\frac{1}{2}(\frac{1}{2}b)(4v_0^2 - v_0^2)}{G} = \frac{\frac{3}{4}bv_0^2}{G}$$

Observation of the motion of the probe has allowed us to determine the mass of the planet.

The total angular momentum of the earth is composed of two parts. Its *orbital angular momentum* is associated with the annual revolution of the earth about the sun, and its *spin angular momentum* arises from the daily rotation of the earth about its axis. Similarly, an electron in an atom has both an orbital angular momentum, due to its motion around the nucleus, and a spin angular momentum. In the absence of any torques, these angular momenta are conserved. Angular momentum considerations play an important role in the description of atomic properties.

SUMMARY

If a net average force $\overline{\mathbf{F}}$ acts for a time Δt on an object, then

$$\overline{\mathbf{F}} \, \Delta t = \mathbf{p}' - \mathbf{p}$$

The product of the average force and the time during which it acts is called the impulse. The linear momentum $\mathbf{p}$ of an object with mass m and velocity $\mathbf{v}$ is $\mathbf{p} = m\mathbf{v}$. The impulse equals the change in the momentum.

When two objects collide, each suffers a change in momentum. However, the total momentum is constant or conserved if no net external force acts on the two objects. Consequently, the total momentum of an isolated system is always conserved. Momentum conservation is particularly useful in collision problems, even though energy may or may not be conserved.

When there is no net external force acting on an object or a system of objects, the total momentum is constant and the velocity of the center of mass remains constant. When there is a net external force, the center of mass moves under its influence in exactly the same way as a single particle with a mass equal to the total mass of the object or objects.

Collisions that conserve mechanical energy are called elastic; those that do not are called inelastic. In a completely inelastic collision, all relative motion ceases and the objects subsequently move together. When an object with a small mass collides completely inelastically with an object with a large mass that is at rest, most of the mechanical energy is dissipated as heat or deformation work. A much smaller fraction of the mechanical energy is dissipated when the larger object is in motion and the smaller is initially at rest. In elastic collisions, the greatest kinetic energy transfer occurs when the two masses are equal.

The angular momentum of a rigid body rotating about a fixed axis is $L = I\omega$. The angular momentum of a particle is $L = r \times p$. The two definitions are equivalent for a system of particles rotating about a common center. If a net torque τ acts for a time Δt, then

$$\tau \, \Delta t = L' - L$$

The angular impulse equals the change in angular momentum. If the net torque on a system is zero, its angular momentum is conserved. Angular momentum is conserved if only a central force acts on an object.

Checklist
Define or explain:

impulse
momentum
collision
momentum conser-
 vation
ballistocardiography
center of mass motion
elastic collision
inelastic collision
completely inelastic
 collision
angular impulse

angular momentum of a
 rigid body
angular momentum
 conservation
external torques
angular momentum of a
 particle
orbital angular
 momentum
spin angular momentum
central force
impact parameter

REVIEW QUESTIONS

Q7-1   The impulse is the product of the _____ and the _____.

Q7-2   The impulse equals the _____.

Q7-3   Momentum is the product of the _____ and _____ of an object.

Q7-4   Momentum is usually conserved in brief collisions because the impulse due to _____ is negligible.

Q7-5   The total momentum of a system is constant if the _____.

Q7-6   If the momentum of a system is conserved, each _____ of the momentum vector is constant.

Q7-7   The center of mass of a system moves like a particle with a mass equal to _____ subjected to the _____.

Q7-8   A completely inelastic collision dissipates the _____ mechanical energy consistent with momentum conservation.

Q7-9   In an elastic collision, _____ mechanical energy is dissipated.

Q7-10   In inelastic collisions, mechanical energy is transformed into _____ and _____.

Q7-11   The angular momentum of a rigid body rotating about a fixed axis is _____.

Q7-12   The angular momentum of a particle relative to a point is _____.

Q7-13   The angular momentum of a system is constant when there is no _____.

EXERCISES

Section 7.1 | Impulse and Linear Momentum

7-1   In a collision, a 1500-kg automobile initially moving at 30 m s^{-1} comes to a stop in 0.1 s. What is the average force on the car during the crash?

7-2   A baseball bat is in contact with a 0.15-kg baseball for 0.00135 s. The ball reverses direction, and its speed changes from 40 m s^{-1} to 50 m s^{-1}. Find the average force on (a) the ball; (b) the bat.

7-3   A golf ball initially at rest is struck with an average force of 2600 N for 1.25×10^3 s. What is the final velocity of the 0.047-kg ball?

7-4   If the momentum of a car increases by 9×10^4 kg m s^{-1} in 12 s, what is the average force accelerating the car?

7-5   A batter hits a baseball of mass m, traveling at a velocity v, directly back toward the pitcher at the same speed. If the ball and bat are in contact for a time Δt, what is the average force exerted by the bat?

7-6 A rubber ball of mass m is thrown against a wall at a speed v and rebounds with the same speed in the opposite direction. (a) How large is the impulse acting on the ball? (b) A ball of putty with the same mass and speed is thrown against the wall and sticks to it. How large is the impulse acting on the ball?

7-7 Why does a hunter press a rifle tightly against his shoulder before firing?

7-8 Air bags inflate very rapidly when a car is in a collision. Give some reasons why they may or may not be better safety devices than harnesses.

Section 7.2 | Momentum Conservation

7-9 A man finds that his weight as indicated on a sensitive scale jiggles slightly no matter how still he attempts to stand. Someone feeling his pulse observes that it is synchronized with the jiggles. What is the cause of these apparent weight fluctuations?

7-10 A man sits on a chair fixed to a cart that is initially at rest on frictionless rails. (a) If he throws a sandbag off the side of the cart, will the cart move? Explain. (b) If he throws a sandbag off the back of the cart, will the cart move? Explain.

7-11 A person seated at the stern of a sailboat attempts to move forward by blowing on the sails. Explain what will happen.

7-12 A rocket of mass M explodes into two pieces just as it reaches its maximum height. Its velocity just before the explosion is v_0. One piece of mass m_1 *stops and then falls* vertically toward the earth. What is the velocity of the other piece of mass m_2 just after the rocket separates?

7-13 A cart of mass m on a frictionless air track has an initial velocity $\mathbf{v}_0$ toward a cart of mass M that is at rest. What are the final velocities of the two carts after they collide if the carts lock together?

7-14 A 1-g $= 10^{-3}$-kg bullet has a horizontal velocity of 200 m s^{-1}. It strikes and becomes embedded in a 1-kg block of wood that rests on a frictionless table top. What is the velocity of the block and bullet after impact?

7-15 A truck of mass 4500 kg moving at 10 m s^{-1} strikes the back of a car that is at rest. The car and occupants have a mass of 950 kg. (a) What is the speed of the car just after impact if the car and truck lock together? (b) If the impact lasts 0.3 s, what is the average force on a 60-kg passenger in the car?

7-16 The engine of a motorboat fails, the boat coming to rest in still water with its bow pointed toward the shore 5 m away. Its disgusted operator hurls a six-pack of beverages horizontally from the stern at a speed of 12 m s^{-1} relative to the water. The mass of the boat plus operator is 240 kg, and that of the six-pack is 3 kg. (a) What is the recoil velocity of the boat? (b) How long would it take the boat to reach the shore at this velocity? (c) Will it actually reach the shore in this time? Explain.

7-17 When the left ventricle of the heart contracts, there is a net displacement of blood toward the head. Suppose a person lies on a horizontal table that can move frictionlessly and that is initially at rest. In a contraction lasting 0.2 s, 0.8 kg of blood is pumped 0.1 m. The mass of the person plus table is 80 kg. What is the velocity of the person and table at the end of the contraction?

7-18 Is momentum conserved when a ball of putty hits a floor? Explain.

7-19 An object collides with a stationary object of the same mass. After the collision, the first object is deflected by an angle θ from its original direction, and the two objects are observed to have the same speed. Find the angle ϕ between the direction of the second object and the original direction of the first object.

7-20 A 2000-kg car and a 1000-kg car traveling at 40 m s^{-1} in opposite directions collide head-on and lock together. What are their speed and direction right after the collision?

7-21 Suppose a large meteor with a mass of 10^{10} kg and a velocity of 2×10^4 m s^{-1} were to hit the earth and disintegrate. (a) With what velocity would the earth recoil? (Use the solar and terrestrial data on the inside back cover.) (b) What fraction of the earth's orbital velocity about the sun does this recoil velocity represent?

7-22 A car traveling north at 30 m s^{-1} has a

mass of 1500 kg. It hits a car of mass 1000 kg, and they both come immediately to rest. What was the speed and direction of the other car just before the collision?

7-23 A car is traveling at a velocity **v**. It is struck from behind by a car of the same mass with a velocity 2**v**. If the cars lock together, what will their velocity be after the collision?

Section 7.3 | Motion of the Center of Mass

7-24 A man with a mass of 70 kg is seated at the center of a stationary canoe of mass 30 kg. If he moves to a seat 2 m forward in the canoe, how far will the canoe move?

7-25 The moon does not rotate about the earth; rather, they both rotate about a common point. (a) What is that point called? (b) What is the radius of the circular path of the earth about that point? (Use the solar and terrestrial data on the inside back cover.)

7-26 An 80-kg man stands on a 120-kg raft that is initially at rest. If the man starts to walk relative to the raft at 1.5 m s^{-1}, how fast will the raft move?

7-27 In Example 7.3, what fraction of the kinetic energy of the system is lost when the neutron is absorbed?

7-28 (a) How much kinetic energy is lost when the bullet lodges in the block in Example 7.5? (b) How much momentum is lost by the bullet and block when they rise a distance h? (c) What has happened to this momentum?

Section 7.4 | Elastic and Inelastic Collisions

7-29 A 1000-kg car moving at 20 m s^{-1} hits a 2000-kg parked car head on. How much mechanical energy is dissipated if the collision is (a) elastic; (b) completely inelastic?

7-30 A ship of mass m and speed v strikes a stationary iceberg of mass 10m. Find the resulting velocity of the iceberg if (a) the collision is completely inelastic; (b) the collision is elastic and the ship bounces off with its direction reversed.

7-31 One of the disadvantages of using the protons in water molecules to slow neutrons in a reactor is that occasionally a proton will capture a neutron when they collide, forming a *deuteron, a heavy hydrogen,* or *deuterium,* nucleus. If the proton is originally at rest when it captures a neutron, what is the ratio of the kinetic energy of the resulting deuteron to that of the neutron? (Take the proton and neutron masses to be half that of the deuteron.)

7-32 The molecules in heavy water contain an oxygen atom plus two atoms of *heavy hydrogen* or *deuterium.* A deuterium nucleus has a mass twice that of a neutron. (a) What fraction of its kinetic energy is transferred when a neutron strikes a stationary deuterium nucleus head-on and collides elastically? (b) What is the ratio of the initial and final neutron velocities in such a collision? (Heavy water is used as a moderator in several nuclear power plants that have been built in Canada.)

Section 7.5 | Angular Momentum of a Rigid Body

7-33 A metrestick with a hole at one end is hung from a nail. The stick is displaced from its equilibrium position, and it swings back and forth. Is its angular momentum about the nail constant? Explain.

7-34 A torque of 100 N m is applied to a wheel with a moment of inertia of 5 kg m^2. (a) What is the resulting angular acceleration? (b) If the wheel is initially at rest, how many rotations will it make in the first 3 s?

7-35 A bicycle wheel has a radius of 0.36 m, and the bicycle is moving at 6 m s^{-1}. The mass of the wheel is 2 kg. (a) What is the angular velocity of the wheel? (b) Assuming the mass of the wheel is entirely at its edge, find its angular momentum.

7-36 An acrobat holds a long pole and walks on a tightrope. (a) Using angular momentum arguments, explain which way he should tip the pole if he starts tipping toward the right side. (b) What effect will weights at the ends of the pole have?

7-37 A tricycle wheel has a moment of inertia of 0.04 kg m^2. If the wheel rotates once per second, what is its angular momentum?

7-38 A 3-kg cylinder of radius 0.2 m is rotating about its axis at 40 rad s^{-1}. Find the angular momentum if the cylinder is (a) solid; (b) a thin shell.

7-39 Why does a girl walking on the top of a fence keep her arms outstretched?

7-40 A car is at rest with the engine idling. If

the accelerator is suddenly depressed, the left side of the car drops slightly and the right side rises. Which way is the crankshaft turning?

7-41   Why must a single-engine plane be trimmed for normal horizontal flight by raising one wing flap, or aileron, and lowering the opposite one? Is this necessary in planes with two engines?

7-42   A grinding wheel has a moment of inertia of 0.5 kg m² and an angular velocity of 120 rad s⁻¹. (a) What is its angular momentum? (b) A tool is pressed against the wheel, and it comes to a stop in 10 s. What is the average torque due to the tool? (Assume no other torques act on the wheel.)

7-43   A flywheel of mass 500 kg and radius of gyration of 0.5 m rotates at 1000 rad s⁻¹. How long can it exert a torque of 250 N m on a shaft?

7-44   A diver leaves a springboard with his body extended, somersaulting at 3 rad s⁻¹. If he bends into a tuck position, his moment of inertia decreases by a factor of 5. (a) By what factor will his angular velocity change? (b) By what factor will his rotational kinetic energy change?

7-45   A woman with her arms outstretched has a moment of inertia of 2 kg m². She rotates on a stool at an angular velocity of 6 rad s⁻¹. At a certain instant she grabs a 3-kg object in each hand, holding them 0.8 m from the axis of rotation. If the objects are initially at rest, what is her angular velocity?

Section 7.6 | Angular Momentum of a Particle

7-46   In a cyclotron, protons move in circular orbits of radius 2 m at 10⁷ m s⁻¹. Find their (a) linear momentum; (b) angular momentum relative to the center of their orbits.

7-47   A binary star system contains two stars that move about each other. Does a planet moving about these two stars have a constant angular momentum? Explain.

7-48   Do objects moving under the influence of electrical forces always have constant angular momentum? Explain.

7-49   Vanguard I, an early artificial earth satellite, moved in an elliptical orbit about the earth. The greatest distance of the satellite from the center of the earth was 1.03×10^7 m, and the mini-

mum distance was 7.02×10^6 m. If its velocity at the greatest distance from the earth was 5600 m s⁻¹, find its velocity at the closest approach.

7-50   A proton is accelerated to a velocity of 3×10^7 m s⁻¹. It approaches a nucleus with an impact parameter of 5×10^{-15} m. However, the electrical repulsion of the protons in the nucleus deflects it, so that at its closest approach it is 7×10^{-15} m away. What is its velocity at this point?

7-51   The motion of the earth about the sun has constant angular momentum relative to an origin at the sun. (More exactly, is constant relative to the C.M. of the earth and the sun.) Is the angular momentum of the earth relative to another origin constant? Explain.

7-52   Calculate (a) the orbital and (b) the spin angular momenta of the earth. (Use the solar and terrestrial data on the inside back cover and assume the earth is a uniformly dense sphere.)

7-53   An artificial satellite moves in an elliptical orbit with the earth at one focal point (Fig. 7-20). At point A, its speed is v and its distance from the center of the earth is r. At point B, its distance from the center of the earth is $2r$. What is its speed?

7-54   In Bohr's model of the hydrogen atom, the electron in its smallest circular orbit has an angular momentum of 1.055×10^{-34} kg m² s⁻¹. The radius of the orbit is 5.29×10^{-11} m, and the mass of the electron is 9.11×10^{-31} kg. (a) What is the speed v of the electron? (b) Find the ratio v/c, where $c = 3.00 \times 10^8$ m s⁻¹ is the speed of light.

7-55   Meteor Crater in Arizona was formed when a 2×10^9-kg meteorite struck the earth at a speed of about 10^4 m s⁻¹. Find (a) the change in the velocity of the earth, assuming the collision was inelastic; (b) the kinetic energy dissipated in joules and in kilotons of TNT (1 kiloton TNT = 4.2×10^9 J).

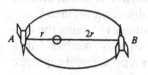

Figure 7.20.   Exercise 7-53.

7-56 Complete the derivation of Eqs. 7.9 and 7.10.

PROBLEMS

7-57 A 1000-kg car and a 2000-kg truck are each moving at 20 m s^{-1} when they collide head-on. Find their final velocities just after the collision, (a) if the collision is elastic; (b) if they remain locked together.

7-58 A man is sitting on a sled on an ice pond so that the frictional forces are zero. He has a machine gun that fires bullets of mass 1.3×10^{-2} kg with a muzzle velocity of 800 m s^{-1}. (a) What is the momentum of each bullet? (b) What is the average force on the man, per bullet, if that force is experienced for 0.2 s? (c) What is the speed of the man on the sled after he fires 100 bullets? Assume that the mass of the man, sled, and gun is 90 kg, and neglect the loss of mass because of the release of 100 bullets.

7-59 A proton is incident on a lead nucleus, which contains 82 protons. Its impact parameter is 8×10^{-15} m. If its point of closest approach is 9×10^{-15} m, what is its velocity far from the lead nucleus? (Assume that the lead nucleus remains at rest and that the collision is elastic.)

7-60 A freight car with a mass of 30,000 kg rolls at 5 m s^{-1} under a grain elevator where 10,000 kg of grain is dropped vertically into the car. (a) Assuming frictional forces between the car and rails are negligible, what is the final velocity of the car? (b) How much kinetic energy is lost by the car, and how is this energy transformed?

*7-61 A billiard ball strikes an identical billiard ball initially at rest and is deflected 45° from its original direction. Show that if the collision is elastic, the other ball must move at 90° to the first and with the same speed.

7-62 (a) If the distance d in Fig. 7.5 is 6 m, how far does the cannonball of Example 7.4 travel before striking the wall? (b) How far do the car and cannon move? (c) Show that the center of gravity of the entire system remains stationary when the ball is fired.

*7-63 A bullet of mass 10^{-2} kg and initial horizontal velocity of 250 m s^{-1} strikes and is embedded in a 1-kg wooden block. The wooden block hangs on the end of a long string. (a) What is the velocity of the block and bullet after impact? (b) How high will the block and bullet swing upward?

7-64 Explain how the toy pictured in Fig. 7.21 operates. The toy is composed of steel balls hung on strings. When one ball is initially raised and released, the last ball at the other end swings up. When two balls are initially displaced, two on the other end swing upward.

7-65 A vehicle with velocity v_0 collides with (a) a stationary vehicle of the same mass, (b) a solid wall, and (c) a vehicle of the same mass moving in the opposite direction with speed v_0. Which is (are) the most severe as far as the effect on passengers is concerned? Explain.

7-66 A carbon-14 nucleus emits a beta particle (electron) and a neutrino (ν) and is transformed into a nitrogen-14 nucleus. The beta particle and nitrogen nucleus can be observed because they leave a trail of ions in a detector. The neutrino, however, is very difficult to detect directly because it rarely interacts with the atoms it passes. Suppose in a particular decay event the beta particle has a momentum **p** and the nitrogen nucleus has a momentum of magnitude $\frac{4}{3}p$ at an angle of 90° to **p**. What is the magnitude and direction of the momentum of the neutrino?

7-67 Two objects with masses m_1 and m_2 are at either end of a spring. If the objects are pulled apart and then released from rest, what is the ratio K_1/K_2 of their kinetic energies at any instant?

7-68 A plutonium-239 nucleus decays at rest into an alpha particle (helium nucleus) plus a ura-

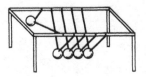

Figure 7.21. When the raised ball is released, it swings downward and collides elastically with the second ball. After a sequence of collisions, the right-hand ball swings upward while the others remain at rest. Problem 7-64.

nium-235 nucleus. The kinetic energy of the alpha particle is found to be 5.06 MeV, where 1 MeV = 10^6 eV = 1.60×10^{-13} J. The mass of a uranium nucleus is $\frac{235}{4}$ times that of an alpha particle; the mass of an alpha particle is 6.64×10^{-27} kg. (a) What is the velocity of the alpha particle? (b) What is the velocity of the uranium nucleus? (c) What is the kinetic energy of the uranium nucleus in MeV?

7-69   A nucleus at rest decays into an alpha particle of mass m and a nucleus of mass M. What fraction of the total kinetic energy of the system is carried by the nucleus of mass M?

7-70   A spaceship initially of mass M and velocity $\mathbf{V}$ fires a projectile of mass m and velocity $\mathbf{v}$. (Both velocities are relative to the earth.) Find the magnitude of the resulting velocity $\mathbf{V}'$ of the spaceship if (a) $\mathbf{v}$ is parallel to $\mathbf{V}$; (b) $\mathbf{v}$ is opposite to $\mathbf{V}$; (c) $\mathbf{v}$ is perpendicular to $\mathbf{V}$.

7-71   A 1000-kg car traveling at 20 m s^{-1} toward the north collides with a 10,000-kg truck heading south at the same speed. Immediately after the collision the car is moving east at 20 m s^{-1}. (a) How fast is the truck moving and in what direction immediately after the collision? (b) How much mechanical energy is dissipated in the collision?

7-72   On a moving bicycle (Fig. 7.22), the angular momentum of the spinning wheels is directed to the rider's left. If the bicycle is ridden "no-handed," what is the effect of the rider leaning to her left? Explain.

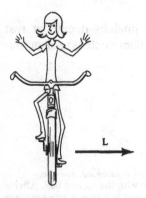

Figure 7.22.   Problem 7-72.

7-73   A girl of mass 50 kg standing at the center of a turntable is spun at 1.5 revolutions per second. In each hand she holds a 6-kg mass, and initially these are close to her body. Estimate her rotational velocity once she extends her arms outward. (Neglect the moment of inertia of the turntable.)

7-74   An insect of mass 10^{-3} kg walks around the edge of a phonograph turntable of mass 0.5 kg and radius 0.15 m. If the insect comes back to the spot on the record it started from, how far has the record turned? (Neglect friction in the bearings, and treat the turntable as a solid cylinder.)

7-75   If the earth's polar ice caps melt, what will happen to the length of the day? Explain.

*7-76   In the Bohr model of the hydrogen atom, the only possible electronic circular orbits are those for which the angular momentum is $nh/2\pi$, where n is an integer and h is Planck's constant. (a) What relation must the radius and linear momentum satisfy in this model? (b) We saw in Chapter Six that the kinetic energy of an electron in an orbit of radius r is $\frac{1}{2}mv^2 = ke^2/2r$. Show that the possible radii of the orbits are $n^2h^2/(4\pi^2kme^2)$. (c) What are the kinetic and total energies for these radii?

*7-77   For some purposes, a diatomic molecule can be thought of as a dumbbell, with two masses at the ends of a rigid rod and a moment of inertia I. According to Bohr's model for such a molecule, such a dumbbell can only have an angular momentum that is an integer multiple of $h/2\pi$, where h is a number called Planck's constant; the angular momentum is said to be *quantized*. What are the possible kinetic energies of such a dumbbell?

7-78   A single-engine airplane is viewed from the front. The propeller begins to rotate counterclockwise. (a) Are the forces due to the ground on the two wheels, one mounted under each wing, the same? If not, which is larger, that on the left wheel or the right? (b) Once the propeller is turning with a constant angular velocity, which wheel experiences the largest force due to the earth?

7-79   A man seated on a stool that rotates freely holds a 5-kg mass in each hand. With his hands in his lap, the moment of inertia about a vertical axis is 20 kg m^2. With his arms outstretched, the total moment of inertia is 35 kg m^2. Initially the man has an angular velocity of 3 rad s^{-1} with his arms in his lap. (a) What is the angular velocity of the man with his arms extended? (b) If the man drops the weights while his arms are extended, what is his angular velocity?

7-80 A high diver of height h wishes to do a forward double flip dive in a tuck position, with her arms around her folded legs. She leaves the board in an erect position with an angular velocity of 2.0 rad s^{-1}. Her radius of gyration is $0.25h$ when she is erect and is $0.1h$ in the tuck position. (a) What is her angular velocity in the tuck position? (b) What is the minimum time necessary for two complete turns? (c) If the diver initially has no vertical translational velocity, what is the minimum height of the diving board above the water if the dive is to be successful? (d) Does a tall person have any advantage in performing this dive?

7-81 Figure 7.23 shows a helicopter in flight. The large propeller that provides the lift force rotates clockwise when viewed from above. Explain, using angular momentum and torque, the function of the small propeller on the tail of the aircraft. This small propeller spins about a horizontal axis.

7-82 A star is initially similar to our sun, with a radius of 7×10^8 m and a period of rotation about its axis of 27 days. It evolves eventually into a neutron star with a radius of only 10^4 m and a period of 0.1 s. Assuming that the mass stays the same, calculate the ratio of its initial and final (a) angular momentum; (b) kinetic energy. (The angular momentum decreases, indicating that some angular momentum must have been carried off by material escaping from the star. The kinetic

Figure 7.23. Problem 7-81. (aragami123345 / iStockphoto)

energy increases as a result of the conversion of gravitational potential energy into other forms of energy as the star collapses.)

*7-83 One of Kepler's laws of planetary motion states that a line joining a planet to the sun sweeps out equal areas in equal times. Show that this law follows from the fact that the angular momentum of the planet is conserved.

*7-84 A long wooden beam of mass m and length $2a$ can pivot in a horizontal plane about its midpoint. A bullet of mass $m/60$ is fired horizontally at a velocity v into the beam at right angles to its length at the end. What is the resulting angular velocity of the beam?

ANSWERS TO REVIEW QUESTIONS

Q7-1, force, elapsed time; **Q7-2**, momentum change; **Q7-3**, mass, velocity; **Q7-4**, external forces; **Q7-5**, net external force is zero; **Q7-6**, component; **Q7-7**, that of the system, net external force; **Q7-8**, maximum; **Q7-9**, no; **Q7-10**, heat, deformation work; **Q7-11**, $I\omega$; **Q7-12**, $r \times p$; **Q7-13**, net external torque.

SUPPLEMENTARY TOPICS

7.7 | MOMENTUM AND THE USE OF THE BODY

In many athletic activities, one tries to maximize the momentum transfer. For example, in boxing, punches thrown by a simple extension of the arm are not nearly as effective in imparting momentum to an opponent as are those thrown in conjunction with body movement. However, in karate, large momentum transfers are often attained by high-speed motion of the limbs instead of by entire body movements.

Contact sports are not the only area where momentum transfer is important. For example, the primary aim of a shot-putter is to transform the low-velocity motion of the mass of the entire body into high-velocity motion of the smaller ball (Fig. 7.24). Momentum also plays an important role in activities where a ball is struck.

Table 7.1 lists the typical velocities and times measured for good athletes in various sports using

Figure 7.24. A shot-putter in action. Ideally, the momentum of the body parts is very small just after release. The momentum of the body is transferred to the ball.

balls. The striker is the instrument used to hit the ball, such as a baseball bat, tennis racket, or foot. To obtain useful information from these data using impulse and momentum, we must recognize that the mass of the striker, and hence its momentum, is somewhat ambiguous. Using tennis as an example, the striker is a racket of mass 0.4 kg. However, in using the racket, the arm and part of the body can be considered as part of the striker; the racket acts as an extension of the body. The effective striker mass depends on what part of the body is used and on how it is used. When a person swings a tennis racket primarily through wrist action, the effective striker mass is small, and the swing cannot be carried through firmly.

It must also be remembered that the person involved in striking the ball will usually be in contact with the ground. This means that the ball and striker cannot truly be regarded as parts of an isolated system with no external forces. When a tennis racket hits a ball, by Newton's third law the ball exerts a force on the racket, the racket exerts a force on the body, and the body exerts a force on the ground. Therefore, if a racket imparts momentum to a ball, momentum is also transferred to the earth.

To avoid the difficult details of this situation, it is convenient to define the *effective mass* of the striker. That is, we pretend the striker and ball are

TABLE 7.1

Masses of balls, velocities of strikers before and after impact, and the impact times during which the balls and strikers are in contact

Ball	Ball Mass (kg)	Ball Velocity (m s⁻¹)		Striker Velocity (m s⁻¹)		Impact Time (s)
		Before	After	Before	After	
Baseball (hit from rest)	0.15	0	39	31	27	1.35×10^{-3}
Football (punt)	0.42	0	28	18	12	$8 \quad \times 10^{-3}$
Golf ball (driver)	0.047	0	69	51	35	1.25×10^{-3}
Handball (serve)	0.061	0	23	19	14	1.35×10^{-2}
Soccer ball (kick)	0.43	0	26	18	13	$8 \quad \times 10^{-3}$
Squash ball (serve)	0.032	0	49	44	34	$3 \quad \times 10^{-3}$
Softball (hit from rest)	0.17	0	35	32	22	$3 \quad \times 10^{-3}$
Tennis ball (serve)	0.058	0	51	38	33	$4 \quad \times 10^{-3}$

two parts of a system on which no external forces act, so the total momentum of the striker and ball can be considered constant. This effective mass is not just a trick to allow us to compute a meaningless number. A detailed study of the motions of an athlete can aid in understanding how to increase the effective mass of the striker and thereby achieve higher ball velocities.

We denote the mass of the ball by m and its final velocity by $\mathbf{v}'$; its initial velocity is zero. The effective mass of the striker is denoted by M and its initial and final velocities by $\mathbf{V}$ and $\mathbf{V}'$. If the motion is in a straight line and momentum is conserved,

$$MV = mv' + MV' \qquad (7.17)$$

Assuming m, v', V, and V' are known, we can solve this equation for the effective mass of the striker,

$$M = \frac{mv'}{V - V'} \qquad (7.18)$$

Note that this effective mass can be increased by performing the motion in such a way as to minimize the change in velocity of the striker during the impact (Fig. 7.25).

Example 7.12

(a) Using the data of Table 7.1 for a tennis serve, calculate the effective mass of the striker. (b) What is the average force on the tennis ball during impact?

(a) With the data of Table 7.1, the effective mass of the striker is

$$M = \frac{mv'}{V - V'} = \frac{(0.058 \text{ kg})(51 \text{ m s}^{-1})}{(38 - 33) \text{ m s}^{-1}} = 0.59 \text{ kg}$$

This is greater than the mass of the racket alone, which is 0.4 kg.

(b) During impact the average force on the ball $\overline{F}$ is found from $\overline{F} \, \Delta t = m(v' - v)$. With $v = 0$ and the impact time of 4×10^{-3} s,

$$\overline{F} = \frac{m(v' - v)}{\Delta t} = \frac{(0.058 \text{ kg})(51 \text{ m s}^{-1})}{4 \times 10^{-3} \text{ s}} = 740 \text{ N}$$

7.8 | GYROSCOPIC MOTION

The relationship between the torque and angular momentum leads to some startling motions. The behavior of a gyroscope is an example of this (Fig. 7.26). A gyroscope is constructed so that a spinning wheel is supported beneath its center of gravity and

Figure 7.25. A batter has his feet firmly set and his body is moving toward the ball on impact. This increases the effective striking mass of the bat.

is isolated from any external torques. Thus the angular momentum of the spinning wheel continues to point in one direction, even if the frame is tilted or rotated.

Gyroscopes of very sophisticated design have virtually no friction and are used in inertial guidance systems for planes, rockets, and ships. Three such gyroscopes can be used to indicate three fixed directions in space. From measurements of a vehicle's acceleration relative to these axes, the velocity and position changes of the vehicle can be computed electronically.

Figure 7.27 shows a toy top on a pedestal. The wheel spins on an axle, which is supported at one end. If the top is placed as shown and released, it will fall if the wheel is not spinning. However, if the wheel is spinning rapidly, the top does not fall. Instead, it *precesses*: the axis slowly turns in the horizontal plane. To analyze this motion, we must see how the torque affects the angular momentum of the wheel.

The gravitational force **w** exerts a torque on the top about the end resting on the pedestal. If the wheel is not spinning, the initial angular momentum **L**$_i$ is zero. The torque produces an angular momentum **L**$_f$ in a time Δt; $\tau \Delta t = $ **L**$_f$. Since the torque $\tau = $ **r** $\times$ **w** and the resulting angular momentum are directed perpendicular to **r** and **w**, the top rotates clockwise and falls.

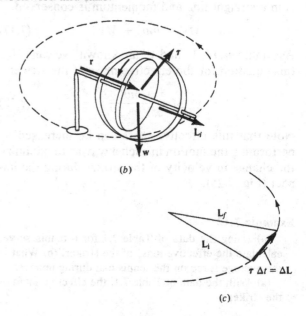

Figure 7.26. A toy gyroscope. Its three pairs of pivots (1, 2, 3) isolate it from any external torques. (Laurent Hamels / Getty Images, Inc.)

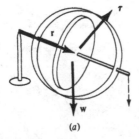

Figure 7.27. (*a*) The torque produced by **w** causes the top to rotate clockwise and fall. The wheel is not spinning. (*b*) and (*c*) When the wheel is spinning, the torque causes the angular momentum to precess in a horizontal plane. The end of the top moves along the dashed circle shown.

When the wheel is spinning, the situation changes. Now there is an initial angular momentum L_i along the top axis. Also, τ is perpendicular to L_i, and the final angular momentum after a short time is $L_f = L_i + \tau \Delta t$. Since $\tau \Delta t$ is perpendicular to L_i, τ acts to change the direction but not the magnitude of the angular momentum. Thus L_f and L_i have the same magnitudes but different directions (Fig. 7.27c). The torque causes the angular momentum and the top to precess in a circle.

Tops are fascinating devices to experiment with, and many different kinds of motion can be produced. When the end of the axis away from the pivot is released with exactly the right initial horizontal velocity, the precessional motion of the axis previously described occurs. If, instead, the end of the axis is simply dropped, the top initially begins to fall, and it then gradually acquires the sideways precessional velocity. The result is a vertical bobbing motion called *nutation*, which occurs along with the horizontal precession. If the top is spinning fast enough, the magnitude of the vertical or nutational displacement is small initially and rapidly diminishes as a result of frictional effects. Only the precessional motion is observed after a brief interval has elapsed.

Precession of the Equinoxes | The earth rotates about its axis in a period of one day. The axis of rotation precesses very slowly, resulting in what is called the precession of the equinoxes.

When the earth was formed, somewhat more mass accumulated along its equator than at the poles because of the centripetal acceleration. The moon and, to some extent, the sun exert unequal forces on the opposite sides of the earth (Fig. 7.28). The net gravitational torque on a spherical planet is zero, so the net torque on the earth results entirely from the unequal forces on the *equatorial bulge* and is quite small.

Because the torque is small, the precession is very slow, with one complete cycle lasting 25,800 years. One effect of this precession is to cause a slow change in the time of year when a star is seen in a given position. Over the last 2000 years this time has shifted about 1 month. A second result is the gradual shifting of the seasons. After 12,900

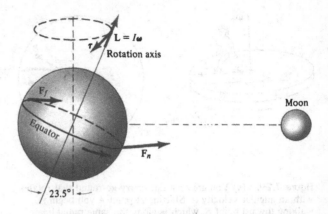

Figure 7.28. The earth's axis of rotation is tilted as shown. The gravitational forces exerted on the equatorial bulge are F_n and F_f. F_n is larger than F_f because the near side of the earth is closer to the moon. The precession is along the dashed curve.

years, winter will occur in the position of the earth's orbit where summer occurs now.

7.9 | CORIOLIS FORCES; LARGE-SCALE WIND PATTERNS

In Chapter Three, we discussed the difference between inertial and noninertial reference frames. Inertial reference frames are nonaccelerating frames. For example, a reference frame moving with a person on a merry-go-round is not an inertial system. In this section, we describe some effects observed in a noninertial reference system.

We begin by imagining that you are on a merry-go-round (Fig. 7.29), a flat rotating platform. As seen from above, you are rotating counterclockwise at a constant angular velocity ω. You begin to walk from point A to point B on the platform. To you, this appears to be a simple walk in a straight line. However, you find that you must force yourself to the left as you walk in order to end up at point B. If you don't, you end up to the right of B.

From our observations on the ground, this is easy to explain. At point A, you have a moment of inertia $I = mr^2$ and an angular velocity ω about the rotational axis. As you walk toward B, your moment of inertia increases. If no forces are exerted perpendicular to your motion in the plane of the platform, there is no torque about the axis, and your angular momentum $I\omega$ must remain constant. Thus since your moment of inertia increases, your angular velocity must decrease. Because the angular velocity

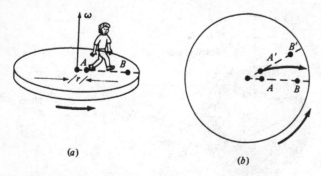

(a)   (b)

Figure 7.29. (a) You are on a flat merry-go-round that rotates with an angular velocity ω. Starting at point A you begin walking toward point B, which is along the same radial line. (b) The view from above. Points A and B rotate after a few seconds to A' and B'. If no horizontal forces act on you perpendicular to your motion, you will slide to your right and will not get to B. The curved path shows your footprints on the merry-go-round.

everywhere on the platform is ω, the only way your angular velocity can decrease is for you to start sliding to your right (Fig. 7.29b).

In order to walk from A to B, you must increase your angular momentum. The only way you can do this is to have the platform push you to your left, in reaction to your pushing on it to the right. This produces a torque on you that increases your angular momentum. Note that we, as inertial observers, do not see any force pushing you toward the right. However, from your point of view in the rotating frame, it seems that there is such a force that you must act against. This apparent "force" is called the *Coriolis force*. It is not really a force but rather an artifact of your observations relative to a noninertial, rotating reference frame.

The rightward tendency is very obvious if you remain at A and attempt to slide a frictionless stone directly toward B. When the stone leaves your hand, it has a certain angular momentum. In order for it to reach B, it must increase its angular momentum. However, since it is not in contact with anything, its angular momentum remains constant. Thus its angular velocity decreases as it moves outward and it passes to the right of B (Fig. 7.30a). The same conclusion is reached if we apply Newton's first law. There is no force on the stone, so it must travel in a straight line relative to the inertial observer. Relative to you on the merry-go-round, the

stone curves to the right, as though a force had acted upon it (Figs. 7.30b, c).

Interestingly, if the stone is thrown by someone at B toward A, it also curves to the right. To reach A, it would have to lose angular momentum as its moment of inertia decreases. Since its angular momentum is in fact constant, the decrease in I means an increase in ω, and again the stone veers past A on the thrower's right (Fig. 7.30d). Similarly, to walk from B to A, you must force yourself to your left to overcome an apparent Coriolis force to the right.

A complete, quantitative discussion of rotating reference frames is beyond the scope of this text. However, it demonstrates that if the sense of rotation is as shown, a thrown stone will always veer toward the right of the target. If the rotation is in the

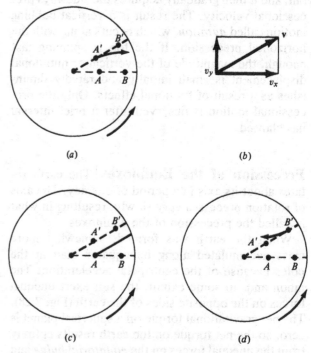

(a)   (b)

(c)   (d)

Figure 7.30. (a) Still on the merry-go-round, you slide a frictionless stone from A toward B. The stone does not reach B but instead veers off to the right. The curved path is its trail left in the dust. (b) Suppose you pushed the stone in the +x direction with a velocity v_x. At the instant you released it, you were moving in the +y direction with a velocity $v_y = r\omega$. Hence the velocity v relative to the ground has both x and y components. (c) Relative to the ground, the stone moves in a straight line since its velocity is constant. (d) If the stone is pushed from B toward A, it again veers to the right of the trajectory expected by an observer on the merry-go-round.

opposite sense, the stone always veers to the left of the target. Thus the direction of the Coriolis force depends on the direction of rotation.

A natural question is why we are not normally aware of Coriolis forces, since we live on a spinning planet, a merry-go-round of sorts. The answer is that the relatively slow rotation of the earth makes its effects very small in situations such as throwing stones or walking. However, many of the atmosphere and oceanic characteristics that we take for granted are due to the effects of the Coriolis force.

Wind Patterns | To discuss wind patterns, we step from the rotating flat platform to the spinning globe. In Fig. 7.31, a person on the surface of a spinning globe is attempting to throw a stone due south, parallel to the surface. From above the north pole this is qualitatively the same situation as the platform rotating counterclockwise. Thus the stone will veer to the thrower's right, to the west.

Storms center on regions of low pressure, and winds move along the earth's surface toward these centers. No matter which direction the wind is incident from, it will veer to the right in the northern hemisphere due to the Coriolis force (Fig. 7.32a). This is the origin of the counterclockwise winds that accompany such low-pressure centers. In the

southern hemisphere, the winds rotate clockwise about low-pressure centers.

Clear, dry weather is associated with centers of high pressure. Surface winds flow away from such centers. In the northern hemisphere this outward flowing air veers to the right again and forms the characteristic clockwise flow around high-pressure centers (Fig. 7.32b).

There are several major prevailing surface wind patterns that are in part due to Coriolis forces. One of these is the trade winds, the prevailing east-to-west winds within about 20° latitude of the equator. Above the equator, the wind is from the northeast, and below, it is from the southeast (Fig. 7.33). The energy source for these winds is the constant heating of the air near the equator. As we shall see in Chapter Twelve, this heated air expands and rises, and cooler, denser air from north and south of the equator moves toward the equator. In the process, this moving air is forced westward in the northern hemisphere and also westward in the southern hemisphere by the Coriolis forces.

One interesting, and to sailors infuriating, feature of the trade winds is that the heated air at the equator is rising so strongly that the winds from the northeast and southeast are drawn off the surface, creating the equatorial doldrums. This region of vir-

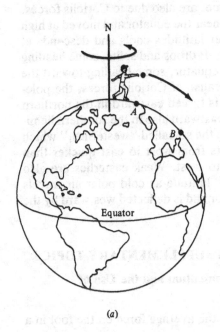

(a)

(b)

Figure 7.31. (a) A stone is thrown due south by someone standing on the earth's surface. (b) From above the north pole, the picture appears much the same as in Fig. 7.30a, as if the thrower were on a flat platform rotating counterclockwise. The stone will veer to the thrower's right, toward the west.

Figure 7.32. (*a*) Low-pressure areas are shown in both the northern and southern hemispheres. In both, surface winds flow toward the low-pressure center, but the Coriolis force deflects them. In the northern hemisphere this causes counterclockwise winds, and in the southern hemisphere the winds are clockwise. (*b*) High-pressure centers have an outward flow of air that is deflected to the right in the northern hemisphere and to the left in the southern hemisphere. The characteristic direction of wind circulation is clockwise in the northern hemisphere and counterclockwise in the southern hemisphere.

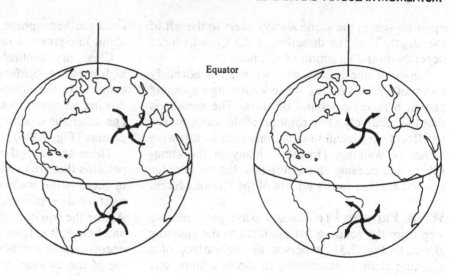

Equator

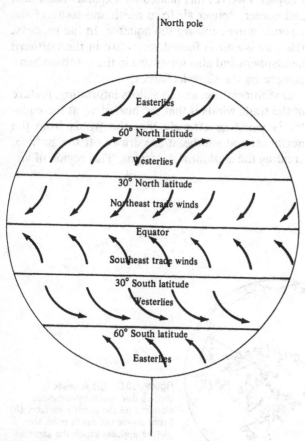

North pole

Easterlies

60° North latitude

Westerlies

30° North latitude

Northeast trade winds

Equator

Southeast trade winds

30° South latitude

Westerlies

60° South latitude

Easterlies

Figure 7.33. A schematic view of the earth showing the prevailing wind patterns. Heated air rises at the equator, flows to higher latitudes, and cools, descending at about 30° latitude. This descending air splits, some returning to the equator, some moving farther poleward. At 60° latitude a similar break in the motion of the air occurs with the air rising at this latitude.

tually no wind at all was a severe problem for sailing ships. The north/south meeting point of the winds is not precisely the equator. The heating is highest in the summer hemisphere, which tends to shift the doldrums toward the summer hemisphere. Also, because there is more land in the northern hemisphere, heating of the air there is greater, and this shifts the median latitude of the doldrums slightly north of the equator.

The prevailing westerlies, found roughly between 30° and 60° latitude, are also due to Coriolis forces. The air that rose near the equator and moved at high altitudes to higher latitudes cools and descends at about 30° latitude. It drops and splits, some heading back toward the equator, some heading toward the poles. Again, because of Coriolis forces, the poleward moving air is forced eastward in the northern hemisphere and eastward also in the southern hemisphere. These are the so-called "westerlies," which make plane flights from west to east quicker than those from east to west. Weak easterlies are also formed above 60° latitude as cold polar air travels toward the equator and is deflected westward by the Coriolis force.

EXERCISES ON SUPPLEMENTARY TOPICS

Section 7.7 | Momentum and the Use of the Body

7-85   What is the average force on the foot in a football punt?

7-86 Using the data of Table 7.1, find the average force on the hand of a handball player when serving.

7-87 Discuss, in terms of impulse and momentum, the difference between boxing with bare knuckles and with gloves.

7-88 What is the effective mass of the striker in a soccer kick?

7-89 Use the data in Table 7.1 for a baseball to find (a) the kinetic energy transferred to the baseball; (b) the mechanical energy lost.

7-90 (a) In a football punt, what is the effective mass of the striker? (b) What percentage of the body weight of an 80-kg person is this?

7-91 Discuss how the concept of effective striker mass applies to boxing techniques.

Section 7.8 | Gyroscopic Motion

7-92 A boy holds a bicycle wheel that is spinning rapidly. The wheel is in the horizontal plane. Viewed from above, the rotation is counterclockwise. (a) Which way does the angular momentum point? (b) The boy tries to turn the plane of rotation of the wheel by pushing to his right on the upper end of the axle and to his left on the lower end. What is the direction of the torque? (c) What happens to the wheel?

7-93 "A top will fall to the floor if released when it is not spinning but will precess if it is spinning." Since this statement does not state any minimum rotational velocity, it suggests that an arbitrarily small rotational speed is sufficient to prevent the top from falling. Explain how nutation resolves this apparent paradox.

Section 7.9 | Coriolis Forces; Large-Scale Wind Patterns

7-94 If the platform of Fig. 7.29 turns clockwise, walking from A to B requires the walker to push to the left. Explain why.

7-95 Show that if the platform of Fig. 7.30 rotates clockwise, a thrown stone veers to the thrower's left, whether it is thrown from A toward B or from B toward A.

7-96 Explain why, in the southern hemisphere, winds rotate clockwise about low-pressure centers.

7-97 What is the direction of the flow around high-pressure centers in the southern hemisphere? Explain.

PROBLEMS ON SUPPLEMENTARY TOPICS

7-98 (a) If a torque applied to the earth reduced the length of the day by 1 hour, how large an angular impulse would be required? (b) If this torque arose from a pair of forces (a couple) applied along the equator on opposite sides of the earth acting for 1 hour, how large would the two forces be? (Use the solar and terrestrial data on the inside back cover.)

7-99 A weight is hung from the free end of the axis of a top similar to the top in Fig. 7.27. What qualitative effect will this have upon its rate of precession?

7-100 In large ships, flywheels are often used to reduce the side-to-side rolling caused by waves. If a large wave approaches the ship from the left in Fig. 7.34, how does the flywheel affect the ship's subsequent motion?

Additional Reading

James G. Hay, *The Biomechanics of Sports Techniques*, Prentice-Hall, Inc., Englewood Cliffs, N.J., 1973. Momentum conservation in athletics.

Stanley Plagenhoef, *Patterns of Human Motion: A Cinematographic Analysis*, Prentice-Hall, Inc., Englewood Cliffs, N.J., 1971. Momentum conservation in athletics.

Jearl D. Walker, Karate Strikes, *American Journal of Physics*, vol. 43, October 1975, p. 845.

F. I. Ordway, Principles of Rocket Engines, *Sky and Telescope*, vol. 14, 1954, p. 48.

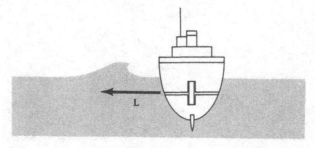

Figure 7.34. A flywheel mounted on a horizontal axle viewed from the rear of the ship. The rotation of the wheel is such that its angular momentum is directed as shown. Problem 7-100.

R. A. R. Tricker and B. J. K. Tricker, *The Science of Movement*, Mills and Boon Ltd., London, 1966. Applications of angular momentum to balance and motion.

R. L. Page, The Mechanics of Swimming and Diving, *The Physics Teacher*, vol. 14, 1976, p. 72.

Chris D. Zafiratos, An Alternative Treatment of Gyroscopic Behavior, *The Physics Teacher*, vol. 20, 1982, p. 34.

Kenneth Laws, The Physics of Dance, *Physics Today*, February 1985, p. 24.

Howard Brody, The Moment of Inertia of a Tennis Racket, *The Physics Teacher*, vol. 23, 1985, p. 213.

Cliff Frohlich, Do Springboard Divers Violate Angular Momentum Conservation? *American Journal of Physics*, vol. 47, July 1979, p. 583.

James Gray, *How Animals Move*, Cambridge University Press, Cambridge, 1953. Gyroscopic effects in insect motion.

David F. Griffing, *The Dynamics of Sports—Why That's the Way the Ball Bounces*, Mohican, Loudonville, Ohio, 1982. Basic physics applied to track and field, swimming, water skiing, football, etc.

Arthur C. Damask, Forensic Physics of Vehicle Accidents, *Physics Today*, March 1987, p. 36.

Scientific American articles:

H. W. Lewis, Ballistocardiography, February 1958, p. 89.

Alfred Gessow, The Changing Helicopter, April 1967, p. 38.

James E. McDonald, The Coriolis Effect, May 1952, p. 72.

Cornelius T. Leondes, Inertial Navigation for Aircraft, March 1970, p. 80.

Cliff Frohlich, The Physics of Somersaulting and Twisting, March 1980, p. 154.

Jearl Walker, The Mysterious "Rattleback": A Stone That Spins in One Direction and Then Reverses, *The Amateur Scientist*, October 1979, p. 172.

Jearl Walker, The Physics of Spinning Topics, Including Some Far-out Ones, *The Amateur Scientist*, March 1981, p. 182.

Jearl Walker, Delights of the "Wobbler," a Coin or a Cylinder That Precesses as it Spins, *The Amateur Scientist*, October 1982, p. 184.

Jearl Walker, The Essence of Ballet Maneuvers Is Physics, *The Amateur Scientist*, June 1982, p. 146.

Jearl Walker, The Physics of the Follow, the Draw, and the Massé (in Billiards and Pool), *The Amateur Scientist*, July 1983, p. 124.

CHAPTER 8
ELASTIC
PROPERTIES
OF MATERIALS

We have discussed the motion of objects using the implicit assumption that these objects never changed in size or shape. However, an object made from any real material will always be deformed at least slightly and may even break when forces or torques are applied. For example, a steel or wooden beam will bend when a weight is hung from it, and a bone will twist and perhaps fracture when subjected to a torque.

Although materials are held together by complicated electric and magnetic forces among the molecules, the effects of these forces can be categorized quite adequately using a few measured quantities. With these quantities one can determine the size and shape of a steel beam needed to safely support a given load or the torque a particular bone can withstand without breaking.

The first portion of this chapter is devoted to the description of the *stresses* that produce deformations, or *strains*, in a material. We find that the strain depends on the way in which the stress is applied. Using experimentally determined parameters, we can then discuss the strength of materials and the optimal design of objects. We also apply our results to find the relation between the lengths and radii of columns. This is used to discuss tree sizes and to develop a very interesting scaling hypothesis relating the structure and function of animals.

8.1 | GENERAL ASPECTS OF STRESS AND STRAIN

If a certain force stretches a rubber band a given distance, then a force twice as great is needed to produce the same elongation in two such bands or,

equivalently, in a *single* band of twice the cross-sectional area. Thus the deformations of materials are determined by the *force per unit area, and not by the total force*. Because of this, it is useful to define the *stress* σ in a bar of cross-sectional area A (Fig. 8.1a) subjected to a force $\mathbf{F}$ as the ratio of the force to the area

$$\sigma = \frac{F}{A} \qquad (8.1)$$

The stress is opposed by the intermolecular forces within the material. For example, if the leg of a table is supporting a 100-N weight, then the intermolecular forces must exert an upward 100-N force on the top layer of molecules in the leg.

Three kinds of stress are commonly defined (Fig. 8.1). *Tension stress* is the force per unit area producing elongation of an object. *Compression stress* acts to compress an object. *Shear stress* corresponds to the application of scissorlike forces.

The change in the length of the bar under tension or compression stress is proportional to its length. For example, if a bar of length l subjected to a tension force $\mathbf{F}$ stretches a distance Δl, then each half of the bar stretches $\frac{1}{2}\Delta l$. The *strain* ε is the *fractional change in length* (Fig. 8.2):

$$\varepsilon = \frac{\Delta l}{l} \qquad (8.2)$$

From this definition, we see that ε is dimensionless and does not depend on the length of the bar. There are three kinds of strains: tension, compression, and shear. Any deformation of an object can be considered as a combination of these three strains. Equation 8.2 defines both tension and compression

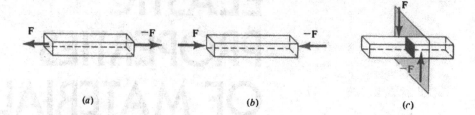

Figure 8.1. A bar subjected to (a) tension; (b) compression; (c) shear forces.

(a)   (b)   (c)

strains. We describe shear strains later in the chapter.

The relation between the stress and the strain for a material under tension can be found experimentally. A bar clamped tightly at each end is gradually stretched, and the applied force F needed to do this is recorded at intervals (Fig. 8.3). The fractional change in length is then the strain, and the force per unit area is the stress. Typical results obtained in this way are shown in Fig. 8.4. Analogous graphs for compression and shear stresses can also be obtained.

Example 8.1

A bar has dimensions 1 cm by 1 cm by 20 cm. It is subjected to a 10,000-N tension force and stretches 0.01 cm (Fig. 8.3). Find (a) the stress; (b) the strain. (c) If the stress–strain graph is a straight line, how much does the bar stretch when the applied force is increased to 50,000 N?

(a) The stress is the ratio of the force applied and the cross-sectional area. Thus, with 1 cm = 0.01 m,

$$\sigma = \frac{F}{A} = \frac{10,000 \text{ N}}{(0.01 \text{ m})^2} = 10^8 \text{ N m}^{-2}$$

This is a tension stress, since the bar is stretched by the force.

(b) The strain is the fractional elongation,

$$\varepsilon = \frac{\Delta l}{l} = \frac{0.01 \text{ cm}}{20 \text{ cm}} = 5 \times 10^{-4}$$

Note that the length units cancel as expected.

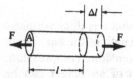

Figure 8.2. A bar of length l and area A subjected to a tension stress has its length increased by Δl. The ratio $\Delta l/l$ is the strain ε.

(c) If the stress–strain graph is a straight line, the two are proportional. When the applied force and the stress increase by a factor of $(50,000 \text{ N})/(10,000 \text{ N}) = 5$, the strain and the elongation change by the same factor. Hence the elongation increases to $5(0.01 \text{ cm}) = 0.05$ cm.

For small values of the strain, the stress–strain graph (Fig. 8.4) is a straight line; the stress σ is linearly proportional to the strain ε. This is called the *linear region* for a material. Beyond the *linear limit A*, the stress is no longer linearly proportional to the strain. However, from A to the *elastic limit*, or *yield point B*, the object still returns to its original dimensions when the applied force F is removed. The deformation up to B is said to be elastic. If the applied force is further increased, the strain increases rapidly. In this region, if the applied force is removed, the object does not return completely to its original dimensions; it retains a permanent deformation. The highest point C on the stress–strain graph is the *ultimate tension strength σ_t* of the material, or its maximum stress. Beyond this point, additional strain is produced even by a reduced ap-

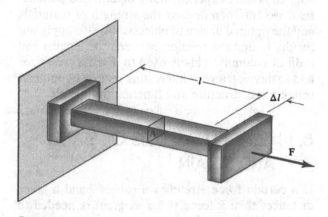

Figure 8.3. An experiment to measure the relationship between stress and strain.

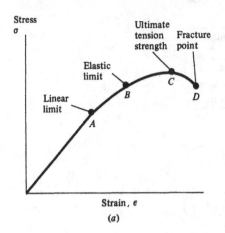

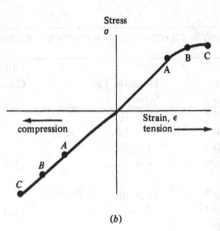

Figure 8.4. (*a*) The stress associated with a given tension strain for a ductile metal. (*b*) Stress–strain graph for a brittle material such as bone. The fracture point *D* (not shown) is now very close to the ultimate strength point *C*. Note that the slopes in the linear portion of the curve are not the same for tension and compression.

plied force, and *fracture* occurs at point *D*. From *B* to *D* the material is said to undergo *plastic deformation*. If the ultimate tension strength and fracture points *C* and *D* are close together, as in Fig. 8.4*b*, the material is *brittle*; if they are far apart, as in Fig. 8.4*a*, the material is said to be *ductile*.

When discussing the properties of materials, it must be remembered that all materials exhibit the phenomenon of *fatigue*. After many cycles of applying and removing a load, their ultimate strength gradually diminishes, and the material finally fails, even under weak stresses. For example, a paper clip bent back and forth several times eventually breaks easily. The effects of fatigue must be considered in situations as diverse as designing a bridge and developing pins to insert into bone fractures.

The reasons for material fatigue are not completely understood, but it is believed that after repeated deformations the internal molecular structure of the material is changed. These changes result in decreased intermolecular forces and hence in a reduction in strength of the material.

8.2 | YOUNG'S MODULUS

The elastic deformations of a solid are related to the associated stresses by quantities called *elastic moduli*. In the linear region of the stress–strain graph for tension or compression, the slope equals the stress-to-strain ratio and is called *Young's modulus E* of

the material:

$$E = \frac{\sigma}{\varepsilon} \qquad (8.3)$$

For homogeneous materials such as steel, the Young's moduli for compression and tension are usually equal. For inhomogeneous materials such as concrete or bone, the moduli for compression and tension are different. Table 8.1 lists representative Young's moduli, ultimate tension strengths σ_t, and ultimate compression strengths σ_c for various materials.

The following examples illustrate these relationships.

Example 8.2

In Example 8.1, a 10^8-N m^{-2} stress produces a strain of 5×10^{-4}. What is Young's modulus for this bar?

Young's modulus is the ratio of the stress to the strain,

$$E = \frac{\sigma}{\varepsilon} = \frac{10^8 \text{ N m}^{-2}}{5 \times 10^{-4}} = 20 \times 10^{10} \text{ N m}^{-2}$$

According to Table 8.1, this is equal to Young's modulus for steel.

Example 8.3

(a) If the minimum cross-sectional area of the femur of a human adult is 6×10^{-4} m^2, what is the compressional load at which fracture occurs? (The femur is the main bone in the upper leg.) (b) Assuming the stress–strain relationship is linear until fracture, find the strain at which the fracture occurs.

TABLE 8.1

Young's moduli and ultimate strengths for representative materials. All quantities have units of N m^{-2}.

Material	Young's Modulus E	Ultimate Tension Strength σ_t	Ultimate Compression Strength σ_c
Aluminum	7×10^{10}	2×10^8	
Steel	20×10^{10}	5×10^8	
Brick	2×10^{10}	4×10^7	
Glass	7×10^{10}	5×10^7	11×10^8
Bone (along axis)			
Tension	1.6×10^{10}	12×10^7	
Compression	0.9×10^{10}		17×10^7
Hardwood	10^{10}		10^8
Tendon	2×10^7		
Rubber	10^6		
Blood vessels	2×10^5		

(a) From Table 8.1, the ultimate compression strength σ_c for bone is 17×10^7 N m^{-2}. This is the force per unit area that will lead to fracture, and the total force is found by multiplying by the cross-sectional area of the bone. Thus

$$F = \sigma_c A = (17 \times 10^7 \text{ N m}^{-2})(6 \times 10^{-4} \text{ m}^2)$$
$$= 1.02 \times 10^5 \text{ N}$$

This force is large; it is about 15 times the weight of a 70-kg person. However, it is readily exceeded if one falls several metres and lands in a rigid position.

(b) Using the definition of Young's modulus, $E = \sigma/\varepsilon$, with $E = 0.9 \times 10^{10}$ N m^{-2} from Table 8.1,

$$\varepsilon = \frac{\sigma}{E} = \frac{17 \times 10^7 \text{ N m}^{-2}}{0.9 \times 10^{10} \text{ N m}^{-2}} = 0.0189$$

Thus the bone is reduced in length by 1.89 percent at the load that will cause fracture. The experimental value of the strain at fracture is slightly larger, since the stress–strain curve is not linear (Fig. 8.4b). It flattens out as shown in Fig. 8.4b as the ultimate strength is approached.

The linear stress–strain region of Fig. 8.4 is also called the *Hooke's law* region. In this region, since the stress is linearly related to the strain, the force is linearly related to the elongation. This can be seen using the definition of Young's modulus rewritten as $\sigma = E\varepsilon$. With the definitions of the stress $\sigma = F/A$ and the strain $\varepsilon = \Delta l/l$, this becomes

$$\frac{F}{A} = E\frac{\Delta l}{l}$$

Thus in tension or compression, the force on an object is proportional to its elongation:

$$F = k\,\Delta l \qquad (8.4)$$

Here k is called the *spring constant*, and

$$k = \frac{EA}{l} \qquad (8.5)$$

Equation 8.4 is called *Hooke's law*. As long as an object under stress is in the linear region, Hooke's law is valid. For example, coil springs, leaf springs, and rubber bands obey this relation if the deformations are not too large. The spring constant k is large for strong springs. From the definition of k, we see that increasing the cross-sectional area and decreasing the length both serve to strengthen the spring properties of the object. Spring forces will be discussed further in Chapter Nine.

8.3 | BENDING STRENGTH

Almost all mechanical structures ranging from beams to tree trunks and human limbs are subjected to various kinds of stresses. When the stress is a simple compression or tension stress, the shape of

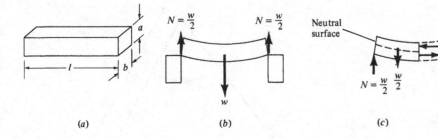

(a)

(b)

(c)

Figure 8.5. (a) and (b) A rectangular bar will bend under its own weight when supported at two points. (c) The left half of the bar experiences forces from one support and its weight. It also experiences forces from the other half of the bar (shown in black).

the object is unimportant because the deformation depends only on the cross-sectional area. However, the ability of an object to resist bending or to bend without breaking depends not only on the composition but also on the shape of the object. For example, a hollow tube made from a given amount of material is stronger than a solid rod of the same length constructed from an equal amount of material. Similarly, there is a definite relationship between the lengths and radii of tree trunks and of animal limbs imposed by their shape and composition. In this section, we see how humans and nature design structures for both strength and lightness.

Figure 8.5 shows a bar of length l and rectangular cross section with sides a and b. Placed on two supports, it bends somewhat under its own weight. When we look at the left half of the bar (Fig. 8.5c), we notice that the vertical force from the left support and the weight of this half are equal and opposite. However, these forces have different lines of action, so they form a couple that rotates the half-bar clockwise. Since the bar is in equilibrium, the right half must exert forces that produce an equal but opposite torque.

From Fig. 8.5c we note that the upper part of the bar is being compressed and the lower part is under tension. The *neutral surface* suffers no change in length. This means that the strength of the bar depends on the elastic properties of the bar.

The upper and lower surfaces of the bar are distorted most, so the largest internal forces will appear at these surfaces (Fig. 8.6b). These forces produce a torque opposing that of the weight and support. The further from the neutral surface they act, the greater will be their contribution to the torque. Thus with thick bars we can obtain large torques with relatively small internal forces, making it possible to support large loads.

To make this idea quantitative, suppose the bar is bent with a radius of curvature R (Fig. 8.7). We mentally divide the cross section into strips like the one shown at a distance x below the neutral surface. At this strip, the bar is stretched a distance Δl, so its total length is $l + \Delta l$. In radians, the angle θ formed by the bar is the arc length l at the neutral surface divided by the radius R, $\theta = l/R$; θ is also equal to $(l + \Delta l)/(R + x)$. Equating the two expressions for θ, we find after some algebra that $\Delta l/l = x/R$. Thus the strain in the strip at x is

$$\varepsilon = \frac{\Delta l}{l} = \frac{x}{R}$$

The strip has an area $\Delta A = b \, \Delta x$. Since the stress σ is $E\varepsilon$, where E is Young's modulus, the force on the strip is

$$\Delta F = \sigma \, \Delta A = E\varepsilon \, \Delta A = \frac{Ex \, \Delta A}{R}$$

The torque due to this force about the neutral surface is $x \, \Delta F = Ex^2 \, \Delta A/R$.

If we sum the torques due to all the strips, the total internal torque is the integral

$$\tau = \int \frac{Ex^2}{R} \, dA$$

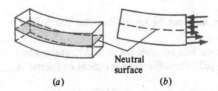

Neutral surface

(a)

(b)

Figure 8.6. (a) The shaded plane, called the neutral surface, suffers no change in dimension as the bar bends. (b) Detailed internal forces acting on the left half of the bar. The pairs of forces at the upper and lower edges produce the largest torques because they are large and far apart.

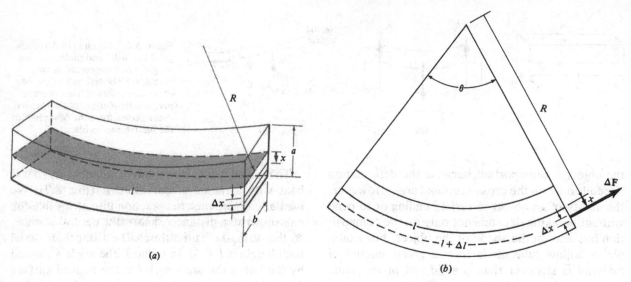

Figure 8.7. (a) A beam of length l is bent with a radius of curvature R. (b) At a distance x below the neutral surface, the bar is stretched so that its length is $l + \Delta l$.

Since E and R are constants, they can be taken out of the integral, leaving

$$\tau = \frac{EI_A}{R} \qquad (8.6)$$

The quantity I_A is called the *area moment of inertia*, and it is defined by

$$I_A = \int x^2 \, dA \qquad (8.7)$$

The integral is over the cross section of the bar. We calculate I_A for a rectangular bar in the next example, and apply the result in the following example to show that thick boards resist bending better than thin ones. Additional area moments of inertia are listed in Table 8.2.

Example 8.4

Find the area moment of inertia for the bar in Fig. 8.7.

The strip shown has an area $\Delta A = b \, \Delta x$, and x goes from $-a/2$ to $+a/2$. Thus the area moment of inertia is

$$I_A = \int_{-a/2}^{a/2} bx^2 dx = b \left[\frac{x^3}{3} \right]_{-a/2}^{a/2} = \frac{a^3 b}{12}$$

Note that I_A increases rapidly as a is increased, since a enters to the third power.

Example 8.5

Two identical wooden 2 cm × 6 cm boards are supported at each end (Fig. 8.8). Each supports its own weight, but one is resting with its wide side down and the other with its narrow side down. Which board bends most and what is the ratio of the radii of curvature for the two boards?

Since each board supports its own weight, the internal torque of each must be the same. Thus from Eq. 8.6, $I_{A1}/R_1 = I_{A2}/R_2$, where R_1 and R_2 are the radii of curvature of the two boards. Using $I_A = a^3b/12$ for each of the two rectangular boards, we see that $I_{A1} = (2 \text{ cm})^3(6 \text{ cm})/12 = 4 \text{ cm}^4$ and $I_{A2} = (6 \text{ cm})^3(2 \text{ cm})/12 = 36 \text{ cm}^4$. Then

$$\frac{4 \text{ cm}^4}{R_1} = \frac{36 \text{ cm}^4}{R_2}$$

or

$$\frac{R_2}{R_1} = 9$$

The radius of curvature of the board with its narrow side down is nine times that of the other. Since a large radius of curvature implies little bending, board 2 does not bend as much as board 1. Consequently, board 2 is less likely to break when a heavy weight is placed upon it.

TABLE 8.2

Area moments of inertia for vertical loading

Cross Section		I_A
Rectangle		$I_A = \dfrac{a^3 b}{12}$
Solid cylinder		$I_A = \dfrac{\pi r^4}{4}$
Hollow cylinder		$I_A = \dfrac{\pi(a^4 - b^4)}{4}$
I beam Each section has a thickness t a is the distance between the midpoints of the members		$I_A = \dfrac{a^2 bt}{2} + \dfrac{a^3 t}{12}$ $\quad (t \ll a, b)$

These results suggest that to construct strong, light structural members, most of the material should be located as far as practical from the neutral surface. A horizontal I beam (Fig. 8.9) is better able to withstand bending torques due to vertical forces than a beam with a square cross section made from the same amount of material. By contrast, the two beams can support the same applied *compressional force* because their cross-sectional areas are the same. Similarly, a hollow tube has more bending strength than a solid rod of the same length and weight. This is why metal chair and table legs are usually hollow (Fig. 8.10). They can better withstand forces applied in any direction perpendicular to their length, since on the average the metal is further from the neutral surface.

From this discussion, it would seem advantageous to make structural members with very large

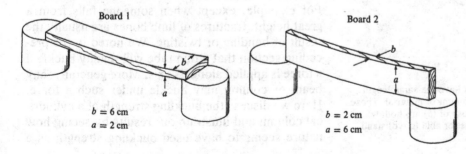

Board 1

$b = 6$ cm
$a = 2$ cm

Board 2

$b = 2$ cm
$a = 6$ cm

Figure 8.8. Identical boards resting flat and on edge.

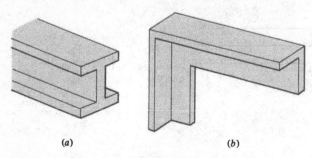

(a)   (b)

Figure 8.9. (a) An I beam is constructed so that most of the material is near the outer surfaces during bending due to a vertical force. (b) Brackets with an L-shaped cross section are designed for the same purpose. This bracket could be used as a wall-mounted support for a shelf.

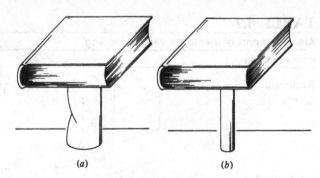

(a)   (b)

Figure 8.11. (a) A large-radius, thin-walled paper tube buckles easily. (b) A narrower tube made from an identical sheet of paper with thicker walls will not buckle under the same load.

diameters and very thin walls. However, a limit to how far one may go in this direction is imposed by the tendency of thin-walled structures to *buckle* under compressional stresses. Figure 8.11 shows an experiment one can readily perform to illustrate this point. One sheet of notebook paper is rolled into a cylinder a single layer thick and fastened with tape. A second sheet is rolled into a cylinder an inch or so in diameter and taped. When the cylinders are stood on end and this textbook is placed on top, the larger cylinder immediately buckles and collapses, while the smaller one is able to support the load. Thus the thinner walls of the larger cylinder are unable to withstand a force applied approximately along its axis. We consider buckling in more detail in the next section.

(a)   (b)

Figure 8.10. The legs of both chairs have the same length and are constructed from the same amount of material. Those of (a) are solid cylinders, whereas those of (b) are hollow cylinders. The hollow cylinders are better able to withstand bending torques.

Nature has made extensive use of the principle that hollow structures are stiffer than solid ones of the same cross-sectional area. Bones are generally hollow. For example, in the human femur, the ratio of the inner and outer radii is about 0.5, and the cross-sectional area is only 78 percent of that of a solid bone with the same bending strength. Smaller mammals and birds have bones with relatively thinner walls. For example, the ratio of the inner to outer radii for the humerus of a swan is 0.9, and the cross-sectional area is 38 percent of that of a solid bone with the same strength. The danger of collapse by buckling in this thin-walled bone is reduced by thin, reinforcing struts of bone extending across the interior of the humerus.

8.4 | BUCKLING STRENGTH AND STRUCTURAL DESIGN IN NATURE

In nature, the failure of structural members usually results from large torques of various types rather than from simple compression or tension stresses. For example, except when someone falls from a great height, fractures of limb bones are usually the result of bending or twisting. We noted in the preceding section that a thin tube will readily buckle if a force is applied along its axis. More generally, any beam or column may buckle under such a force. Here we discuss the buckling strength of a cylindrical column and illustrate our results by seeing how nature seems to have used buckling strength as a criterion in designing the approximately cylindrical trunks of trees.

To understand how buckling occurs, consider the long, thin cylindrical column in Fig. 8.12. It is held almost but not exactly vertically, so that its center of gravity is not quite over the center of the base, point P. The weight therefore exerts a torque about P that causes the column to bend. If the material is strong enough, the bending stops when the torques due to the internal forces in the material become large enough to balance the torque due to the weight. However, if the column is very tall and thin, as it bends the torques due to the weight will grow faster than will the torques due to the internal forces. The column will then buckle and collapse.

More generally, any vertical column supporting a load or even just its own weight will eventually buckle if its radius is held fixed and its height is increased. This *critical height* is determined by the Young's modulus of the material. This is because Young's modulus determines the internal forces for a given deformation.

For a solid cylinder of radius r supporting only its own weight, the critical height is shown in Section 8.7 to be

$$l_{cr} = cr^{2/3} \qquad (8.8)$$

Here c is a constant that depends on the weight per unit volume and the Young's modulus of the material composing the column. This result implies, for example, that if a column is just barely stable against buckling, doubling its radius does not permit doubling its height. This is illustrated in the following example.

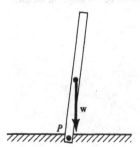

Figure 8.12. A cylindrical column tilted so that its weight is not directly over the center of its base, point P.

Example 8.6

Two columns are made of the same material. One has a radius r_1 and the other has a radius of $2r_1$. If both columns can just support their own weight without buckling, what is the ratio of their lengths?

The length of the column of radius r_1 is $l_1 = cr_1^{2/3}$. The other column has a length $l_2 = c(2r_1)^{2/3}$. The ratio l_2/l_1 is

$$\frac{l_2}{l_1} = \frac{(2r_1)^{2/3}}{r_1^{2/3}} = (2)^{2/3} = 1.59$$

Thus the column with twice the radius can only be about 1.6 times as long.

The Height of Trees

The result $l_{cr} = cr^{2/3}$ is quite general. For example, with suitable values of the constant c, it holds true for tapered columns, hollow columns, and columns supporting loads. It must also hold true for trees; that is, the maximum height a tree can have and be stable against buckling must vary as $r^{2/3}$. Whether buckling is, in fact, the limiting factor in determining the height of trees can be investigated by comparing their measured heights and radii (Fig. 8.13). While there is considerable scatter in the data, the results support the idea that buckling strength is the key factor in deter-

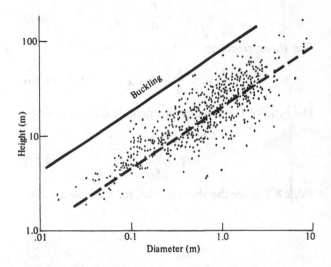

Figure 8.13. Data for North American trees. The dashed line is that of $l = cr^{2/3}$, with $c = 34.9$ chosen to fit the data. The solid line is the theoretical result for a tapered column that is just on the verge of buckling. Presumably no data points appear above this line since such trees would buckle under their own weight. (From T. McMahon, *Science*, vol. 179, pp. 1201–1204, March 23, 1973. Copyright 1973 by the American Association for the Advancement of Science.)

mining the proportions of trees. We see in Section 8.6 that there is evidence that buckling strength also determines the body proportions of animals.

8.5 | SHEARING AND TWISTING TORQUES

Thus far, we have only considered compression and tension stress. However, it is also common to have forces acting on an object that cause shearing or twisting. In this section, we describe shear forces qualitatively and twisting torques more analytically.

A simple example of shearing stresses and strains that you can easily try is provided by placing a book on a table and exerting equally large forces in opposite directions on its covers (Fig. 8.14). Each page moves slightly relative to the next one, and the shape of the book changes even though its height h and width w stay nearly the same.

In Fig. 8.14, the book is deformed through an angle α. The upper cover moves a distance δ relative to the lower one. The *shear stress* on the upper cover is

$$\sigma_s = \frac{F}{A} \qquad (8.9)$$

The *shear strain* is

$$\varepsilon_s = \frac{\delta}{h} = \tan \alpha \qquad (8.10)$$

The ratio of these quantities defines the *shear modulus*

$$G = \frac{\sigma_s}{\varepsilon_s} \qquad (8.11)$$

Table 8.3 gives the shear moduli for some materials.

TABLE 8.3
Shear moduli for some materials in N m^{-2}

Material	Shear Modulus G
Aluminum	2.4×10^{10}
Bones (long)	10^{10}
Copper	4.2×10^{10}
Glass	2.3×10^{10}
Hardwood	10^{10}
Steel	8.4×10^{10}
Tungsten	11.4×10^{10}

Usually the shear modulus is between one third and one half of Young's modulus for the material.

The next example illustrates shear stresses and strains.

Example 8.7

A skyscraper has an outer skin of brick-faced concrete panels attached to a structural frame by steel pins. Each pin is a cylinder of radius 0.01 m and supports a mass of 1000 kg. (a) What is the shear stress on a pin? (b) What is its shear strain? (c) If the maximum shear stress for the pins is 2×10^8 N m^{-2}, how large a safety factor is built into design?

(a) The shear force on a pin is equal to the weight it supports. Thus the stress is

$$\sigma_s = \frac{F}{A} = \frac{mg}{\pi r^2} = \frac{(1000 \text{ kg})(9.8 \text{ m s}^{-2})}{\pi (0.01 \text{ m})^2}$$
$$= 3.12 \times 10^7 \text{ N m}^{-2}$$

(b) With $G = \sigma_s / \varepsilon_s$, the strain is

$$\varepsilon_s = \frac{\sigma_s}{G} = \frac{3.12 \times 10^7 \text{ N m}^{-2}}{8.4 \times 10^{10} \text{ N m}^{-2}}$$
$$= 3.71 \times 10^{-4}$$

Since $\varepsilon_s = \tan \alpha$, this corresponds to an angular deformation $\alpha = 0.02°$.

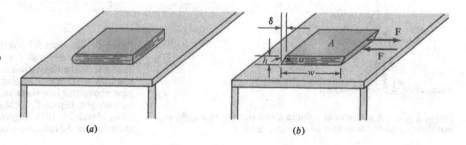

Figure 8.14. A book subjected to shearing forces changes its shape. The upper cover is displaced a distance δ relative to the lower, and the back of the book makes an angle α with the vertical direction.

(a)   (b)

(c) The ratio of the maximum sheer stress to its actual value is

$$\frac{2 \times 10^8 \text{ N m}^{-2}}{3.12 \times 10^7 \text{ N m}^{-2}} = 6.41$$

The pins can support over six times their load without breaking. Buildings are designed conservatively to allow for fatigue and abnormal stresses.

Even though an object is subjected only to shearing forces, compression or tension stresses may result on various planes in the object. For example, the cube in Fig. 8.15 is in translational and rotational equilibrium under the action of four shearing forces of equal magnitude acting along the faces. The cube is deformed slightly by these forces as shown. If we examine an imaginary cut along a diagonal plane as in Fig. 8.15b, then the shaded part of the cube must experience a compressive force **F** in the direction shown, since this part is in equilibrium. Similarly, for the plane in Fig. 8.15c, the shaded part experiences a tension force. The net result is that the square shown on the side of the cube in Fig. 8.15d becomes a rectangle when the cube is deformed by shearing forces.

From this discussion it is clear that stress and strain are complex quantities except in rather special cases. As we saw, externally applied shear forces result in both compressive and tension forces inside the material. Full specification of the stress must include the three components of the force on each of three perpendicular planes at each point in the object. Such complete analyses of stress–strain relations are beyond the scope of this textbook.

Twisting Torques | We now briefly discuss the

effect of a torque directed along the axis of a cylinder arising from twisting forces. Such torques occur when a skier's leg is twisted in a fall or when power is transmitted by a rotating shaft. Figure 8.16 shows a cylinder fixed at one end. A couple is applied at the free end, so that there is a torque directed along the axis. If the resulting deformation is not too large, it is found that a plane drawn along the axis of the cylinder becomes twisted, as in Fig. 8.16b. The angle of twist increases linearly with the distance from the fixed end, so that the radial lines remain straight. Lines originally drawn along the outside of the cylinder parallel to the axis become slightly curved.

To find the relation between the torque τ and the deformation or twisting angle α, we divide the cylinder into thin concentric cylindrical layers, seen at the end as narrow concentric rings (Fig. 8.16c). The layers are twisted by shear forces, so their stress and strain are related by the shear modulus: $\sigma_s = G\varepsilon_s$. A ring of radius r has a width Δr and an area $\Delta A = 2\pi r\, \Delta r$. The ring rotates through an angle α and a distance $r\alpha$. With the replacements $\delta = r\alpha$ and $h = l$, the shear strain of the ring is $\varepsilon_s = \delta/h = r\alpha/l$. The corresponding shear stress, the force per unit area needed to cause this deformation, is $\sigma_s = G\varepsilon_s = G(r\alpha/l)$. The torque about the axis on this ring is then $\Delta\tau = r\sigma_s\, \Delta A = r(Gr\alpha/l)(2\pi r\, \Delta r)$. Summing over the rings gives the total torque needed to cause this deformation:

$$\tau = \int_0^a \frac{G\alpha}{l} 2\pi r^3 \, dr = \frac{G\alpha\pi a^4}{2l}$$

Figure 8.15. (a) A cube subjected to four shearing forces of equal magnitude. The cube deforms slightly, but it is in static equilibrium. (b) The parts formed by an imaginary cut along a diagonal plane are subjected to compressive stresses. (c) The other diagonal plane forms parts that experience tension stresses. (d) The dashed lines show a square on the side of the cube before the shearing forces are applied. A square drawn with this orientation is deformed into a rectangle by the shearing forces, even though the cube face itself is deformed from a square into an equilateral parallelogram or rhombus.

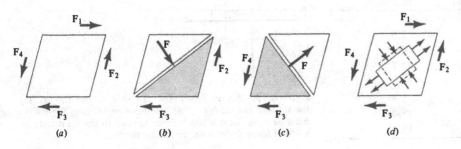

(a) (b) (c) (d)

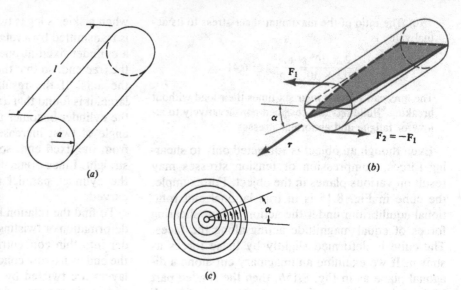

Figure 8.16. (s) A cylinder of length l and radius a. (b) The far end of the cylinder is held fixed by a constraint (not shown), and the near end is subjected to forces producing a torque along the axis. The resulting twist of the planes in the cylinder increases linearly with the distance from the fixed end if the applied torque is not too large. (c) The near end. Adjacent cylindrical layers deform more as one goes farther from the cylinder axis. This is a shearing deformation.

We can rewrite this result as

$$\tau = GI_p \frac{\alpha}{l} \qquad (8.12)$$

This is similar in form to the result for bending torques, but I_p is the *polar moment of inertia*. For a cylinder of radius a,

$$I_p = \frac{\pi a^4}{2} \qquad \text{(solid cylinder)} \qquad (8.13)$$

Since the polar moment of inertia increases with the fourth power of the radius, doubling the radius of a cylinder increases its resistance to twisting by a factor of $2^4 = 16$.

TABLE 8.4

The breaking torque and breaking angle for twisted bones in humans

Bone	Breaking Torque (N m)	Breaking Angle of Twist
Leg		
Femur	140	1.5°
Tibia	100	3.4°
Fibula	12	35.7°
Arm		
Humerus	60	5.9°
Radius	20	15.4°
Ulna	20	15.2°

If an object is subjected to an increasingly large twisting torque, it will eventually fracture. The torques and corresponding angles at which this happens for several human limb bones are listed in Table 8.4. Under the right conditions, a relatively small force can lead to a fracture. For example, a ski tip is about a metre from the heel of a skier's boot, so a 100-N force·at the tip produces a torque of 100 N m. According to the table, this is sufficient to break the tibia, the larger of the two bones in the lower leg.

The toe of the boot is about 0.3 m from the heel. If the foot and ski do not rotate, an applied torque of 100 N m requires that the skier exert a force of 100 N m/0.3 m = 330 N at the toe (Fig. 8.17). If the toe release is set to open at a lower force level, the risk of injury is reduced.

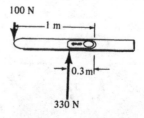

Figure 8.17. An overhead view of a skier's boot and ski. If the ski and foot do not rotate, the net torque about the heel must be zero. Thus a 100-N force applied to the ski results in a 330-N force exerted on the ski by the toe.

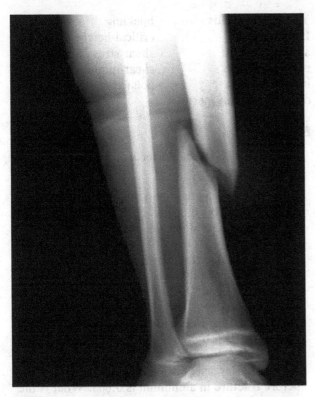

Figure 8.18. A spiral fracture of a tibia. (Scott Camazine / Alamy Limited)

Twisting fractures in bones or metal cylinders normally are not breaks at right angles to the axis, but instead are spiral fractures (Fig. 8.18). The explanation for this phenomenon is suggested by our discussion of the stresses and strains in a cube subjected only to shearing forces. We saw that for some surfaces in the cube, there was pure tension or compression stress, and a square drawn appropriately on a face of the cube was deformed into a rectangle. Similarly, when a rod is twisted, planes drawn at 45° angles to the axis experience pure tension or compression. Fracture occurs when the

smaller of the ultimate strengths for tension and compression is exceeded on one of these planes (Fig. 8.19).

SUMMARY

Objects subjected to forces or torques change their shape and may break. The fractional change in size or shape is the strain ε, and the force per unit area producing the deformation is the stress σ. For small applied forces or torques, the stress and strain in a material are usually linearly related. The proportionality constant relating stress and strain in the linear region is Young's modulus for compression or tension,

$$E = \frac{\sigma}{\varepsilon}$$

In the presence of a shear stress, the relationship is

$$G = \frac{\sigma_s}{\varepsilon_s}$$

where G is the shear modulus.

When a beam bends with a radius of curvature R, the torque due to the internal force is

$$\tau = E\frac{I_A}{R}$$

where I_A is the area moment of inertia. If the area moment of inertia of the beam is large, the radius of curvature for a given torque is also large, and the beam does not bend much.

A column of radius r supporting its own weight has a maximum or critical length

$$l_{cr} = cr^{2/3}$$

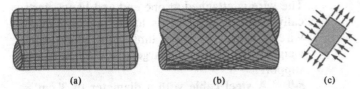

     (a)   (b)   (c)

Figure 8.19. (a) When a cylinder is twisted, lines parallel to the axis are twisted, but lines in planes perpendicular to the axis are unaffected. (b) When the cylinder is twisted, one set of parallel lines drawn at 45° to the axis is pushed together and the other set is stretched out. (c) A single square from part (b) becomes deformed into a rectangle. The stress is pure tension along the long sides and pure compression along the short sides.

c depends on Young's modulus for the material and on the weight per unit volume. If the length exceeds l_{cr}, the column will buckle. This criterion appears to be a limiting factor in the growth of trees.

A twisting torque τ applied to a uniform cylinder of length l is related to the angle α through which the cylinder twists by

$$\tau = GI_p \frac{\alpha}{l}$$

I_p is the polar moment of inertia and depends on the radius of the cylinder.

REVIEW QUESTIONS

Q8-1   If a force F is applied to a bar of cross section A, the stress is _____.

Q8-2   The strain in an object subjected to a stress is the _____.

Q8-3   The three types of stress are _____, _____, and _____.

Q8-4   In the linear region, the _____ and _____ are linearly proportional.

Q8-5   Up to the _____, an object returns to its original length when the stress is removed.

Q8-6   If a material is easy to compress, it has a small _____.

Q8-7   If the force needed to stretch an object is proportional to the elongation, the object obeys _____.

Q8-8   A bar with a large area moment of inertia is _____ to bend than one with a small area moment of inertia.

Q8-9   Buckling of a column refers to collapse under forces approximately along its _____.

Q8-10   The shear modulus is the ratio of the _____ to _____.

Q8-11   Twisting a cylinder produces _____ stresses.

Checklist
Define or explain:

tension stress and strain ultimate tension
compression stress and   strength
  strain   brittle
linear limit   ductile
elastic limit   fatigue

Young's modulus   buckling
Hooke's law   critical height
spring constant   shear stress and strain
neutral surface   shear modulus
internal torque   polar moment of inertia
area moment of inertia

EXERCISES

Section 8.1 | General Aspects of Stress and Strain

8-1   A 2-m long bar has a rectangular cross section, 0.02 m by 0.04 m. If it is subjected to a 10,000-N force along its length, what is the stress?

8-2   A pipe has an inner radius of 0.02 m and an outer radius of 0.023 m. If it is subjected to a tension stress of $5 \times 10^7 \ N \ m^{-2}$, how large is the applied force?

8-3   A 0.4-m pipe under compressional stress changes length by 0.005 m. What is the strain in the pipe?

8-4   The largest tension strain that can occur before fracture in aluminum is 0.003. What is the maximum change in length of a 1-m aluminum pipe?

8-5   A man's leg can be thought of as a shaft of bone 1.2 m long. If the strain is 1.3×10^{-4} when the leg supports his weight, by how much is his leg shortened?

8-6   A rubber rod of length 0.5 m and radius 10^{-3} m stretches 0.1 m when a 140 N force is applied. How large a force is needed to stretch a rubber rod 0.1 m if its length is 0.5 m and its radius is 2×10^{-3} m?

8-7   An automobile jack supports half the weight of a 1500-kg vehicle. If the stress is not to exceed $10^8 \ N \ m^{-2}$, and the jack has a solid circular cross section, what is its minimum radius?

8-8   A steel wire 10 m long has a radius of 1 mm = 10^{-3} m. Its linear limit is $2.5 \times 10^8 \ N \ m^{-2}$, and its ultimate tension strength is $5 \times 10^8 \ N \ m^{-2}$. The wire is attached at one end and hangs vertically with a weight at its lower end. (a) If the wire is just at its linear limit, how large is the weight? (b) What is the largest load the wire can support?

8-9   A steel cable with a diameter of 3 cm =

3×10^{-2} m supports a chairlift at a ski area. If the maximum stress is not to exceed 10^8 N m^{-2}, what is the greatest load the cable can support?

8-10 A bar stretches 0.01 cm when a 10,000-N tension force is applied and stretches 0.3 cm when a 25,000-N tension force is applied. Is the stress-strain graph linear? Explain.

Section 8.2 | Young's Modulus

8-11 A rod with a radius of 0.005 m and a length of 2 m stretches 0.002 m when subjected to a tension force of 10,000 N. What is Young's modulus for this rod?

8-12 When a steel rod is at its ultimate tension strength, what is its strain?

8-13 A steel post is compressed by 0.001 cm when it supports a compressive load. (a) If it is replaced by a hardwood post with the same dimensions, how much is the hardwood post compressed? (b) If, instead, a steel post is used with the same length but half the radius, by how much is it compressed?

8-14 An aluminum wire is 20 m long and has a radius of 2 mm = 2×10^{-3} m. The linear limit for aluminum is 0.6×10^8 N m^{-2}. (a) How large a tension force must be applied to stretch the wire to its linear limit? (b) How much will the wire stretch when this force is applied?

8-15 A 100-kg mass is suspended from the end of a vertical, 2-m-long steel post with a cross-sectional area of 0.1 m^2. (a) Find the stress and strain in the post. (b) How much does the post stretch? (c) What is the maximum mass that can be suspended from this post?

8-16 A hardwood post with dimensions 10 cm by 15 cm by 3 m supports a load of 1000 N along its length. (a) Find the stress and strain in the post. (b) What is its change in length?

8-17 If the minimum cross-sectional area of a human femur is 6.45×10^{-4} m^2, what is the tension load at which fracture occurs?

8-18 A sheet of glass has an area of 0.5 m^2 and is 0.005 m thick. (a) If it is placed horizontally, what is the uniformly distributed load at which fracture occurs? (b) What is the change in thickness if half that load is applied?

8-19 A vertical steel post is 3 m long and has a radius of 0.1 m. It is supporting a load of 10^5 N.

(a) Find the stress and strain in the post. (b) Find the change in length.

8-20 The average cross-sectional area of a woman's femur is 10^{-3} m^2, and it is 0.4 m long. The woman weighs 750 N. (a) What is the length change of this bone when it supports half of the weight of the woman? (b) Assuming the stress-strain relationship is linear until fracture, what is the change in length just prior to fracture? (c) Is the answer to part (b) an overestimate or underestimate?

8-21 What is the spring constant of a human femur under compression of average cross-sectional area 10^{-3} m^2 and length 0.4 m?

8-22 A rubber band has a circumference of 0.4 m when it is unstretched. The rubber has a rectangular cross section, 0.01 m by 0.001 m. (a) What is the spring constant of the rubber band? (b) How large a force must be applied to increase its length by 0.05 m?

8-23 A shock cord used to tie luggage onto an auto roof rack is made up of 20 cylindrical strands of rubber. Each strand is 0.002 m in radius and 0.5 m long when unstretched. If the cord is stretched 0.3 m from its equilibrium length, how large a force does it exert?

Section 8.3 | Bending Strength

8-24 A cylindrical rubber rod is 0.5 m long and has a radius of 0.005 m. (a) What is its area moment of inertia? (b) What torque is exerted by the internal elastic forces on the ends of a rod when it is bent into a circle?

8-25 A cylindrical steel rod 2 m long has a radius of 0.01 m. If it is loaded so that it bends elastically with a 20-m radius of curvature, what is the torque due to this load?

8-26 A board is 1 cm by 6 cm in cross section. (a) Compute the area moments of inertia for loads parallel to the longer dimension and for loads parallel to the shorter dimension. (b) What is the ratio of the radii of curvature for the two deflections if equal loads are applied to the board in both orientations?

8-27 Two boards have the same length. (a) Board A has a 4-cm-by-4-cm cross section. What is its area moment of inertia for forces perpendicular to one of its sides? (b) Board B has a 2-cm-by-8-cm cross section. Find its two area moments of inertia for forces perpendicular to its shorter and longer sides. (c) Which board would be stronger if forces were always applied along a given direction perpendicular to its length? (d) Which board would be the best choice if the forces were to be applied in various directions perpendicular to its length?

8-28 A 10-m-long hollow steel cylinder is secured to a concrete base and used as a flagpole. Its inner and outer radii are 7 and 8 cm, respectively. (a) What is its area moment of inertia? (b) If the wind exerts a horizontal force at the top of 10^3 N, what is the radius of curvature of the flagpole?

8-29 In Fig. 8.14, two equal but opposite forces of magnitude F are shown acting on a book that remains at rest although it is deformed. (a) Is the book in equilibrium? (b) What are the other two forces acting on the book? (c) Do the other forces have the same line of action? Explain.

Section 8.4 | Buckling Strength and Structural Design in Nature

8-30 In a monument, a column is just strong enough to withstand buckling under its own weight. The column is 10 m tall and 0.1 m in radius. If a similar column is to be 40 m tall, what is its minimum radius?

8-31 A tall, slender column or tower is less likely to buckle if it is supported by guy wires attached to its top and to the ground some distance from the bottom. Why is a relatively small amount of material in the form of guy wires more effective than adding a similar amount to the structure itself?

8-32 A tree is just stable against buckling. If it grows until its height is doubled, and again it is just stable against buckling, by what factor does its cross-sectional area at the base change?

8-33 Using $l = cr^{2/3}$ with the experimental value $c = 34.9$ $m^{1/3}$, find the height of a tree of trunk radius $\frac{1}{8}$ m. Comment on whether your answer seems reasonable.

8-34 Give an argument as to why the data of Fig. 8.13 do not fall on a single straight line.

8-35 A uniform column will buckle under its own weight when

$$l = \left(\frac{2E}{w_0}\right)^{1/3} r^{2/3}$$

For hardwood, $E = 10^{10}$ N m^{-2} and $w_0 = 5900$ N m^{-3}. Compare the length of a uniform column of wood of radius $\frac{1}{8}$ m with that of a typical tree of the same trunk radius for which $l = cr^{2/3}$ and $c = 34.9$ $m^{1/3}$.

Section 8.5 | Shearing and Twisting Torques

8-36 Two bones of equal radius are subjected to equal twisting torques. If one is longer than the other, which will fracture first?

8-37 A steel bar is clamped in a vise, so that a cube with sides 0.01 m protrudes above the jaws of the vise. (a) If a force of 100 N is applied along the top face of the cube, what are the stress and strain? (b) What is the horizontal displacement of the top face?

8-38 A 75-kg bicyclist puts all her weight on one pedal. (Fig. 8.20) The diameter of the central shaft of the pedal is 1.5 cm. (a) Find the shear stress on the pedal shaft. (b) Find the ratio of this stress to the maximum shear stress, 10^8 N m^{-2}.

8-39 Two metal plates overlap slightly and are attached by a row of 10 rivets. Each rivet has a radius of 3 mm = 3×10^{-3} m. If the shearing stress on the rivets is not to exceed 10^8 N m^{-2}, what is the greatest force that can be applied to the ends of the plates?

8-40 A brake block on a bicycle has a shear modulus of 10^7 N m^{-2}. When the brake is applied, the block exerts a 100-N force on the wheel rim. The surface in contact with the rim is 1 cm by 5 cm, and the block is 0.8 cm thick. (a) What is the shear stress on the block? (b) By what distance is the surface in contact displaced?

  Pedal shaft

Figure 8.20. Exercise 8-38.

8-41 A truck pulls a travel trailer with a mass of 2000 kg. They are connected by a hitch whose weakest link is a steel pin 2 cm in diameter that slides through a hole across the shaft of the hitch. The maximum shearing stress for the steel is 10^8 N m^{-2}. (a) During a panic stop, the hitch must support a load equal to 20 percent of the weight of the trailer. What is the shearing stress on the pin? (b) Find the ratio of this stress to the maximum shearing stress.

8-42 A steel rod is 0.4 m long and has a radius of 0.5 cm. (a) Find its polar moment of inertia. (b) One end is held fixed and the other is twisted. How large a torque must be applied to twist the end 0.1 radians (5.7°)? (c) This torque is applied by a wrench. If the force applied normal to the wrench is 100 N, how long is the wrench?

8-43 How large a force is required to shear a bolt with a radius of 0.005 m if it breaks when the shearing stress is 2×10^8 N m^{-2}?

8-44 A steel plate is 0.002 m thick and breaks when the shearing stress is 2×10^8 N m^{-2}. (a) A force is applied uniformly at right angles to a circle of radius 0.005 m on the plate. How large is the area that must be used in calculating the corresponding shear stress? (b) How large a force must be applied to punch out a hole of radius 0.005 m?

PROBLEMS

8-45 Three vertical 10-m-long steel tubes support a water tank. The inner and outer radii of the tubes are 15 and 17 cm, respectively. The tank is designed so that the stress on the tubes will not exceed 10^8 N m^{-2}. (a) Find the maximum volume of water the tank can hold, assuming the weight of the tank is negligible compared to that of the water. (The density of water is 1000 kg m^{-3}.) (b) By how much are the tubes shortened when they support the maximum load?

8-46 Suppose the I beam shown in Table 8.2 is rotated 90° about a horizontal axis, so that the "I" becomes an "H." Its area moment of inertia for supporting a vertical load is then $b^3t/6$, assuming $t \ll a, b$. For an I beam with $a = b$, find the ratio of this area moment of inertia to that of the I beam in its original orientation.

8-47 An amusement park ride whirls a car and its passengers with a total mass of 700 kg in a vertical circle of radius 8 m. At the bottom of the circle the car is moving at 12 m s^{-1}. The car is at the end of a steel arm. (a) If the maximum stress is to be 1 percent of the ultimate tension strength of the arm, what is its cross-sectional area? (b) What is the maximum elongation of the arm due to the moving car?

8-48 A freight elevator and its contents have a mass of 10,000 kg and are at rest. The steel cable supporting it has a stress equal to 10 percent of its ultimate tension strength. (a) What is the radius of the cable? (b) Find the fractional change in length $\Delta l/l$ of the cable when the motor is turned on and it accelerates the elevator upward at 2 m s^{-2}.

8-49 Two stone columns are barely stable against buckling under their own weight. If one is twice as tall as the other, find the ratio of the weight of the taller column to that of the other.

8-50 Estimate the twisting torques on the femur of a football player when he makes a sharp pivot on one foot. Does your result have any bearing on the types of cleats and playing surfaces that should be used?

8-51 The I beam in Fig. 8.21 is constructed from plates 0.003 m thick and is 0.3 by 0.4 m. (a) Calculate its area moment of inertia for loads applied vertically. (b) Calculate the area moment of inertia for a beam with square cross section having the same weight per unit length.

8-52 A 100-N bar is 5 m long. What is the magnitude of the torque on one half due to forces from the other half when it is supported horizontally? (*Hint*: See Fig. 8.5c and assume that the bar bends very little.)

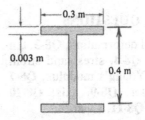

Figure 8.21. Problem 8-51.

*8-53 Two cylinders are constructed, one solid with radius r and one hollow with radii $a = 2r$ and $b = 3r/2$. If both cylinders are subjected to the same load, perpendicular to their long axes, what is the ratio of their radii of curvature?

8-54 A rod of radius a is replaced by a hollow tube of the same length with inner radius a. (a) If the tube is to have the same area moment of inertia as the rod, what must its outer radius be? (b) What is the ratio of the weights of the tube and rod?

8-55 The inner radius of a bone is half the outer radius. What would the outer radius of the bone be if, for a given torque, it were to twist through the same angle as a steel rod of the same length with a 1-cm radius? (The polar moment of inertia of a hollow cylinder is $\pi(a^4 - b^4)/2$, where a and b are the outer and inner radii, respectively.)

8-56 A steel shaft connecting an electric motor to a machine rotates at 1800 revolutions per minute. The shaft is 0.4 m long, has a radius of 1 cm, and delivers 2 kW of power. What is the twisting angle at the end of the shaft?

ᶜ8-57 Show that the polar moment of inertia of a hollow cylinder with outer radius a and inner radius b is $\pi(a^4 - b^4)/2$.

*ᶜ8-58 Derive the formula in Table 8.2 for the area moment of inertia of an I beam.

ᶜ8-59 Show that the area moment of inertia of a solid cylinder of radius r is $\pi r^4/4$. (*Hint:* Work in polar coordinates.)

ᶜ8-60 Show that the area moment of inertia of a hollow cylinder with outer radius a and inner radius b is $\pi(a^4 - b^4)/4$. (*Hint:* Work in polar coordinates.)

ANSWERS TO REVIEW QUESTIONS

Q8-1, F/A; **Q8-2,** fractional deformation; **Q8-3,** tension, compression, shear; **Q8-4,** stress and strain; **Q8-5,** elastic limit; **Q8-6,** Young's modulus; **Q8-7,** Hooke's law; **Q8-8,** harder; **Q8-9,** axis; **Q8-10,** shear stress, shear strain; **Q8-11,** shear.

SUPPLEMENTARY TOPICS
8.6 | STRUCTURE AND FUNCTION

The buckling strength criterion was employed in Section 8.4 to relate structure and size in trees. It can also be used to relate structure and physiological function in animals with a different form of the scaling concept introduced in Chapter Six. We shall see that this different scaling approach leads to much better agreement with observations.

The simple version of scaling adopted earlier assumes that all of an animal's body dimensions scale with a single characteristic length l. Thus the body volume, and hence the mass m, varies as l^3; the length varies as $l \propto m^{1/3}$. Any area A then varies as l^2 or as $m^{2/3} = m^{0.67}$, so it is predicted that the body surface area will vary as $m^{0.67}$. It is also predicted that the *metabolic rate*—the rate at which food energy is used in the body—will vary in the same way, because the rate of oxygen absorption must vary as the surface area of the lungs, and the rate of heat loss must vary as the body surface area.

The actual scaling laws found by experiment are not always in exact agreement with the predictions of this simple model (Fig. 8.22). For example, one failure of the simple scaling procedure was observed by Kleiber in 1932. He found that the rate of heat production in mammals ranging in size from mice to elephants is not proportional to $m^{0.67}$ but to $m^{0.75}$. This difference is small, but it is sufficient to raise doubts about the validity of the model.

Recently, McMahon suggested that one should take account of the fact that most body segments are cylindrical and are perhaps built to withstand buckling. If this is true, the length l and radius r of each body segment are related as we found in Section 8.4, $l \propto r^{2/3}$. Because the volume of a cylindrical body segment is $\pi r^2 l$, the mass m should be proportional to $r^2 l$. Using $r \propto l^{3/2}$ we find $m \propto r^2 l = (l^{3/2})^2 l = l^4$. This is significantly different from the other scaling assumption, $m \propto l^3$.

In this model, since $m \propto l^4$, lengths should scale as $l \propto m^{1/4}$. Also because $l \propto r^{2/3}$, $r^{2/3} \propto m^{1/4}$ or $r \propto m^{3/8}$. Thus our scaling assumption is that lengths and radii of body segments scale with mass as

$$l \propto m^{1/4}, \qquad r \propto m^{3/8} \qquad (8.14)$$

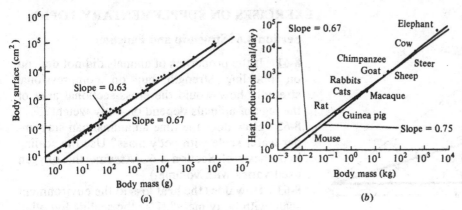

Figure 8.22. (a) The body surface area of mammals of various sizes. (b) The metabolic rates of various mammals versus mass. The black lines are the predictions of the buckling strength model: the colored lines are those of the simple scaling model. (From T. McMahon, *Science*, vol. 179, pp. 1201–1204, March 23, 1973. Copyright 1973 by the American Association for the Advancement of Science.)

We can use these results to find how the body surface area of mammals with cylindrical body segments scales with their mass.

To find the surface area, we note that most cylindrical body segments are connected to other segments at either one or both ends. The surface area of one segment will then be proportional to the area of the sides of the cylinder: $A_{surf} = 2\pi rl$. Using the relations of Eq. 8.14, $A_{surf} \propto rl$, so

$$A_{surf} \propto m^{3/8}m^{1/4} = m^{5/8}$$

This $\frac{5}{8} = 0.625$ is very close to 0.63 and fits the surface area data in Fig. 8.22a quite well.

To find the metabolic rate, we calculate not the surface area but the power used to flex a muscle. This power $\mathcal{P}$ is the force exerted F times the velocity of muscle contraction v. Since all mammalian muscles are found to exert the same force per unit area $\sigma = F/A$, we write the force as $F = \sigma A$, where A is the cross-sectional area of the muscle. Thus

$$\mathcal{P} = Fv = \sigma Av$$

For voluntary muscle fiber, it has been found experimentally that the velocity of muscle contraction is also the same for all mammals. Thus σ and v do not depend on the mass and $\mathcal{P} \propto A$. The cross-sectional area A depends on the square of the radius of the muscle, $A \propto r^2$, so

$$\mathcal{P} \propto A \propto r^2 \propto m^{0.75}$$

This is the result shown in Fig. 8.22b, if we assume that the power expended and the heat production

scale in the same way. The rate of work done by the heart muscle should also vary as $m^{0.75}$; and, because metabolic processes use oxygen absorbed through the lung wall, the lung area should depend on $m^{0.75}$. Both of these results have been well established experimentally.

From these results, we can also find how pulse rates scale. The metabolic rate, and hence the oxygen demand of the body, is proportional to $m^{0.75}$. The volume of blood pumped per heartbeat is proportional to the heart volume or to m. The blood pumped per second will vary as mf, where f is the heart rate. Then $mf \propto m^{0.75}$ or $f \propto m^{-0.25}$. This means that larger animals should have lower pulse rates. Again, this has been observed experimentally.

To summarize, the assumption that the cylindrical segments of animals have their shape determined by the buckling criterion gives rise to scaling laws that are in good agreement with a variety of experiments. Even if further study should show that this model is not adequate to explain other kinds of data, it does illustrate clearly how physical principles can influence the relationship between size and function in biological systems.

8.7 DERIVATION OF $l_{cr} = cr^{2/3}$

We consider the particular example of a uniform column of radius r and length l that bends under its own weight with a radius of curvature R (Fig. 8.23). The torque due to the weight w is $\tau = wd$ and must be counteracted by a torque acting at the base of the column equal to $\tau = EI_A/R$. For a cylinder, $I_A =$

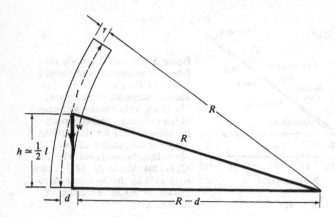

Figure 8.23. A column of length l and radius r, supported at its base, bends with a radius of curvature R.

$\pi r^4/4$. Thus when the column is just at the buckling point,

$$\frac{E\pi r^4}{4R} = wd \qquad (8.15)$$

We now need to find expressions for w and d.

If the weight per unit volume is w_0, the total weight is w_0 times the volume, or $w = w_0(\pi r^2 l)$. The distance d can be found from the colored triangle in Fig. 8.23. The sides of the triangle have lengths R, $R - d$, and h. If the radius of curvature is large compared to l, then $h \simeq \frac{1}{2}l$. Using the Pythagorean theorem,

$$(R - d)^2 + (\tfrac{1}{2}l)^2 = R^2$$

Squaring and neglecting the term d^2, we find $d = l^2/8R$.

Using our results for w and d in Eq. 8.15,

$$\frac{E\pi r^4}{4R} = w_0(\pi r^2 l)\frac{l^2}{8R}$$

or

$$l = \left(\frac{2E}{w_0}\right)^{1/3} r^{2/3}$$

This is the critical length l_{cr} of Eq. 8.8 for a uniform column. Here $c = (2E/w_0)^{1/3}$, where E is Young's modulus and w_0 is the weight per unit volume of the column.

EXERCISES ON SUPPLEMENTARY TOPICS

Section 8.6 | Structure and Function

8-61 If the properties of animals did not depend on buckling strength but on compressional strength, how would the cross-sectional area of the legs of animals depend on body weight?

8-62 How does the time an animal can stay under water scale with body mass? Use the scaling hypothesis of Section 8.6. (Assume the oxygen used varies with volume.)

8-63 How does the heat loss to the environment scale with body mass? (Use the scaling hypothesis of Section 8.6.) Are your results consistent with the fact that small animals are not generally found in arctic areas?

8-64 If all mammals lived the same number of heartbeats, which animals would live longest?

PROBLEMS ON SUPPLEMENTARY TOPICS

8-65 Find how the speed with which an animal can run uphill varies with its mass, assuming (a) the simplest scaling law; (b) the buckling strength criterion.

8-66 Assume that as a human grows from an infant to an adult, the bones grow according to the relationship $l \propto r^{2/3}$. (a) If the breaking angle during twisting is always the same, are adults or infants more susceptible to fractures due to twisting forces? (b) How does the twisting torque scale with body mass?

8-67 If the proportions of animal body segments are determined by the structural buckling strength criterion, how does the height jumped vary with the mass? Compare your result with that of Chapter Six.

8-68 The column of Fig. 8.23 will fracture when the stress at the outer (and inner) edges reaches the maximum σ_t. Show that this occurs when $\sigma_t = Er/R$.

8-69 Using the results of Problem 8-68, find the maximum radius of curvature for a hardwood tree with $r = 0.25$ m. Use $E = 10^{10}$ N m^{-2} and $\sigma_t = 10^8$ N m^{-2}.

8-70 What is the radius of a cylindrical steel rod that fractures when the radius of curvature is 4 m? (Use the results of Problem 8-68).

Additional Reading

Harold M. Frost, *An Introduction to Biomechanics*, Charles C Thomas, Springfield, Ill., 1967. Brief introduction to the properties of biological materials.

Hiroshi Yamada, in F. Gaynor Evans (ed.), *Strength of Biological Materials*, Williams and Wilkins Co., Baltimore, 1970. Results of extensive research.

T. McMahon, Size and Shape in Biology, *Science*, vol. 179, 1973, p. 1201. Buckling strength and scaling.

R. McNeill Alexander, *Animal Mechanics*, University of Washington Press, Seattle, 1968. Chapters 3 and 4 discuss elastic properties, strength.

Francis Gaynor Evans, *Stress and Strain in Bones*, Charles C Thomas, Springfield, Ill., 1957.

Haywood Blum, Physics and the Art of Kicking and Punching, *American Journal of Physics*, vol. 45, 1977, p. 61. Karate and the strength of materials.

John R. Cameron and James G. Skofronick, *Medical Physics*, John Wiley & Sons, Inc., New York, 1978, Chapter 3 on composition and strength of bones.

Horace Freeland Judson, "Take That, King Richard!" *Science 80*, July/August 1980, p. 44.

Scientific American articles:

John J. Gilman, Fracture in Solids, February 1960, p. 94.

Carl W. Condit, The Wind Bracing of Buildings, February 1974, p. 93.

Francis P. Bundy, Superhard Materials, August 1974, p. 62.

Thomas A. McMahon, The Mechanical Design of Trees, July 1975, p. 92.

Tsu-Wei Chou, Roy L. McCullough, and R. Byron Pipes, Composites, October 1986. One of several interesting articles in an issue devoted to new materials.

Jearl Walker, Strange to Relate, Smokestacks and Pencil Points Break in the Same Way, *The Amateur Scientist*, February 1979, p. 158.

CHAPTER 9
VIBRATIONAL MOTION

When an object moves back and forth repeatedly over the same path, it is said to be oscillating or vibrating. Some familiar examples are a child on a swing, a clock pendulum, and a violin string. Oscillations also play an important role in many physical phenomena outside the field of mechanics. For example, the molecules of solids vibrate about their equilibrium positions and the currents in electrical circuits can reverse directions or oscillate. There are also many biological examples of oscillations, such as the production of sound by the human vocal cords and the motions of insect wings.

Although the physical nature of vibrating systems can vary greatly, the equations describing small oscillations of an object about an equilibrium position often relate its acceleration, velocity, and displacement in exactly the same special way. A vibration of this kind is called *simple harmonic motion*, and its mathematical description is always the same except for differences in the symbols used.

Simple harmonic motion is characterized by several quantities. The *amplitude* is the maximum displacement of the oscillating object from equilibrium. A complete oscillation back and forth, which returns the system to its original state, is called a *cycle*. The *period T* is the time needed for one full cycle. The *frequency f* of the oscillation is the number of cycles in a unit time. If the period is $\frac{1}{2}$ s, there are two full oscillations per second. In general, the period and the frequency are related by $f = 1/T$. Frequencies are measured in cycles per second of Hertz (Hz).

In this chapter, we first find the general relations describing simple harmonic motion and discuss several examples of this motion. We then discuss the effects of a frictional force that dissipates energy

and of external forces that vary in time and provide energy. We find that there is a special frequency of the external force for which the oscillations have the greatest amplitude. Examples of this *resonance* phenomenon occur in molecular, mechanical, biological, and other systems.

9.1 | SIMPLE HARMONIC MOTION

In Chapter Eight, we found that many objects, when stretched or compressed, exert a force opposing this action that is directly proportional to the distance they are stretched or compressed. Simple coil springs have this property. When a mass at the end of a coil spring is displaced from its equilibrium position and released, the resulting oscillatory motion is referred to as *simple harmonic motion*. This means the position, velocity, and acceleration are related in a specific way that we now determine.

When a coil spring is stretched by the application of a force, the resulting elongation x and the applied force F are proportional:

$$F = kx \tag{9.1}$$

The proportionality factor k is called the *spring constant*.

The spring exerts a restoring force that is opposite in direction:

$$F_r = -kx \tag{9.2}$$

The minus sign indicates that the restoring force is always opposite to the displacement, or toward the equilibrium point.

In Fig. 9.1, a mass resting on a frictionless table is attached to a spring. Suppose now we pull the mass away from its equilibrium point and release it. Then

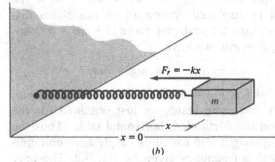

Figure 9.1. (a) A mass on a frictionless horizontal table. (b) When the spring is stretched a distance x, it exerts a restoring force $F_r = -kx$ opposite to the displacement.

it will move under the influence of the restoring force $-kx$ in accordance with Newton's second law of motion, $F = ma$. Thus the motion will satisfy $-kx = ma$, or

$$a = -\frac{kx}{m} \quad \text{(simple harmonic motion)} \quad (9.3)$$

This equation states that the acceleration a is proportional to the magnitude of the displacement x from the equilibrium position and is opposite in direction. Whenever such a relationship holds, the object undergoes a specific type of motion called *simple harmonic motion*. Equation 9.3 can be considered a definition of simple harmonic motion (SHM).

To find the explicit description of this motion, we recall that $v = dx/dt$ and that $a = dv/dt = d^2x/dt^2$. Hence $a = -kx/m$ implies that the second derivative of x is proportional to $-x$. Two functions that have this property are sines and cosines. For example, we can try a solution of the form

$$x = A \cos \omega t \quad (9.4)$$

where A and ω are constants that we determine shortly. Then, using Eq. B.26 in Appendix B, $(d/dt) \cos \omega t = -\omega \sin \omega t$ and

$$v = \frac{dx}{dt} = -A\omega \sin \omega t \quad (9.5)$$

Similarly, $(d/dt) \sin \omega t = \omega \cos \omega t$ and

$$a = \frac{dv}{dt} = -A\omega^2 \cos \omega t \quad (9.6)$$

Thus we have found a solution of the SHM equation of motion, $a = -kx/m$, if the constant ω satisfies $\omega^2 = k/m$, or

$$\omega = \sqrt{\frac{k}{m}} \quad (9.7)$$

If we had chosen $x = B \sin \omega t$, we would again have had a satisfactory solution, but with peak values of x and v at different times from those of a cosine solution. A linear combination of a sine and a cosine is the most general solution.

Now let's see what the constants A and ω mean. The cosine varies from -1 to $+1$, so x varies from $-A$ to $+A$ (Fig. 9.2). Thus A is the *amplitude*, the maximum displacement in either direction from the equilibrium point. The cosine function repeats itself when its argument ωt goes through 360° or 2π radians, or after a time T that satisfies $\omega T = 2\pi$. The time $T = 2\pi/\omega$ required for one full cycle is called the *period*. Its reciprocal, $f = 1/T$, the number of oscillations per second, is the *characteristic frequency* of the oscillator. Thus

$$f = \frac{1}{T} = \frac{\omega}{2\pi} = \frac{1}{2\pi}\sqrt{\frac{k}{m}} \quad (9.8)$$

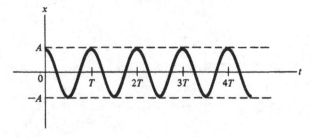

Figure 9.2. A plot of $x = A \cos \omega t$ versus t. The cosine varies from -1 to $+1$, so x varies from $-A$ to $+A$. Since the cosine repeats when its argument increases by 2π, the time for one full oscillation is $T = 2\pi/\omega$.

This equation shows that if the mass is increased, the frequency decreases, and the spring oscillates less rapidly. If the spring is made stiffer so that k is increased, the spring oscillates more rapidly. The quantity $\omega = 2\pi f$ is measured in radians per second and is called the *angular frequency*. The oscillator is not undergoing angular motion, so the name is somewhat inappropriate. However, an object undergoing circular motion at a constant angular velocity ω in the x–y plane has x and y coordinates that undergo SHM with a frequency $f = \omega/2\pi$ (Fig. 9.3).

In summary, SHM occurs whenever the acceleration is related to the displacement by $a = -kx/m$, or with $\omega^2 = k/m$, by

$$a = -\omega^2 x = -(2\pi f)^2 x \qquad (9.9)$$

The following example shows how the spring constant and frequency of a mass and spring may be found.

Example 9.1

The object in Fig. 9.1 has a mass of 0.1 kg and is on a frictionless table. If a 5-N force is applied, the spring is stretched 0.2 m. (a) What is the spring constant? (b) Find the characteristic frequency and period of oscillation when the mass is set in motion.

(a) The force applied and the elongation are related by $F = kx$, so

$$k = \frac{F}{x} = \frac{5 \text{ N}}{0.2 \text{ m}} = 25 \text{ N m}^{-1}$$

(b) The characteristic frequency is

$$f = \frac{1}{2\pi} \sqrt{\frac{k}{m}} = \frac{1}{2\pi} \sqrt{\frac{25 \text{ N m}^{-1}}{0.1 \text{ kg}}} = 2.52 \text{ Hz}$$

The period is $T = 1/f = 0.397$ s.

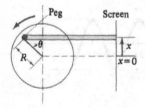

Figure 9.3. A peg at distance R from the center of a wheel that is rotating with a constant angular velocity ω. The peg is illuminated by a lamp at the left, and it casts a shadow on the screen at the right. If $\theta = \omega t$, the position of the shadow is $x = R \cos \omega t$.

9.2 | THE WEIGHT ON A SPRING

It is much easier in practice to illustrate oscillatory motion with an object hanging on a spring than it is to arrange for nearly frictionless horizontal motion. We see now that despite the complication of the weight of the object, the motion is essentially the same.

In Fig. 9.4, a weight $w = mg$ is hung on a spring. In equilibrium, the spring will be stretched a distance d such that its restoring force $F_r = -kd$ balances the weight mg, or $-kd + mg = 0$. If the weight is displaced downward an *additional* distance x, then the restoring force is $-k(d + x)$. Applying $F = ma$, we have

$$-k(d + x) + mg = ma$$

Since $-kd + mg = 0$, this reduces to $-kx = ma$, exactly the same result we just obtained for the mass on the frictionless horizontal table. Thus the hanging weight also executes simple harmonic motion with a frequency given by Eq. 9.8. The only difference is that here it oscillates about an equilibrium point displaced a distance d from the end of the unstretched spring. *The frequencies and periods are the same for vertical and horizontal motions.*

Example 9.2

In the preceding example, a 0.1-kg mass moved horizontally on a frictionless table at the end of a spring with spring constant 25 N m^{-1}. Suppose instead the mass is hung from the spring as in Fig. 9.4. (a) How far is the spring stretched when the mass is in equilibrium? (b) Find the characteristic frequency when the mass is set into motion.

(a) In equilibrium, the restoring force balances the weight, or $-kd + mg = 0$. Solving for d,

$$d = \frac{mg}{k} = \frac{(0.1 \text{ kg})(9.8 \text{ m s}^{-2})}{25 \text{ N m}^{-1}} = 0.0392 \text{ m}$$

(b) Since the frequency is the same whether the motion is horizontal or vertical, the frequency has the same value as in Example 9.1, or 2.52 Hz.

9.3 | THE PHYSICAL PENDULUM

An object swinging back and forth also undergoes simple harmonic motion. Such an object is called a *physical pendulum*. We will find that the physical pendulum serves as a useful model for the analysis

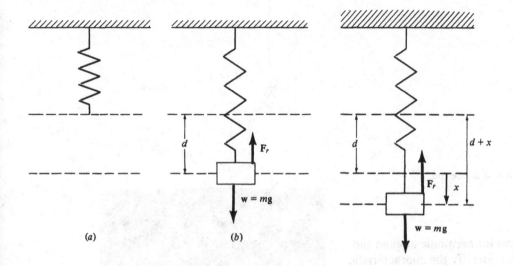

Figure 9.4. (a) A spring with constant k. (b) A weight w is hung from the spring. It is in equilibrium and remains at rest when $kd = mg$. (c) The weight is displaced a distance x from the equilibrium position. The force F_r due to the spring is $-k(d + x)$.

of certain kinds of body motions. A *simple pendulum* is an idealized example of a physical pendulum, consisting of a massless rod with a point mass at its end. Results for the simple pendulum can be obtained directly from those for the physical pendulum.

We consider an object of arbitrary shape that can swing frictionlessly about an axis A (Fig. 9.5). The object has mass m and moment of inertia I about A. The distance from A to the center of mass C.G. is d.

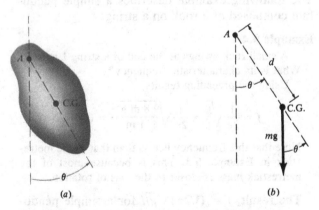

Figure 9.5. (a) An object of mass m and moment of inertia I with respect to the axis at A. (b) A schematic diagram showing the force $w = mg$. The distance from A to the center of gravity (C.G.) is d. At equilibrium the C.G. is on the vertical dashed line beneath A.

The object is initially displaced and released. Figure 9.5 shows the object when the displacement is θ, which is taken to be positive when the C.G. is to the right of the vertical line through A. Since the motion is not linear but angular, we must compute torques and angles rather than forces and distances.

The torque is $\tau = rF \sin \theta$, where r is the length of the line from A to C.G. and $F \sin \theta$ is the component of the force perpendicular to this line. From the figure, we see that $r = d$ and $F = mg$. The torque is then $\tau = -mgd \sin \theta$, where the minus sign indicates that the torque is clockwise. Using the angular form of Newton's second law, $\tau = I\alpha$, we have

$$-mgd \sin \theta = I\alpha$$

or

$$\alpha = -\frac{mgd}{I} \sin \theta$$

This is not the equation for harmonic motion even though α is the angular acceleration associated with the displacement θ. However, at small angles $\sin \theta$ and θ are almost equal. If θ is measured in radians, for example, $\sin \theta$ and θ differ by only about 1 percent at 15° and by about 5 percent at 30°. Thus for *small angles*, we have

$$\alpha = -\frac{mgd}{I} \theta$$

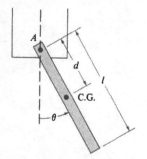

Figure 9.6.   A metrestick pivoted at one end.

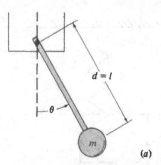

(a)

This has the correct form for harmonic angular motion, $\alpha = -(2\pi f)^2 \theta$, if we identify the characteristic frequency as

$$f = \frac{1}{T} = \frac{1}{2\pi}\sqrt{\frac{mgd}{I}} \qquad (9.10)$$

A metrestick swinging about one end is an example of a physical pendulum.

Figure 9.7.   (a) A simple pendulum is a point mass at the end of a massless rod. (b) The period of a simple pendulum is independent of its mass. Swing (Courtesy of M. Sternheim)

Example 9.3

A metrestick suspended from one end is displaced slightly and released (Fig. 9.6). When does the metrestick first become vertical?

According to Table 5.3, the moment of inertia I for a rod of mass m and length l rotating about an axis through its end is $\frac{1}{3}ml^2$; the distance d from the C.G. to the axis of rotation is $\frac{1}{2}l$. With Eq. 9.10,

$$f = \frac{1}{2\pi}\sqrt{\frac{mgd}{I}} = \frac{1}{2\pi}\sqrt{\frac{mgl/2}{ml^2/3}} = \frac{1}{2\pi}\sqrt{\frac{3g}{2l}}$$

$$= \frac{1}{2\pi}\sqrt{\frac{3(9.8 \text{ m s}^{-2})}{2(1 \text{ m})}} = 0.61 \text{ Hz}$$

Note that the frequency does not depend on the mass. The metrestick is vertical after one quarter of a period, or $t = T/4 = 1/4f$. Thus

$$t = \frac{1}{4f} = \frac{1}{4(0.61 \text{ s}^{-1})} = 0.41 \text{ s}$$

Simple Pendulum | The simple pendulum is an idealized system that is also sometimes a good approximation to a real system. It consists of a point mass m at one end of a massless rod of length l pivoted about the other end. Its moment of inertia is ml^2 and $d = l$ (Fig. 9.7).

Using the results for the physical pendulum, the frequency of the simple pendulum is

$$f = \frac{1}{T} = \frac{1}{2\pi}\sqrt{\frac{mgl}{ml^2}} = \frac{1}{2\pi}\sqrt{\frac{g}{l}} \qquad (9.11)$$

The following example describes a simple pendulum composed of a rock on a string.

Example 9.4

A small rock swings at the end of a string 1 m long. What is its characteristic frequency?

Using the preceding results,

$$f = \frac{1}{2\pi}\sqrt{\frac{g}{l}} = \frac{1}{2\pi}\sqrt{\frac{9.8 \text{ m s}^{-2}}{1 \text{ m}}} = 0.5 \text{ Hz}$$

Note that this frequency is less than that of the metrestick in Example 9.3. This is because most of the metrestick mass is closer to the axis of rotation.

The result, $f = (1/2\pi)\sqrt{g/l}$ for a simple pendulum, is particularly simple and interesting. Since g is nearly constant over the earth's surface, f depends only on the length of the simple pendulum.

The mass is not important except that it must be much larger than that of the rod or string, so that we may assume $I = ml^2$. One way of observing this is to note that the period of oscillation of different people on identical swings is nearly independent of their weight. The dependence of the period on length may also be verified roughly by observing the way the period of a weight tied to a string varies as the length of the string is changed.

The implications of the variation of period with length are often important in our daily activities. Normal walking speeds are very nearly those determined by considering the legs as swinging rigid rods. In running, the leg is bent during its forward motion. This reduces its length and hence its period. The bent leg moves forward more quickly than a rigid leg, reducing the effort required. Furthermore, the arms are moved in opposition to the legs to provide balance but are kept bent to reduce their period and the effort required to move them back and forth.

9.4 | ENERGY IN SIMPLE HARMONIC MOTION

In the preceding section, we discussed a pendulum executing simple harmonic motion. It is convenient to define the potential energy to be zero when the pendulum is at its lowest point, so its energy is entirely kinetic at this position. When the pendulum is at its highest point, the velocity is zero, and the energy is entirely potential. Since no forces other than gravity do work, the total mechanical energy is conserved, and the maximum potential energy is equal to the maximum kinetic energy. As the pendulum swings back and forth, there is a continual conversion of kinetic to potential energy and then back to kinetic energy (Fig. 9.8).

Similarly, when a mass oscillates on a spring, the total energy is constant, and there is a continual interchange of potential and kinetic energy. For a mass on a spring sliding on a frictionless table, we choose the origin at the equilibrium position where the spring force is zero. Again, it is convenient to define potential energy to be zero at the equilibrium point. As the mass passes through $x = 0$, its energy is entirely kinetic. At the points of maximum dis-

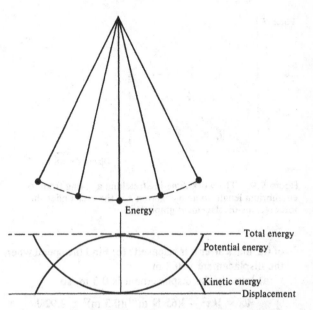

Figure 9.8. As a pendulum swings farther from its equilibrium point, the potential energy increases and the kinetic energy decreases. Their sum, which is the total energy, remains constant throughout the motion.

placement, the mass is momentarily at rest, and the kinetic energy is zero. All the energy is then potential energy stored in the spring.

The potential energy at a displacement x is equal to the work that must be done against the restoring force to stretch the spring to the extent. We saw in Section 6.1 that when an object is displaced, the work done by a force $\mathbf{F}$ is $\int \mathbf{F} \cdot \mathbf{ds}$. The force needed to stretch a spring a distance x' is $F = kx'$, so the work done in stretching the spring from 0 to x is

$$W = \int_0^x F \, dx' = \int_0^x kx' \, dx' = \tfrac{1}{2}kx^2$$

(This result can also be obtained by using geometric arguments to find the area under the F–x graph, Fig. 9.9.) Hence the potential energy at x is

$$\mathcal{U} = \tfrac{1}{2}kx^2 \tag{9.12}$$

The following example illustrates this result.

Example 9.5

A mass of 2 kg on a spring is extended 0.3 m from the equilibrium position and released from rest. The spring constant is 65 N m^{-1}. (a) What is the initial potential energy of the spring? (b) What is the maximum speed

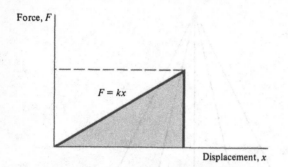

Figure 9.9.   The work done in stretching a spring from its equilibrium length to an elongation x is the area under the force-versus-displacement graph.

of the mass after it is released? (c) Find the speed when the displacement is 0.2 m.

(a) Initially the displacement is 0.3 m, so

$$\mathcal{U}_0 = \tfrac{1}{2}kx^2 = \tfrac{1}{2}(65 \text{ N m}^{-1})(0.3 \text{ m})^2 = 2.92 \text{ J}$$

(b) The energy is totally kinetic when the spring and mass pass through the unstretched position, $x = 0$. The kinetic energy there is $\tfrac{1}{2}mv^2$ and is equal to the initial potential energy. Thus

$$\tfrac{1}{2}mv^2 = \mathcal{U}_0$$

or

$$v = \sqrt{\frac{2\mathcal{U}_0}{m}} = \sqrt{\frac{2(2.92 \text{ J})}{2 \text{ kg}}} = 1.71 \text{ m s}^{-1}$$

(c) When $x = 0.2$ m, the system has both potential and kinetic energies that are nonzero. The potential energy can readily be calculated from $\tfrac{1}{2}kx^2$. Because the total energy is conserved, it is equal to the initial potential energy $\mathcal{U}_0$ found in (a). Hence we can get the kinetic energy and determine the speed:

$$\tfrac{1}{2}mv^2 + \tfrac{1}{2}kx^2 = \mathcal{U}_0$$

$$v = \sqrt{\frac{2}{m}\left(\mathcal{U}_0 - \tfrac{1}{2}kx^2\right)}$$

$$= \sqrt{\frac{2}{2 \text{ kg}}\left[2.92 \text{ J} - \tfrac{1}{2}(65 \text{ N m}^{-1})(0.2 \text{ m})^2\right]}$$

$$= 1.27 \text{ m s}^{-1}$$

Example 9.6

A spring with a mass m attached oscillates at a characteristic angular frequency ω. It is stretched a distance R and released at $t = 0$. At a later time t, find the

(a) potential energy; (b) kinetic energy; (c) total energy.

(a) The frequency and spring constant are related by

$$\omega = \sqrt{\frac{k}{m}}$$

Squaring and solving for k, we find

$$k = m\omega^2$$

Using Eq. 9.6, the displacement at time t is

$$x = R \cos \omega t$$

Hence the potential energy is

$$\mathcal{U} = \tfrac{1}{2}kx^2 = \tfrac{1}{2}m\omega^2 R^2 \cos^2 \omega t$$

(b) Since $v = -\omega R \sin \omega t$,

$$K = \tfrac{1}{2}mv^2 = \tfrac{1}{2}m \omega^2 R^2 \sin^2 \omega t$$

(c) The total energy is

$$E = K + \mathcal{U}$$

$$= \tfrac{1}{2}m\omega^2 R^2 \sin^2 \omega t + \tfrac{1}{2}m\omega^2 R^2 \cos^2 \omega t$$

$$= \tfrac{1}{2}m\omega^2 R^2 [\sin^2 \omega t + \cos^2 \omega t]$$

Now $\sin^2 \vartheta + \cos^2 \vartheta = 1$ for any value of ϑ, so

$$E = \tfrac{1}{2}m\omega^2 R^2$$

The total energy E is constant. Note that $\sin^2 \vartheta$ and $\cos^2 \vartheta$ each have maximum values of 1. Hence K and $\mathcal{U}$ each have maximum values equal to $\tfrac{1}{2}m\omega^2 R^2 = E$, as expected.

Energy conservation can be applied to problems involving more than one kind of potential energy, as in the next example.

Example 9.7

A toy gun fires 0.05-kg darts tipped with suction cups. The spring constant is 400 N m^{-1}, and it is compressed 0.1 m. If all the stored energy of the spring is transferred to a dart, how high will it rise when the gun is fired straight up?

Here spring potential energy is converted first into kinetic energy and then into gravitational potential energy. At the highest point reached, $v = 0$, and the kinetic energy is zero. Since energy is conserved throughout, we can equate the initial energy of the spring and the increase in gravitational potential energy. Thus if the increase in height is h, we have

$$\tfrac{1}{2}kx^2 = mgh$$

Solving for h,

$$h = \frac{\frac{1}{2}kx^2}{mg}$$

$$= \frac{\frac{1}{2}(400 \text{ N m}^{-1})(0.1 \text{ m})^2}{(0.05 \text{ kg})(9.8 \text{ m s}^{-2})}$$

$$= 4.08 \text{ m}$$

9.5 | DAMPED OSCILLATIONS

Most real situations involving vibrational motion cannot be described precisely by the equations of simple harmonic motion because of the presence of dissipative forces such as friction or air resistance. For example, a child on a swing, a clock pendulum, and a violin string all gradually come to rest unless energy is supplied to replace the losses. In this section, we briefly describe the reduction in amplitude, or *damping*, caused by dissipative forces. In the next section, we discuss what happens when energy is fed into a system by an external source.

Dissipative forces typically depend on the velocity, but the exact dependence varies and can be quite complicated for some systems. Often it is assumed that the dissipative force F_d is linearly proportional to v, or $F_d = -\gamma v$. (The qualitative behavior of an oscillator does not greatly depend on the exact form of the force law.) Here γ is the *damping constant*, and the minus sign indicates that the damping force opposes the motion.

The effect of including the damping force in the equation of motion for a weight on a spring is illustrated in Fig. 9.10. If γ is zero, oscillations continue with the same amplitude indefinitely. When a small amount of damping is present, the oscillations steadily decrease in amplitude until they are negligibly small. If γ is larger, then the oscillations diminish faster. Oscillations cannot occur at all when γ is very large; if displaced, the weight returns to its equilibrium position without oscillating.

The theory of damped oscillations has some interesting biological applications. For example, it provides a way of measuring the friction present in the joints of mammalian limbs. As we noted in Chapter Three, this friction is quite small because of the lubricating effects of synovial fluid. If you sit so that your lower leg can swing freely from the knee and

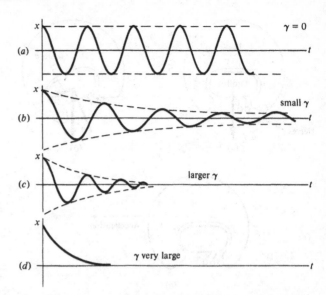

Figure 9.10. The displacement of a weight on a spring versus time. (*a*) No dissipative forces. The displacement is alternately positive and negative with constant amplitude. (*b*) With a dissipative or damping force, the amplitude gradually diminishes. (*c*) With more damping, the amplitude diminishes more rapidly. (*d*) If the damping is very large, no oscillations occur.

set it in motion, it will gradually come to rest if no muscular forces are exerted. Measurement of the rate at which the amplitude diminishes leads to information about the frictional forces. In a normal knee, there is very little friction, and the oscillations damp out slowly, much as in Fig. 9.10*b*.

An example of strongly damped motion is provided by the cupola in the inner ear of vertebrates. We learned in Chapter Five that this is a swinging door type of structure that is easily displaced from its equilibrium position by the relative motion of the endolymph fluid and the semicircular canal. Here the spring constant k is very small, and the damping due to the fluid is comparatively large. As a result, the cupola returns very slowly over a period of about 20 s to its equilibrium position, and it does not oscillate at all. This is similar to the situation shown in Fig. 9.10d.

Another structure in the ear of vertebrates, the *otolith*, provides an example of an intermediate amount of damping. All vertebrates have two or three otoliths, which provide information about ac-

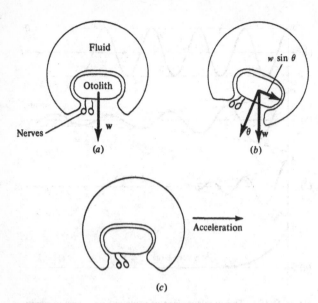

Figure 9.11. (a) The otolith is denser than the surrounding fluid. Tilting (b) or accelerating (c) causes the otolith to move. Nerve endings adjacent to the otolith sense its motion. Note that in (b) and (c) the side portions of the fluid-filled chamber change size. (Adapted from Alexander.)

celeration and tilting of the animal. The otolith is made of calcium carbonate and is about three times as dense as water. It is connected by springlike tissue to a cavity filled with watery fluid (Fig. 9.11). When the head tilts or accelerates, the otolith moves relative to the fluid, and this motion is detected by sensory nerves. Although the otolith does go past the new equilibrium position when the head tilts or accelerates, it oscillates only a few times before coming to rest. This is the kind of situation shown in Fig. 9.10c. Thus evolution has arranged that, in a very short time, information about the amount of tilt or acceleration will be available to the brain without significant ambiguity due to continued oscillations.

9.6 | FORCED OSCILLATIONS AND RESONANCE

We saw in the preceding section that unless energy is supplied, the amplitude of an oscillator usually decreases in time because of frictional effects. To overcome such losses, clock pendulums are driven by coiled springs, and children on swings pump their feet. When energy is fed into a vibrating system, the system is said to be undergoing *forced oscillations*.

A singer holding a note of a certain frequency can set up vibrations in a glass. If the singer persists, the energy absorbed by the glass may cause large enough vibrations so that the glass will shatter (Fig. 9.12). This is only true of well-made glassware. In poorer-quality glasses, which are less homogeneous in composition, various portions of the glass have different characteristic frequencies, and no single frequency will cause shattering.

Soldiers crossing bridges break step because the regular march step may be at just the right frequency to set the bridge vibrating and perhaps cause its ultimate destruction. A spectacular example of a bridge being set into motion and collapsing is that of the Tacoma Narrows Bridge in Washing-

Figure 9.12. A trained singer can break a glass by sustaining the right note. (Foodcollection RF / Getty Images, Inc.)

Figure 9.13. Winds caused the Tacoma Narrows Bridge to collapse after several hours of increasing vibrations. After this disaster, which occurred in 1940, some similar bridges were substantially modified. (©AP / Wide World Photos)

ton. The wind set the bridge oscillating with a steadily increasing amplitude (Fig. 9.13).

Insect wings may vibrate at up to 120 times per second, although only about three nerve impulses per second trigger the wing muscles. The nerve impulses arrive at just the right frequency to maintain the natural vibrational motion of the wing.

In all these examples, there are both dissipative forces that reduce the vibrations and external forces that supply energy. Depending on the physical circumstances, there may be a balance of these two energies, so that the amplitude of the motion is constant, as with the clock or the insect wing. Sometimes energy enters the system faster than it is dissipated, and disaster follows, as with the glass and the Tacoma Narrows Bridge. Finally, if the energy does not enter the system at very nearly the right

frequency, little or no vibration occurs, since the energy supplied is immediately dissipated.

As we have seen, energy is most effectively supplied to an oscillator when the external force acts at the correct frequency, which is usually close to the frequency of the oscillator with no external force. This phenomenon is called *resonance*, and the optimum frequency is referred to as the *resonant* frequency (Fig. 9.14). A child pumping a swing or a parent pushing from behind learns to apply forces at just the right interval to attain the maximum amplitude. Similarly, people trying to push a car stuck in snow or mud are most successful when they allow the car to rock back and forth and time their pushes appropriately.

A spectacular example of resonance is provided by the enormous tides in Canada's Bay of Fundy.

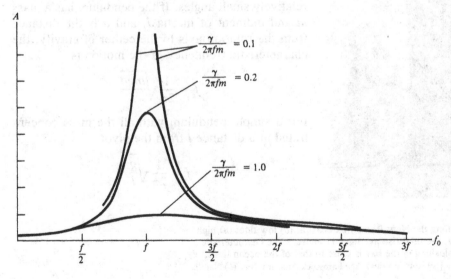

Figure 9.14. The amplitude of an oscillator versus the frequency f_0 of the external force driving the oscillator. The amplitude has its greatest value at the resonant frequency, which is very close to the characteristic frequency of the oscillator. Note that as the damping constant γ is reduced, the amplitude at resonance becomes larger.

(a)

(b)

The tidal rise in the ocean averages about 0.3 metre, but at the head of the bay it averages 11 metres. One reason for this is that the characteristic frequency of oscillation of the water as it sloshes back and forth in the bay is about 13 hours, just slightly more than the 12.4 hours between successive high tides. Since the driving force—the ocean tide—has a frequency close to the characteristic frequency, large resonant amplitudes result. Proposals have been made to dam up part of the flow and use it to drive electric generators. It is expected that the dams would in effect shorten the bay and decrease the period. In that event, the frequencies would be even closer, and the tidal rise might increase farther! (Fig. 9.15).

SUMMARY

Any motion in which the displacement x and acceleration a are related by

$$a = -\omega^2 x = -(2\pi f)^2 x$$

is simple harmonic motion; f is the natural or characteristic frequency of the motion. The period T is the time for one full cycle, and $f = 1/T$.

A mass attached to a spring undergoes simple harmonic motion. If the mass is m and the spring constant is k, the frequency of the motion is

$$f = \frac{1}{2\pi}\sqrt{\frac{k}{m}}$$

A common example of simple harmonic motion is a physical pendulum that swings back and forth at relatively small angles. If the pendulum has a mass m and moment of inertia I, and d is the distance from the rotation axis to the center of gravity, the characteristic frequency of the motion is

$$f = \frac{1}{2\pi}\sqrt{\frac{mgd}{I}}$$

For a simple pendulum with all the mass concentrated at a distance l from the pivot,

$$f = \frac{1}{2\pi}\sqrt{\frac{g}{l}}$$

Figure 9.15. The Hopewell Rocks along the New Brunswick coast at (a) low tide; (b) high tide. At the head of the Bay of Fundy, the tidal rise averages 11 metres. The characteristic frequency of oscillation of the water sloshing in the bay is close to that of the ocean tides, resulting in large resonant amplitudes. [(a) Ron de Vries / Age Fotostock America, Inc., (b) Natalia Bratslavsky / Age Fotostock America, Inc.]

The total mechanical energy of an object undergoing simple harmonic motion is constant. There is a repeated interchange between the kinetic and potential energy portions. The potential energy is

$$\mathcal{U} = \tfrac{1}{2} kx^2$$

If dissipative forces are present, the energy of an oscillating system is not constant, and the motion is said to be damped. The rate at which the motion dies out is proportional to the magnitude of the dissipative force.

If an external driving force is also present, the motion is again quite similar. However, the amplitude of the motion depends on the frequency of the external force. When the frequency of the external force is equal to the resonant frequency of the oscillator, the amplitude is largest, and the system is at resonance.

Checklist

Define or explain:

simple harmonic motion	restoring force
amplitude	physical pendulum
cycle	simple pendulum
frequency	potential energy of a spring
hertz	damping
period	forced oscillations
spring motion	resonance
spring constant	resonant frequency

REVIEW QUESTIONS

Q9-1 The time needed for one complete oscillation is the _____; its reciprocal is the _____.

Q9-2 The shadow of a peg on a rotating wheel executes _____.

Q9-3 An object will undergo simple harmonic motion if its acceleration is proportional to _____.

Q9-4 The force needed to change the length of a spring is proportional to the _____.

Q9-5 Comparing an object hanging from a spring with a similar system moving horizontally without friction, the characteristic frequencies of oscillation are _____.

Q9-6 The characteristic frequency of oscillation of a mass on a spring decreases if the mass is

_____ and increases if the spring constant is _____.

Q9-7 If the length of a simple pendulum is increased, its period _____.

Q9-8 The kinetic energy of a simple harmonic oscillator is greatest when the displacement equals _____ and least when the displacement equals _____.

Q9-9 Oscillations die out quickly if the _____ is large.

Q9-10 When an external force acts on an oscillator, the amplitude is greatest at the _____.

EXERCISES

Section 9.1 | Simple Harmonic Motion; An Experiment

9-1 An object is undergoing simple harmonic motion with an amplitude R. (a) In one complete cycle, what is its displacement? (b) In one complete cycle, what is the total distance it travels back and forth?

9-2 An object undergoes simple harmonic motion with an amplitude of 0.1 m. Its maximum acceleration is 2 m s^{-2}. Find (a) the frequency of the oscillations; (b) the maximum velocity.

9-3 An object undergoes simple harmonic motion, with the displacement a maximum at $t = 0$. For which parts of a cycle (if any) do the following quantities have the same sign or direction: (a) displacement and velocity; (b) displacement and acceleration; (c) velocity and acceleration?

9-4 A mass on the end of a spring moves according to Eqs. 9.4, 9.5, and 9.6 at a frequency $f = 1.5$ Hz. (a) What is the angular frequency ω? (b) If the amplitude of the oscillation is 0.2 m, what is the displacement at $t = \tfrac{1}{3}$ s?

9-5 An object oscillates according to Eqs. 9.4, 9.5, and 9.6. Its frequency is $f = 0.5$ Hz and the amplitude is 0.1 m. Find its displacement and velocity at (a) $t = 0$ s; (b) $t = 0.5$ s; and (c) $t = 1$ s.

9-6 An object undergoing simple harmonic motion has its greatest displacement, 0.2 m, at $t = 0$. Its characteristic frequency is 8 Hz. (a) Find the earliest times at which the displacements will be 0.1 m, 0 m, -0.1 m, and -0.2 m. (b) Find the velocities at those times.

9-7 An object undergoing simple harmonic motion with an amplitude of 0.5 m and a period of 2 s has a velocity of 1.11 m s^{-1}. What is its displacement?

9-8   An object undergoing simple harmonic motion with a frequency of 10 Hz has a maximum velocity of 3 m s^{-1}. What is the amplitude of the motion?

9-9   At what displacement of an object undergoing simple harmonic motion is the magnitude greatest for (a) the velocity; (b) the acceleration?

Section 9.2 | The Weight on a Spring

9-10   Masses m and M are suspended from two identical springs of spring constant k. When set in motion, the characteristic frequency of M is three times that of m. What is the ratio M/m?

9-11   The characteristic frequency of a mass on a spring is 5 Hz. What is the acceleration of the mass when the displacement is 0.15 m?

9-12   A spring stretches 0.05 m when a 0.3-kg mass is suspended from it. (a) What is the spring constant? (b) What is the characteristic frequency of this mass on the spring?

9-13   A spring oscillates with an amplitude of 0.2 m. Its maximum velocity is 3 m s^{-1}. Find the spring constant if the mass on the spring is 0.01 kg.

9-14   When a 3-kg mass is hung from a spring, it oscillates once every 4 s. What is the spring constant?

9-15   When a 30-N force is applied to a spring, it stretches 0.2 m. (a) If a 5-kg mass is hung from the spring and remains at rest, how much is the string stretched from its original length? (b) What is the period of oscillation of the mass and spring?

9-16   By what factor must the mass of an object attached to a spring be increased to double the period of oscillation?

9-17   When a passenger with a mass of 80 kg enters a car, the springs are compressed by his weight a distance of 1.2 cm. If the total mass supported by the springs (including the passenger) is 900 kg, find the characteristic frequency of oscillation of the car and passenger.

9-18   An object of mass 10 kg hanging on a spring has a characteristic frequency of 2 Hz. How much will the length of the spring change when the object is detached?

Section 9.3 | The Physical Pendulum

9-19   A small weight swings at the end of a string. If the period is 1 s, how long is the string?

9-20   A simple pendulum has a 1.5-s period on earth. When it is set swinging at the surface of another planet, the period is found to be 0.75 s. What is the acceleration of gravity on this planet?

9-21   A steel ball on the end of a cable is used in demolition work. The period of swing is found to be 7 s. What is the length of the cable? (Neglect the mass of the cable.)

9-22   (a) Estimate the moment of inertia of your lower leg and foot when pivoted at the knee. (b) What is your estimate of the characteristic frequency of the lower leg and foot when pivoted at the knee? (c) How does your estimate in part (b) compare to your observations?

9-23   A uniform rod is suspended at one end. The characteristic period of its swing is 2 s. What is the length of the rod?

9-24   What is the percentage error in using sin $\theta = \theta$, where θ is in radians, at (a) 10°; (b) 20°; (c) 30°; (d) 40°?

9-25   By what factor must the length of a simple pendulum be changed to double the period of oscillation?

9-26   The gravitational acceleration g increases by 0.44 percent when one goes from the equator to Greenland. If a pendulum has a period of 1 s at the equator, what is its period in Greenland?

9-27   A wrench is allowed to pivot about a hole through one end. Its radius of gyration is 0.15 m and its center of gravity is 0.1 m from the end. If it swings as a physical pendulum, what is its frequency?

9-28   A pendulum has a period of 1 s on the earth. What is its period on the moon? (Use the solar and terrestrial data on the inside back cover.)

9-29   A man hangs 10 m below a parachute that is falling at a constant velocity. If we treat his sideways motion as that of a simple pendulum, what is his period of oscillation?

9-30   By what factor must the length of a simple pendulum be changed to double its frequency?

Section 9.4 | Energy in Simple Harmonic Motion

9-31 An oscillator has an amplitude of 0.2 m and a maximum velocity of 4 m s^{-1}. What is the magnitude of the velocity when the displacement is 0.15 m?

9-32 A pendulum has an amplitude θ_0. At what displacement will its angular velocity be half the maximum value?

9-33 In Example 9.7, what is the speed of the darts as they leave the gun?

9-34 A 0.5-kg mass on a spring has a period of 0.3 s. The amplitude of the motion is 0.1 m. (a) What is the spring constant? (b) What is the potential energy stored in the spring at maximum displacement? (c) What is the maximum speed of the mass?

9-35 A 0.05-kg mass is hung from a massless rubber band and stretches it 0.1 m. (a) What is the spring constant of the rubber band? (b) What is the characteristic frequency of oscillation of the system? (c) What is the period of the oscillation? (d) If the mass is pulled 0.05 m below the equilibrium position and released, what will be the energy associated with the oscillations?

9-36 A 5-kg mass is attached to a spring with a spring constant of 100 N m^{-1}. If it oscillates with a maximum velocity of 4 m s^{-1}, what is the amplitude of the motion?

9-37 A simple harmonic oscillator has an amplitude of 0.1 m. At what displacement will its kinetic and potential energies be equal?

9-38 When the displacement of a simple harmonic oscillator is half its amplitude, what fraction of the total energy is kinetic energy?

9-39 A 10-kg mass is attached to a spring with spring constant 50 N m^{-1}. It is pulled 0.2 m from its equilibrium position and released. Find its velocity (a) at the equilibrium position; (b) at a displacement of -0.1 m.

9-40 In a pinball machine, a spring is compressed and then released so that a ball is fired. A player shoots a ball that just reaches the top of the machine, stopping after traveling 0.5 m. The surface of the machine makes an angle of 10° with the horizontal direction, and the mass of the ball is 0.1 kg. If the spring is compressed 0.02 m be-fore it is released, what is its spring constant? (Assume all the stored energy of the spring is tranferred to the ball and neglect friction.)

9-41 A 50-kg boy rides on a Pogo stick, a pole with a spring on its bottom end. He jumps into the air 0.3 m and lands on the ground, compressing the spring 0.05 m. (Neglect the mass of the stick.) (a) How much energy is stored in the spring? (b) What is its spring constant? (c) What is the characteristic frequency of oscillation?

Section 9.5 | Damped Oscillations

9-42 The otolith in a fish has a mass of 0.022 g = 2.2×10^{-5} kg, and the effective spring constant is 3 N m^{-1}. (a) What is the characteristic frequency of the otolith? (b) Is the frequency consistent with the idea that the otolith should respond rapidly to accelerations or changes in orientation?

9-43 The characteristic frequency of a man's lower leg and foot, when swung at the knee, is 1.3 Hz. The motion is damped out after six swings. (a) What is the period of the motion? (b) How long does the leg swing?

9-44 The otolith of a fish has a mass of 0.1 g = 10^{-4} kg and a spring constant of 3 N m^{-1}. (a) Find the characteristic frequency. (b) Assuming the damped otolith comes to rest in a time equal to twice its natural period, how long is the otolith in motion after the fish's head is tilted?

9-45 A damped oscillator has its amplitude reduced by a factor of 10. By what factor is its energy reduced?

9-46 The otolith of a fish has a mass of 0.3 g = 3×10^{-4} kg and an effective spring constant $k = 3$ N m^{-1}. The damping constant $\gamma = 1.5 \times 10^{-2}$ N m^{-1} s. (a) What is the characteristic frequency of the otolith? (b) What is the ratio $\gamma/(2\pi f m)$? (c) Does the otolith have a fairly sharp resonance?

PROBLEMS

9-47 During the motion of a weight on a spring, the position, velocity, and acceleration are given by

$$x = x_0 \cos \omega t$$
$$v = -\omega x_0 \sin \omega t$$
$$a = -\omega^2 x_0 \cos \omega t$$

Evaluate x, v, and a for (a) $t = 0$; (b) $t = \pi/\omega$. (c) In words, describe how x, v, and a change with time between $t = 0$ and $t = \pi/\omega$.

9-48 Sketch the x–t, v–t, and a–t graphs for an object undergoing simple harmonic motion for one full cycle.

9-49 Equations 9.4, 9.5 and 9.6 were obtained assuming the clock was started at $t = 0$ when the displacement of the spring had its greatest value. Find the analogous equations for the case when the velocity has its greatest value at $t = 0$.

9-50 An object of mass m is connected to two springs with constants k and k' (Fig. 9.16). (a) Show that when the mass is displaced a distance x from its equilibrium position, the restoring force exerted by the pair of springs is $-(k + k')x$. (b) Find the frequency of oscillation of the object.

9-51 Using sense organs in their legs, spiders can detect vibrations in their webs when their prey is captured. When trapped in one web, a 1-g $= 10^{-3}$-kg insect causes the web to vibrate at 15 Hz. (a) What is the spring constant of the web? (b) What would be the frequency of a 4-g insect caught in the web?

9-52 Young's modulus for bone is $E = 1.6 \times 10^{10}$ N m^{-2}. The tibia is 0.2 m long and has an average cross-sectional area of 0.02 m^2. (a) What is the spring constant of the bone? (b) A man weighs 750 N. How much is the bone compressed if it supports half his weight? (c) If the bone oscillates lengthwise with half the body weight on it, what is the characteristic frequency of oscillation?

9-53 An instructor wishes to prepare a class demonstration of simple harmonic motion. She has only a 2-kg mass available but has a selection of springs. (a) What spring constant should she choose to have a period of 2 s? (b) She selects the spring by measuring the extension of the available springs with the 2-kg mass. What extension is she seeking?

Figure 9.16.   Problem 9-50.

9-54 The characteristic frequency of the simple pendulum of a clock is 0.7 Hz. The pendulum is 0.5 m long. How should the length be changed to change the frequency to 0.8 Hz?

9-55 The human leg can be approximated by a cylinder. (a) Estimate the characteristic frequency of your legs when swung from the hip with the knee locked. (b) If normal walking were performed with the legs swinging at their natural frequency, how far could you walk in 1 hour?

9-56 (a) If one assumes that the arm is a uniform rod, estimate the characteristic frequency of the extended arm. (b) Estimate the frequency if the forearm is at a right angle with the upper arm as in running.

9-57 A ball on a 30-m cable is used for demolition work. If the maximum angular displacement is 20°, what is the velocity of the ball at its lowest point? (Neglect the mass of the cable.)

9-58 A 1-m-long rod is suspended about a pivot at one end and has a small sphere attached at the other. The rod and sphere have the same masses. What is the frequency of oscillation?

9-59 A metrestick of mass m is hung on a nail through a hole located 0.25 m from an end. (a) What is its moment of inertia about this point? (b) Find the characteristic frequency if it is displaced slightly and released.

9-60 A uniform disk of radius R is suspended from a point on its edge. What is its characteristic frequency for oscillations in the plane of the disk?

9-61 A simple pendulum is displaced 30° and then released. Its period differs by 1.7 percent from that predicted by Eq. 9.11. (a) Is its period longer or shorter than the prediction? Explain your reasoning. (b) A second pendulum with the same length is started in motion at the same time with a very small displacement. How many cycles will it take for the first pendulum to be at its starting position whent he second is at its lowest point?

9-62 A weight hung from a spring stretches it a distance d when it is in equilibrium. Show that when the weight is set into motion, its characteristic frequency is

$$f = \frac{1}{2\pi}\sqrt{\frac{g}{d}}$$

9-63 Show   that the potential energy of a simple pendulum displaced from equilibrium by a small angle θ is

$$\mathcal{U} = \tfrac{1}{2}mgl\theta^2$$

9-64 Using the result of the preceding problem, find the maximum angular velocity of a simple pendulum if its amplitude of oscillation is θ_0.

*9-65 Derive a formula for the potential energy of a physical pendulum displaced from equilibrium by a small angle θ.

9-66 Sketch the graph of $\mathcal{U}$ and K versus time for an object undergoing simple harmonic motion for one full cycle.

9-67 The simple harmonic oscillation provides a good approximation to the motion of many complex vibrational systems. This is because, for small displacements, the restoring force can usually be approximated by $F_r = -kx$. To show this, consider an object whose equilibrium position is $x = 0$ and that experiences a restoring force when displaced slightly to either side. The restoring force, for small x, can be expanded generally as a series, $F_r = a + bx + cx^2 + dx^3 + \cdots$. (a) Show that the coefficient a must be zero. (b) Show that b must be negative. (c) Show that $c = 0$. (d) Show that the dx^3 term can be neglected for small enough displacements, assuming $b \neq 0$.

9-68 The physical pendulum illustrates the point made in the preceding problem: the simple harmonic oscillator provides a good approximation to the motion of many complex systems. (a) Using the series expansion for $\sin \theta$ in Appendix B.6, write the restoring torque in the form $\tau_r = a + b\theta + c\theta^2 + d\theta^3 + \cdots$. Verify that $a = 0$, $b < 0$, and $c = 0$. (b) Find the ratio of the magnitudes of $d\theta^3$ and of $b\theta$. (c) Find the angle in degrees for which this ratio is 0.1.

9-69 The simple harmonic oscillator provides a good model for small oscillations about equilibrium in many systems, including molecules. In the H_2 molecule, the two hydrogen atoms can

Figure 9.17.   An oscillator model for the hydrogen molecule. Problem 9-69.

oscillate toward and away from each other, so that their center of mass remains stationary (Fig. 9.17). Each moves as though connected to a spring with constant 1130 N m^{-1}. (a) Find the frequency of oscillation. (b) If the vibrational energy of the molecule is 1.23 eV, what is the amplitude of the oscillations for each atom? (*Hint*: Each atom has half the total energy.) (c) Find the maximum velocity of the atoms relative to the C.M.

9-70 In a torsional pendulum, an object rotates about a fixed axis, with a restoring torque provided by a spring rather than by gravity. When the object is displaced from equilibrium by an angle θ, the restoring torque is $-\kappa\theta$, where κ is the torsional constant of the spring. (a) Show that the object will undergo simple harmonic motion. (b) If its moment of inertia is I, show that the characteristic frequency is $f = (\kappa/I)^{1/2}/2 \pi$.

9-71 In an experiment designed to measure G, a thin rod with masses at each end is hung from a very find quartz fiber. The masses are each 0.03 kg, and the rod is 0.5 m long. If the period of oscillation of the rod is 4 minutes, what is the torsional constant of the fiber? (*Hint*: Use the result of the preceding problem.)

9-72 The torsional pendulum is defined in Problem 9-70. Show that its potential energy is $\tfrac{1}{2}\kappa\theta^2$. (*Hint*: The work done in a displacement is the area under the F–x curve; the work done in a rotation is the area under the τ–θ curve.)

°9-73 (a) Show that $x = A \cos (\omega t + \alpha)$ is a solution of the SHM equation $a = -kx/m$. (b) What is the significance of α?

9-74 Show that the area under the F–x curve (Section 9.4) is $kx^2/2$ using geometric arguments.

9-75 Show from the motion of the peg in Fig. 9.3 that its shadow has (a) a velocity of $v = -\omega R \sin \omega t$; (b) an acceleration $a = -\omega^2 R \cos \omega t = -\omega^2 x$.

9-76 Using the series $\sin\theta = \theta - (\theta^3/6) + \cdots$, estimate the angle in radians and in degrees at which the approximation $\sin\theta = \theta$ is in error by 10 percent.

ANSWERS TO REVIEW QUESTIONS

Q9-1, period, frequency; **Q9-2,** simple harmonic motion; **Q9-3,** the negative of the displacement; **Q9-4,** elongation; **Q9-5,** equal; **Q9-6,** increased, increased; **Q9-7,** increases; **Q9-8,** zero, the amplitude; **Q9-9,** damping constant; **Q9-10,** resonant frequency.

SUPPLEMENTARY TOPICS

9.7 | THE EFFECTS OF VIBRATION ON HUMANS

People have always experienced vibrational motion in activities such as walking or running. However, they are now routinely subjected to vibrational motion when they travel in cars or airplanes, operate tractors, use power tools, or work near machinery. The effects of vibration may range from mild annoyances to injury or death, depending on the amplitude, frequency, and duration of the vibration. Considerable research has been directed at measuring these effects, so that safer and more comfortable vehicles and machines can be designed.

Discussions of the effects of vibration normally use the peak acceleration a_{max} rather than the amplitude as a variable. According to Eq. 9.9, the acceleration is related to the displacement by $a = -(2\pi f)^2 x$. When x is equal to the amplitude A or to $-A$, the magnitude of the acceleration is

$$a_{max} = (2\pi f)^2 A \qquad (9.13)$$

Laboratory experiments are usually done with platforms or seats that vibrate at a single frquency, although practical vibrational motion situations often involve a combination of oscillations with many different frequencies. Figure 9-18 shows the reactions to vertical oscillations for subjects sitting on a hard seat. The greatest sensitivity occurs at 6 to 7 Hz; larger accelerations can be tolerated at higher or lower frequencies.

These ideas are illustrated in the following example.

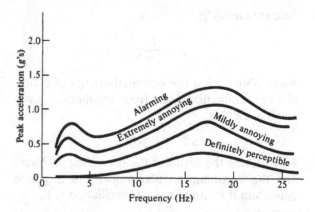

Figure 9.18. The average reactions of men to simple harmonic motion. The subjects are on hard seats that vibrate vertically. (Adapted from S. Lippert, *Vibration Research*.)

Example 9.18

What peak acceleration is perceived as alarming at 6 Hz? What is the corresponding vibrational amplitude?

From Fig. 9.18, the peak acceleration at 6 Hz that is perceived as alarming is about $0.65g$, where g is the acceleration due to gravity. With Eq. 9.13, the amplitude is

$$A = \frac{a_{max}}{(2\pi f)^2} = \frac{(0.65)(9.8 \text{ m s}^{-2})}{[2\pi(6 \text{ s}^{-1})]^2}$$

$$= 4.48 \times 10^{-3} \text{ m}$$

Mathematical models can correlate the observations of the response of the body to vibrations. (Fig. 9.19). At frequencies up to 2 Hz, the body reacts as though it were a single mass attached to a spring with some damping present. Above 2 Hz, there is relative motion of the body parts, and a much more complex model is needed. The body as a whole has a resonance at about 6 Hz, but the abdominal mass resonates at 3 Hz, the pelvis at 5 and 9 Hz, the head relative to the shoulders at 20 Hz, and the eyeballs in their sockets at 35 and 75 Hz (Fig. 9.20). Vibration well below the "alarming" level causes physiological changes in the circulatory and nervous systems and impairs coordination, vision, and speech. High levels of vibration can cause serious or even fatal lung, heart, intestinal, and brain damage.

Above 20 Hz it is relatively easy to protect people from excessive vibration using cushioned seats and

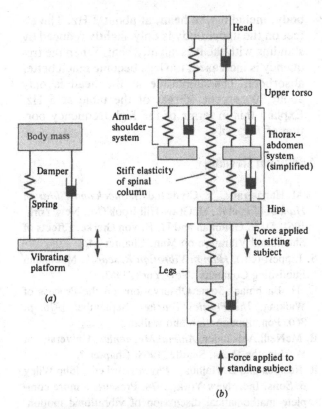

Figure 9.19. (a) A model that treats the body as a single mass describes the motion adequately for frequencies up to 2 Hz. The device resembling a piston in a fluid symbolizes the damping. (b) A more elaborate model that takes into account the relative motion of the body parts. (Adapted from R. R. Coermann et al., *Aerospace Med.*, vol. 31, p. 443, 1960.)

various simple suspension arrangements. However, tractors and trucks have most of their vibration at 1 to 7 Hz, and peak accelerations up to $1g$ sometimes occur. Springs with low resonant frequencies and hydraulic shock absorbers can be used to construct seats that reduce these vibrations to acceptable levels.

It is useful to know that when a person's legs are slightly bent, considerably less vibration is transmitted to the upper body than when the person stands or sits erect. Operators of farm machinery sometimes stand in this way to reduce the vibration to a level lower than that they experience when sitting. Similarly, if one rides a bicycle on a rough road, the discomfort can be reduced by supporting

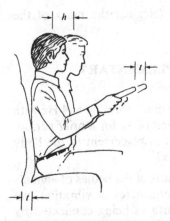

Figure 9.20. The amplitude of the motion of various body parts can exceed that of the original vibration. This often happens when the frequency is close to the resonant frequency of a particular part. Here a subject is seated on a test platform built to resemble an automobile. The figure shows the maximum displacements of the car and the subject. Note that the subject's head moves a distance h that is larger than the distance t moved by the test car.

part or all of the weight on the pedals rather than on the seat.

EXERCISES ON SUPPLEMENTARY TOPICS

Section 9.7 | The Effects of Vibration on Humans

9-77 When a man is placed on a shaking platform, his head is observed to oscillate relative to the shoulders with an amplitude that is greatest at 20 Hz. Estimate the spring constant for this motion.

9-78 A tractor seat is mounted on springs. When a 70-kg adult sits on the seat, the characteristic frequency is 7 Hz. What is the characteristic frequency when a child of mass 25 kg sits on the seat? (Neglect the mass of the seat itself.)

9-79 A 50-kg woman sits on a spring mounted seat. The spring is compressed 5×10^{-3} m. (Neglect the mass of the seat itself.) (a) What is the spring constant? (b) What is the characteristic frequency of the motion? (c) Would this be an approxiate size spring for use in a vehicle?

9-80 What is the spring constant of a tractor seat if the resonant frequency is 2 Hz with a 70-kg person seated on it? (Neglect the mass of the seat.)

PROBLEMS ON SUPPLEMENTARY TOPICS

9-81   A human can endure vibration at 4 Hz with a maximum acceleration of $4g$ for a brief period. What is the maximum displacement of the body under these conditions?

9-82   Since various parts of the bodies of animals have characteristic frequencies of vibration, we can think of these parts as being connected by springs (Fig. 9.19b). The spring is formed by the flexible connections of these parts of the body. In Chapter Eight, we learned that the spring constant is proportional to the cross-sectional area divided by the length of the spring material. (a) Using the scaling hypothesis of Section 8.6, $l \propto r^{2/3}$, show that the spring constant $k \propto m^{1/2}$, where m is the body mass. (b) Show that the characteristic frequencies should scale as $f \propto m^{-1/4}$.

9-83   The abdomen and thorax of a 60-kg human has a resonance at about 3 Hz. (a) Using the results of Problem 9-82, what would you expect the corresponding characteristic frequency to be in a 20-g = 2×10^{-2}-kg mouse? (b) Experimentally the frequency in mice is between 18 and 25 Hz. How does this compare to the result in part (a)?

9-84   When a person stands erect on a vibration table, there is a resonant vibration of the entire body, including the head, at about 2 Hz. The effect on the upper body is only slightly reduced by standing with the legs slightly bent. When the frequency is increased, the legs become much better absorbers. The amplitude at the head is only about 30 percent of that of the table at 5 Hz. Explain this in terms of the high-frequency portion of Fig. 9.14.

Additional Reading

C. M. Harris and C. E. Crede (eds.), *Shock and Vibration Handbook,* vol. 3, McGraw-Hill Book Co., New York, 1961, D. E. Goldman and H. E. von Gierke, Effects of Shock and Vibration on Man, Chapter 44.

S. Lippert (ed.), *Human Vibration Research,* Macmillan Publishing Company, New York, 1963.

C. H. Bachman, Some Observations on the Process of Walking, *The Physics Teacher,* September 1976, p. 360. Pendulum motion and walking.

R. McNeill Alexander, *Animal Mechanics,* University of Washington Press, Seattle, 1968, Chapter 7.

R. Resnick and D. Halliday, *Physics,* 3rd ed., John Wiley & Sons, Inc., New York, 1978. Presents a more complete mathematical discussion of vibrational motion, including a quantitative discussion of forced oscillations and resonance.

Scientific American Article:

Jearl Walker, Strange Things Happen When Two Pendulums Interact Through a Variety of Interconnections, *The Amateur Scientist,* October 1985, p. 176.

UNIT THREE

UNIT THREE

HEAT

The study of heat and the thermal properties of matter is actually a study of energy and energy transfer. Heat phenomena can be interpreted on a molecular basis; for example, a warm substance has a greater degree of molecular motion than a cold one. The temperature can then be thought of as a measure of the kinetic energy of this motion.

In the first chapter of this unit (Chapter Ten), we develop the molecular basis for thermal phenomena and temperature. This is accomplished by considering a simplified model of real gases, the *ideal gas*. This model is a good approximation to a real gas at low pressures and densities. Surprisingly, the ideal gas model also gives a very good description of the phenomena of diffusion and osmosis.

Long before the relationship between molecular energies and thermal phenomena was understood or even recognized, a great deal of effort went into the study of what is now called *thermodynamics*. Recognizing that the thermal properties of materials could be characterized by such general quantities as the pressure, volume, and temperature, it was found that very general and amazingly important predictions could be made about how systems exchange thermal energy and do work. At the basis of these studies are the first and second laws of thermodynamics, which are covered in Chapter Eleven. As an example of the generality of thermodynamics, we show how Carnot, in 1824, predicted the maximum possible efficiency for a heat engine. Such engines are used in automobiles and in the production of electricity in power plants. Carnot's result shows that the optimal operation of such engines depends only on the operating temperatures. Thermodynamics has proved to be a powerful and useful approach to many problems. This is particularly evident to students of chemistry, since thermodynamics is frequently used to study chemical reactions.

In the final chapter of this unit, we examine the thermal properties of various kinds of materials. We consider thermal expansion, the absorption of heat, and phase changes such as melting or vaporization. We also discuss the three types of heat transport: conduction, convection, and radiation. The phenomena discussed in this chapter are all well understood at the molecular level. However, we do not concentrate on this molecular description but describe, in terms of the temperature, the transfer of energy from one object to another and its effects.

CHAPTER 10
TEMPERATURE AND THE BEHAVIOR OF GASES

The concept of temperature plays an important role in the physical and biological sciences. As we learn in this chapter, this is because the temperature of an object is directly related to the average kinetic energy of the atoms and molecules composing the object. Since natural processes often involve energy changes, the temperature plays the role of a label for these changes.

In our everyday experience, this same idea holds true. Our perception of hot and cold is actually a measure of how rapidly energy exchange occurs between objects. Touching something hot results in a rapid and sometimes damaging transfer of energy into our bodies.

In this chapter, we first discuss several temperature scales. The measurement of temperature is based on the variation of physical properties of materials with temperature. *Dilute gases*—those with average intermolecular separations that are very large compared to the molecular dimensions, so that molecular forces are unimportant—are sometimes used to measure temperature. This is because their pressure and temperature are related accurately by a simple expression called the *ideal gas law*. The ideal gas law can be derived by applying Newton's laws of motion to a model that depicts gas molecules as particles that do not interact with each other except during occasional brief elastic collisions. This analysis also makes clear the relationship between temperature and energy and provides a framework for discussing the processes of diffusion and osmosis.

10.1 | TEMPERATURE SCALES

Many physical quantities always have the same value at a given temperature. For example, the length of a rod varies with the temperature, but it has the same value every time it is placed in a container of ice and water. Because of the reproducibility of experiments of this nature, these properties may be used to define a temperature scale.

One common thermometer uses the volume of a fixed mass of mercury to indicate the temperature. A fine glass tube is attached to a larger bulb. The bulb and part of the tube are filled with mercury, and the rest of the tube is evacuated and sealed. As the temperature increases, the volume of mercury increases faster than that of the bulb, so the mercury rises in the tube.

To calibrate the thermometer, one usually chooses two reference temperatures and divides the interval between them into some number of equal steps. Thus we might take the freezing and boiling points of water at normal atmospheric pressure as our reference temperatures and divide the interval between them into 100 equal steps. We would then have the *Celsius* (centigrade) temperature scale if we set the freezing temperature equal to 0°C and the boiling temperature equal to 100°C. This scale is in everyday use in most of the world and is widely used in scientific work. The *Fahrenheit* (°F) scale used in the United States was originally defined by setting the lowest temperature obtained with a prescribed ice water–salt mixture equal to 0°F and the temperature of the human body to 96°F. Because of the variability of the body temperature, this scale was later redefined, so that water freezes at 32°F and boils at 212°F. The relationship between the Celsius temperature T_C and the Fahrenheit temperature T_F is given exactly by the equation

$$T_C = \tfrac{5}{9}(T_F - 32°F) \qquad (10.1)$$

For example, normal body temperature is 98.6°F. On the Celsius scale, this is

$$T_C = \tfrac{5}{9}(T_F - 32°F)$$
$$= \tfrac{5}{9}(98.6°F - 32°F)$$
$$= 37.0°C$$

The procedure for defining a temperature scale does not clarify the meaning of temperature and depends on the choice of materials. For example, suppose the length of a steel rod were chosen to measure the temperature, with the same calibration procedure used again. Although the steel and mercury thermometers would necessarily agree at the two reference points, they might differ slightly at intermediate temperatures. In the following sections, we shall see how these difficulties can be avoided by using the properties of gases to define a temperature scale.

Later in this chapter, we also introduce a third temperature scale, the Kelvin, or absolute, scale. This scale is intimately related to the molecular motion and hence is used extensively in scientific work.

10.2 | MOLECULAR MASSES

The kinetic energy of a molecule depends on its mass, and the net kinetic energy of a collection of molecules also depends on the mass of the molecules. As a result, the temperature and pressure of a collection of molecules depend on the mass of the molecules. Before discussing these relationships, we describe the *molecular mass* and the *gram-mole*.

Even a relatively small sample of a pure gas contains a large number of molecules. Some gases such as helium (He) and argon (A) are *monatomic*; that is, their molecules are single atoms. Molecules of *polyatomic* gases such as oxygen (O_2), nitrogen (N_2), and ammonia (NH_3) contain two or more atoms.

The masses of atoms and molecules are tabulated using a scale defined so that the mass of a ^{12}C atom is exactly 12 atomic mass units (u). It has been determined that

$$1 \text{ u} = 1.660 \times 10^{-27} \text{ kg} \qquad (10.2)$$

In addition to ^{12}C, naturally occurring carbon contains a small amount of ^{13}C, which has one more neutron in its nucleus. The average mass of natural carbon is therefore 12.011 u.

Atomic masses for the elements are tabulated in Appendix A and on the inside back cover. The *molecular mass* (often imprecisely termed the molecular weight) of a molecule is the sum of the masses of its constituent atoms in atomic mass units. Molecular masses are calculated in the following example.

Example 10.1

Find the molecular masses of carbon dioxide (CO_2) and molecular hydrogen (H_2). The atomic masses of H, O, and C are 1.008 u, 15.999 u, and 12.011 u, respectively:

$$M(CO_2) = M(C) + 2\,M(O)$$
$$= 12.011 \text{ u} + 2(15.999 \text{ u})$$
$$= 44.009 \text{ u}$$
$$M(H_2) = 2M(H) = 2(1.008 \text{ u}) = 2.016 \text{ u}$$

A *gram-mole*, or more simply a mole, of a substance is an amount whose mass in grams is *numerically equal* to the molecular mass in atomic mass units. Thus 1 mole of CO_2 has a mass of 44.009 g, and 20.16 g of H_2 is 10 moles. Because of its definition, 1 mole of CO_2 contains exactly the same number of molecules as does 1 mole of H_2 or 1 mole of any other substance. The number of molecules in 1 mole is called *Avogadro's number* N_A, where

$$N_A = 6.02 \times 10^{23} \text{ molecules mole}^{-1} \qquad (10.3)$$

More generally, if the particles of a substance are ions or atoms rather than molecules, or a mixture of several kinds of particles, a mole still consists of N_A particles.

In the next example, we find the number of moles in a sample to determine how many molecules it contains.

Example 10.2

A tank contains 2 kg of CO_2 gas. How many molecules are in the tank?

We saw in the preceding example that the molecular mass of CO_2 is 44.0 g. The mass of the gas is 2 kg = 2000 g. In terms of moles, this amount is

$$n = \frac{2000 \text{ g}}{44.0 \text{ g mole}^{-1}} = 45.5 \text{ moles}$$

Since each mole contains N_A molecules, the total number of molecules is the product of n and Avogadro's number,

$$N = nN_A$$
$$= (45.5 \text{ moles})(6.02 \times 10^{23} \text{ molecules mole}^{-1})$$
$$= 2.74 \times 10^{25} \text{ molecules}$$

10.3 | PRESSURE

When we refer to the pressure of a gas on its container walls, or to the pressure exerted on a liquid to produce flow, we usually think of a force. In fact, the pressure of a fluid (a liquid or gas) is intimately related to but not the same as a force. The pressure is related to the magnitude of the forces a sample exerts in all directions on its surroundings. The surroundings may be the remainder of the sample or the walls of a container.

To illustrate the first case, consider a fluid in equilibrium as in Fig. 10.1a. Suppose we wished to remove a spherical portion of the fluid in such a way as to leave the remaining fluid undisturbed. Then we would have to apply, in some manner, forces such as those shown in Fig. 10.1b. *These forces would replace the actual effect of the removed fluid* and would be perpendicular or normal to the spherical surface at each point.

The sum of the *magnitudes* of the normal forces divided by the surface area is the *average pressure* $\bar{P}$ on the surface of the sphere:

$$\bar{P} = \frac{\text{magnitude of normal forces on surface}}{\text{surface area}}$$

$$= \frac{F_N}{A} \qquad (10.4)$$

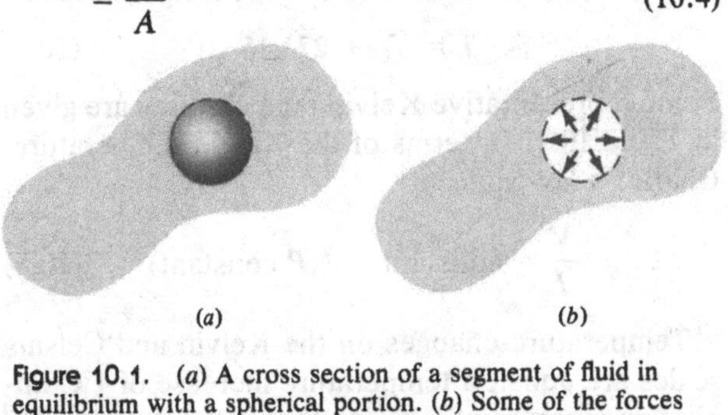

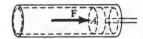

Figure 10.2. The pressure on the piston is equal to the force **F** exerted on it by the gas divided by the area A of the piston.

To obtain the *pressure* P *at a point*, we shrink the imaginary sphere until its radius and area are arbitrarily small.

The pressure exerted by a gas on its container walls is similarly defined. Figure 10.2 shows a gas in a cylinder fitted with a piston of area A. The magnitude of the force F the gas exerts on the piston divided by A is the *pressure P*:

$$P = \frac{F}{A} \qquad (10.5)$$

The gas exerts a force per unit area equal to P in magnitude and normal to the walls of its container at every point. Methods for measuring pressures are discussed in Chapter Thirteen.

The S.I. unit of pressure is the *pascal*; $1 \text{ Pa} = 1 \text{ N m}^{-2}$. Normal atmospheric pressure is

$$1 \text{ atmosphere} = 1 \text{ atm} = 1.013 \times 10^5 \text{ Pa}$$
$$= 1.013 \text{ bar}$$
$$= 760 \text{ torr}$$
$$= 760 \text{ mm Hg}$$

The *bar* and *millibar* are used extensively in meteorology. The *torr*, or the *millimetre of mercury* (mm Hg), is used in medicine and physiology. Normal atmospheric pressure will support a column of mercury of height 760 mm = 0.76 m.

The relationship between force and pressure is used in the following example.

Example 10.3

A gas at a pressure of 10 atm is in a cubical container of side 0.1 m. If the pressure outside is atmospheric pressure, what is the net force on one wall of the container?

The force due to the gas inside is

$$F_i = P_i A = (10 \text{ atm})(1.013 \times 10^5 \text{ Pa atm}^{-1})(0.1 \text{ m})^2$$
$$= 1.013 \times 10^4 \text{ N}$$

The force on the outside due to the atmosphere is

$$F_a = P_a A = (1.013 \times 10^5 \text{ Pa})(0.1 \text{ m})^2$$
$$= 0.1013 \times 10^4 \text{ N}$$

Figure 10.1. (a) A cross section of a segment of fluid in equilibrium with a spherical portion. (b) Some of the forces necessary to maintain equilibrium when the portion is removed.

(a)
(b)

The net outward force is the difference

$$F_i - F_a = 1.013 \times 10^4 \text{ N} - 0.1013 \times 10^4 \text{ N}$$
$$= 0.912 \times 10^4 \text{ N}$$

In this example, the force on the wall is proportional to the difference between the internal pressure P_i and the atmospheric pressure P_a. The difference $P_i - P_a$ is called the *gauge pressure* of the gas. For example, the gauge on a tire pump registers the gauge pressure. In this textbook, the term "pressure" without any modifier usually means the *absolute pressure*, not the gauge pressure.

10.4 | THE IDEAL GAS LAW

Suppose that we have a fixed quantity of a gas in a tank. We may vary the temperature T_C or the volume V of the gas. We discover that for any gas, at low enough densities, its pressure P is related to T_C and to V in a specific fashion. A gas that behaves in this way is called an *ideal gas*, and the equation relating these quantities is called the *ideal gas law*. Real gases under many conditions behave much like ideal gases.

The ideal gas law actually summarizes two kinds of experiments. First, if the temperature of the gas is kept constant and its volume is decreased, then the pressure increases so that the product PV is constant (Fig. 10.3):

$$PV = \text{constant} \qquad (T \text{ constant}) \qquad (10.6)$$

This was discovered by Robert Boyle (1627–1691) and is called *Boyle's law*.

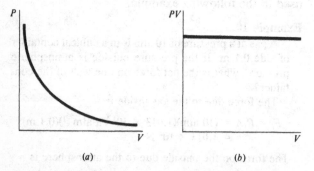

Figure 10.3. Boyle's law, for a gas at fixed temperature. (a) P is inversely proportional to V; (b) PV is constant.

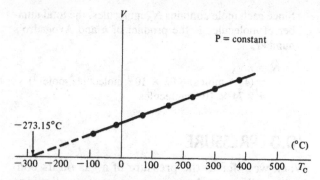

Figure 10.4. The volume of a gas decreases uniformly as the temperature decreases. The solid line is drawn through actual data points, and the dashed line is the extension down to zero volume. This dashed line intersects the temperature axis at $-273.15°C$.

The second experiment involves keeping the pressure fixed and changing the temperature. The temperature change and the volume change are proportional; each 1° temperature decrease produces the same volume decrease. This is *Charles's law*, discovered by Jacques Charles (1746–1823) and Joseph Guy-Lussac (1778–1850). Thus the plot of the measured volumes versus T_C is a straight line (Fig. 10.4).

If we extend the line through the data points toward lower temperatures and pressures, it eventually reaches $V = 0$ at $T_C = -273.15°C$. Since it is not possible to have a negative volume, this requires the existence of a minimum or *absolute zero* of temperature. It is convenient then to define a new temperature scale that measures temperatures from absolute zero. Temperatures on this *absolute*, or *Kelvin*, *scale* are related to Celsius temperatures by

$$T = T_C + 273.15 \qquad (10.7)$$

Some representative Kelvin temperatures are given in Table 10.1. In terms of the Kelvin temperature, Charles's law states

$$\frac{V}{T} = \text{constant} \qquad (P \text{ constant}) \qquad (10.8)$$

Temperature changes on the Kelvin and Celsius scales are equal; a temperature increase of 1°C implies an increase of 1 K. (Note that the degree symbol ° is usually not written with Kelvin temperatures

TABLE 10.1

Kelvin temperatures at which representative physical and biological phenomena occur

Description	T
Absolute zero	0
Melting point of nitrogen	67
Gasoline freezes	123
Dry ice (CO_2 freezes)	195
Water freezes	273.15
Hibernating squirrel	275
Body temperature in man	310
Body temperature in birds	315
Water boils	373.15
Fireplace fire	1,100
Gold melts	1,336
Gas flame (stove)	1,900
Surface of sun	6,000
Center of earth	16,000
Center of sun	10^7

or temperature changes. The kelvin, or K, is treated as a unit.) However, 0° on the Celsius scale is assigned arbitrarily to the freezing point of water, while $T = 0$ K represents absolute zero, the minimum possible temperature. Extensive study has confirmed that no process can bring the temperature below absolute zero, although experiments have been performed at a few millionths of a degree above this temperature.

We can now state the ideal gas law that contains both Boyle's law and Charles's law:

$$\frac{PV}{T} = \text{constant} \qquad (10.9)$$

If T is fixed, this gives $PV = $ constant; when P is fixed, V/T is constant. Note that when we double the amount of the gas (the number of moles, n) while keeping the pressure and temperature the same, V doubles. Hence we may write the constant on the right side of Eq. 10.9 as nR, where R is found by experiment. Thus the ideal gas law becomes

$$PV = nRT \qquad \text{(ideal gas law)} \qquad (10.10)$$

where R is called the *universal gas constant*. For all *dilute* gases, that is, real gases at low densities and

pressures, it has the same value:

$$R = 8.314 \text{ J mole}^{-1} \text{ K}^{-1}$$
$$= 0.08207 \text{ litre atm mole}^{-1} \text{ K}^{-1}$$
$$(1 \text{ litre} = 10^{-3} \text{ m}^3 = 10^3 \text{ cm}^3)$$

Defining a temperature scale using the ideal gas law has the advantage of not depending on the properties of any one material such as mercury or steel. Gas thermometers are maintained at standards laboratories and are used to calibrate more convenient thermometers, such as mercury thermometers. Another important advantage of defining temperature in this way is that it enables us to relate temperature to molecular quantities, as shown in Section 10.6.

Standard conditions for a gas are defined to be $P = 1$ atm and $T_C = 0°C$. The following example illustrates an important property of ideal gases at standard conditions.

Example 10.4

What is the volume of 1 mole of an ideal gas at standard conditions?

From Eq. 10.7, $T = T_C + 273.15 = 273.15$ K. The ideal gas law then gives

$$V = \frac{nRT}{P}$$

$$= \frac{1 \text{ mole}}{1 \text{ atm}} (0.08207 \text{ litre atm mole}^{-1} \text{ K}^{-1})(273.15 \text{ K})$$

$$= 22.4 \text{ litres}$$

Thus under standard conditions, a mole of an ideal gas occupies 22.4 litres.

As long as the number of moles remains fixed, the combination PV/T is constant. This fact is useful in solving many ideal gas problems.

Example 10.5

An ideal gas in a cylinder is initially at a temperature of 27° C. It is heated and allowed to expand so that its volume is doubled and its temperature is increased to 127° C. If it was originally at a pressure of 10 atm, what is its new pressure?

Since the amount of the gas is fixed, the initial value of PV/T equals the final value, $P'V'/T'$. Solving for P', and converting to Kelvin temperatures, we have

$$P' = P\left(\frac{T'}{T}\right)\left(\frac{V}{V'}\right) = (10 \text{ atm}) \left(\frac{400 \text{ K}}{300 \text{ K}}\right)\left(\frac{V}{2V}\right)$$

$$= 6.67 \text{ atm}$$

Note we do not need to know the actual amount of the gas or the volume to find P'.

In summary, all real gases satisfy the ideal gas law to a high degree of accuracy if they are sufficiently dilute. The ideal gas law also provides a good approximation to the behavior of real gases at moderate pressures and temperatures.

10.5 | GAS MIXTURES

Very often, particularly in considering life-supporting processes, we must deal with mixtures of gases. For example, each mole of dry air contains 0.78 mole of nitrogen (N_2), 0.21 mole of oxygen (O_2), 0.009 mole of argon, 0.0004 mole of carbon dioxide, and traces of several other gases. These proportions are nearly constant up to an altitude of 80 km.

Discussions of dilute gas mixtures are simplified by the fact that each constituent behaves as though the others were not present. This follows from the ideal gas model in which we assume that molecules do not interact with one another. Thus suppose there are $n(O_2)$ moles of oxygen and $n(N_2)$ moles of nitrogen in a volume V of air at a temperature T. The *partial pressures* of oxygen and nitrogen, $P(O_2)$ and $P(N_2)$, will *each* satisfy an ideal gas law:

$$P(O_2)V = n(O_2)RT$$
$$P(N_2)V = n(N_2)RT \qquad (10.11)$$

The total pressure P (ignoring the small amount of other gases present) of the air is the sum $P = P(O_2) + P(N_2)$. The number of moles of air is $n = n(O_2) + n(N_2)$, so by adding Eqs. 10.11, we recover $PV = nRT$ for the air.

The partial pressure of oxygen is easy to calculate if the total air pressure is known, as shown in the following example.

Example 10.6

What are the partial pressures of oxygen at sea level and at an altitude of 7000 m, where the air pressure is 0.45 atm?

Dividing $P(O_2)V = n(O_2)RT$ by $PV = nRT$, we have at sea level, where $P = 1$ atm,

$$\frac{P(O_2)}{P} = \frac{n(O_2)}{n} = \frac{0.21 \text{ mole}}{1 \text{ mole}} = 0.21$$

Thus $P(O_2) = 0.21$ atm. The ratio is the same at 7000 m, but $P = 0.45$ atm, so $P(O_2) = (0.21)(0.45 \text{ atm}) = 0.096$ atm, less than half the pressure at sea level.

The amount of a gas present in our bodies is directly proportional to the partial pressure of the gas in the air we breathe. Thus any time the air pressure changes, so does the oxygen and nitrogen content of our bodies. This is of great importance to divers.

As a diver descends, the water pressure increases rapidly. The pressure of the air the diver inhales also increases, since the pressures inside and outside the lungs must be kept equal. For example, the pressure 10.3 m below the surface of a lake is 2 atm, and the partial pressures of oxygen and nitrogen in a diver's lungs must be twice normal. This increased nitrogen pressure can lead to problems because nitrogen is much more soluble in the bloodstream and body tissues than oxygen.

As the diver in this example breathes the high-pressure air, the amount of nitrogen in the body tissue and blood gradually increases to a level twice normal. If the diver now ascends too rapidly to the surface, the external partial pressure of nitrogen drops and the excess nitrogen in the body comes out of solution. Since it cannot escape rapidly, it forms bubbles in tissues and in the blood stream, causing the severe symptoms called "bends." A slow ascent and gradual decompression avoid this problem.

10.6 | TEMPERATURE AND MOLECULAR ENERGIES

The ideal gas law, $PV = nRT$, was originally obtained from several types of experiments. However, it is also possible to construct a theoretical model of a gas that yields the ideal gas law. A byproduct of this model is the direct identification of the average kinetic energy of the gas molecules with the Kelvin temperature.

In the ideal gas model, the molecules are assumed to not exert forces on each other except during occasional brief elastic collisions. The molecules also suffer elastic collisions with the walls of their container. Thus when the molecules strike a wall, they lose no energy, but they do change direction. The change in direction involves a change in momentum of the molecules, and this means that there is a reaction force on the container walls. The average force per unit area exerted by the molecules on the walls is the pressure of the gas.

In Section 10.9, we use this model to derive the expression for the pressure on the walls due to the colliding molecules. The result of that calculation is that the product of the pressure and volume PV is related to the mean or average kinetic energy of the molecules $(K)_{ave}$ by

$$PV = \tfrac{2}{3}nN_A(K)_{ave} \qquad (10.12)$$

where n is the number of moles of gas present, N_A is Avogadro's number, m is the mass of a molecule, and

$$(K)_{ave} = \tfrac{1}{2}m(v^2)_{ave} \qquad (10.13)$$

The quantity $(v^2)_{ave}$ is called the mean square speed, and it represents the average value of v^2.

If we compare these results of the model with the ideal gas law, $PV = nRT$, we have

$$nRT = \tfrac{2}{3}nN_A(K)_{ave}$$

Thus

$$(K)_{ave} = \frac{3}{2}\frac{R}{N_A}T = \tfrac{3}{2}k_BT \qquad (10.14)$$

The ratio $k_B = R/N_A$ is called *Boltzmann's constant* and has the value

$$k_B = 1.38 \times 10^{-23} \text{ J K}^{-1}$$

This is an extremely important result. It gives us a direct interpretation of the absolute temperature in terms of the average kinetic energy of the molecules in a gas.

The thermal energy k_BT is a ubiquitous factor in the natural sciences. By knowing the temperature we have a direct measure of the energy available for initiating chemical, physical, and biological processes.

We can also use Eqs. 10.13 and 10.14 to identify what is called the root mean square (rms) speed for the molecules at a given temperature. With the rms speed defined by $(v_{rms})^2 = (v^2)_{ave}$, we have

$$v_{rms} = \sqrt{(v^2)_{ave}} = \sqrt{\frac{2(K)_{ave}}{m}} = \sqrt{\frac{3k_BT}{m}} \qquad (10.15)$$

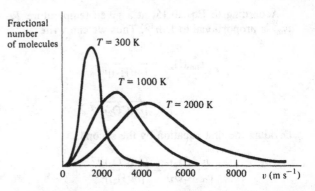

Figure 10.5. The distribution of molecular speeds of diatomic hydrogen gas H_2. At higher temperatures, the rms speed is greater and there is a greater spread.

Individual molecules of a gas can have much larger or smaller speeds. However, as shown in Fig. 10.5, there is a speed at which the largest number will be found for a given temperature. The peaks in the curves occur at speeds that are slightly below v_{rms}. Thus in an approximate sense we can think of v_{rms} as a typical speed of a molecule in the gas.

These relationships allow us to compute the average molecular energy and the rms speed of molecules of any ideal gas at a given temperature.

Example 10.7
(a) What is the average kinetic energy of a hydrogen molecule at $27°$ C $= 300$ K? (b) What is the rms speed?
(a) From $(K)_{ave} = \tfrac{3}{2}k_BT$,

$$\begin{aligned}(K)_{ave} &= \tfrac{3}{2}k_BT \\ &= \tfrac{3}{2}(1.38 \times 10^{-23} \text{ J K}^{-1})(300 \text{ K}) \\ &= 6.21 \times 10^{-21} \text{ J}\end{aligned}$$

(b) In Example 10.1, we found that the molecular mass of H_2 is

$$\begin{aligned}2.016 \text{ u} &= (2.016 \text{ u})(1.66 \times 10^{-27} \text{ kg u}^{-1}) \\ &= 3.35 \times 10^{-27} \text{ kg}\end{aligned}$$

Thus using $v_{rms} = \sqrt{2(K)_{ave}/m}$,

$$v_{rms} = \sqrt{\frac{2(6.21 \times 10^{-21} \text{ J})}{(3.35 \times 10^{-27} \text{ kg})}} = 1930 \text{ m s}^{-1}$$

Example 10.8
Find the ratio of the rms velocities of H_2 and CO_2 molecules if both gases are at the same temperature.

According to Eq. 10.15, at a given temperature T, v_{rms} is proportional to $1/m^{1/2}$. Thus we can write

$$v_{rms}(H_2) = \frac{c}{[m(H_2)]^{1/2}}$$

$$v_{rms}(CO_2) = \frac{c}{[m(CO_2)]^{1/2}}$$

Dividing the first equation by the second,

$$\frac{v_{rms}(H_2)}{v_{rms}(CO_2)} = \frac{[m(CO_2)]^{1/2}}{[m(H_2)]^{1/2}}$$

Now we saw in Example 10.1 that the molecular masses of H_2 and CO_2 are 2.016 u and 44.009 u, respectively. Thus the ratio is

$$\frac{v_{rms}(H_2)}{v_{rms}(CO_2)} = \left(\frac{44.009}{2.016}\right)^{1/2} = 4.67$$

The lighter molecules move faster on the average.

We calculated $(K)_{ave}$ and v_{rms} for the molecule H_2 in Example 10.7. Our calculations are correct for the *translational* motion, but molecules containing two or more atoms can also *rotate* and *vibrate*, and each of these motions has kinetic energy. In the equations we have developed, $(K)_{ave}$ should be interpreted as the translational kinetic energy only.

Two processes that depend on the thermal energy and are very important in biological systems are *osmosis* and *diffusion*. Both may be understood from the kinetic theory of an ideal gas and are described in the next two sections.

10.7 | DIFFUSION

When perfume is sprayed into still air, the scent eventually spreads to all parts of a room. Similarly, a drop of dye placed in a solvent will gradually spread throughout the container, even though we are careful not to disturb or stir the liquid. The rather slow process by which the molecules spread out evenly is called *diffusion*.

We may visualize the diffusion process for a typical gas by referring to Fig. 10.6. A small amount of helium gas is released at point A in an air-filled container. At a given moment, we draw an imaginary hemispherical surface so that most of the helium

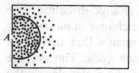

Figure 10.6. A container of air has some helium atoms released into it at A. The helium atoms spread out, and at some instant, we draw an imaginary hemispherical surface approximately separating the regions of high and low concentrations of helium.

atoms are inside the surface, but a few are outside. These helium atoms are in constant random motion, bouncing off air molecules, other helium atoms, and the walls. A certain number of helium atoms will cross the surface from the inside outward and some from the outside inward. Because most of the helium is inside, more helium atoms will pass outward than inward, increasing the number outside. We see that there is a net drift of helium atoms away from A into the remainder of the container. *This flow from higher to lower concentrations is diffusion.*

The average distance the helium atoms diffuse increases with the time, but in a somewhat surprising fashion. Consider the path of a typical atom as illustrated in Fig. 10.7. The atom makes many collisions and changes direction repeatedly. Often the effect of one straight-line section or *step* is nearly canceled by a later step. On the average, the distance l from the initial point 0 increases, but much more slowly than the number of steps N_s. When statistical methods are applied to such a path, it is found that l increases as the square root of the num-

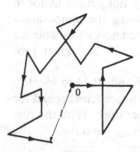

Figure 10.7. The random motion of an atom. On the average the distance l is proportional to the square root of the number of straight-line steps.

ber of steps, or $l^2 \propto N_s$. Since the number of steps is proportional to the time, l^2 is proportional to t. This result for the case of *random motion* is quite different from the relationship $l \propto t$ that holds true for straight-line motion.

Conventionally, instead of $l^2 \propto t$, one writes an equation for the *mean squared displacement* x_{rms}^2 in one direction,

$$x_{rms}^2 = 2Dt \qquad (10.16)$$

where D is called the *diffusion constant*. Similar equations hold for y_{rms}^2 and z_{rms}^2. The value of D depends on the nature of the diffusing atom or molecule and the choice of the solvent or medium (Table 10.2). The following numerical example illustrates how slow the diffusion process is in a typical situation.

Example 10.9

How long will it take a hemoglobin molecule to diffuse an rms distance of 1 cm = 10^{-2} m along the x direction in water?

Using Eq. 10.16 with $D = 6.9 \times 10^{-11}$ m^2 s^{-1} and $x_{rms} = 10^{-2}$ m, we have

$$t = \frac{x_{rms}^2}{2D} = \frac{(10^{-2} \text{ m})^2}{2(6.9 \times 10^{-11} \text{ m}^2 \text{ s}^{-1})} = 7.24 \times 10^5 \text{ s}$$

This is 201 hours, or about 8.4 days!

Even though diffusion is a slow process, it is the primary mechanism used by the body in absorbing and distributing the substances required by living cells. The release of the by-products of cellular function, such as carbon dioxide, also proceeds by diffusion.

TABLE 10.2

Representative values of the diffusion constant D at 20°C = 293 K

Molecule	Solvent	D (m^2 s^{-1})
Hydrogen (H$_2$)	Air	6.4×10^{-5}
Oxygen (O$_2$)	Air	1.8×10^{-5}
Oxygen (O$_2$)	Water	1.0×10^{-9}
Glucose (C$_6$H$_{12}$O$_6$)	Water	6.7×10^{-10}
Hemoglobin	Water	6.9×10^{-11}
DNA	Water	1.3×10^{-12}

It is the slow process of diffusion that determines the rate at which nitrogen is absorbed and released during diving, as described in Section 10.5. Diffusion is also an important factor in nerve conduction, as we shall see in Chapter 18, and is the controlling factor in osmosis, which we discuss next.

10.8 | DILUTE SOLUTIONS; OSMOTIC PRESSURE

The behavior of real gases can often be closely approximated by the ideal gas law, which is derived with a model that depicts the gas molecules as small, noninteracting particles. Somewhat surprisingly, the *osmotic pressure of dilute solutions* can also be accurately predicted using a form of the ideal gas law.

Figure 10.8 illustrates the meaning of osmotic pressure. The outer vessel contains water, and the inner one is filled initially to the same height with a solution of water and sugar. Water molecules can pass freely through the membrane separating the two vessels, but the larger sugar molecules cannot. Because the membrane is *permeable* to water molecules and *impermeable* to sugar molecules, it is called *semipermeable*.

Since the concentration of water molecules is greater in the outer vessel, there is a net diffusion of

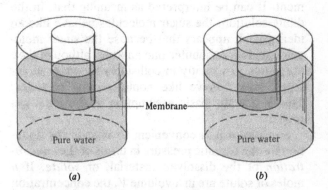

Figure 10.8. (a) Initially the levels of the water outside the container and the sugar solution inside are the same. (b) The membrane at the bottom of the inner vessel is not permeable to sugar molecules. Water molecules enter the container until equilibrium is reached, with the level of the solution inside higher than that of the pure water.

water molecules into the inner vessel raising the level of the solution until an equilibrium level is reached (Fig. 10.8b). At this point, equal numbers of water molecules cross the membrane in each direction. The additional pressure in the solution just above the membrane due to the weight of the raised column of solution is called the *osmotic pressure* π. In other words, the osmotic pressure is the extra pressure that must be applied to stop the flow of water into the solution.

The osmotic pressure can be predicted on the basis of a surprisingly simple model. We associate a pressure P_w^o with the pure water in the outer vessel and a pressure P_w^i with the water inside. The sugar inside has a pressure P_s, so the total pressure inside is $P_w^i + P_s$. In equilibrium (Fig. 10.8b), the pressure difference across the membrane is the osmotic pressure:

$$\pi = (P_w^i + P_s) - P_w^o \qquad (10.17)$$

If we assume that the net flow of water across the membrane stops when the water pressures are the same and that the sugar obeys the ideal gas law, we find

$$\pi = P_s = \frac{nRT}{V} \qquad (10.18)$$

where n is the number of moles of sugar and V is the volume of the fluid in the inner vessel.

This prediction is in good agreement with experiment. It can be interpreted as meaning that, in the dilute solution, the sugar molecules behave like an ideal gas. It appears that because the sugar molecules seldom encounter one another, although they are almost constantly in collision with water molecules, they behave like noninteracting particles. This is just the basic assumption of the ideal gas model.

Sometimes it is convenient to rewrite the equation for the osmotic pressure in terms of the *concentration* of the dissolved material, or *solute*. If n moles of solute are in a volume V, the concentration is

$$c = \frac{n}{V} \qquad (10.19)$$

The S.I. units of c are moles per cubic metre. The osmotic pressure is then given by

$$\pi = cRT \qquad (10.20)$$

The following example illustrates the use of this result and shows the role that osmosis plays in maple trees.

Example 10.10

Sap rises in the early spring in maple trees as a result of the osmotic pressure difference between the sugar solution (sap) within the tree and the water in the ground around the roots. The sap contains 1 percent by weight of sucrose ($C_{12}H_{22}O_{11}$) in water. Assuming the temperature is 27°C find (a) the concentration in moles m^{-3}; (b) the osmotic pressure; (c) the height the sap rises.

(a) The molecular mass of sucrose is [12(12 u) + 22(1 u) + 11(16 u)] = 342 u, so a mole has a mass of 342 g. One cubic metre of solution has a mass nearly equal to that of 1 m^3 of water, or 10^3 kilograms. The mass of the sucrose is 1 percent of that, or 10 kg = 10^4 g. Thus 1 m^3 of solution contains (10^4 g)/(342 g $mole^{-1}$) = 29.2 moles of sucrose. Its concentration is 29.2 moles m^{-3}.

(b) The osmotic pressure is

$$\pi = cRT$$
$$= (29.2 \text{ moles m}^{-3})(8.314 \text{ J mole}^{-1} \text{ K}^{-1})(300 \text{ K})$$
$$= 7.28 \times 10^4 \text{ Pa}$$

(c) The weight of the column of sap divided by the area A of its base equals the osmotic pressure. The weight can be written as $w = mg = \rho V g$, where ρ is the density of sap and is well approximated by that of water, 1000 kg m^{-3}. If the height of the tree is h, $V = Ah$, and

$$\pi = \frac{w}{A} = \frac{\rho A h g}{A} = \rho h g$$

Then

$$h = \frac{\pi}{\rho g} = \frac{7.28 \times 10^4 \text{ Pa}}{(1000 \text{ kg m}^{-3})(9.8 \text{ m s}^{-2})} = 7.43 \text{ m}$$

The concentration of sugar in maple trees can be higher than 1 percent, and it may be that osmosis is largely responsible for the spring flow of sap in maples. In most other trees, the concentration of solutes that will not pass through the root wall is much smaller. In these cases, osmotic pressure is insufficient to account for the movement of fluids in trees. We discuss another mechanism for this fluid transport in Chapter Fifteen.

Osmosis is extremely important in understanding a wide variety of biological processes. Both plant and animal tissues are composed of cells containing complex solutions. Solutes that can pass through the cell membrane are present along with impermeable solutes. The fluids surrounding the cells are also complex solutions but with different compositions. In equilibrium the total osmotic pressures due to impermeable molecules and ions must be the same inside and outside the cell; otherwise, the difference in osmotic pressures will cause water to enter or leave the cell, along with dissolved permeable materials.

To illustrate this, suppose a person drinks a large quantity of water. Water enters the blood, thereby reducing the concentration of solutes relative to the body tissue. Consequently the body tissues take on water. The flow of water into the kidneys is also increased because of the increased osmotic pressure difference. The kidneys then excrete more dilute urine until the blood concentration returns to equilibrium values. By contrast, a person with a high fever may lose a great deal of water from the tissues and hence from the blood until it is impossible for the kidneys to absorb water and dissolved permeable solutes.

Fluids given to a patient intravenously are usually adjusted so their concentrations of impermeable solutes and osmotic pressures balance those of the tissues. Such solutions are called *isotonic*. If a cell is placed in a solution with a lower concentration of impermeable solutes, there will be a tendency for water to enter the cell. A red blood cell has relatively rigid walls. When it is placed in pure water, an influx of water molecules occurs, which raises the internal pressure since the cell cannot expand appreciably. Equilibrium would occur at about 8 atm, but the cells will usually rupture before this pressure is reached. Cells that can change volume readily will expand or contract when placed in solutions that are not isotonic.

Osmotic Pressure and Energy
Recently there has been a revived interest in the osmotic pressure difference between fresh water and sea water. Where a large river empties into the sea, the large osmotic pressure difference combined with

the enormous amounts of water involved suggest that energy may be extracted in large amounts.

In its simplest form, we may envision an apparatus such as that of Fig. 10.8 where the pure water is river water and the solution is sea water. As the fresh water flows through the membrane, the solution can be drawn off at the top of the cylinder so the flow never stops. The concentration of the solution can be maintained since the volume of fresh water is small compared to the volume of sea water. Using a turbine, energy could then be extracted from the flowing water. Recalling from Chapter Six that power is force times velocity, $\mathscr{P} = Fv$, and writing the force as the pressure times the area, we have the power and pressure related by

$$\mathscr{P} = PAv \qquad (10.21)$$

where P is the osmotic pressure, A is the membrane area, and v is the velocity of flow. In the following example we estimate the power available where a major river empties into the ocean.

Example 10.11
Sea water contains approximately 1000 moles m^{-3} of salt ions. The mouth of a typical major river has a cross-sectional area of 900 m^2 and an average flow velocity of 0.5 m s^{-1}. (a) What is the osmotic pressure at the freshwater–seawater junction? (b) How much power is available? (Assume a temperature of 300 K.)

(a) The osmotic pressure is found from

$$\pi = cRT$$
$$= (1000 \text{ moles } m^{-3})(8.314 \text{ J mole}^{-1} \text{ K}^{-1})(300 \text{ K})$$
$$= 2.5 \times 10^6 \text{ Pa}$$

This is almost 25 atmospheres!

(b) Using Eq. 10.21,

$$\mathscr{P} = PAv = (2.5 \times 10^6 \text{ Pa})(900 \text{ m}^2)(0.5 \text{ m s}^{-1})$$
$$= 1.125 \times 10^9 \text{ W} = 1125 \text{ MW}$$

This is roughly the output of a very large fossil fuel or nuclear power plant.

In practice, harnessing this energy is not easy. For example, the difficulties in constructing a membrane of appropriate size and its maintenance under actual conditions could preclude its use. However, this energy may still be available using vapor pressure differences between sea water and fresh water, which does not involve a membrane.

SUMMARY

Temperature is a measure of the average translational kinetic energy of the molecules in a substance. The temperature scale that most directly characterizes the energy is the Kelvin scale, which starts at absolute zero.

Atomic and molecular masses are measured in terms of atomic mass units, where the mass of a ^{12}C atom is defined to be exactly 12 u. A mole of any substance is an amount whose mass in grams is numerically equal to its molecular mass in atomic mass units, and it contains a number of molecules equal to N_A, Avogadro's number.

The pressure of a gas or liquid is the force it exerts per unit area on its surroundings or on the walls of its container.

The ideal gas model assumes that the gas molecules do not interact with each other except during collisions. The model predicts that the pressure, volume, amount of gas, and temperature are related by

$$PV = nRT$$

The ideal gas law holds very well for dilute real gases.

When a dilute real gas is composed of several types of molecules, the net pressure is just the sum of the ideal gas pressures for each type of molecule. The ideal gas model also leads to the identification of the Kelvin temperature with the average kinetic energy per molecule,

$$(K)_{ave} = \tfrac{3}{2} k_B T$$

Molecules diffuse slowly from regions of high to low concentrations. The root mean squared diffusion distance in one direction, x_{rms}, is related to the time by

$$x_{rms}^2 = 2Dt$$

Diffusion also plays a role in the osmotic flow of fluids through semipermeable membranes. The solvent will flow as if there were a pressure difference across the membrane equal to the osmotic pressure,

$$\pi = cRT$$

where c is the concentration of the solute.

Checklist

Define or explain:

Celsius (centigrade)	Boltzmann's constant
Fahrenheit	root mean square speed
molecular mass	diffusion
mole	diffusion constant
Avogadro's number	osmosis
pressure	osmotic pressure
gauge, absolute pressure	random motion
dilute gas	semipermeable
ideal gas	membrane
Kelvin temperature	concentration
absolute zero	solute
partial pressure	isotonic

REVIEW QUESTIONS

Q10-1   For use as a thermometer, a substance must have some characteristic property that changes with _____.

Q10-2   The Fahrenheit temperature scale is based on defining _____ fixed and reproducible temperatures.

Q10-3   The atomic mass unit is chosen so the mass of a ^{12}C atom is exactly _____.

Q10-4   The molecular mass is the sum of the _____.

Q10-5   The S.I. unit of pressure is the pascal, which is 1 _____ per _____.

Q10-6   Gas station attendants check tires for the correct _____ pressure.

Q10-7   A collection of noninteracting molecules and/or atoms is _____.

Q10-8   Under some conditions, _____ gases behave like _____ gases.

Q10-9   For constant pressure, absolute zero is the extrapolated temperature at which the _____ becomes zero.

Q10-10   Boyle's and Charles's laws are special cases of the _____ law.

Q10-11   For a gas with several types of molecules, the total gas pressure is the _____ of the partial pressures.

Q10-12   The amount of dissolved gas in a liquid in contact with that gas is directly proportional to the _____ of the gas.

Q10-13   The Boltzmann constant k_B is the proportionality constant relating the _____ and the _____ of gas molecules.

Q10-14 The root mean square speed for the molecules of a gas is proportional to the _____ of the Kelvin temperature.

Q10-15 Diffusion occurs from regions of _____ concentration to regions of _____ concentration.

Q10-16 A _____ membrane is one through which only certain types of molecules can move.

Q10-17 The osmotic pressure equation $\pi = cRT$ makes it appear as if the molecules of the solute behaved like an _____.

Q10-18 A solution with the same concentrations of impermeable solutes on both sides of a semi-permeable membrane is _____.

EXERCISES

Section 10.1 | Temperature Scales

10-1 A room is at 70°F, a comfortable temperature for many people. What is the Celsius temperature?

10-2 A Paris weather report predicts a high temperature of 27°C. What is this temperature on the Fahrenheit scale?

10-3 At what temperature are the readings on Celsius and Fahrenheit thermometers the same?

10-4 (a) Which is hotter, 100°C or 100°F? (b) Which is colder, −100°C or −100°F?

10-5 Alcohol boils at 78°C. What is this temperature on the Fahrenheit scale?

Section 10.2 | Molecular Masses

Refer to Appendix A or to the inside back cover for atomic masses where needed.

10-6 In a crude experiment, the molecular mass of NH_3 is found to be 17.5 u. If the accepted value is used for the hydrogen mass, what is the atomic mass of nitrogen from this experiment?

10-7 What is the mass of 2 moles of H_2?

10-8 What is the mass of 0.3 mole of ammonia, NH_3? (The molecular mass of NH_3 is 17.03 u.)

10-9 How many molecules are in 3 moles of sucrose?

10-10 How many molecules are in 0.7 mole of mercury?

10-11 (a) What is the molecular mass of O_2? (b) What is the mass of 10^{24} O_2 molecules?

10-12 (a) Find the molecular mass of H_2O. (b) How many molecules are there in 10 kg of H_2O?

10-13 How many molecules are there in 4 moles of CCl_4?

10-14 (a) Find the molecular mass of sucrose, $C_{12}H_{22}O_{11}$. (b) How many molecules are there in 1 kg of sucrose?

Section 10.3 | Pressure

10-15 The owner's manual says to inflate the tires on a car to a pressure of 200 kPa. (a) What is the recommended gauge pressure? (b) What is the recommended absolute pressure?

10-16 A driver inflates her tires at sea level to the recommended pressure 180 kPa. She then drives up to a mountain peak where the atmospheric pressure is 10 percent below that at sea level. Assuming the air in the tires has not changed its absolute pressure, what will her tire gauge read when she checks the tires at the peak?

10-17 A submarine deep below the surface of the sea is at a gauge pressure of 40 atm. The air inside the submarine is at normal atmospheric pressure. What is the net force on a flat hull plate 2 m by 6 m?

10-18 What is the force due to the atmosphere on one side of a door of area 2 m²?

10-19 If the difference in pressure on the two sides of a closed door of area 2 m² is 0.01 atm, what is the net force on the door? Do you think you could open it by hand?

10-20 What pressure on the 12-m² base of an automobile of mass 1300 kg would be necessary to support it?

10-21 Estimate the pressure you exert on the ground (a) when standing erect on both feet; (b) when lying down.

Section 10.4 | The Ideal Gas Law

10-22 A gas occupies 5 m³ at a pressure of 1 atm. What is the pressure when the volume is 1.5 m³ if the temperature is held constant?

10-23 The pressure of a gas changes from 1.5 atm to 0.3 atm at constant temperature. What is the ratio of the final and initial volumes?

10-24 The volume of a gas doubles at constant pressure. What is the final temperature if the gas was initially at 30°C?

10-25 If the temperature of a gas is raised from 0°C to 100°C at constant pressure, by what factor is its volume changed?

10-26 What is the volume of 3 moles of an ideal gas at $P = 2$ atm and $T = 300$ K?

10-27 What is the temperature of 1 mole of an ideal gas with a pressure of 0.3 atm in a volume of 3 m^3?

10-28 One mole of an ideal gas occupies 2.24×10^{-2} m^3 at standard conditions. What will the pressure be if the volume is increased to 1 m^3 at constant temperature?

Section 10.5 | Gas Mixtures

10-29 A tank of gas at a pressure of 3 atm is composed of 0.35 mole of oxygen and 0.65 mole of helium. What is the partial pressure of oxygen?

10-30 Normal air contains 0.21 mole of oxygen per mole of air. It is desired to change this proportion so that at an altitude where the air pressure is 0.40 atm, the oxygen partial pressure is the same as at sea level. How many moles of oxygen per mole of air are needed?

10-31 If each increase in altitude of 1000 m resulted in an air pressure drop of 0.078 atm, above what altitude would even the use of pure oxygen result in a below normal oxygen intake?

10-32 A human will suffer from oxygen toxicity when the partial pressure of oxygen reaches about 0.8 atm. If the pressure increases 1 atm for each 10.3 m below the water surface, at what depth would breathing air lead to oxygen toxicity?

Section 10.6 | Temperature and Molecular Energies

10-33 Find the rms speed of a CO_2 molecule at 0°C.

10-34 Air contains a mixture of nitrogen (N_2), oxygen (O_2), and argon (Ar). Which molecules have the (a) largest rms speed; (b) smallest rms speed?

10-35 If the average kinetic energy of a gas is doubled and the volume remains constant, what is the change in pressure?

10-36 What is the ratio of the rms speeds of hydrogen gas (H_2) and oxygen gas (O_2) if both gases are at the same temperature?

10-37 Natural uranium is composed of 99.3 percent ^{238}U, with a mass of 238 u, and 0.7 percent ^{235}U, with a mass of 235 u. It is the ^{235}U that is mainly used in reactors and weapons. The two isotopes are separated using diffusion processes. This method utilizes the fact that the rms speed of the gas UF_6 is different for the two isotopes. What is the ratio of their speeds at 37°C?

10-38 Suppose that all the translational molecular kinetic energy of 1 mole of an ideal gas at a temperature of 300 K could be used to raise a 1-kg mass. How high would the block be raised?

10-39 The rms speed of the molecules in an ideal gas with molecular mass 32.0 u is 400 m s^{-1}. (a) What is the average translational kinetic energy? (b) What is the temperature of the gas?

Section 10.7 | Diffusion

10-40 What average distance will O_2 molecules diffuse in air in 1 hour? Assume $T_C = 20$°C.

10-41 How long will it take glucose molecules to diffuse an average distance of 1 mm = 10^{-3} m in water at 20°C?

10-42 If a solute diffuses through water an average distance of 10^{-2} m in 6 hours, what is its diffusion constant?

Section 10.8 | Dilute Solutions; Osmotic Pressure

10-43 What is the osmotic pressure of a brine solution with an ion concentration of 1500 moles m^{-3} separated by a semipermeable membrane from pure water? Assume $T_C = 27$°C.

10-44 A sugar solution in an apparatus such as that of Figure 10.8 will support a water column 14 m high. What is the sugar concentration? Assume $T_C = 27$°C.

10-45 What concentration difference of impermeable solutes across a cell membrane would result in an osmotic pressure of 5 atm? Assume $T_C = 37$°C.

PROBLEMS

10-46 One of the earliest temperature scales was the Réaumur scale, which set the freezing point

of water at 0°R and the boiling point at 80°R.
(a) What is 40°C on the Réaumur scale? (b) What
is 40°R on the Celsius scale?

10-47 (a) What temperature on the Fahrenheit
scale corresponds to absolute zero? (b) The
Rankine scale is defined so that 0° is at absolute
zero and that its degree is equal to the Fahrenheit
degree. What is 0°F on the Rankine scale?
(c) What is the boiling point of water on the
Rankine scale?

10-48 (a) Find the molecular mass of ethyl alcohol, C_2H_5OH. (b) How many molecules are there
in 1 litre of ethyl alcohol? (The density of ethyl
alcohol is 791 kg m^{-3}.)

10-49 A 1-litre tank contains oxygen gas at a
temperature of 27° C and a pressure of 3 atm.
How many oxygen molecules are in the tank?

10-50 (a) Assuming air contains 78 percent N_2,
21 percent O_2, and 1 percent Ar molecules, find
its average molecular mass. (b) What is the density of air at standard conditions?

10-51 A house is approximately a rectangular
box 20 m long, 8 m wide, and 3 m high. The air in
the house is initially at the same temperature and
pressure as that outside, 12°C and 1 atm. Its occupants turn on the heat, and the temperature rises
to 21°C. (a) If the air is allowed to escape, what
fraction will leak out? (b) If the air could not leak
out, what would be the net force on a wall 3 m
high and 8 m long?

10-52 A cylinder contains 0.02 m^3 of oxygen at a
temperature of 25°C and a pressure of 15 atm.
(a) What volume does this gas occupy at 25°C and
a pressure of 1 atm? (b) A man is breathing pure
oxygen through a face mask at a rate of
0.008 m^3 min^{-1} at atmospheric pressure. How
long will the cylinder of gas last?

10-53 A diver, originally 20 m below the surface, ascends, expelling air as she rises to keep
her lung volume constant. The air bubbles rise
faster than she does. If her lung volume is
2.4 litres, what is the total volume of expelled air
in the bubbles at the water surface? (The pressure
changes by 1 atm for each 10.3 m of depth change
in water.)

10-54 Mixtures of oxygen and helium can be tolerated by divers. What proportion should be oxygen if the diver works 50 m below the surface and
the partial pressure of oxygen should be 0.3 atm?
(The pressure changes by 1 atm for each 10.3 m of
depth change in water.)

10-55 In Example 10.7, the rms speed of hydrogen molecules (H_2) at 27°C (300 K) was calculated
to be 1930 m s^{-1}. At what temperature would hydrogen molecules have an rms speed of $1.1 \times
10^4$ m s^{-1}, which is sufficient to escape from the
earth?

*10-56 The walls of blood capillaries are impermeable to proteins. The two major protein groups
in blood plasma are

Protein Group	Concentration	Ave. Molecular Mass
Albumin	0.045 g m^{-3}	69,000 u
Globulin	0.025 g m^{-3}	140,000 u

(a) Calculate the concentration of each protein
group in moles m^{-3}. (b) Calculate the osmotic
pressure of blood plasma at a temperature of
310 K due to the proteins dissolved in it. (c) How
tall a column of water can this pressure support?

10-57 The alveoli of the lungs are small air sacs
about 10^{-4} m in radius. The membrane walls of
the sacs that separate the air space from the blood
capillaries are about 0.25×10^{-4} m thick. The
capillaries themselves have a radius of about $5 \times
10^{-6}$ m. (a) Assuming that O_2 diffuses through the
wall and blood as it does through water, what
average time is required for O_2 to diffuse from the
center of an alveolus to the center of a capillary?
(b) How does this compare with the time, 0.1 s,
that the blood is in transit around an alveolus?

10-58 The osmotic pressure of ocean water is
22 atm at 300 K. What is the salt concentration?
(*Hint*: NaCl dissociates in water into Na$^+$ and Cl$^-$
ions.)

*10-59 A solution of sodium chloride (NaCl) in
water of 160 moles m^{-3} concentration is isotonic
with blood cells. What is the osmotic pressure in
atmospheres in the cells if the temperature is
300 K? (*Hint*: NaCl dissociates in water into Na$^+$
and Cl$^-$ ions.)

*10-60 The osmotic pressure of a red blood cell is 8 atm. The cell is placed in a water solution containing 100 moles m^{-3} of a solute to which the cell membrane is impermeable. Will the cell tend to expand, contract, or remain the same size? Explain. (Assume $T = 300$ K.)

10-61 How much energy must be added to 1 mole of an ideal monatomic gas to raise its temperature 1 K? (The volume is kept fixed.)

*10-62 The earth's atmosphere contains only small traces of hydrogen (H_2) and helium (He) gases, even though these were once present. What happened to these gases? (*Hint*: How do the rms speeds for H_2 and He compare with the rms speeds for N_2 and O_2?)

ANSWERS TO REVIEW QUESTIONS

Q10-1, temperature; **Q10-2**, two; **Q10-3**, 12; **Q10-4**, atomic masses; **Q10-5**, newton, square metre; **Q10-6**, gauge; **Q10-7**, an ideal gas; **Q10-8**, real, ideal; **Q10-9**, volume of an ideal gas; **Q10-10**, ideal gas law; **Q10-11**, sum; **Q10-12**, partial pressure; **Q10-13**, temperature, average kinetic energy; **Q10-14**, square root; **Q10-15**, high, low; **Q10-16**, semipermeable; **Q10-17**, ideal gas; **Q10-18**, isotonic.

SUPPLEMENTARY TOPICS

10.9 | MODEL DERIVATION OF THE IDEAL GAS LAW

One of a large number of molecules that collide only with the walls of a container is shown in Fig. 10.9. The volume of the container is $V = Al$, and there are nN_A molecules inside.

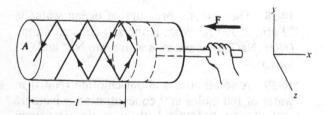

Figure 10.9. A single molecule moving in a container of area A and length l. The molecule collides elastically with the walls and with the piston. The piston must be held in place with a force **F** to offset the force due to the molecule.

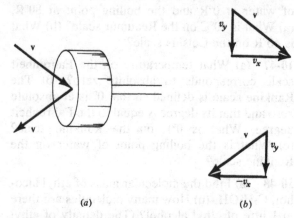

Figure 10.10. (*a*) When a molecule collides with a piston, its speed does not change, but the molecule does change directions. (*b*) v_y is the same before and after the collision, but v_x is reversed.

Each time a molecule hits the piston, its x component of velocity reverses itself (Fig. 10.10). Since the y component of the velocity is unchanged, the momentum change in one collision is $2mv_x$.

We can find the force on the piston due to one molecule from Newton's second law in the form $F \Delta t = \Delta p$, where Δp is the momentum change and Δt the time interval. The time interval Δt between impacts with the pistons is the time for the molecule to travel the length of the container and back, so $2l = v_x \Delta t$. Thus the force is

$$F = \frac{\Delta p}{\Delta t} = \frac{2mv_x}{2l/v_x} = \frac{mv_x^2}{l}$$

For the nN_A molecules actually present, the total force on the piston is nN_A times the average value of mv_x^2/l:

$$F = \frac{nN_A}{l} (mv_x^2)_{ave}$$

The pressure is the force per unit area. Using $V = Al$,

$$P = \frac{F}{A} = \frac{nN_A}{V} (mv_x^2)_{ave}$$

Since m is the same for each molecule, we need to compute $(v_x^2)_{ave}$. This average can be more conveniently written by noting that $(v_x^2)_{ave}$ should be just the same as $(v_y^2)_{ave}$ and $(v_z^2)_{ave}$. Since v^2, the total velocity squared, is the sum of the squares of its components, we can use $(v_x^2)_{ave} = \frac{1}{3}(v^2)_{ave}$ and then write

$$PV = \frac{2nN_A}{3}\left(\frac{mv^2}{2}\right)_{ave}$$

$$= \frac{2}{3}nN_A(K)_{ave} \qquad (10.12)$$

This is the result we quoted earlier.

Additional Reading

R. E. Wilson, Standards of Temperature, *Physics Today*, vol. 6, January 1953, p. 10.

Leslie A. Guildner, The Measurement of Thermodynamic Temperature, *Physics Today*, December 1982, p. 24.

Robert H. Romer, Temperature Scales: Celsius, Fahrenheit, Kelvin, Reámur, and Rømer, *The Physics Teacher*, vol. 20, 1982, p. 450.

D. K. C. MacDonald, *Near Zero: The Physics of Low Temperatures*, Science Study Series, Doubleday and Co., Garden City, N.Y., 1961. Paperback.

Mark W. Zemansky, *Temperatures Very High and Very Low*, Momentum Series, D. Van Nostrand and Co., Princeton, N.J., 1964. Paperback.

C. Barber Jorgensen and Erik Skadhauge, *Osmotic and Volume Regulation* (Proceedings of a Symposium, Copenhagen, June 1977), Academic Press, New York, 1978.

Ultrahigh Pressure: New Highs Spur Pursuit of Exotic Goals, *Science*, vol. 201, 1978, p. 429.

T. H. Maugh II, Birds Fly, Why Can't I? *Science*, vol. 203, 1979, p. 1230.

Gerald L. Wich and John D. Isaacs, Salt Domes: Is There More Energy Available from Their Salt than from Their Oil? *Science*, vol. 199, 1978, p. 1436.

W. Gary Williams, Mineral Salt: A Costly Source of Energy? *Science*, vol. 203, 1979, p. 376.

Mark Olsson, Gerald L. Wich, and John D. Isaacs, Salinity Gradient Power: Utilizing Vapor Pressure Differences, *Science*, vol. 206, 1979, p. 452.

Eric Perlman, Walking on Thin Air, *Science 80*, July/August 1980, p. 89.

Scientific American articles:

Marie Boas Hall and Robert Boyle, August 1967, p. 84.

Arthur K. Solomon, The State of Water in Red Cells, February 1971, p. 88.

Reuben Hersh and Richard J. Griego, Brownian Motion and Potential Theory, March 1969, p. 66.

Bernard H. Lavenda, Brownian Motion, February 1985, p. 70.

Holger W. Iannosch and Carl O. Wirsen, Microbial Life in the Deep Sea, June 1977, p. 42.

Warren M. Zapol, Diving Adaptations of the Weddell Seal, June 1987, p. 100.

Warren G. Proctor, Negative Absolute Temperatures, August 1978, p. 90.

CHAPTER 11
THERMODYNAMICS

Thermodynamics originated as the study of the relationship between mechanical and *thermal energy*—the energy associated with the disordered motions of the atoms and molecules within a substance. Today, its scope is much broader, and it is important wherever temperature plays a role. It has major applications in virtually every field of basic and applied science.

Thermodynamics describes the behavior of matter in terms of a few macroscopic variables such as the temperature, volume, and pressure that define its *thermodynamic state*. This description is complete when there is equilibrium, and it provides a starting point for the study of nonequilibrium processes such as chemical reactions. In general, thermodynamics defines a broad framework for relating changes in the macroscopic properties of a substance to its energy exchanges with the surroundings.

No direct reference is made in thermodynamics to the underlying atomic and molecular physics. Indeed, its principles were understood long before the development of our modern picture of the microscopic world. *Statistical mechanics*, a much newer branch of physics, starts with the molecular interactions and calculates quantities that are taken from experiment in traditional thermodynamics.

A good deal of conventional jargon or terminology appears in discussions of thermodynamics. A "system" may refer to a single substance or object or to a more general situation involving several substances or components. "Heat" is a popular but often poorly defined term. Historically, heat was thought to be a property of an object that could be transferred to another as a sort of fluid, called "caloric." The caloric theory was long ago discarded after the equivalence of heat and mechanical energy was realized. Today, *heat flow* refers to energy transferred from one substance to another because of a temperature difference between them. The quantity of energy transferred in this way is the amount of *heat* entering or leaving a substance.

The first law of thermodynamics generalizes the fundamental law of energy conservation introduced in Chapter Six to include thermal energy explicitly. It states that the change in the *internal energy* of a system is equal to the heat entering the system minus the work done by the system. A given change in the state of a substance can be brought about by doing work, or by heat transfer, or by some of each. Hence the concept of an amount of heat in an object is not meaningful, although its internal energy is well defined.

The second law of thermodynamics can be phrased in several ways. In terms of the macroscopic description of a system, it states that a quantity called the *entropy* tends to increase in all processes. The entropy change is related to the heat entering or leaving a system divided by its absolute temperature. At the microscopic level, entropy is closely related to the randomness or disorder of the constituents; all systems tend toward states of greater disorder. The second law sets limits on the efficiency of converting thermal energy to work that are independent of the materials used in the process. Such processes are used in automobile engines and in both fossil fuel and nuclear electrical power-generating plants.

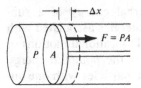

Figure 11.1.   The work done by a gas or a piston during a small displacement Δx is $\Delta W = F\,\Delta x = P\,\Delta V$.

11.1 | MECHANICAL WORK

Work can be done on or by a system in many ways. A gas may be compressed or allowed to expand against a piston. A liquid may be stirred, and a solid may be pounded with a hammer. Electric charges may be brought near a material, so that the electric forces alter the arrangements of charges inside the material. Thus the kinds of work that can be done are as varied as the forces that can be exerted on a system. In this section, we obtain an expression for the work done by a substance or system when its volume changes.

When a substance or system expands or contracts, the work W done by the system can be related to the volume change of the material. It is conventional in thermodynamics to take W as positive when work is done *by* the system. Note by contrast that in Chapter Six we took W to be positive when work was done *on* an object.

It is most convenient to develop our ideas using the example of a gas. Figure 11.1 shows a gas at a pressure P in a closed cylinder. A movable piston of cross-sectional area A forms one end of the enclosure. The gas exerts a force $F = PA$ on the piston. When the piston moves a small distance Δx parallel to the force, the work done by the gas is $\Delta W = F\,\Delta x = PA\,\Delta x$. Since $\Delta V = A\,\Delta x$ is the

change in volume of the gas, the work done by the gas is

$$\Delta W = P\,\Delta V \qquad (11.1)$$

A large displacement can be broken up into a series of small displacements Δx_j, with volume changes $\Delta V_j = A\,\Delta x_j$ and work $\Delta W_j = P\,\Delta V_j$. If we sum over these, in the limit as ΔV_j approaches zero, the work done by the system when its volume changes from V_1 to V_2 is the integral

$$W = \int_{V_1}^{V_2} P\,dV \qquad (11.2)$$

The work done by the system is equal to the area under the P–V curve (Fig. 11.2). This result is valid for a gas in a container of any shape and also for volume changes in liquids and solids.

Equation 11.2 has a simple form if the work is done in an *isobaric* process, that is, at constant pressure. If the initial and final volumes of the system are denoted by V_i and V_f, then the work done is

$$W = P(V_f - V_i) \qquad (11.3)$$

For an isobaric process, W is positive and work is done by the system if $(V_f - V_i)$ is positive; work is done on the system if $(V_f - V_i)$ is negative.

The following example describes an isobaric process.

Example 11.1

A gas at a pressure of 2 atm = 2.02×10^5 Pa is heated and is allowed to expand against a frictionless piston at constant pressure. If the volume change is 0.5 m^3, how much work is done by the gas?

Using Eq. 11.3,

$$W = P(V_f - V_i) = (2.02 \times 10^5 \text{ Pa})(0.5 \text{ m}^3)$$
$$= 1.01 \times 10^5 \text{ J}$$

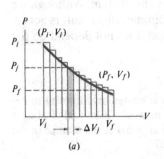

(a)

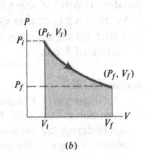

(b)

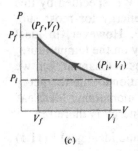

(c)

Figure 11.2. (a) The work done by the system is the sum of the areas of the small segments. In each segment, P_j is assumed constant, and for the colored segment shown, $\Delta W_j = P_j\,\Delta V_j$. (b) The total work is exactly equal to the total colored area under the P-versus-V curve. W is positive in this example. (c) A process in which work is done on the system, so W is negative.

Another illustration of the formula for the work is provided by the expansion of an ideal gas kept at a constant temperature, an *isothermal* process. From the ideal gas law, $PV = nRT$, we have $P = nRT/V$. Hence the work done by the gas is

$$W = \int_{V_1}^{V_2} P\, dV = \int_{V_1}^{V_2} nRT\, \frac{dV}{V}$$

$$= nRT \ln V \Big|_{V_1}^{V_2} = nRT \ln \frac{V_2}{V_1}$$

where ln is the natural logarithm (see Appendix B.10). Since $P_1V_1 = P_2V_2$ when T is constant, $V_2/V_1 = P_1/P_2$. Thus the work done by an ideal gas in an isothermal expansion can also be written as

$$W = nRT \ln\left(\frac{P_1}{P_2}\right) \quad \text{(ideal gas, constant } T\text{)} \quad (11.4)$$

If the gas expands, the pressure drops. Then $P_1/P_2 > 1$, and $\ln(P_1/P_2)$ is positive. As we would expect, the gas does positive work as it expands.

11.2 | THE FIRST LAW OF THERMODYNAMICS

The first law of thermodynamics is a generalization of the energy conservation law introduced in our study of mechanics. It provides a relationship between the heat transferred to a system, the work it performs, and the change in its *internal energy* associated with the motions of its molecules.

The internal energy U varies with the *state* of a system, as described by macroscopic variables such as the temperature, pressure, and volume. These variables are related for any system by an *equation of state*. For example, the equation of state for an ideal gas is $PV = nRT$. For a given number of moles n, if T and P are known, then V is specified by this equation. Thus the internal energy for most substances depends on T and P. However, in ideal gases, U actually depends only on the temperature. In our discussion of ideal gases in Chapter Ten, we found that the average translational kinetic energy of a molecule is $\frac{3}{2}k_BT$. For N monatomic ideal gas molecules, the total internal energy is therefore

$$U = \tfrac{3}{2}Nk_BT \quad \text{(monatomic ideal gas)} \quad (11.5)$$

More generally, the internal energy of a substance includes the kinetic energies associated with translational, rotational, and vibrational motions of the particles. It also includes the potential energy due to the interactions of the particles with one another. Just as in our discussion of potential energy in Chapter Six, the internal energy is defined with respect to some reference configuration. Usually this choice is of no practical importance because only changes in internal energy affect the properties of the system.

The heat Q added to or taken from a system is the amount of thermal energy transferred due to a temperature difference. For example, we may say that heat flows from a wood stove to the air and to objects in a room because they have a lower temperature than the stove.

We now discuss the first law of thermodynamics, using a gas as an example. Consider a container of gas fitted with a movable piston (Fig. 11.3). If we add heat Q to the system, but do not allow the piston to move, the temperature and hence the internal energy U of the gas will increase. We can also change the internal energy by doing work on the gas. Thus, if we insulate the container walls and push the piston in, we compress the gas. The work done on the system equals the change in internal energy (Fig. 11.3*b*), since no heat enters or leaves the gas.

More generally we may add heat Q to the gas and have the gas do work W (Fig. 11.3*c*). The difference is the change in internal energy of the gas, $\Delta U = U_f - U_i$. U_f and U_i are the final and initial energies of the gas, respectively. This is the *first law of thermodynamics*:

$$U_f - U_i = Q - W \quad (11.6)$$

Q is positive if heat is *added* to the system, and W is positive if work is *done* by the system. Although we have used a gas in this example, this result is generally true for all systems and does not depend on the presence of a gas.

Example 11.2

In Example 11.1, a gas is heated and allowed to expand, doing 1.01×10^5 J of work. If 3×10^5 J of heat enters during the expansion, what is the change in the internal energy of the gas?

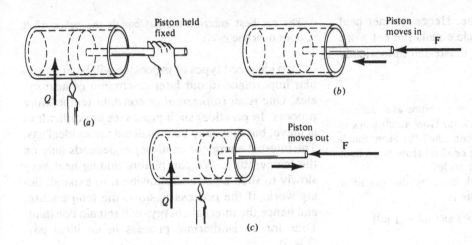

Figure 11.3. (a) With the piston held fixed, the heat added Q equals the internal energy increase ΔU. (b) The walls are insulated. The force **F** does work on the piston and hence on the gas. This work is equal to the internal energy increase. (c) Heat Q is added to the gas, and it expands against the external force **F**. The gas does work W. The difference between Q and W is the change in internal energy of the gas ΔU.

From the first law, the change in the internal energy is $U_f - U_i = Q - W$. Here heat *enters* the system, so Q is positive. Also work is done *by* the system, and W is positive as well. Hence

$$U_f - U_i = Q - W = (3 \times 10^5 \text{ J}) - (1.01 \times 10^5 \text{ J})$$
$$= 1.99 \times 10^5 \text{ J}$$

Since the heat entering is greater than the work done by the expanding gas, its internal energy has increased.

Two statements about the physical world are contained in the first law. First, heat and work are equivalent; they are to be treated on the same basis. They are both forms of energy. Second, the same change in the internal energy can be achieved by adding heat, or by doing work, or by some of each, but the internal energy change is independent of how that change was achieved. This means that the internal energy depends only on the thermodynamic state of the system: its temperature, pressure, and volume in the case of a gas. In other words, going

from a given initial state to a particular final state does not require a definite amount of heat or work, but rather a specific total of the two. It is meaningful to speak of the internal energy of a substance, but not of how much heat it contains. You cannot say an object contains a certain amount of heat.

This idea is illustrated in Fig. 11.4. Suppose a system undergoes two processes, represented by curves (1) and (2), in which the initial and final pressures and volumes are (P_i, V_i) and (P_f, V_f). Along path (1) the area beneath the curve is larger than that beneath curve (2). Hence more work is done by the system in process (1) than in (2). From the first law, since $U_f - U_i$ is the same for both processes, more heat must be added to the system in process (1) than in (2) to achieve the same final state.

If a gas or other substance experiences a series of pressure and volume changes and eventually comes back to its initial state, it has gone through a *cycle*. Its internal energy cannot change over a full cycle,

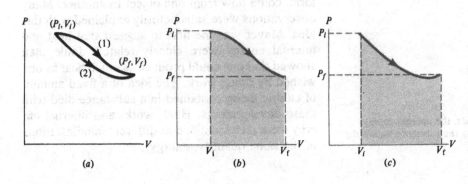

Figure 11.4. (a) A system can change from a state (P_i, V_i) to state (P_f, V_f) by many paths, two of which are shown. (b) The work done by the system is the area beneath the $P-V$ curve and is greater for process (1) than for process (2) shown in (c).

since U_f and U_i are the same. Hence the net heat entering a system over a cycle equals the net work done by the system. This is illustrated numerically in the next example.

Example 11.3

A gas undergoes a series of pressure and volume changes as shown in Fig. 11.5. (a) How much work is done by the gas along the path *abc*? (b) How much work is done by the gas along *cda*? (c) How much heat enters the gas during one full cycle?

(a) From *a* to *b*, the work done by the gas as it expands at a constant pressure is

$$W_{ab} = P \, \Delta V = (2 \times 10^5 \text{ Pa})(4 \text{ m}^3 - 1 \text{ m}^3)$$
$$= 6 \times 10^5 \text{ J}$$

From *b* to *c*, the volume does not change, so no work is done. Hence

$$W_{abc} = W_{ab} = 6 \times 10^5 \text{ J}$$

(b) From *b* to *c*, the volume is decreasing, and ΔV is negative. Thus

$$W_{cd} = P \, \Delta V = (10^5 \text{ Pa})(1 \text{ m}^3 - 4 \text{ m}^3) = -3 \times 10^5 \text{ J}$$

The minus sign indicates work is done *on* the gas as it is compressed to a smaller volume. Note that this work done on the gas is less than the work it did as it expanded, since the pressure is lower. Again, no work is done in the constant volume part of the cycle from *d* to *a*, so

$$W_{cda} = W_{cd} = -3 \times 10^5 \text{ J}$$

(c) Since we have gone through a full cycle, $U_f - U_i = 0$. Hence the first law, $U_f - U_i = Q - W$, becomes $Q - W = 0$. The net heat entering is

$$Q = W = W_{abc} + W_{cda}$$
$$= (6 \times 10^5 \text{ J}) + (-3 \times 10^5 \text{ J}) = 3 \times 10^5 \text{ J}$$

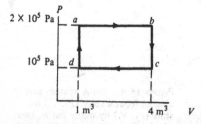

Figure 11.5. Over a full cycle *abcda*, the internal energy change is zero. The net heat entering the substance equals the net work done by it.

The net heat entering the gas equals the net work it does over the cycle.

Two idealized types of processes will be of particular importance in our later discussion of heat cycles. One is an *isothermal* or constant temperature process. In practice, such processes are difficult to achieve, but they may be visualized for an ideal gas. The internal energy of an ideal gas depends only on the temperature. We can picture adding heat very slowly to such a gas and allowing it to expand, doing work. If the process is slow, the temperature, and hence the internal energy, will remain constant. Thus for an isothermal process in an ideal gas, $Q = W$.

A second, more easily approximated process is an *adiabatic* process. This is one in which no heat enters or leaves the system. Thus $U_f - U_i = -W$ for an adiabatic process. This condition is common because we can insulate systems to minimize heat transfer. Alternatively, processes may occur so rapidly that no heat flow occurs. If we pinch the hose on a bicycle pump, pushing the plunger once results in a sudden increase in the internal energy of the air. It will take a few seconds before heat flow from the inside to outside of the pump will be noticed. This flow results from the fact that the air inside is at a higher temperature.

From our presentation of the concepts of heat and temperature, the first law seems an almost obvious statement of the conservation of energy. Nevertheless, the first law forms one of the most fundamental cornerstones of thermodynamics. Historically, the first law was by no means obvious. Until the work of Mayer, Joule, and Helmholtz in the 1840s, heat was regarded as a material substance inside an object. This substance, called caloric, could flow from one object to another. Many observations were satisfactorily explained with this idea. Mayer was the first to suggest that heat and internal energy were closely related. Joule then showed that one could produce as much heat as one wished by doing work. The idea of a fixed amount of caloric being contained in a substance died with these developments. Heat, work, and internal energy were then identified as different manifestations of the same quantity, energy.

Until nearly the middle of the nineteenth century, heat was generally regarded as a fluid called *caloric*. This weightless fluid, which could flow from one object to another but could neither be created nor destroyed, provided a rather complete explanation of many experiments of this period. The three men pictured above are now linked historically with the demise of the caloric theory and with extending the conservation of energy principle to include thermal phenomena.

Mayer was the first to suggest that the energies associated with gravity, electricity, heat, and motion are intimately connected; when one kind of energy disappears, an equivalent amount of other types appears. However, Mayer and his ideas both suffered from neglect. Educated in Germany as a physician, Mayer became interested in physics and published his observations in 1842. His article was written in a metaphysical style and was not viewed as very convincing. Part of the resistance to Mayer's ideas arose because it was not even clear that he understood Newton's laws, much less the concepts involved in a theory of energy conservation.

While the caloric theory was dying even before Mayer's work, the real acceptance of heat as another form of energy came as a result of the independent work of Joule and Helmholtz in 1847. Joule was an English brewery owner and amateur scientist who had built a reputation as a careful and ingenious experimenter. By 1847, Joule had very accurately shown that mechanical work, in this case the work required to turn a paddle wheel immersed in water, is equivalent to heat, since the temperature of the water increased.

While Joule provided the most convincing experimental evidence for the equivalence of mechanical energy and heat, Helmholtz systematically developed the concept of the conservation of energy in one of the most important scientific papers of the nineteenth century.

Helmholtz was also a physician, serving as a surgeon in the Prussian army. In 1849, he became a professor of physiology in Konigsberg. His work on energy conservation, stimulated by his observations on muscle motion, was only one example of his remarkable ability to understand the physics behind biological systems. Helmholtz invented the ophthalmoscope for peering into the eye and also developed the ophthalmometer for measuring the curvature of the eye. In addition, he revived a theory of color vision credited to Young and expanded on it. Helmholtz's study of the ear included the role played by the bones of the middle ear and the cochlea and went on into the difficult but important subject of the quality of sounds. His book, *Sensations of Tone*, is a cornerstone of physiological acoustics. He was the first to measure the speed of a nerve impulse. In his later life, his interests and research led directly to the experimental discovery of electromagnetic waves by one of his students.

While Joule and Helmholtz pursued successful scientific careers, Mayer did not fare so well. Mayer was deeply affected by his lack of recognition and attempted suicide in 1849. After a period of mental illness from which he never fully recovered, he lived out his life in obscurity.

11.3 | THE SECOND LAW OF THERMODYNAMICS

The first law of thermodynamics is useful in understanding the flow of energy during a given process. However, it yields no information about which energy-conserving processes are possible nor does it allow us to predict what state a system will be in under a given set of conditions. The second law can be used to answer some of these questions.

For example, suppose fuel is burned and the heat produced is supplied to a steam engine. The first law requires that the work done by the engine plus the heat rejected by it to the surroundings must equal the heat added, since the internal energy of the engine does not change. However, the first law gives no clue as to the ratio of the work done to the heat supplied, that is, the *efficiency* of the engine. The second law makes it possible to calculate the efficiency for an idealized engine and to set limits on the efficiencies of real engines.

A second example of its use is in chemical reactions. When a reaction occurs, the first law allows one to predict how much energy is absorbed or liberated. However, the second law allows one to predict, for given conditions of temperature and pressure, what the equilibrium state of this system will be.

In this section, we discuss the microscopic and macroscopic forms of the second law. The efficiency of heat engines is discussed in the next section. Applications to chemical systems are treated in detail in chemistry and biochemistry texts.

Microscopic Form of the Second Law

The microscopic form of the second law is a statement about the probable behavior of a large number of molecules or other particles. It states that systems tend to evolve from highly ordered, relatively improbable configurations to more disordered, more statistically probable configurations. Equivalently, systems tend toward states of maximum mo-

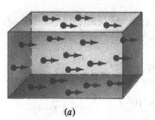
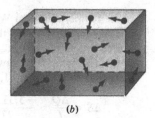

Figure 11.6. Two patterns of molecular motion in a gas. (*a*) Highly ordered. (*b*) Much less ordered or more chaotic.

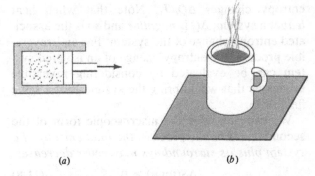

(*a*)   (*b*)

Figure 11.7. In a reversible process, the system and surroundings can both be restored to their original states. (*a*) A frictionless adiabatic expansion is reversible. (*b*) Heat transfer between objects at different temperatures is irreversible.

lecular disorder or chaos. For example, Fig. 11.6 shows two ways in which the molecules of a gas may move. Both pictures show a gas with the same internal energy, but Fig. 11.6*a* represents a highly ordered situation unlike Fig. 11.6*b*. The second law says that a situation *similar* to the disordered state is *more probable* than one similar to the ordered state. Thus it is possible to imagine a great many pictures similar to 11.6*b*, but only a few like Fig. 11.6*a*. Poker players will recognize an equivalent idea: there are only a few hands with a royal flush, but many hands with no value at all, so the odds strongly favor hands of the latter type. Similarly, from this point of view, parking in a tight space at a curb is more difficult than moving onto the street, because there are many more moving configurations than parked ones.

Macroscopic Form of the Second Law

The second law was first formulated as a statement about large or macroscopic systems. This form is easier to use for many applications, although its physical interpretation is perhaps more subtle than that of the molecular chaos previously discussed. The two forms have been shown to be equivalent using microscopic statistical theories.

The macroscopic form of the second law is a statement that a quantity called the *entropy* tends to assume a maximum value. Like the internal energy, the entropy of a system depends only on its state and not on how that state is achieved.

The definition of entropy involves the concept of *reversible* and *irreversible* processes. A reversible process is one in which the system can be returned to its original state with no net change in either the system or its surroundings. For example, if no fric-

tion, turbulence, or other dissipative effect is present, the adiabatic expansion of a gas is reversible (Fig. 11.7). This is because an adiabatic compression can return the system to its original state. The work done on the gas during the compression is equal to that done by the gas during the expansion; the net work done by the gas and its surroundings is zero.

No known natural process is reversible. When heat is transferred between objects at different temperatures, the heat can be returned to the higher-temperature object, but to do so requires that the surroundings do work, as in a refrigerator. Thus the surroundings must be modified to return the system to its original state. Reversible processes, like frictionless systems in mechanics, are an idealization only approximately realized in real systems.

We can now define the entropy of a system. Suppose that a small quantity of heat ΔQ is added to a system at a Kelvin temperature T during a reversible process. We use ΔQ to emphasize the small changes involved. The entropy change of this system is then defined by

$$\Delta S = \frac{\Delta Q}{T} \qquad \text{(reversible process)} \qquad (11.7)$$

If a large quantity of heat is transferred, it can be divided into many small amounts ΔQ_i such that the temperature T_i is nearly constant during the transfer of ΔQ_i. Then, in a reversible process, the total change in entropy is found by summing the small entropy changes $\Delta Q_i/T_i$. Note that when heat *leaves* a system, ΔQ is *negative* and so is the associated entropy change of the system. For an irreversible process, the entropy change of an isolated system can be evaluated by considering reversible processes that would bring the system to the same final state.

We can now give the macroscopic form of the second law. For any process, *the total entropy of a system plus its surroundings may never decrease*:

$$\Delta S(\text{total}) \geq 0 \qquad (11.8)$$

The total entropy change is zero for a reversible process and positive for an irreversible process. This is called the *second law of thermodynamics.* Microscopically this is equivalent to saying that the molecular disorder of a system and its surroundings remains constant if the process is reversible and increases if it is not.

It is possible to derive Eq. 11.8 starting from either of two experimental observations. One is that heat never flows spontaneously from a colder to a hotter object. This is called the Clausius form of the second law. The second observation is that it is impossible to extract heat from an object and convert it *entirely* into work. This is the Kelvin form of the second law. The path from either of these statements of the second law to the entropy or molecular chaos forms is complex and beyond the scope of this textbook. We can, however, see that Eq. 11.8 is indeed satisfied in some simple processes. The following examples also show how one computes entropy changes in reversible and irreversible processes.

Example 11.4

Find the entropy changes of the system and of its surroundings for a reversible adiabatic process.

In an adiabatic process, the heat entering a system is zero. Since the process is reversible, by Eq. 11.7 the entropy change of the system is zero. Similarly, since the surroundings transfer no heat, their entropy change is also zero. Thus $\Delta S(\text{total}) = 0$ as required for reversible processes by the second law.

Example 11.5

If 3.33×10^5 J of heat is removed from a kilogram of liquid water at 0° C, it will turn to ice. Suppose heat is reversibly withdrawn from 10^{-2} kg of liquid water at 0° C until it is entirely converted to an ice cube at the

same temperature. (a) What is the entropy change of the water? (b) What is the net entropy change of the water and surroundings?

(a) The heat withdrawn is $(3.33 \times 10^5$ J kg^{-1}) $\times$ $(10^{-2}$ kg) $= 3.33 \times 10^3$ J, so the entropy change is

$$\Delta S = \frac{\Delta Q}{T} = \frac{-3.33 \times 10^3 \text{ J}}{273 \text{ K}} = -12.2 \text{ J K}^{-1}$$

The minus sign appears because heat is withdrawn from the water, and its entropy decreases.

(b) The process occurs reversibly, so the net entropy change of the water plus surroundings is zero. Since the entropy of the water decreases, the entropy of the surroundings must *increase* by the same amount, $\Delta S = 12.2$ J K^{-1}.

In this example, we can see the relationship between entropy and order. When the water solidifies to an ordered solid phase, the entropy decreases. Since the net change in entropy is zero, the entropy of the surroundings increases. Conversely, when the ice melts, its entropy increases. If the melting occurs reversibly, the entropy of the surroundings decreases.

Example 11.6

Two large objects are isolated from their surroundings. They are at temperatures T_1 and T_2 with $T_2 > T_1$ and are placed in thermal contact. A small quantity of heat Q is transferred, leaving their temperatures nearly unchanged. Find the entropy changes.

The entropy change of the surroundings is zero, since the system is isolated. This is an irreversible process, so we calculate the entropy changes for reversible paths leading to the same final states. We may, for example, consider the case where heat Q is reversibly removed from the object at T_2 by placing a cylinder of gas in contact with it and allowing the gas to expand isothermally. This gives an entropy change $\Delta S_2 = -Q/T_2$. Similarly, a second cylinder can be placed in contact with the cooler object and heat transferred reversibly. The entropy change of the cooler object is then $\Delta S_1 = Q/T_1$. Thus the total entropy change of the two objects is

$$\Delta S(\text{total}) = -\frac{Q}{T_2} + \frac{Q}{T_1} = Q\left(\frac{1}{T_1} - \frac{1}{T_2}\right)$$

$$= Q\frac{(T_2 - T_1)}{T_1 T_2}$$

Since T_2 is greater than T_1, this is positive as predicted for an irreversible process.

Although the second law of thermodynamics in the form of Eq. 11.8 states that no *net* decrease in entropy can occur, it is not true that the entropy of a *system* cannot be reduced. When water is frozen, the entropy of the water is lowered. However, if careful consideration is taken of the surroundings, it is found that the *total entropy of the system plus its surroundings remains constant or increases*.

11.4 | THE CARNOT THEOREM AND CONVERSION OF ENERGY

If one applies the second law of thermodynamics to an idealized reversible heat engine, one finds that the efficiency of the engine in converting heat into mechanical work is always less than 100 percent. Real heat engines, such as automobile engines and electrical power-generating plants, always have some friction or turbulence and are therefore irreversible. Their efficiencies are necessarily still lower. This remarkable property of heat engines was discovered by Sadi Carnot (1796–1832) in 1824 and is called *Carnot's theorem*.

Carnot's theorem shows that the conversion of thermal energy into other forms of energy is qualitatively different from other kinds of energy conversion. For example, a swinging pendulum can completely convert mechanical potential energy into mechanical kinetic energy and back again. The kinetic energy of moving water in a turbine can be transformed into electrical energy by a generator; the efficiency is limited only by friction and turbulence and can be quite high in practice. Electrical energy can also be converted into mechanical energy by a motor; again there is no theoretical limit on the efficiency, and the actual efficiencies can be 90 percent or better. Also, chemical energy can be

converted into electrical energy with very high efficiency, as in a fuel cell where hydrogen and oxygen combine and produce an electrical current. Electrical energy can also be transformed into chemical energy without any fundamental limitation. In the human body the conversion of chemical energy from food into mechanical work is usually done at an efficiency of about 30 percent at most. This limit on the efficiency does not arise from the second law. It occurs because the body loses energy in converting foods into compounds that the body can utilize effectively at the cellular level.

Any heat engine can be thought of as acting in a *cycle*. First, a substance at a high temperature is permitted to do work and also to transfer heat to its surroundings; then the cycle is completed by returning the substance to its original state while transferring enough heat to it to replace the lost energy.

Carnot's theorem is proved by considering a particular reversible heat engine, called a *Carnot engine*, or a *Carnot cycle*. This cycle consists of four reversible processes, which are illustrated in Fig. 11.8 for the special case of an ideal gas. However, the *calculated efficiency is independent of the material* used in the engine; we only use the ideal gas because it is easy to discuss.

The path from a to b is an isothermal expansion in which heat Q_2 is absorbed from a reservoir at T_2. The path bc is an adiabatic expansion; no heat is transferred. The path cd is an isothermal compression in which heat Q_1 leaves the system at a lower temperature T_1. (Note that in contradiction to our earlier convention, we take Q_1 to be positive here even though heat is *leaving* the system.) Finally, the material is returned to its original state

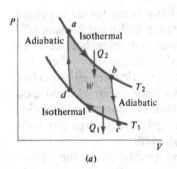

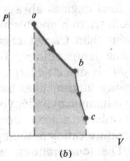

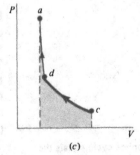

Figure 11.8. (a) The Carnot cycle for an ideal gas. (b) The work done by the gas during the expansion equals the colored area. (c) The work done on the gas during the compression equals the colored area.

by an adiabatic compression da; again, no heat is transferred.

In expanding, the gas does work equal to the area under the curve abc (Fig. 11.8b). When it is compressed, work must be done on the gas equal to the smaller area under the curve cda (Fig. 11.8c). The net work W done by the gas over one full cycle therefore equals the shaded area enclosed by the path (Fig. 11.8a). Because the gas at the end of the cycle is in its original state, the net change in internal energy is zero. The first law therefore requires that the net work done by the gas must equal the heat absorbed minus the heat rejected, or

$$W = Q_2 - Q_1 \qquad (11.9)$$

This is shown symbolically in Fig. 11.9.

Since the Carnot cycle is reversible, the total entropy change of the system is zero. For the reservoir at T_2 the entropy change is $\Delta S_2 = -Q_2/T_2$. The entropy change of the lower-temperature reservoir is $\Delta S_1 = Q_1/T_1$. The gas returns to its original state, so its entropy change is zero. Thus

$$\Delta S(\text{total}) = \Delta S_1 + \Delta S_2 = -\frac{Q_2}{T_2} + \frac{Q_1}{T_1} = 0$$

or

$$\frac{Q_1}{Q_2} = \frac{T_1}{T_2}$$

The efficiency is defined as the work done divided by the heat absorbed, $e = W/Q_2$. Using $W = Q_2 - Q_1$, we find

$$e = \frac{W}{Q_2} = 1 - \frac{Q_1}{Q_2} = 1 - \frac{T_1}{T_2} \qquad (11.10)$$

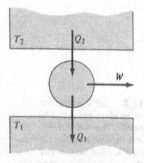

Figure 11.9. The work done in a complete cycle equals the heat absorbed at T_2 less the heat rejected at T_1.

This ratio of the work done to the heat supplied is the *efficiency* of the Carnot engine. According to Eq. 11.10, the efficiency is always less than 1 unless the colder reservoir is at absolute zero, which is, in fact, unattainable even in principle.

The following example shows the efficiency of a Carnot engine operating between two easily achieved temperatures.

Example 11.7

A Carnot engine operates between 100°C and 0°C. What is its efficiency?

Converting the temperatures to the Kelvin scale, $T_1 = 273$ K and $T_2 = 373$ K. Then

$$e = 1 - \frac{T_1}{T_2} = 1 - \frac{273}{373} = 0.268$$

Only 26.8 percent of the heat supplied is converted into mechanical work; the remainder is rejected into the colder reservoir.

11.5 | IMPLICATIONS OF CARNOT'S THEOREM

As we noted earlier, the efficiency of a Carnot engine is independent of the substance used. This is clear from the derivation, because the calculation of the efficiency used only the fact that the cycle consisted of two isothermal and two adiabatic processes and did not rely on any properties of the material. This means that one cannot hope to improve the efficiency of an engine by an ingenious choice of materials if that engine is already fairly close to the Carnot efficiency for the temperatures of its cycle. Carnot also showed that *no heat engine operated cyclically between two temperature reservoirs is more efficient than that described by the Carnot cycle.*

Real engines always have some losses resulting from friction and turbulence and must be less efficient than Carnot engines operating between the same temperatures. To maximize the efficiency, T_2/T_1 is made as large as practicable. High-performance auto engines have large ratios of maximum to minimum cylinder volumes or compression ratios in order to achieve correspondingly large gas temperature ratios in the cylinders.

The temperatures and pressures of the steam boilers in electrical power-generating plants are also very high. Modern fossil fuel electrical power-generating plants are about 40 percent efficient; the excess heat lost when the steam condenses is given off into a lake or river or transferred to the atmosphere with cooling towers. Present commercial nuclear power plants are at best 34 percent efficient, so the thermal pollution problems they pose are somewhat larger. These efficiencies should be compared with the ideal Carnot efficiencies of 52 percent and 44 percent, respectively, for the two types of plants.

The lower efficiency of the nuclear plants is related to limitations on the high temperatures allowable for the uranium in the reactor. The uranium oxide in the center of the fuel rods must be kept well below melting temperature. This limits the temperature at the outside of the fuel rods. In all power plants the maximum temperature is limited by design and materials problems, and the exhaust temperature is determined by the available cooling water in lakes and rivers. The components of a major steam-generating plant are shown in Fig. 11.10.

Example 11.8

A nuclear power plant generates 500 MW = 5×10^8 W at 34 percent efficiency. The waste heat goes into a river, such as the Connecticut River, with an average flow of 3×10^4 kg s^{-1}. How much does the water temperature rise? (It requires 4.18×10^3 J to raise the temperature of 1 kg of water 1 K.)

If the plant operates at 34 percent efficiency, it must have a total heat input of 1.47×10^9 W. Of this, 66 percent, or 9.7×10^8 W, must go into the river. In

1 second the heat $\Delta Q = 9.7 \times 10^8$ J will raise the water temperature by ΔT. With $m = 3 \times 10^4$ kg,

$$\Delta T = \frac{\Delta Q}{(4.18 \times 10^3 \text{ J kg}^{-1} \text{ K}^{-1})m}$$
$$= \frac{9.7 \times 10^8 \text{ J}}{(4.18 \times 10^3 \text{ J kg}^{-1} \text{ K}^{-1})(3 \times 10^4 \text{ kg})}$$
$$= 7.7 \text{ K}$$

This temperature rise could cause serious damage to the organisms in the river. In a case such as this, cooling towers are used to dissipate heat to the atmosphere rather than the river. A 40 percent efficient fossil fuel plant of the same output power would raise the river temperature by almost 6 K.

The expression $e = 1 - (T_1/T_2)$ for the efficiency of a Carnot engine provides a useful way of interpreting the second law. If heat is transferred from a hotter object to a colder one, reducing their temperature difference, then the efficiency of a Carnot engine operating between these two heat reservoirs decreases. This means that less work can be done with a given heat input and that the energy stored in these objects is therefore less available. For example, with tanks of water at 0°C and 100°C, we can operate an engine; this cannot be done if we mix these tanks together so that they are at a common temperature. The statement that systems tend toward states of maximum entropy therefore implies that *energy tends to become less and less available for doing mechanical work.*

Ocean Thermal Differences

The intensifying search for alternative energy sources often involves consideration of the limits imposed by the Carnot theorem. One source of power now under investigation employs the temperature differences between the ocean surface and water layers deep below. The warm surface water evaporates a working fluid such as ammonia. The gas drives a turbine, much as steam does in a conventional power plant, and is then condensed using the colder water from lower levels. The temperature differences range from 18°C to 25°C in tropical waters. Assuming a surface temperature of 30°C, or 303 K, the ideal Carnot efficiency of the scheme is at best

$$e = 1 - \frac{T_1}{T_2} = 1 - \frac{278}{303} = 0.0825$$

Since the theoretical Carnot efficiency is only 8.25 percent and there are other unavoidable losses,

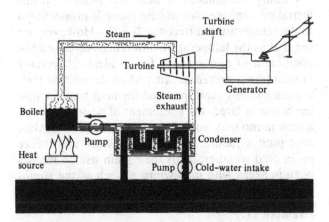

Figure 11.10. The major components of a steam electrical power-generating plant. The heat source may be coal or oil or a uranium-fueled reactor.

a 3 percent efficiency in producing electrical power is considered somewhat optimistic. For such a plant to produce 500 MW of electrical power requires pumping approximately 200,000 litres of water per second through the heat exchangers. In a small-scale 1979 test of this scheme in the Pacific Ocean near Hawaii, the pumps used 80 percent of the electrical power generated; eventually, this might be reduced to 30 percent. By contrast, conventional power plants use about 1 percent of their output on site. Thus while the supply of thermal energy in the oceans is enormous, the problems inherent in using it are very large.

11.6 | REFRIGERATORS AND HEAT PUMPS

Refrigerators and heat pumps are devices that remove heat from a low-temperature region or reservoir and release it into a higher temperature reservoir. The refrigerator removes heat from the cooling compartment and freezer section and releases it into the room. The heat pump, usually operating between the inside and outside of a building, can be used to cool the inside during hot weather and to heat the inside during cold weather.

If one of these devices removes heat Q_1 from a low-temperature reservoir at T_1 and releases heat Q_2 into a high-temperature reservoir at T_2, from the first law of thermodynamics the work done *by* the system is

$$W = Q_1 - Q_2$$

The internal energy change is zero because the device acts cyclically, returning the system to the same thermodynamic state repeatedly.

The *coefficient of performance* (C.P.), which gives a useful measure of effectiveness, is defined differently for the refrigerator and heat pump. For the refrigerator, C.P.$_R$ is defined as the ratio of the heat absorbed at the *lower temperature* to the work done *on* the system. The work done on the system is $-W = Q_2 - Q_1$, so

$$\text{C.P.}_R = \frac{Q_1}{-W} = \frac{Q_1}{Q_2 - Q_1} \qquad (11.11)$$

A typical refrigerator has C.P.$_R \simeq 5$.

For the heat pump, C.P.$_{HP}$ is defined as the ratio of the heat released at the *higher temperature* to the work done *on* the system. Thus

$$\text{C.P.}_{HP} = \frac{Q_2}{-W} = \frac{Q_2}{Q_2 - Q_1} \qquad (11.12)$$

Commercially available heat pumps have C.P.$_{HP}$ in the range of 2 to 4.

We can find the theoretical limits on the performance of ideal refrigerators and heat pumps just as we did for the Carnot engine. An ideal device operates reversibly so the total entropy change of the system plus surroundings per cycle is zero. Adding the entropy changes of the low- and high-temperature reservoirs,

$$\Delta S = \frac{-Q_1}{T_1} + \frac{Q_2}{T_2} = 0$$

Hence $Q_1/T_1 = Q_2/T_2$. Using this result, the work done on the system per cycle is $-W = Q_2 - Q_1$ or

$$-W = Q_2 \left(1 - \frac{T_1}{T_2} \right) = Q_1 \left(\frac{T_2}{T_1} - 1 \right)$$

The corresponding ideal coefficients of performance are

$$\text{C.P.}_R = \frac{T_1}{T_2 - T_1} \qquad \text{(ideal)} \qquad (11.13)$$

and

$$\text{C.P.}_{HP} = \frac{T_2}{T_2 - T_1} \qquad \text{(ideal)} \qquad (11.14)$$

Usually the amount of heat that must be transferred by a refrigerator or heat pump is proportional to the temperature difference $T_2 - T_1$. However, we see that as the temperature difference *increases*, the coefficient of performance for an ideal refrigerator or heat pump *decreases*. Just when the outside temperature is low, and the need for heat transfer into the house is large, the coefficient of performance of a heat pump may not be much greater than 1. Also, heat pumps tend to condense moisture and freeze up in cold weather. Thus their main use so far has been in areas with mild winters, such as the southern parts of the United States.

Example 11.9
A commercial heat pump has C.P.$_{HP} = 3$ when the indoor temperature is 20°C and the outdoor tempera-

ture is 6°C. (a) What is the ideal value of C.P.$_{HP}$? (b) How much work is required to operate the commercial heat pump if 3×10^6 J of heat must be transferred to the room each hour?

(a) The indoor and outdoor temperatures are 293 K and 279 K, respectively. For an ideal heat pump,

$$C.P._{HP} = \frac{T_2}{T_2 - T_1} = \frac{293 \text{ K}}{293 \text{ K} - 279 \text{ K}} = 20.9$$

(b) The work done on the heat pump in an hour is

$$-W = \frac{Q_2}{C.P._{HP}} = \frac{3 \times 10^6 \text{ J}}{3} = 10^6 \text{ J}$$

Thus energy must be provided to operate the heat pump at the rate of 10^6 J per hour, or 278 W. In one hour, the heat transferred from the outdoors to the room is $Q_1 = Q_2 + W = 3 \times 10^6$ J $- 10^6$ J $= 2 \times 10^6$ J.

SUMMARY

Thermodynamics is the study of the transformation of energy from one form to another. In this chapter, we were specifically concerned with internal energy, heat, and mechanical work. The first law is a relationship between these quantities: the internal energy change of a system is equal to the heat added to the system less the work done by the system,

$$\Delta U = U_f - U_i = Q - W$$

The work done by a system at a pressure P when a small volume change ΔV occurs is

$$\Delta W = P \, \Delta V$$

The second law of thermodynamics is expressed in terms of the entropy. In its microscopic form, it is a statement that systems tend to evolve toward increasing disorder. The macroscopic statement of the second law, while it is somewhat subtle in its content, can be used to make very general statements about processes and their efficiencies.

Macroscopically, if a small amount of heat ΔQ is added to a system in a reversible process, the entropy change of the system is

$$\Delta S = \frac{\Delta Q}{T}$$

The second law states that the total entropy of a system and its surroundings will never decrease.

Using the first and second laws of thermodynamics, Carnot showed that the maximum efficiency of a heat engine operating with high and low temperatures of T_2 and T_1, respectively, is

$$e = 1 - \frac{T_1}{T_2}$$

Refrigerators and heat pumps can also be described and analyzed in terms of the first and second laws. The maximum possible coefficients of performance for these devices are

$$C.P._R = \frac{T_1}{T_2 - T_1} \quad \text{(ideal)}$$

and

$$C.P._{HP} = \frac{T_2}{T_2 - T_1} \quad \text{(ideal)}$$

Checklist

Define or explain:

work	Carnot efficiency
internal energy	isothermal process
first law of	disordered state
thermodynamics	reversible and
adiabatic process	irreversible processes
entropy	refrigerator
second law of	heat pump
thermodynamics	coefficient of
Carnot's theorem	performance

REVIEW QUESTIONS

Q11-1 When a gas at a constant pressure P expands by an amount ΔV, the work done by the system is _____.

Q11-2 What is meant by the word heat?

Q11-3 What is the internal energy?

Q11-4 If heat is added to a system and some work is done by the system, what is the difference between these quantities?

Q11-5 The _____ is a measure of the disorder in a system.

Q11-6 If a small amount of heat ΔQ enters a system at an absolute temperature T, what is the entropy change of the system if the process is reversible?

Q11-7 The second law of thermodynamics states that the entropy of a system plus its surroundings may never _____.

Q11-8 If a heat engine takes in heat at a higher

temperature T_2 and loses heat at a lower temperature T_1, what is its maximum possible efficiency?

Q11-9 How is the coefficient of performance of a refrigerator defined?

EXERCISES

Section 11.1 | Mechanical Work

11-1 In Fig. 11.11, how much work is done by the system in the process (a) along path (2) from A to B? (b) If the system is returned from B to A along the same path, how much work is done by the system?

11-2 A gas does work in an isobaric process at $P = 10^5$ Pa. How much work is done by the gas if (a) $V_i = 10^{-2}$ m^3 and $V_f = 2.24 \times 10^{-2}$ m^3; (b) $V_i = 2 \times 10^{-2}$ m^3 and $V_f = 0.5 \times 10^{-2}$ m^3?

11-3 A 10-N force directed to the left is applied to the piston of Fig. 11.1. If the piston moves 0.14 m, how much work is done on the gas?

11-4 A gas at a pressure of 10 atm has a volume of 0.5 m^3. (a) If it is allowed to expand at a constant pressure to a volume of 2 m^3, how much work does it do? (b) If instead the gas is compressed at a constant pressure to a volume of 0.25 m^3, how much work does it do?

11-5 A gas is allowed to expand at a constant pressure of 10^7 Pa, its volume increasing by 2 m^3. It is then cooled at a constant volume, and its pressure drops to 5×10^6 Pa. Finally, it is returned at constant pressure to its original volume. What is the net work done by the gas during the entire process?

Section 11.2 | The First Law of Thermodynamics

11-6 In Fig. 11.11, a system undergoes a process from point A to point B. How much work is

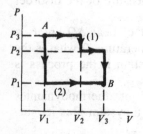

Figure 11.11. Exercises 11-1 and 11-6.

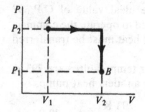

Figure 11.12. $P_1 = 1$ atm, $P_2 = 3$ atm, $V_1 = 0.02$ m^3, and $V_2 = 0.10$ m^3. Exercise 11-7.

done by the system on (a) path (1); (b) path (2)? (c) If process (1) is carried out adiabatically, what is the change in the internal energy?

11-7 In undergoing the process from A to B in Fig. 11.12, the increase in internal energy of a substance is 3×10^5 J. How much heat is absorbed by the system?

11-8 Find the change in internal energy of the system when (a) a system absorbs 2000 J of heat and produces 500 J of work; (b) a system absorbs 1100 J of heat and 400 J of work is done on it.

11-9 An electric heater supplies heat to a gas at a rate of 100 W. If the expanding gas does 75 joules of work in each second, at what rate is the internal energy increasing?

11-10 If the gas of Exercise 11-9 has a constant pressure of 1 atm, by how much does it expand in 10 s?

11-11 The gas of Figure 11.1 is heated. Under which condition will the internal energy increase most rapidly, when the piston is held fixed or when the piston is allowed to move to the right? Explain your reasoning.

11-12 An inventor has a system in which water comes down from a reservoir through a pipe, turns a turbine to generate electricity, and is then pumped back to the reservoir. "Free power," he claims. What is wrong with this scheme?

Section 11.3 | The Second Law of Thermodynamics

11-13 An inventor announces to the press a wonderful new machine for generating electric power. Water taken in from the surface of the ocean cools as it passes through the device, and the energy released is converted into electricity. A reporter who studied physics in college says this idea can't work because of the first law of thermodynamics. Another disagrees, claiming it violates the second law but not the first. Who is correct? Explain.

11-14 A large pot of boiling water is placed on a block of ice at 0°C, and 1000 J of heat goes from the pot to the ice. (a) Is this process reversible? (b) Find the entropy change of the pot of water. (c) Find the entropy change of the ice. (d) Find the net entropy change of the pot of water plus the ice.

11-15 A 10-kg rock falls off a cliff, coming to rest after dropping a vertical distance of 50 m. All its kinetic energy is converted to heat. What is the change in entropy of the rock and its surroundings if the temperature is 27°C?

11-16 Worldwide, humans use energy in all forms at a rate of about 10^{13} W. Estimate the annual increase in entropy associated with this energy usage.

11-17 An electrically heated house maintains a temperature of 20°C by using electrical energy at a rate of 5 kW. The air outside is at 0°C. At what rate is the entropy of the house plus surroundings changing?

11-18 A new deck of playing cards has cards of each suit together and ordered numerically. The deck is then shuffled. Has its entropy changed? If so, why?

11-19 The second law of thermodynamics states that the disorder of the universe is always either constant or increasing. (a) How is this compatible with the fact that plants and animals develop into highly ordered systems? (b) How can the second law of thermodynamics be compatible with the theory of evolution, which states that more highly ordered complex living things evolve from simpler species?

11-20 A system at a constant temperature of 300 K absorbs 10^4 J of heat, and no work is done. (a) What is the change in entropy of the system? (b) What is the change in its internal energy?

11-21 A helium-filled balloon is punctured, and the gas spreads uniformly throughout a room. (a) Is the process reversible? Explain. (b) Has the entropy of the helium and the air in the room increased or decreased? Explain.

11-22 In terms of the microscopic form of the second law of thermodynamics, explain why repeatedly tossing a coin should yield heads about as often as tails.

11-23 A coin is flipped six times. (a) How many ways can these flips result in all tails, one head and five tails, two heads and four tails . . . to five heads and one tail, and to all heads? (b) From your results, what is the most probable result of the six flips? Explain.

Section 11.4 | The Carnot Theorem and Conversion of Energy

11-24 What does the second law imply about the efficiency of hydroelectric power plants?

11-25 A child leaves a refrigerator door open in an attempt to cool off a hot kitchen. What will this actually do to the temperature in the room if the door is left open for several hours?

11-26 An inventor announces a new kind of steam engine that uses chicken soup instead of water and has twice the efficiency of conventional steam engines. Furthermore, it uses steam at lower temperatures and pressures, reducing construction costs. Would you buy stock in his company? Explain.

11-27 An internal combustion engine using natural gas and air as a working substance has a temperature in the spark-ignited firing chamber of 2150 K and an exhaust temperature of 900 K. The difference between the heat supplied and the work done by the engine in each second is 4.6×10^6 J. (a) What is the ideal Carnot efficiency of this engine? (b) How much work is actually done per second if the heat input is 7.9×10^6 W? (c) What is the actual efficiency of this engine?

11-28 If a heat engine operates at 40 percent efficiency and it absorbs 10^4 W from the high-temperature reservoir, at what rate does it do mechanical work?

Section 11.5 | Implications of Carnot's Theorem

11-29 If fossil fuel and nuclear power-generating plants operate with efficiencies of 40 percent and 30 percent, respectively, and the low-temperature reservoir is at 300 K for both, what is the minimum temperature of the steam produced by the fuel in each case?

11-30 If the power plant of Example 11.8 were a fossil fuel plant operating at 40 percent efficiency, what would the temperature rise of the water be as a result of the waste heat?

11-31 The temperature difference between the surface and deep water behind large dams could be used to produce power in the same way as described for ocean water. If the deep water is assumed to always be at 5°C, what is the ideal efficiency for utilizing this energy source in January and in July if the surface temperature of the water is 8°C and 23°C, respectively, in these two months?

Section 11.6 | Refrigerators and Heat Pumps

11-32 A refrigerator takes heat from the freezer unit at −3°C at a rate of 100 W. The heat is released to a room at 26°C. (a) What is the maximum possible coefficient of performance of the refrigerator? (b) If the actual C.P.$_R$ is 4, how much power is needed to maintain the freezer unit at −3°C?

11-33 A heat pump is used to provide heat to the inside of a house at a rate of 5000 W. If energy is provided to operate the heat pump at a rate of 2000 W, what is the coefficient of performance of the heat pump?

11-34 A heat pump has a C.P.$_{HP}$ of 3 when the temperature is 20°C indoors and 10°C outside. (a) Find the coefficient of performance for an ideal heat pump operating at these temperatures. (b) What is the C.P.$_{HP}$ for the ideal heat pump if the outside temperature drops to −15°C? (c) What is the ratio of these two C.P.$_{HP}$s? (d) If the same ratio also applies to the actual heat pump, what is its C.P.$_{HP}$ when the outside temperature is −15°C?

PROBLEMS

11-35 A system goes from state a to c via path abc in Fig. 11.13. 10^5 J of heat flow into the system, and 4×10^4 J of work are done. (a) How much heat flows into the system along path adc if 10^4 of work are done? (b) If the system returns to state a from state c via the zigzag path, the work is 2×10^4 J. How much heat enters or leaves the system? (c) If $U_a = 10^4$ J and $U_d = 5 \times 10^4$ J, what is the heat absorbed along the paths ad and dc?

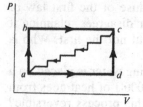

Figure 11.13. Problem 11-35.

11-36 Eight litres of air at room temperature and atmospheric pressure are compressed isothermally to a volume of 3 litres. The air then expands adiabatically to a volume of 8 litres. Show the process on a P–V diagram.

11-37 An engine operates on the cycle shown in Fig. 11.14, a temperature-entropy diagram. What is the efficiency of the engine?

11-38 Draw a schematic T–S diagram for a Carnot engine operating between temperatures T_2 and T_1, where $T_2 > T_1$.

11-39 Two dice, each having the numbers one through six on its sides, are thrown together. (a) In how many ways can the two dice be thrown so that the "up" numbers total 2, 3, 4, . . ., 12? (b) Which total is most probable? (c) What is the implication of part (b) in terms of entropy and disorder?

11-40 A heat pump is used to heat a building when the outdoor temperature is 0°C and the indoor temperature is 25°C. The coefficient of performance for the pump under these conditions

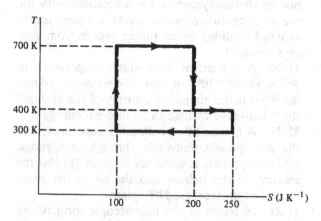

Figure 11.14. Problem 11-37.

is 3.2. (a) If the heat pump delivers heat inside at a rate of 5×10^6 J per hour, at what rate must work be done to run the heat pump? (b) How much electrical energy would be used to heat the building directly? (c) A litre of oil provides 3.7×10^7 J of energy when burned. How many litres of oil per hour must be burned at 80 percent efficiency to provide the heat needed for the building? (d) If the oil is burned to produce electrical power at 40 percent efficiency and used to run the heat pump, how much oil per hour must be burned?

11-41 About 2×10^5 J of heat must be removed from a tray of water to produce ice cubes. (a) How long will it take to remove this much heat in a 200-W input Carnot refrigerator operating between inner and outer temperatures of 270 K and 310 K, respectively? (b) Is this time consistent with your estimate of how long it takes to freeze an ice tray? Explain the difference, if any.

11-42 The motor in an ideal (Carnot) refrigerator delivers 200 W of useful power. The freezing compartment of the refrigerator is at $T_1 = 270$ K, and the room air is at $T_2 = 300$ K. Find the maximum amount of heat that can be removed from the refrigerator in 1 minute.

11-43 A nuclear boiling water reactor heats steam to 285°C, and the cooling water is at 40°C. The actual operating efficiency of the power plant is 34 percent. (a) What is the ideal efficiency of the plant? (b) What is the ratio of the power actually lost to that lost in the ideal situation?

11-44 Using the temperature difference between surface and deep ocean water to produce electricity involves transferring the heat from the higher-temperature water to a working substance and finally to the cooling water. To increase the temperature of a kilogram of water by 1 K requires 4.169×10^3 J. In order to produce 500 MW (500×10^6 W) of electricity at 4 percent efficiency, a mass m of cooling water must have its temperature raised from 12°C to 30°C each second. What is m?

11-45 An automobile burns gasoline, producing gases at 2100°C. The atmosphere is at 27°C. (a) Find the efficiency of a Carnot engine operating between these temperatures. (b) If this Carnot

engine were to deliver 10 kW of usable power, what thermal power input would it require? (c) The actual efficiency of automobile engines is only 20 percent. When the losses in the drive train and transmission and the requirements of the lights, water pump, generator, and other accessories are included, the overall system efficiency drops to about 12.5 percent. At what rate must energy be supplied by burning gasoline if the car requires 10 kW to overcome dissipative forces and maintain its speed?

11-46 Converting 1 kg of water at 20°C to ice at −10°C requires removing 4.37×10^5 J from the water. An ice-making machine operates in a room where the air temperature is 25°C and maintains an interior temperature of −10°C. It produces 200 kg of ice per day. (a) If the refrigerator achieved the limits set by the second law, what would its coefficient of performance be? (b) The actual C.P.$_R$ for the refrigerator is 4.5. How much energy must be supplied to it daily?

11-47 A coal-fired electrical power plant heats steam and exhausts waste heat into a river where the temperature is 10°C. (a) The efficiency of a Carnot engine operating at the temperatures of the plant is 52 percent. What is the temperature of the steam? (b) The plant has an actual efficiency of 40 percent and produces 750 MW of electrical power. At what rate is it consuming energy obtained from burning coal? (c) Burning 1 kg of coal produces 4.4×10^7 J of heat. How much coal is burned in 24 hours by the plant?

^{c}11-48 For real gases, an improvement over the ideal gas equation of state is given by the *van der Waal's equation*,

$$\left(P + \frac{a}{V^2}\right)(V - b) = RT$$

Here a and b are constants. Show that the work done when a gas expands from initial volume V_0 to a volume V at a constant temperature T is

$$W = \frac{a}{V} - \frac{a}{V_0} + RT \ln\left[\frac{(V - b)}{(V_0 - b)}\right].$$

^{c}11-49 In an adiabatic expansion of an ideal gas, the pressure and volume are related by $PV^\gamma = K$, where K and γ are constants. Show that when the pressure and volume change in an adiabatic expansion from P_0, V_0 to P, V, the work done by the gas is

$$W = \frac{(PV - P_0V_0)}{(1 - \gamma)}$$

ANSWERS TO REVIEW QUESTIONS

Q11-1, $P \Delta V$; **Q11-2**, the thermal energy transferred; **Q11-3**, the energy of a system due to the translational, rotational, and vibrational kinetic energy of its molecules plus that due to molecular interactions, **Q11-4**, the change in internal energy; **Q11-5**, entropy; **Q11-6**, $\Delta Q/T$; **Q11-7**, decrease; **Q11-8**, $1 - T_1/T_2$; **Q11-9**, the ratio of the heat absorbed at the low temperature to the work done on the system.

SUPPLEMENTARY TOPICS
11.7 | HUMAN METABOLISM

All living things require energy to sustain the life process. Green plants obtain their energy directly from the sun through the process of photosynthesis. Plants such as mushrooms, which do not utilize photosynthesis, as well as animals require food capable of providing chemical energy. In all cases, living plants and animals operate within the constraints described by thermodynamics.

The first law of thermodynamics provides a convenient scheme for cataloging the factors that enter the complex subject of human metabolism. Suppose that in a time Δt, a person does an amount of mechanical work ΔW. This can be directly measured in activities such as bicycling, shoveling snow, or pushing a cart. Heat will usually leave the body, so ΔQ will be negative. It can be measured by finding the amount of heat that must be removed to keep the temperature constant in a room in which the person is working. From the first law, the internal energy change ΔU will be given by $\Delta U = \Delta Q - \Delta W$. Dividing by Δt, this becomes a relation among the rates of change:

$$\frac{\Delta U}{\Delta t} = \frac{\Delta Q}{\Delta t} - \frac{\Delta W}{\Delta t} \qquad (11.15)$$

The rate of change of internal energy can be measured accurately by observing the rate at which a person uses oxygen in converting food into energy and waste materials. For example, a mole (180 g) of glucose, which is a typical carbohydrate, combines with 134.4 litres of oxygen gas in a series of steps to form carbon dioxide and water. In the process, 2870 kJ of energy are released. The *energy equivalent of oxygen* is defined as the ratio of the energy released to the oxygen consumed. For glucose, this ratio is 2870 kJ/134.4 litres = 21.4 kJ litre^{-1}. The *energy content per unit mass* is defined as the energy released divided by the mass. For glucose, this ratio is 2870 kJ/180 g = 15.9 kJ g^{-1}.

Table 11.1 lists the average energy content per unit mass and energy equivalent of oxygen for the carbohydrates, proteins, and fats usually consumed. The calorific equivalent of oxygen of all these is the same to within a few percent. Thus an average value of 20.2 kJ litre^{-1} is used in converting measured oxygen consumption rates to rates of internal energy change. For example, if a person consumes oxygen at the high rate of 100 litres h^{-1}, the rate of internal energy change is (100 litres h^{-1}) × (20.2 kJ litre^{-1}) = 2020 kJ h^{-1} = 561 W.

Basal Metabolic Rate | All animals, including humans, use internal energy even while sleeping. The rate of energy consumption while resting but awake is called the basal metabolic rate. It is about 1.2 W kg^{-1} for an average 20-year-old man and 1.1 W kg^{-1} for a woman of the same age. In the units often used in discussions of nutrition, kilocalories, this corresponds to about 1700 kcal per day and 1400 kcal per day for a 70-kg man and a 60-kg woman, respectively. Much of the energy consumed by a resting person is converted directly into heat. The remainder is used to do work in the body and then converted into heat.

TABLE 11.1

The average energy content per unit mass of food and the energy equivalent of oxygen for a typical diet

Food	Energy Content per Unit Mass (kJ g^{-1})	Energy Equivalent of Oxygen (kJ litre^{-1})
Carbohydrate	17.2	21.1
Protein	17.6	18.7
Fat	38.9	19.8
Ethanol	29.7	20.3
Standard average		20.2

Food materials are not used directly in the body. Instead they are converted into materials such as ATP (adenosine triphosphate), which can be used in the tissues. About 55 percent of the internal energy is lost as heat in this conversion. The remaining 45 percent is available to do internal work in the body organs or to enable the skeletal muscles to contract and do work on an external object.

When a person is performing an activity such as running up stairs or doing housework, the metabolic rate increases (Table 11.2). Part of the increased conversion of internal energy is needed to provide the mechanical work done by the person. The remainder results from the increased internal demands of the body. For example, in shoveling, the metabolic rate is about eight times the basal metabolic rate, but little mechanical work is actually done. The metabolic energy is used primarily by the skeletal muscles in changing and maintaining the body position.

The following example illustrates some of the ideas we have developed to this point.

Example 11.10

(a) How much internal energy is used by a 65-kg man when bicycling for 4 hours? (b) If this energy is obtained by the metabolism of body fat, how much fat is used in this period?

(a) From Table 11.2, the metabolic rate while cycling is 7.6 W kg^{-1}. A 65-kg man then uses energy at a rate

of (7.6 W kg^{-1})(65 kg) = 494 W. Four hours is 1.44×10^4 s, so the net energy usage is

$$
\begin{aligned}
-\Delta U &= (494 \text{ W})(1.44 \times 10^4 \text{ s}) \\
&= 7.1 \times 10^6 \text{ J} \\
&= 7100 \text{ kJ}
\end{aligned}
$$

(b) The energy equivalent of fat is 38.9 kJ g^{-1} so the mass of fat needed to supply the necessary energy is

$$
\text{mass of fat} = \frac{7100 \text{ kJ}}{38.9 \text{ kJ g}^{-1}}
$$

$$
= 180 \text{ g} = 0.18 \text{ kg}
$$

To appreciate this result, it is useful to compare it with the energy equivalent of the food required by a fairly sedentary man during a 24-hour day, which is 10,500 kJ, or 2500 kcal. Hence the exercise of bicycling for 4 hours will use up about two thirds of the daily energy required by a sedentary man. This indicates that limiting food intake is a more practical way to decrease body weight than is exercise for most people.

The Efficiency of Food Utilization

The efficiency of a human using the chemical energy in food to do useful work can be defined in several ways. The usual convention is to compare the measured rate at which mechanical work is done with the actual metabolic rate during the activity minus the basal metabolic rate. The efficiency e in percent is then

$$
e = \frac{100 \dfrac{\Delta W}{\Delta t}}{\left| \dfrac{\Delta U}{\Delta t} - \dfrac{\Delta U}{\Delta t}_{\text{basal}} \right|} \% \qquad (11.16)
$$

The denominator is the magnitude of the difference in actual and basal metabolic rates. The efficiency would be 100 percent if all the additional energy were converted to mechanical work. Table 11.3 lists some measured efficiencies.

The following example illustrates the calculation of efficiency for hiking up a mountain.

Example 11.11

A 20-year-old woman of mass 50 kg climbs a mountain 1000 m high in 4 hours. Her metabolic rate per unit mass during this activity is 7 W kg^{-1}. (a) What is the difference between her actual and basal metabolic rate? (b) How much work is done in the climb? (c) What is her efficiency?

(a) Since the woman's basal rate is 1.1 W kg^{-1}, the difference per unit mass is $(7 - 1.1)$ W kg^{-1} = 5.9 W kg^{-1}. The total difference in rates is this times

TABLE 11.2

Approximate metabolic rates per unit mass of a 20-year-old man during various activities

Activity	$-\dfrac{1}{m} \dfrac{\Delta U}{\Delta t}$ (W kg^{-1})
Sleeping	1.1
Lying awake	1.2
Sitting upright	1.5
Standing	2.6
Walking	4.3
Shivering	Up to 7.6
Bicycling	7.6
Shoveling	9.2
Swimming	11.0
Lumbering	11.0
Skiing	15.0
Running	18.0

TABLE 11.3
Maximum efficiencies for physical work

Activity	Efficiency in Percent
Shoveling in stooped posture	3
Weight lifting	9
Turning a heavy wheel	13
Climbing ladders	19
Climbing stairs	23
Cycling	25
Climbing hills with a 5° slope	30

Adapted from E. Grandjean, *Fitting the Task to the Man; An Ergonomic Approach*, Taylor and Francis, London, 1969.

her mass or

$$\left| \frac{\Delta U}{\Delta t} - \frac{\Delta U}{\Delta t}_{basal} \right| = (50 \text{ kg})(5.9 \text{ W kg}^{-1})$$

$$= 295 \text{ W}$$

(b) The work done during the climb is equal to the change in the woman's potential energy so

$$\Delta W = mgh = (50 \text{ kg})(9.8 \text{ m s}^{-2})(1000 \text{ m})$$
$$= 4.9 \times 10^5 \text{ J}$$

The rate at which she does work in 4 hours = 1.44×10^4 s is

$$\frac{\Delta W}{\Delta t} = \frac{4.9 \times 10^5 \text{ J}}{1.44 \times 10^4 \text{ s}} = 34 \text{ W}$$

(c) Her efficiency is found from the definition

$$e = \frac{100 \dfrac{\Delta W}{\Delta t}}{\left| \dfrac{\Delta U}{\Delta t} - \dfrac{\Delta U}{\Delta t}_{basal} \right|} = \frac{100(34 \text{ W})}{295 \text{ W}} = 11.5\%$$

Thus the woman is utilizing food energy for mechanical work at 11.5 percent efficiency. In general the efficiencies in human activities are below 30 percent.

It is important to notice that the rate at which work can be done depends on how long the activity is continued. A person in good condition can produce a power of nearly 21 W kg^{-1} during bicycle racing, but only for about 5 or 6 seconds. When doing work for a period of as long as 5 hours, the maximum metabolic rate is 6 or 7 W kg^{-1}. For a person doing physical labor the annual average metabolic rate should be 4 W kg^{-1} or less to be safe.

EXERCISES ON SUPPLEMENTARY TOPICS

Section 11.7 | Human Metabolism

11-50   A woman of mass 55 kg produces heat at a rate of 1.1 W kg^{-1} while lying at rest on a hot day. If her body temperature is constant, (a) what is the rate at which her internal energy changes? (b) How much internal energy will she use up in 8 hours? (c) If all of this energy is produced by metabolizing carbohydrates, what mass of carbohydrate is consumed?

11-51   A woman with a normal diet uses internal energy at a rate of 3 W kg^{-1} and has a mass of 50 kg. (a) What is her rate of oxygen consumption? (b) How much oxygen does she use in 8 hours?

11-52   A 60-kg man shovels dirt with an efficiency of 3 percent, and his metabolic rate is 8 W kg^{-1}. (a) What is his power output? (b) How much work does he do in 1 hour? (c) How much waste heat does his body produce in 1 hour?

11-53   A resting 45-kg woman has a normal basal metabolic rate. (a) What volume of oxygen does she use in 1 hour? (b) If she walks for 1 hour and has a metabolic rate of 4.3 W kg^{-1}, how much oxygen does she consume?

11-54   If a 70-kg, 20-year old man uses 1 litre of oxygen per minute, (a) what is his metabolic rate? (b) If he could do work at 100 percent efficiency, what would his mechanical power output be?

11-55   Experimentally, it was found by J. P. Joule in 1846 that in 24 hours a horse was capable of doing work equivalent to raising a weight of 10^8 N to a height of 0.3 m. The hay and corn consumed during this period were equivalent to a reserve of internal energy of 1.2×10^8 J. (a) What fraction of this internal energy was used by the horse to do mechanical work? (b) If the horse's actual efficiency was 30 percent, what is the basal metabolic rate of the horse?

PROBLEMS ON SUPPLEMENTARY TOPICS

11-56   The basal metabolic rate for most humans steadily decreases after age 20, decreasing by about 20 percent by age 70. (a) Will an older person become cold on a winter day more quickly than a younger person? Why? (b) If a 70-year-old man does work at the same rate as a younger man and both work with the same efficiency, which man will have the higher metabolic rate? Explain.

11-57 If a 70-kg person's diet yields a food energy equivalent of 1.25×10^7 J, how much work can that person do at 15 percent efficiency with a metabolic rate of 250 W before all of the food energy is used up?

11-58 If a 90-kg man exercises with a metabolic rate of 7.5 W kg^{-1}, how long must he continue to use up 1 kg of fat?

11-59 A 70-kg sprinter does work at a rate of 820 W during a bicycle dash lasting 11 s. If the efficiency is 20 percent and only carbohydrates are consumed, what mass of carbohydrates is used?

11-60 A 45-kg woman runs up a flight of stairs 5 m high in 3 s. (a) What is her mechanical power output? (b) If the woman's basal metabolic rate is 1 W kg^{-1} and she works with 10 percent efficiency, what is her metabolic rate when ascending the stairs? (c) What is the total amount of oxygen consumed by the woman during the climb?

11-61 If the woman of Problem 11-60 descends the stairs, her change in potential energy is negative. Is any metabolic energy required in this process? Explain.

11-62 In Chapter Eight, the buckling strength scaling model led to the conclusion that the metabolic rate of an animal of mass m should vary as $m^{0.75}$. This also means that the metabolic rate per unit mass varies as $m^{0.75}/m = m^{-0.25}$. The basal metabolic rate of a 60-kg man is 1.2 W kg^{-1}. What is the basal metabolic rate per unit mass of a 960-kg horse?

11-63 Using the scaling law described in Problem 11-62, what is the expected basal metabolic rate of a 6400-kg elephant if that of a 0.04-kg mouse is 0.3 W?

11-64 A hummingbird requires an expenditure of 0.06 W to hover. The measured oxygen consumption rates for a hummingbird at rest and hovering are 5×10^{-6} litre s^{-1} and 35×10^{-6} litre s^{-1}, respectively. What is the efficiency of the hummingbird while hovering?

11-65 A dieter consumes 10,500 kJ or 2500 kcal per day and uses 12,600 kJ per day. If the deficit is made up by the use of stored body fat, in how many days will the dieter lose 1 kg?

Additional Reading

W. F. Magie, *A Source Book in Physics*, McGraw-Hill Book Co., New York, 1935, pp. 196–211. Excerpts from papers by Mayer and Joule.

V. V. Raman, Where Credit Is Due—The Energy Conservation Principle, *The Physics Teacher*, vol. 13, 1975, p. 80.

T. C. Ruch and H. D. Patton (eds.), *Physiology and Biophysics*, vol. 3, W. B. Saunders Co., Philadelphia, 1973. Chapter 5 by Arthur C. Brown discusses human metabolism.

George B. Benedek and Felix M. H. Villars, *Physics: With Illustrations from Medicine and Biology*, vol. I, Addison-Wesley Publishing Co., Reading, Mass., 1973, pp. 5–115. Human metabolism.

Knut Schmidt-Nielsen, *Animal Physiology*, 3rd ed., Prentice-Hall, Inc., Englewood Cliffs, N.J., 1970. Human and animal metabolism.

I. Prigogine, G. Nicolis, and A. Babloyantz, Thermodynamics of Evolution, *Physics Today*, November 1972, p. 23; December 1972, p. 38. Difficult but interesting articles.

Beverly Karplus Hartline, Tapping Sun-Warmed Ocean Water for Power, *Science*, vol. 209, 1980, p. 794. The first demonstration that power can actually be generated from ocean thermal differences.

The Science-and-Art-of Keeping Warm, *Natural History*, vol. 90, October 1981. A special issue about how people, plants, and animals survive cold weather.

John Tierney, Perpetual Commotion, *Science 83*, May 1983, p. 30. Thermodynamics and perpetual motion.

Ronald Giedd, Real Otto and Diesel Engine Cycles, *The Physics Teacher*, vol. 21, 1983, p. 29.

Thomas U. Ayres and Indira Nair, Thermodynamics and Economics, *Physics Today*, November 1984, p. 62.

Bjarne Andresen, Peter Salamon, and Stephen R. Berry, Thermodynamics in Finite Time, *Physics Today*, September 1984, p. 62.

Scientific American articles:

Mitchell Wilson, Count Rumford, October 1960, p. 158.

J. W. L. Köhler, The Stirling Refrigeration Cycle, April 1965, p. 119.

Graham Walker, The Stirling Engine, August 1973, p. 80.

C. M. Summers, The Conversion of Energy, September 1971, p. 148.

Lynwood Bryant, Rudolf Diesel and His Rational Engine, August 1969, p. 108.

Freeman Dyson, Energy in the Universe, September 1971, p. 50.

W. Ehrenberg, Maxwell's Demon, November 1967, p. 103.

Charles H. Bennett, Demons, Engines and the Second Law, November 1987, p. 108.

Terry R. Penney and Desikan Bharathan, Power from the Sea, January 1987, p. 86.

Stanley W. Angrist, Perpetual Motion Machines, January 1968, p. 114.

O. V. Lounasmaa, New Methods for Approaching Absolute Zero, December 1969, p. 26.

John R. Clark, Thermal Pollution and Aquatic Life, March 1969, p. 18.

James B. Kelley, Heat, Cold and Clothing, February 1956, p. 107.

R. E. Newell, The Circulation of the Upper Atmosphere, March 1964, p. 62.

C. B. Chapman and J. H. Mitchell, The Physiology of Exercise, May 1965, p. 88.

J. R. Brett, The Swimming Energetics of Salmon, August 1965, p. 80.

John W. Kanwisher and Sam H. Ridgway, The Physiological Ecology of Whales and Porpoises, June 1983, p. 110.

Vance A. Tucker, The Energetics of Bird Flight, May 1969, p. 70.

David M. Gates, The Flow of Energy in the Biosphere, September 1971, p. 88.

Bernd Heinrich, The Energetics of the Bumblebee, April 1973, p. 97.

Eugene S. Ferguson, The Measurement of the Man-Day, October 1971, p. 96.

Rudolfo Margaria, The Sources of Muscular Energy, March 1972, p. 84.

Salvador E. Luria, Colicins and the Energetics of Cell Membranes, December 1975, p. 30.

Jules Janick, Carl H. Noller, and Charles L. Rhykerd, The Cycles of Plant and Animal Nutrition, September 1976, p. 74.

S. S. Wilson, Sadi Carnot, August 1981, p. 134.

The September 1970 issue of Scientific American deals with The Biosphere and has several articles relating to energy cycles and life.

CHAPTER 12
THERMAL PROPERTIES
OF MATTER

In Chapter Ten, we described the relationship between the temperature of a substance and the average energy of its molecules, using an ideal gas as an example. The relationship connecting this internal energy, the thermal energy transferred, and the work done by the system was discussed in Chapter Eleven. Most of these discussions make little reference to specific materials. Here we focus on how several properties of materials vary with temperature and how materials transfer thermal energy. In each case, account is taken of the nature of the material involved.

Because the properties of matter depend on temperature, the exchange of thermal energy is extremely important. Since biological process can only function properly over a small temperature range, both people and nature have devised ways of either limiting or improving the means by which this energy is transferred. For example, we insulate our homes, and our bodies respond to high temperatures by perspiring.

We begin our study of the thermal properties of matter with the thermal expansion of solids and liquids. We then discuss how the temperature of an object changes as thermal energy or *heat* is added or withdrawn. This leads us to a discussion of the transfer of thermal energy, and we use our ideas to study temperature control in warm-blooded animals.

12.1 | THERMAL EXPANSION

When a substance is heated, its volume usually increases, and each dimension increases correspondingly. This increase in size can be understood in terms of the increased kinetic energy of the atoms

or molecules. The additional kinetic energy results in each molecule colliding more forcefully with its neighbors. The molecules effectively push each other farther apart, and the material expands.

At the macroscopic level, we can find a convenient relationship between a small temperature change and the resulting change in the length of an object. Suppose the original length of the object in Fig. 12.1 is l, and a small increase in length Δl occurs when the temperature increases by a small amount ΔT. If we divide the object into two equal parts, each part will have length $l/2$ and will expand by $\Delta l/2$. Consequently, the change in length Δl is directly proportional to the length l. In addition, we find from experiment that if we double the temperature change by raising the temperature by $2\,\Delta T$, the expansion also doubles. A single equation expressing both proportionalities is

$$\Delta l = \alpha l\, \Delta T \qquad (12.1)$$

The constant α is the *coefficient of linear expansion*. It is a property of a given material and depends somewhat on the temperature. Typical values of α are given in Table 12.1. We see that α has the dimensions of inverse temperature, so its units are K^{-1}. *Since only the change in temperature is important, we can measure ΔT in Kelvins or in Celsius degrees.* We use this fact throughout this chapter.

Since α depends somewhat on temperature, the proportionality of the length and temperature changes is exact only for infinitesimal changes. Thus Eq. 12.1 should be replaced by

$$dl = \alpha l\, dT$$

However, Eq. 12.1 is often quite accurate if an average value of α is used even when ΔT is 100 K or

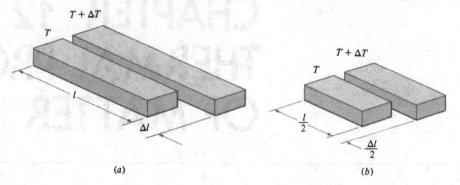

Figure 12.1. The expansion of a bar is proportional to its length. When the bar is halved in length, the expansion is also halved.

(a)   (b)

more. We assume the validity of this approximation in our examples and problems.

The following example illustrates the importance of thermal expansion.

Example 12.1

The roadbed of the Golden Gate Bridge is 1280 m long. During a certain year the temperature varies from −12°C to 38°C. What is the difference in the lengths at those temperatures if the road is supported by steel girders? For steel, $\alpha = 1.27 \times 10^{-5}$ K^{-1}.

With $\Delta T = 38°C − (−12°C) = 50°C = 50$ K,

$$\Delta l = \alpha l \, T$$
$$= (1.27 \times 10^{-5} \text{ K}^{-1})(1280 \text{ m})(50 \text{ K})$$
$$= 0.81 \text{ m}$$

This substantial change in the roadbed length must be allowed for in the design of the bridge. If the structure could not alter its length with changes in temperature, huge forces would be developed and severe damage would result.

TABLE 12.1

Coefficient of linear expansion for various materials

Material	Temperature (°C)	α (K^{-1})
Aluminum	−23	2.21×10^{-5}
	20	2.30×10^{-5}
	77	2.41×10^{-5}
	527	3.35×10^{-5}
Diamond	20	1.00×10^{-6}
Celluloid	50	1.09×10^{-4}
Glass (most types)	50	$8.3 \ \times 10^{-6}$
Glass (Pyrex)	50	$3.2 \ \times 10^{-6}$
Ice	−5	5.07×10^{-5}
Steel	20	1.27×10^{-5}
Platinum	20	$8.9 \ \times 10^{-6}$

Two interesting applications of thermal expansion are the *thermostat* and the *ultramicrotome*. A thermostat has two metal strips with different coefficients of linear expansion attached to each other (Fig. 12.2). When they are heated the unequal expansion causes the strips to bend; if they bend far enough, they open or close a switch that may, for example, control a heating system or air conditioning.

The *ultramicrotome* is an apparatus designed to make very thin tissue slices for use in microscopes. A sample, mounted on a rotating metal arm, passes a knife edge (Fig. 12.3). If the metal arm is heated at a constant rate, it will expand uniformly, and a thin specimen slice will be cut on each turn. The metal arm can be extended as slowly as 1 micrometre (10^{-6} m) per minute.

Area and Volume Expansion
When an object is heated, all of its dimensions increase (Fig. 12.4). Thus the lengths of the sides increase, the

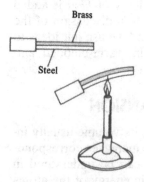

Figure 12.2. Brass and steel strips attached to each other expand at different rates when heated ($\alpha_{\text{brass}} > \alpha_{\text{steel}}$).

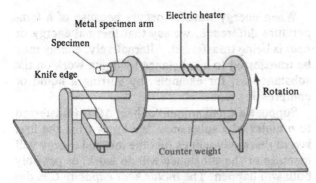

Figure 12.3. A schematic view of an ultramicrotome. The mechanism for turning the holder is not shown.

areas of surfaces increase, and the volume increases.

Consider what happens to a square surface of a cube with an initial area $A = l^2$. If a temperature increase dT changes l by $dl = \alpha l\, dT$, then the area expands by

$$dA = \frac{dA}{dl}\, dl = 2l\, dl$$

$$= 2l(\alpha l\, dT) = 2\alpha l^2\, dT$$

Using $A = l^2$, the change in area is $dA = 2\alpha A\, dT$. For a finite temperature change ΔT, the change in area is approximately

$$\Delta A = 2\alpha A\, \Delta T \qquad (12.2)$$

Thus the area increases at twice the rate of a linear dimension. Note that although we obtained Eq. 12.2 by considering a square area, it is correct for any shape. We use this result in the following example.

Example 12.2

A circular steel disk has a circular hole through its center. If the disk is heated from 10°C to 100°C, what is the fractional increase in the area of the hole?

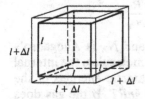

Figure 12.4. When the temperature is increased, each dimension of a cube changes from l to $l + \Delta l$.

When the disk is heated, all of its dimensions increase. The area of the hole increases also, just as the area inside a penciled circle on a solid disk increases. The area of the hole increases as if it were filled with steel. Using Eq. 12.2 and α from Table 12.1, the fractional increase in the area of the hole is

$$\frac{\Delta A}{A} = 2\alpha\, \Delta T = 2(1.27 \times 10^{-5}\ \mathrm{K}^{-1})(90\ \mathrm{K})$$

$$= 2.29 \times 10^{-3}$$

The rate at which the volume $V = l^3$ expands as the cube is heated is also determined by α. A temperature change dT causes a length change $dl = \alpha l\, dT$, and a volume change

$$dV = \frac{dV}{dl}\, dl = 3l^2\, dl$$

$$= 3l^2(\alpha l\, dT) = 3\alpha l^3\, dT$$

$$= 3\alpha V\, dT$$

We define the *coefficient of volume expansion* β by

$$dV = \beta V\, dT$$

Comparing this with the equation above, we have

$$\beta = 3\alpha$$

Thus the volume increases three times as fast as the length. Again, for most applications it is adequate to use the approximation

$$\Delta V = \beta V\, \Delta T \qquad (12.3)$$

Water | In discussing thermal expansion, special mention must be made of liquid water because it is one of the very few substances with a negative coefficient of volume expansion at some temperatures. Figure 12.5 shows both β and the density (mass per unit volume) of water plotted against the temperature; β varies as the temperature changes and even reverses sign at 3.98°C. Thus as T rises from 0°C, water *contracts* up to 3.98°C and then expands as the temperature increases further; water has its greatest mass per unit volume at 3.98°C.

This characteristic of water is extremely important for aquatic life. As the air temperature decreases in early winter, the surface water of lakes cools. When this surface water reaches 3.98°C, it sinks to the bottom; the warmer, less dense water from beneath floats to the surface. The cool de-

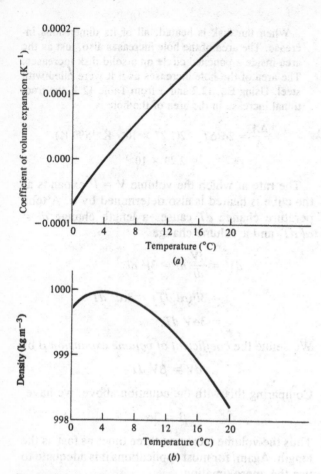

Figure 12.5. (a) Coefficient of volume expansion for water. (b) The density (mass per unit volume) of water.

scending water carries oxygen with it. Once the entire lake has undergone this mixing and has reached 3.98°C, further cooling occurs at the surface and ice forms. The lower-density ice floats, so that lakes freeze from the surface downward. Aquatic life survives the winter in the freshly oxygenated water beneath the ice.

12.2 | HEAT CAPACITY

When an object at one temperature is placed near or in contact with another object at a higher temperature, energy is transferred to the cooler object, and its temperature rises. The ratio of the amount of energy transferred to the temperature change is called the *heat capacity*.

When energy transfer occurs because of a temperature difference, we say that thermal energy or *heat* is being transferred. Alternatively, energy may be transferred to a substance by doing work on the substance as, for example, by stirring a liquid or compressing a gas.

Suppose a small amount of heat ΔQ is transferred to n moles of a substance. We know from the first law of thermodynamics that the internal energy will increase or the substance will do work, or possibly both will happen. The *molar heat capacity C* is defined as

$$C = \lim_{\Delta T \to 0} \frac{1}{n} \frac{\Delta Q}{\Delta T} = \frac{1}{n} \frac{dQ}{dT} \qquad (12.4)$$

That is, C is the ratio of the heat added per mole to the rise in temperature. Substances such as water, which have a high molar heat capacity, experience relatively small temperature changes when a given amount of heat is transferred.

In practice the heat capacity is usually measured under one of two special conditions. If heat is added with the *volume* of the substance kept *constant*, no work is done. Then the heat dQ added is equal to the internal energy change dU, and the molar heat capacity at constant volume is

$$C_V = \frac{1}{n} \frac{dU}{dT} \qquad \text{(constant volume)} \qquad (12.5)$$

More often, the heat capacity is measured at *constant pressure*. Here when heat is added, there is an increase in internal energy and also some work is done by the substance. The heat capacity at constant volume is easiest to calculate theoretically, while the heat capacity at constant pressure is easiest to measure. However, for the special case of an ideal monatomic gas, we can easily derive both results.

We found in Chapter Ten that the average kinetic energy per molecule in an ideal monatomic gas is

$$(K)_{ave} = \frac{3}{2} \frac{R}{N_A} T$$

Here R is the gas constant and N_A is Avogadro's number. For n moles or nN_A molecules, the internal energy U is the sum of the kinetic energies of the molecules $U = nN_A(K)_{ave} = \frac{3}{2}nRT$. If the gas does not change its volume as the heat is added, and the temperature increases by dT, the change in internal energy is $dU = \frac{3}{2}nR\, dT$. Hence the molar heat capacity at constant volume is

$$C_V = \frac{1}{n}\frac{dU}{dT} = \frac{3}{2}R \quad \text{(ideal monatomic gas)} \quad (12.6)$$

If the pressure, not the volume, is held constant when heat dQ is added to a substance, the internal energy increases and some work is done; $dQ = dU + W$. Using the ideal gas law, $PV = nRT$, the work done at constant pressure when the temperature changes by dT is $W = P\, dV = nR\, dT$. Thus $dQ = dU + nR\, dT$, and the molar heat capacity at constant pressure is

$$C_P = \frac{1}{n}\frac{dQ}{dT} = \frac{1}{n}\frac{dU}{dT} + R$$

But dU/ndT is C_V, so

$$C_P = C_V + R = \frac{5}{2}R \quad \text{(ideal monatomic gas)} \quad (12.7)$$

This result is in very good agreement with experiments on real monatomic gases at low to moderate densities. The relationship $C_P = C_V + R$ also agrees well with measurements on real polyatomic gases.

While we have been able to calculate the heat capacity of a monatomic gas from first principles, the problem of calculating the energy required to raise the temperature of a polyatomic gas, a liquid, or a solid is more difficult. For example, we noted that for polyatomic molecules the rotational and vibrational energies must be included in the internal energies. Modern theory predicts that at low temperatures the molar heat capacity of any gas results entirely from the translational motion, and C_V is $\frac{3}{2}R$. At intermediate temperatures rotations also contribute and C_V is $\frac{5}{2}R$ for a diatomic gas. At high temperatures, vibrational, rotational, and translational motions all contribute to the specific heat, and C_V is $\frac{7}{2}R$ for a diatomic gas. The molar heat capacity of hydrogen gas H_2 versus temperature is shown in Fig. 12.6, where the three contributions are clearly seen.

As a gas is cooled and becomes a liquid, further difficulties in making accurate calculations are encountered. For example, the heat capacity of steam is only half as large as that of liquid water. The difference arises from a change in the effects of the forces among molecules. In the gas, the molecules are far apart, and the forces are negligible. In a

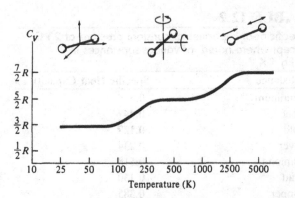

Figure 12.6. Molar heat capacity at constant volume of hydrogen gas H_2. At low temperatures, the heat capacity is due to the translational kinetic energy. At higher temperatures, the rotational kinetic energy must be included, and the vibrational kinetic energy is important at still higher temperatures. Note that the temperature scale is logarithmic.

liquid, the molecules are closer to each other, so their mutual attraction becomes significant, adding to the internal energy and making specific heat calculations very difficult. Oddly enough, in the solid form, specific heats are again relatively easy to calculate.

A quantity closely related to the molar heat capacity is the *specific heat capacity c*. This is the heat required for a unit temperature change in a unit mass of a substance. It is related to C by

$$c = \frac{C}{M} \quad (12.8)$$

where M is the mass of 1 mole. For example, helium gas has a molecular mass of 4 u; 1 mole is 4 g = 4×10^{-3} kg, and $C_V = 12.47$ J mole^{-1} K^{-1}. Thus

$$c_V = \frac{12.47 \text{ J mole}^{-1} \text{ K}^{-1}}{4 \times 10^{-3} \text{ kg mole}^{-1}}$$

$$= 3.12 \times 10^3 \text{ J kg}^{-1} \text{ K}^{-1}$$

In terms of c, the heat required for a temperature change ΔT in a mass m is

$$\Delta Q = mc\, \Delta T \quad (12.9)$$

Because c depends on the temperature, this equation is exact only for very small ΔT. However, like the thermal expansion formula, it is usually adequate for large values of ΔT if the average specific heat capacity is used. Specific heat capacities of representative substances are given in Table 12.2.

TABLE 12.2

Specific heat capacities at constant pressure at 25°C, except where noted, of various substances in kJ kg $^{-1}$ K $^{-1}$

Substance	Specific Heat Capacity c_P
Aluminum	0.898
Steel	0.447
Gold	0.129
Silver	0.234
Diamond	0.518
Lead	0.130
Copper	0.385
Helium (gas)	5.180
Hydrogen (H₂) (gas)	14.250
Iron	0.443
Nitrogen (N₂) (gas)	1.040
Oxygen (O₂) (gas)	0.915
Water (liquid)	4.169
Ice (−10° to 0°C)	2.089
Steam (100° to 200°C)	1.963

A simple but effective way of measuring heat capacities at constant pressure uses a *calorimeter* (Fig. 12.7). Heat ΔQ is supplied by an electrical heater to a well-insulated calorimeter that holds the sample, and a thermometer measures the temperature rise ΔT. A sample with mass m and specific heat capacity c absorbs an amount of heat equal to $mc \, \Delta T$. The container also absorbs some heat; if its mass is m_c and its specific heat capacity is c_c, this heat equals $m_c c_c \, \Delta T$. Adding the heat absorbed by

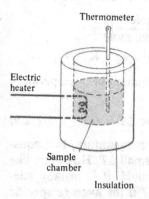

Thermometer

Electric heater

Sample chamber

Insulation

Figure 12.7. A calorimeter.

the sample and the container, we have

$$\Delta Q = mc \, \Delta T + m_c c_c \, \Delta T \qquad (12.10)$$

This result may be used to find the specific heat capacity as illustrated in the next example.

Example 12.3

There are 0.1 kg of carbon in a calorimeter at 15°C. The container has a mass of 0.02 kg and is made of aluminum. The addition of 0.892 kJ of heat energy brings the temperature to 28°C. What is the specific heat capacity of carbon? Assume that the specific heat capacity of aluminum in this temperature range is 0.9 kJ kg^{-1} K^{-1}.

Substituting in Eq. 12.10, with $\Delta T = 28°C - 15°C = 13$ K,

$$
\begin{aligned}
c &= \frac{\Delta Q - m_c c_c \, \Delta T}{m \, \Delta T} \\
&= \frac{0.892 \text{ kJ} - (0.02 \text{ kg})(0.9 \text{ kJ kg}^{-1} \text{ K}^{-1})(13 \text{ K})}{(0.10 \text{ kg})(13 \text{ K})} \\
&= 0.506 \text{ kJ kg}^{-1} \text{ K}^{-1}
\end{aligned}
$$

When the specific heat capacities are known, the same ideas can be used to predict the final temperature, as shown in the next example.

Example 12.4

A copper pipe of mass 0.5 kg is originally at 20°C. If its ends are capped after 0.6 kg of water at 98°C is poured into it, what is the final temperature of the pipe? (Assume the pipe is insulated so no heat is lost to the surroundings.)

Thermal energy is transferred from the water to the pipe until both are at the same temperature, T_f. The heat transferred to the pipe is its mass times its specific heat capacity times its temperature change, which is $T_f - 20°C$. The heat lost by the water is its mass times specific heat capacity times its temperature change, $98°C - T_f$. No heat enters or leaves through the insulation. Thus, using Table 12.2,

$$(0.5 \text{ kg})(0.385 \text{ kJ kg}^{-1} \text{ K}^{-1})(T_f - 20°C)$$
$$= (0.6 \text{ kg})(4.169 \text{ kJ kg}^{-1} \text{ K}^{-1})(98°C - T_f)$$

Multiplying this out and solving for T_f, we find

$$T_f = 92.43°C$$

In our discussion of heat capacities based on the ideal gas model, the relationship between heat and energy is quite clear. Historically, scientists studied heat long before any molecular theory was developed. Since it was not realized that heat is just another form of energy, a separate set of units was developed to measure heat. The gram-calorie (cal) was defined as the heat required to heat 1 g of water from 14.5°C to 15.5°C. Later, it was discovered that the energy represented by 1 calorie is equivalent to 4.18 J. The first suggestion of this equivalence was made in 1842 by Julius Robert Mayer (1814–1878), a German physician, on the basis of physiological observations. Mayer also suggested that energy can be neither created nor destroyed. His work was largely ignored, and it was not until the work of James Prescott Joule (1818–1889) several years later that the equivalence of heat and energy was accepted. The principle of the conservation of energy was also independently proposed by Hermann von Helmholtz (1821–1894).

Although 125 years have elapsed in which scientists could have adopted a common energy unit for both heat and work, it is still common to measure mechanical and electrical energies in joules and heat energies in calories. To make matters worse, American engineers frequently use the British thermal unit (BTU), defined as the heat required to heat 1 lb of water from 63°F to 64°F, and the kilowatt-hour (kW h), which is equal to 3.6×10^6 J. Further, nutritionists measure the energy supplied by food in kilo-calories (kcal), which are 10^3 times as large as the gram-calorie. Conversion factors for these energy units may be found on the inside of the front cover of this book.

12.3 | PHASE CHANGES

Most substances can exist in solid, liquid, or gas *phases*. For example, water may be ice, liquid, or steam. A transition from one of these phases to another is called a *phase change*. Many other kinds of phase changes occur in nature. A solid may change from one crystalline structure to another; at low temperatures, a material may become magnetic or lose its electrical resistance. All these changes take place very abruptly at a sharply defined temperature.

The temperature at which a phase change occurs usually depends on additional variables, such as pressure. This is illustrated by the *phase diagram* for water (Fig. 12.8). At the temperature and pres-

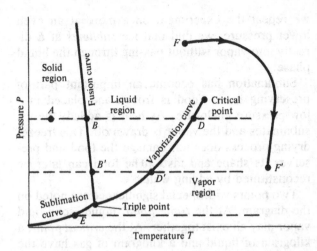

Figure 12.8. Phase diagram for water. The lines indicate the temperature and pressures at which phase changes occur.

sure corresponding to point A, water can exist only as ice. If we keep the pressure fixed and add heat, the temperature rises until point B is reached. Now as more heat is added, the temperature does not rise. Instead, the ice gradually melts into water, and the *temperature remains constant until all the ice is melted* (Fig. 12.9). As more heat is added, the temperature of the liquid again steadily increases until point D is reached. *Here again the temperature remains constant* until all the liquid has been converted into water vapor. Additional heat will now increase the temperature of the gas.

If we repeat this experiment at a lower pressure, the phase changes occur at B' and D', which correspond to different temperatures than do B and D. If

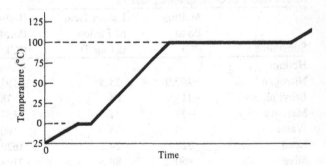

Figure 12.9. The temperature of a sample of water versus time. Heat is added at a uniform rate and the pressure is held constant at 1 atm.

we repeat the experiment once more at an even lower pressure, we find that ice *sublimes* at E directly into vapor without passing through the liquid phase.

Sublimation has become an important part of preserving food. Food is frozen and placed in a low-pressure enclosure. As heat is added, the ice sublimates and the vapor is drawn off. This freeze-drying process does not damage the food and preserves its shape and taste. The food can later be reconstituted by adding water.

Two points with special significance are noted on the diagram. At the *triple point*, liquid, solid, and vapor may all exist together. At the *critical point*, a kilogram of liquid and a kilogram of gas have the same volume, and the distinction between the two phases vanishes. Then if the pressure and temperature are adjusted so that a sample passes from point F to F' along the path shown in Fig. 12.8, the change of phase from liquid to vapor is never observed.

The energy absorbed or liberated in a phase change is called the *latent heat*. At atmospheric pressure, the *latent heat of fusion* L_f needed to melt ice is 333 kJ kg^{-1}. The *latent heat of vaporization* L_v needed to boil water at atmospheric pressure is 2255 kJ kg^{-1}. Some other latent heats are given in Table 12.3. The heat ΔQ needed to change the phase of a mass m is

$$\Delta Q = Lm \qquad (12.11)$$

where L is the appropriate latent heat. The role of the latent heat of fusion is illustrated in the following example.

Example 12.5

How much heat is required to melt 5 kg of ice at 0°C?

Since the latent heat of fusion L_f is 333 kJ kg^{-1}, $Q = Lm$ gives

$$Q = L_f m = (333 \text{ kJ kg}^{-1})(5 \text{ kg}) = 1665 \text{ kJ}$$

The latent heat and specific heat capacity are both important in determining the equilibrium state of a system. This is shown in the following example.

Example 12.6

If 20 kg of water at 95°C is mixed with 5 kg of ice at 0°C, what is the final temperature of the mixture?

In this example it is useful to determine first whether enough thermal energy is available in the water to melt the ice. If not, the equilibrium temperature will be 0°C with only a portion of the ice melting. From the previous example, we know that 1665 kJ is required to melt 5 kg of ice. If the water is cooled to 0°C, it gives up

$$\Delta Q = mc_P \Delta T = (20 \text{ kg})(4.169 \text{ kJ kg}^{-1} \text{ K}^{-1})(95 \text{ K})$$
$$= 7921 \text{ kJ}$$

This is more than enough to melt the ice so the final temperature will be above 0°C.

If the final temperature is T_f, the heat transferred to the ice is 1665 kJ + $m_i c_P(T_f - 0°C)$. The heat given up by the water is $mc_P(95°C - T_f)$, so equating these gives

$$1665 \text{ kJ} + m_i c_P(T_f - 0°C) = mc_P(95°C - T_f)$$

TABLE 12.3

Latent heats at atmospheric pressure

Substance	Melting Point (°C)	Latent Heat of Fusion (kJ kg^{-1})	Boiling Point (°C)	Latent Heat of Vaporization (kJ kg^{-1})
Helium			−268.9	21
Nitrogen	−209.9	25.5	−195.8	201
Ethyl alcohol	−114	104	78	854
Mercury	−39	11.8	357	272
Water	0	333	100	2255
Lead	327	24.5	1620	912
Silver	960	88.3	2193	2335
Gold	1063	64.4	2660	1580

Substituting $m_i = 5$ kg, $m = 20$ kg, and $c_P = 4.169$ kJ kg^{-1} K^{-1}, multiplying, and solving for T_f, we find $T_f = 60.0°$C.

The following example shows how to find the mass of ice melted when the final temperature is 0°C.

Example 12.7

A 0.6-kg pitcher of tea at 50°C is cooled with 0.4 kg of ice cubes at 0°C. What is the equilibrium condition if no heat is lost to the surroundings?

The heat needed to melt all of the ice is $\Delta Q = L_f m_i = (333$ kJ kg$^{-1})(0.4$ kg$) = 133.2$ kJ. The heat given up by the tea if it is cooled to 0°C is $\Delta Q = (0.6$ kg$)(4.169$ kJ kg^{-1} K$^{-1})(50$ K$) = 12.51$ kJ, not enough to melt all the ice. Thus some of the ice will not melt and the final temperature will be 0°C.

To find the mass of the melted ice, we equate the heat loss of the cooled tea to the heat needed to melt a mass m_1 of ice, 125.1 kJ $= m_1 L_f$. Thus with $L_f = 333$ kJ kg^{-1}, the mass of ice melted is

$$m_1 = \frac{125.1 \text{ kJ}}{333 \text{ kJ kg}^{-1}} = 0.376 \text{ kg}$$

12.4 | HEAT CONDUCTION

Heat transfer always occurs from regions of higher temperature to regions of lower temperature, so that two objects isolated from their surroundings gradually approach a common temperature. In this section, we discuss heat *conduction* between objects in contact. Heat transfer by *convection* and *radiation* is considered in the following two sections.

When two objects at temperatures T_1 and T_2 are connected by a rod, their temperature difference $\Delta T = T_2 - T_1$ will steadily diminish (Fig. 12.10). If we cut the rod lengthwise so that each section has a cross section of $A/2$, then half the heat flow will be conducted in each section. Thus the *rate* at which heat flows from the hotter to the colder object must be proportional to the cross-sectional area A.

The rate of heat flow also depends on ΔT and the length l. If we double ΔT and double the length at the same time, the heat flow is unchanged. If the temperature difference is doubled and the length is unchanged, the heat flow doubles. The same thing

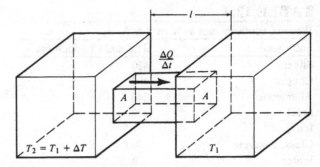

Figure 12.10. A rod of cross-sectional area A and length Δl conducts heat from the higher- to the lower-temperature object.

happens if ΔT is unchanged and the length is halved. Thus the heat flow must depend on the ratio $\Delta T/l$, which is called the *temperature gradient*. We can summarize these observations algebraically in an equation for the *heat flow* $H = \Delta Q/\Delta t$:

$$H = \kappa A \frac{\Delta T}{l} \qquad (12.12)$$

where κ is a proportionality constant called the *thermal conductivity*. Equation 12.12 is exact when ΔT is very small. However, the discussion of heat flow becomes more complicated if κ varies with temperature or when the geometry is not so simple. In this chapter, we assume that κ is constant in the temperature range of interest.

Representative values of κ are given in Table 12.4. Typically, metals are good thermal conductors. Their conductivities are greater by factors of 10^3 or 10^4 than those of thermal insulators such as asbestos or rock wool.

One of the most important insulators is air. Insulation in homes and in the material for warm clothing utilize this fact. The fibers of the material trap air in the material, and this air acts as an insulator. Storm or double-pane windows use air trapped between two glass panes to reduce conductive heat losses.

Body tissue is also a good insulator. When the environment is warm, the interior body temperature is quite uniform (Fig. 12.11a). Because body tissues are poor conductors, the inner core of the body can be kept warm in a cold environment (Fig. 12.11b).

TABLE 12.4

Thermal conductivities in W m⁻¹ K⁻¹

Substance	Thermal Conductivity κ
Silver	420
Copper	400
Aluminum	240
Steel	79
Ice	1.7
Glass, concrete	0.8
Water	0.59
Animal muscle, fat	0.2
Wood, asbestos, fiberglass	0.08
Felt, rock wool	0.04
Air	0.024
Down	0.019
Styrofoam	0.01

Example 12.8

A person walking at a modest speed generates heat at a rate of 280 W. If the surface area of the body is 1.5 m² and if the heat is assumed to be generated 0.03 m below the skin, what temperature difference between the skin and interior of the body would exist

if the heat were conducted to the surface? Assume the thermal conductivity is the same as that for animal muscle, 0.2 W m⁻¹ K⁻¹.

Despite the dissimilarity between humans and the rod in Fig. 12.10, we may still apply Eq. 12.12 to a small section of tissue. Summing over the sections is approximately equivalent to using the total body surface area for the area A.

Solving $H = \kappa A \, \Delta T/l$ for ΔT,

$$\Delta T = \frac{lH}{\kappa A} = \frac{(0.03 \text{ m})(280 \text{ W})}{(0.2 \text{ W m}^{-1}\text{ K}^{-1})(1.5 \text{ m}^2)}$$
$$= 28 \text{ K}$$

Since the actual temperature difference is only a few degrees (Fig. 12.11), we can conclude that heat is not removed from the body by conduction through tissue from the interior to the exterior of the body. In fact, the flow of warm blood from the interior of the body to the cooler exterior is the major factor in body heat transport.

Example 12.9

A copper hot-water pipe is 2 m long and 0.004 m thick, and has a surface area of 0.12 m². If the water is at 80°C and the temperature in the room is 15°C, at what rate is heat conducted through the pipe wall?

If we assume provisionally that the outside surface of the pipe is at 15°C, then Eq. 12.12 yields

$$H = \kappa A \frac{\Delta T}{l} = (400 \text{ W m}^{-1}\text{ K}^{-1})(0.12 \text{ m}^2)\left(\frac{65 \text{ K}}{0.004 \text{ m}}\right)$$
$$= 780{,}000 \text{ W}$$

This is a huge heat loss rate, much larger than is actually observed. As we will find, the air cannot carry off heat at this rate, nor can radiation, and the outer surface of the pipe is actually at a temperature much higher than 15°C. The resulting smaller temperature difference reduces the rate of conduction. This also corresponds to our experience; if we touch a heating pipe the outer surface feels very hot.

The quantity l/κ in Eq. 12.12 is sometimes called the "R-value." Using this definition, the heat flow can be written as

$$H = \frac{A \, \Delta T}{R} \tag{12.13}$$

For example, a 3-cm-thick section of rock wool has

$$R = \frac{l}{\kappa} = \frac{0.03 \text{ m}}{0.04 \text{ W m}^{-1} K^{-1}} = 0.75 \text{ m}^2 \text{ K W}^{-1}$$

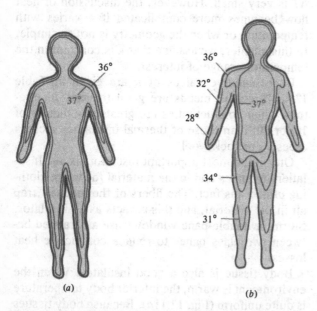

Figure 12.11. Isotherms (surfaces of constant temperature) in the body for (a) a warm environment and (b) a cold environment. (Adapted from Aschoff and Wever, *Naturwissenschaften*, vol. 45, p. 477, 1958.)

It can be shown that R-values are additive (Problem 12-82). For example, if the thickness of a wall is doubled, the R-value is doubled, and the heat loss through the wall is halved. If a second layer of attic insulation is placed over the original insulation, the net R-value is the sum of the two R-values. Recommended R-values have steadily increased as energy costs have risen.

12.5 | HEAT TRANSFER BY CONVECTION

Although some heat is transported by conduction in liquids and gases, a much larger quantity may be carried by the motion of the fluid itself. This is called *convection*. In Fig. 12.12a, the liquid near the heat source is heated and expands slightly, becoming lighter than the overlying cooler fluid. It then rises and is replaced by cooler, heavier fluid. When the warmer fluid arrives at the cooler region of the container, it cools, contracts, and begins to sink again. Had the container been heated from the top, convection would not have occurred, and the bulk of the fluid would have been heated by the much slower conduction process.

A hot-water or steam radiator provides another illustration of convection (Fig. 12.12b). Air near the radiator is heated and rises, while air near the outside walls and the windows is cooled and sinks. This establishes the flow pattern shown.

There are many difficulties in developing a quantitative theory of convection. For example, a given surface loses heat slower when it is vertical than when it is horizontal. Despite such difficulties, we can make some progress using an approximate formula. In still air, the rate of convective heat transfer for a surface area A is given approximately by the empirical formula

$$H = qA\,\Delta T \qquad (12.14)$$

where ΔT is the temperature difference between the surface and the air distant from the surface. The *convective heat transfer constant* q depends on the shape and orientation of the surface and to some extent on ΔT. For a naked human, we use the average value $q = 7.1$ W m^{-2} K^{-1}. Heat loss by convection is important for humans, as shown in the following example.

Example 12.10

In a warm room, a naked resting person has a skin temperature of 33°C. If the room temperature is 29°C and the body surface area is 1.5 m², what is the rate of heat loss due to convection?

Using $q = 7.1$ W m^{-2} K^{-1}, we have

$$\begin{aligned} H &= qA\,\Delta T \\ &= (7.1 \text{ W m}^{-2}\text{ K}^{-1})(1.5 \text{ m}^2)(33°C - 29°C) \\ &= 43 \text{ W} \end{aligned}$$

A resting person in this situation will generate heat at about twice this rate. Thus under these moderate conditions, convection provides the mechanism for about 50 percent of the body's heat loss. If there is a breeze or if the room temperature is lower, convective heat losses will increase correspondingly.

We can return to the question of the water-filled pipe to gain some insight into the interplay between conduction and convection. In Example 12.9, we found that conduction from a heating pipe would be enormous if the outside of the pipe were at room temperature. Suppose we assume instead that the outside of the pipe is at the water temperature, 80°C. The maximum convective heat loss would then be, using a typical value of $q = 9.5$ W m^{-2} K^{-1} for the pipe,

$$\begin{aligned} H &= qH\,\Delta T = (9.5 \text{ W m}^{-2}\text{ K}^{-1})(0.12 \text{ m}^2)(65 \text{ K}) \\ &= 74.1 \text{ W} \end{aligned}$$

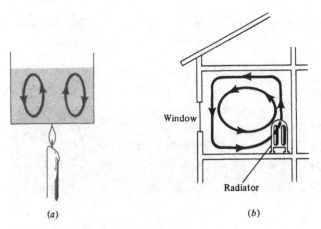

(a)   (b)

Figure 12.12. Paths of convective flow in (a) a container of liquid; (b) in a room heated by a radiator.

This is smaller than the conductive heat loss estimated in Example 12.9 by a factor of more than 10^4.

Radiation, discussed in the next section, transfers a comparable amount of heat (Exercise 12-49). Thus we can conclude that radiation and convection are limiting factors in the heat loss from any metal hot-water or steam-heating element. In most baseboard-heating systems, many thin metal fins project from the heating pipe. This effectively increases the surface area and hence the rate of convective and radiative heat loss. On the other hand, the section of pipe in Example 12.9 is still losing heat at an appreciable rate. If this pipe is used to transport hot water, considerable heat loss will occur in the process. To analyze this problem exactly, it is necessary to equate the heat conduction through the pipe wall to the convective heat loss plus the radiative heat loss and then solve for the temperature of the outside of the pipe (see Problem 12-81).

Convection plays a significant role in many everyday experiences. In a warm room the air a centimetre or so away from a cold windowpane feels rather cold. The air in contact with the glass has the same temperature as the pane; the air temperature rises perceptibly for some distance moving away from the window (Fig. 12.13). A similar gradual decrease in air temperature occurs outside if there is no wind. However, because the conduction of heat across the glass is very efficient, only a small temperature difference exists across the window.

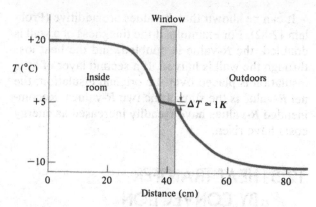

Figure 12.13. Air and glass temperatures near a window on a cold windless day. For clarity, the window thickness has been exaggerated.

If there is a wind, the nearly stagnant layer of warm air just outside the window is removed more rapidly than when convective forces alone are acting. This results in a lower temperature at the outside window surface and hence increases the rate of heat loss from the window. This is equivalent to having a lower outside temperature and is referred to in weather reports as the *wind chill factor*. The *effective temperature* decreases rapidly as the wind velocity increases, as shown in Table 12.5. Skiers and snowmobilers who create their own wind must be conscious of the potential hazards. Exposed flesh can freeze in about a minute at an effective

TABLE 12.5

Effect of moving air on temperature									
Wind Speed (km h^{-1})					**Actual Temperature (°C)**				
Calm	−10	−15	−20	−25	−30	−35	−40	−45	−50
					Effective Temperature (°C)				
10	−15	−20	−25	−30	−35	−40	−45	−50	−55
20	−20	−25	−35	−40	−45	−50	−55	−60	−65
30	−25	−30	−40	−45	−50	−60	−65	−70	−75
40	−30	−35	−45	−50	−60	−65	−70	−75	−80
50	−35	−40	−50	−55	−65	−70	−75	−80	−85

—*Moderate danger*   —*Great danger*

temperature of −30°C, which can, for example, be achieved by moving at 40 km h⁻¹ in air at −10°C. Effective temperatures below −60°C are extremely dangerous, since freezing can occur in seconds.

Convection plays a major role in the determination of weather patterns. Moist warm air masses heated over bodies of water are relatively light and tend to rise. As they rise into regions of lower pressure, they expand, doing work in the process. According to the first law of thermodynamics, if an air mass does work when no heat enters it, the internal energy must decrease. Thus the temperature of the air mass drops, causing some of the moisture to condense into clouds and release its heat of vaporization to the air mass. This slows the cooling of the air mass, permitting it to rise still further. Under some conditions this process will continue until large thunderclouds form and violent showers result.

12.6 | RADIATION

Conduction and convection require the presence of some material, be it solid, liquid, or gas. However, we know that heat can also be transmitted through a vacuum, since the sun's energy traverses millions of kilometres of space before reaching the earth. The process by which this occurs is called *radiation*. Radiant heat transfer also occurs in transparent media.

The term "radiation," as used in this chapter, is another word for electromagnetic waves. These are waves that are of electrical and magnetic origin and carry energy. In a hot object, the atomic charges oscillate rapidly, sending out energy as electromagnetic waves, somewhat like ripples on a pond. These waves travel with the speed of light, $c = 3 \times 10^8$ m s⁻¹. Visible light, radio waves, and X rays are all examples of electromagnetic waves (Fig. 12.14). The energy carried by the waves depends on the motion of the charges and hence on the temperature. These electromagnetic waves are discussed further in later chapters.

A wave is characterized by its *wavelength* λ and *frequency f*. The wavelength is the distance between successive wave crests; the frequency is the number of crests passing a given point each second and is equal to the frequency of vibration of the

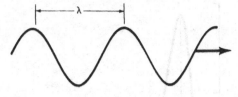

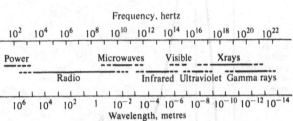

Figure 12.14. Frequencies and wavelengths of various kinds of electromagnetic waves. The scales are logarithmic.

charge producing the electromagnetic wave. The distance between crests, λ, times f, the number of crests per second passing a point, must equal the velocity of the wave, so

$$f\lambda = c \qquad (12.15)$$

For example, red light has a wavelength of about 7×10^{-7} m, which corresponds to a frequency

$$f = \frac{c}{\lambda} = \frac{3 \times 10^8 \text{ m s}^{-1}}{7 \times 10^{-7} \text{ m}} = 4.3 \times 10^{14} \text{ Hz}$$

In principle, every object at a nonzero temperature emits some radiation at all wavelengths. However, the amount of energy radiated at each wavelength depends on the temperature (Fig. 12.15). An object at 800°C looks red since it emits some radiation in the longest wavelength or red portion of the visible spectrum but very little in the blue portion. An object heated to 3000°C looks white because it is emitting substantial amounts of radiation throughout the visible light range. Similarly, very hot stars appear relatively blue, while cooler ones are somewhat red.

The wavelength at which the radiation is most intense is given by the *Wien displacement law*,

$$\lambda = \frac{B}{T} \qquad (12.16)$$

The constant B has a numerical value of 2.898×10^{-3} m K.

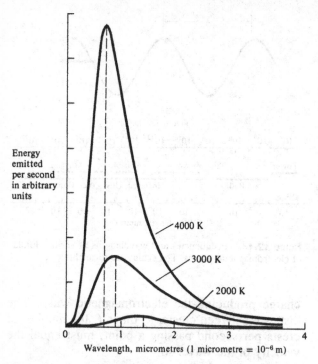

Figure 12.15. The heat energy radiated per second by 1 m² of surface. As the temperature increases, λ_{max} shifts to shorter wavelengths (vertical dashed lines), and the total energy radiated increases rapidly.

The temperature of the sun determines the wavelength at which most of its radiation reaches us. This is shown in the following example.

Example 12.11

The sun has a surface temperature of 6000 K. What is the wavelength of maximum radiation?

From the Wien displacement law,

$$\lambda_{max} = \frac{2.898 \times 10^{-3} \text{ m K}}{6000 \text{ K}} = 4.83 \times 10^{-7} \text{ m}$$

Thus the maximum solar radiation is in the visible portion of the spectrum as noted earlier. It is no accident that the eyes of animals are most sensitive very near the wavelength at which there is the most radiation available for seeing.

This variation of λ_{max} with temperature has many extremely important consequences. One is commonly called the *greenhouse effect*. In a greenhouse, the incident radiation from the sun is most intense at $\lambda_{max} = 4.83 \times 10^{-7}$ m and readily passes through glass. Inside, the radiation is absorbed by objects that in turn reemit radiation. However, since the average temperature in the greenhouse is approximately 300 K, the wavelength of greatest radiation intensity is much longer:

$$\lambda_{max} = \frac{2.898 \times 10^{-3} \text{ m K}}{300 \text{ K}} = 96.6 \times 10^{-7} \text{ m}$$

This is in the infrared part of the radiation spectrum and *will not* readily pass through glass. Since the incident radiation enters the greenhouse and the radiation from the objects within is trapped inside, the greenhouse warms up. Of course, the outside of the glass radiates energy, but this balances the input from the sun only after the greenhouse temperature has risen considerably. The glass also prevents convective losses by stopping the upward flow of warm air.

In a sense, the earth is a huge greenhouse, with the atmosphere replacing the glass. The water vapor and carbon dioxide in the air are good absorbers of infrared radiation. Thus sunlight passes through the atmosphere more readily than infrared, and the temperature at the surface is higher and more stable than it would be without an atmosphere. Burning fossil fuels increases the carbon dioxide level. This could significantly increase the average temperature of the earth and lead to major climatic changes. This is an important and complex problem, and it is the subject of considerable research.

In Fig. 12.15, we note that the area beneath the curves increases very rapidly as the temperature increases. The area represents the energy emitted per second. There is a simple formula for this emission rate. The rate at which energy radiates from a surface of area A at temperature T was given by Josef Stefan (1835–1893) in 1879 and is called *Stefan's law*,

$$H = e\sigma A T^4 \qquad (12.17)$$

where

$$\sigma = 5.67 \times 10^{-8} \text{ W m}^{-2} \text{ K}^{-4}$$

is *Stefan's constant*. The quantity e is called the *emissivity*; its value depends on the surface, but it is always between 0 and 1.

Before illustrating Eq. 12.17 with an example, we remark on several features of radiating objects in general and Stefan's law in particular.

Note first that Stefan's law contains only the absolute temperature of the emitting object, not a temperature difference as found for conduction and convection. At first glance Stefan's law thus apparently means that an object will radiate energy until its temperature reaches absolute zero. In fact, the object does radiate energy to its surroundings, *but it also absorbs energy from those same surroundings.* Consider an object at a temperature T_2 that is in a large container kept at a temperature T_1. If initially $T_2 > T_1$, one finds that the temperature of the object decreases until the object and the container are both at a common temperature T_1; afterward, no further temperature change occurs. At this stage the object is emitting energy at a rate given by $e\sigma A T_1^4$, and it is absorbing radiated energy from the container at the same rate, $e\sigma A T_1^4$.

A single result contains all the information about this process. At a time that the object's temperature T is between T_2 and T_1, its net rate of heat loss is

$$H_{net} = H_{out} - H_{in} = e\sigma A(T^4 - T_1^4) \quad (12.18)$$

When $T = T_1$, the net heat leaving the object becomes zero. Equation 12.18 is indeed correct, but we have not explained why the same value of e, the emissivity, can be used for emission and absorption.

The value of the emissivity depends on the surface of the object. A shiny surface has a small value of e; a black surface has e near 1. Because the object reaches equilibrium at the temperature of the walls, it must absorb energy at the same rate as it is emitted. Thus, a good emitter must also be a good absorber. Conversely, a good reflector is a poor emitter; therefore, small values of e correspond to surfaces that emit radiation poorly and reflect radiation well. Large values of e describe surfaces with the opposite characteristics.

A perfect absorber (emitter) is one for which $e = 1$ and all incident radiation is absorbed; none is reflected. Any object that absorbs all incident radiation appears black (unless it is hot enough to radiate visibly); hence, a perfect absorber (and emitter) is called a *blackbody*. A blackbody has $e = 1$.

The emissivity usually varies somewhat with the wavelength. Sunlight is most intense in the visible light region, which corresponds approximately to wavelengths from 4×10^{-7} m to 7×10^{-7} m. The darkest human skin has an emissivity of 0.82 for visible light and the lightest skin has $e = 0.65$. The radiation from objects at or near typical room or body temperatures is predominantly in the longer infrared wavelengths. All human skin has an emissivity of nearly 1 at these wavelengths.

Radiation losses are important for people. This is illustrated in the following example.

Example 12.12

The person in Example 12.10 had a skin temperature of 33°C = 306 K and was in a room where the walls were at 29°C = 302 K. If the emissivity is 1 and the body surface area is 1.5 m², what is the rate of heat loss due to radiation?

We must consider two competing processes. First, the person at a temperature $T_2 = 33°C = 306$ K will radiate heat at a rate

$$\begin{aligned} H_{out} &= e\sigma A T_2^4 \\ &= (1)(5.67 \times 10^{-8} \text{ W m}^{-2} \text{ K}^{-4})(1.5 \text{ m}^2)(306 \text{ K})^4 \\ &= 746 \text{ W} \end{aligned}$$

This is roughly six times the typical heat output of a human; a person losing this much heat would quickly freeze. However, heat is also received from the surroundings. If these are at temperature $T_1 = 29°C = 302$ K, heat will be received at the rate

$$\begin{aligned} H_{in} &= e\sigma A T_1^4 \\ &= (1)(5.67 \times 10^{-8} \text{ W m}^{-2} \text{ K}^{-4})(1.5 \text{ m}^2)(302 \text{ K})^4 \\ &= 707 \text{ W} \end{aligned}$$

Thus the net rate of heat loss is (746 W − 707 W) = 39 W. This is roughly equal to the convective loss rate calculated in Example 12.10.

In almost all radiation problems, one must compute the difference between the rates at which energy is emitted at two temperatures. Thus if one temperature is $T + \Delta T$ and the other is T, the difference is $\Delta H = e\sigma A[(T + \Delta T)^4 - T^4]$. In many such problems, ΔT is very much less than T, and it is a good approximation to write $(T + \Delta T)^4 - T^4 \approx 4T^3 \Delta T$. Then

$$\Delta H = 4e\sigma A T^3 \Delta T \quad (\Delta T \ll T) \quad (12.19)$$

The fractional error introduced by the approximation leading to this result is of the order $\Delta T/T$. In the preceding example, $\Delta T/T = 0.013$, so the error would be about 1.3 percent if the approximate formula was used. The following example illustrates a situation where this approximate result can be used accurately.

Example 12.13

Comparing two patches of skin of area A on a person's chest, the radiation rate is found to differ by 1 percent. What is the difference in skin temperature?

Suppose the lower temperature patch is at $T = 37°C = 310$ K, and the temperature of the other is $T + \Delta T$. Then the difference divided by the heat loss at 310 K is

$$\frac{\Delta H}{H} \simeq \frac{4e\sigma A T^3\, \Delta T}{e\sigma A T^4} = \frac{4\,\Delta T}{T} = 0.01$$

Solving for ΔT,

$$\Delta T = 0.01\,\frac{T}{4} = (0.01)\,\frac{(310\text{ K})}{4} = 0.775\text{ K}$$

Thus a temperature change of less than 1 K alters the radiation rate by 1 percent.

The preceding example illustrates the physical principle underlying *thermography*, a technique with uses in many fields. In medical applications, special infrared detectors are used to produce a photographic record of the infrared radiation emitted by a patient (Fig. 12.16). In photos of this type, areas with higher temperatures appear darker; differences as small as 0.1°C are detectable. The photographs can show, for example, how circulation is reduced by smoking.

Thermography has in some cases led to the early

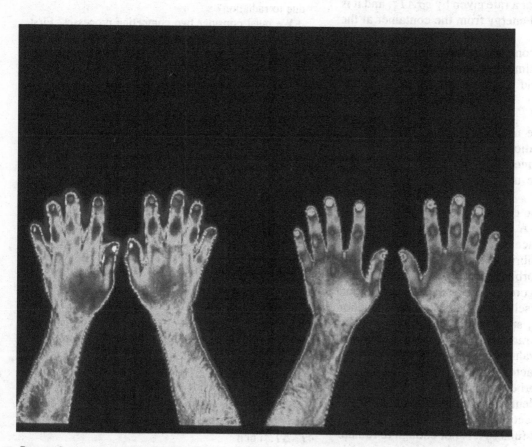

Figure 12.16.   Smoker's forearms. Thermogram of forearms seen before (left) and 5 minutes after smoking a cigarette (right). The thermograms show the skin's temperature by recording its emission of infrared radiation. (Dr. Arthur Tucker / Photo Researchers, Inc.)

Figure 12.17. (a) Thermogram of a building showing the distribution of heat over its exterior. (Alfred Pasieka / Photo Reseachers, Inc.) (b) A thermogram shows the differences in temperature on the exterior of a building, measured by the long-wave infrared radiation it emits. (Tony McConnell / Photo Researchers, Inc.)

detection of breast and thyroid cancer, but its use has not become widespread because its reliability has not been adequate. It has enjoyed somewhat greater success in the detection of circulatory problems in the legs of diabetics, allowing corrective medical procedures to be performed at an early stage of the disease.

Thermography has also recently been used in the area of energy conservation. Ground-level and aerial thermographic pictures show buildings and parts of buildings that lose excessive amounts of heat (Fig. 12.17).

It is also possible to measure accurately the weak radiation emitted by the body at microwave wavelengths, which are longer than those of infrared radiation. Recent experiments show that such measurements may help doctors to detect tumors up to 10 cm below the surface. By contrast, infrared radiation is absorbed more readily in body tissues, so thermography is sensitive only to tumors closer to the skin. Both techniques are noninvasive and intrinsically safe, since the patient is not subjected to any external source of radiation or other probe.

Wien's and Stefan's laws together can be used to explain many phenomena of our everyday experience. Consider, for example, why clear nights are cooler than cloudy nights. On a clear night the earth radiates energy into space at a rate proportional to the fourth power of its temperature, about 300 K. The incoming radiation from space is very small because its average temperature is near absolute zero. On the other hand, with cloud cover, the earth radiates at 300 K, but the radiation is absorbed in the clouds, which radiate energy back to earth. Again the radiation is trapped, rather like the greenhouse effect. The cooling that occurs on clear nights is often referred to as radiational cooling.

SUMMARY

Many properties of materials depend on temperature. The temperature is a measure of the different states of motion of the molecules. For example, most objects will experience a fractional change in length $\Delta l/l$ proportional to the temperature change ΔT,

$$\frac{\Delta l}{l} = \alpha \, \Delta T$$

Similarly, fractional changes in the area and volume of uniform materials are given by

$$\frac{\Delta A}{A} = 2\alpha \, \Delta T$$

and

$$\frac{\Delta V}{V} = \beta \, \Delta T = 3\alpha \, \Delta T$$

where α is the linear expansion coefficient and β is the volume expansion coefficient.

When heat is added to an object, its temperature will change or it will undergo a phase change. If n moles of a substance change temperature by dT when heat dQ is transferred, the molar heat capacity is given by

$$C = \frac{1}{n} \frac{dQ}{dT}$$

The specific heat capacity is the molar heat capacity divided by the mass of one mole of the substance, $c = C/M$. The heat ΔQ entering or leaving an object of mass m when the temperature changes by ΔT is

$$\Delta Q = mc \, \Delta T$$

In practice, molar and specific heat capacities are measured or calculated either at constant pressure or at constant volume.

If heat ΔQ is added to a substance but no temperature change occurs, then a mass m of the substance undergoes a phase change, where

$$\Delta Q = Lm$$

Here L is the latent heat for the phase change.

Heat is transferred between objects at different temperatures by conduction, convection, and radiation. If a sample of material of cross-sectional area A has a temperature difference ΔT along its length, the rate of heat transfer from the high- to low-temperature end by conduction is

$$H = \kappa A \frac{\Delta T}{l}$$

where κ is the thermal conductivity of the material. The factor l/κ is called the R-value and is a measure of the resistance of the material to the flow of heat.

An object may transfer heat by convection. If the object has a surface area A and is at a temperature

ΔT above that of a fluid that can circulate, the heat loss rate is given approximately by

$$H = qA \, \Delta T$$

Convective heat transfer increases dramatically if the fluid is forced to move. For example, convective losses are much greater on windy days than on calm days.

Heat transfer by radiation occurs through the emission and absorption of electromagnetic radiation. An object at a temperature T will emit most of its radiation at wavelengths near

$$\lambda = \frac{B}{T}$$

where B has a value 2.898×10^{-3} m K. Knowledge of this wavelength is very useful since materials transmit, absorb, and reflect radiation differently at different wavelengths. The total rate at which energy is emitted depends on the fourth power of the temperature,

$$H = e\sigma A T^4$$

Here A is the surface area, e is the emissivity of the surface, and $\sigma = 5.67 \times 10^{-8}$ W m^{-2} K^{-4} is Stefan's constant. The heat lost by radiation is the difference between that emitted by the object and that absorbed from the object's surroundings.

Checklist
Define or explain:

linear expansion	conduction
thermostat	thermal conductivity
volume expansion	R-value
internal energy	convection
molar heat capacity	radiation
specific heat capacity	frequency
calorimeter	wavelength
phase change	emissivity
sublimation	blackbody
triple point	Wien displacement law
critical point	Stefan's law
latent heat	

REVIEW QUESTIONS

Q12-1 The fractional change in length of an object is proportional to the temperature change. The proportionality constant is called the _____.

Q12-2 The change in length of a heated object is proportional to α, the coefficient of linear expansion. The fractional area change is proportional to _____, and the fractional volume change is proportional to _____.

Q12-3 The ratio of the heat added to 1 mole of a substance to the temperature change is called the _____.

Q12-4 The specific heat capacity is defined as the molar heat capacity divided by the _____ of the substance.

Q12-5 The heat capacity is usually measured or calculated under the conditions of constant _____ or constant _____.

Q12-6 The latent heat of vaporization of a substance is the heat required to change 1 kg of a substance from _____ to _____.

Q12-7 The transfer of heat from one place to another by the actual movement of material is called _____.

Q12-8 Heat conduction refers to the transfer of thermal energy between objects in _____.

Q12-9 The wavelength at which the radiation from an object is most intense increases as the temperature _____.

Q12-10 Stefan's law describes the fact that the rate of heat loss through radiation is proportional to the _____ power of the temperature.

EXERCISES

Section 12.1 | Thermal Expansion

12-1 A steel railroad track is 20 m long at 20°C. How much longer is it at 40°C?

12-2 A steel railroad track is 30 m long at 0°C. How much shorter is it at −20°C?

12-3 An aluminum metrestick is exactly 1 m long at 20°C. How much shorter is it at 0°C? Use $\alpha = 2.30 \times 10^{-5}$ K^{-1}.

12-4 For Pyrex glass, β is about one third that of ordinary glass. What does this imply about thermal stresses?

12-5 Why does heating a jar lid make it easier to open?

12-6 By how much does the area of a rectangular steel plate 0.5 m by 2.5 m change when it is heated from 0°C to 40°C?

12-7 A common lecture demonstration uses a

steel ball that will not fit through a steel ring unless the ring is heated. If the diameter of the ball is 3 cm = 0.03 m at 20°C, what is the inner diameter of the ring at 20°C if the ball slips through when the ring reaches 250°C?

12-8 A container of water is filled to the top. The temperature increases 8 K, but no water spills. What was the original temperature of the water? (Neglect the expansion of the glass.)

12-9 Both iron and concrete have coefficients of linear expansion that are approximately 1.2×10^{-5}. Reinforced concrete, which is very widely used in buildings and other structures, consists of thin iron rods imbedded in masses of concrete. If the coefficients were not nearly equal, how would that affect the usefulness of reinforced concrete as a construction material?

12-10 A thermometer has a mercury-filled glass bulb with a volume of 2×10^{-7} m³ attached to a thin glass capillary tube with an inner radius of 5×10^{-5} m. If the temperature increases by 100°C, how far will the mercury rise in the tube? ($\beta = 1.82 \times 10^{-4}$ K⁻¹ for mercury; neglect the expansion of the glass.)

Section 12.2 | Heat Capacity

12-11 How many kilojoules are needed to heat 0.15 kg of helium gas from 20°C to 80°C at constant pressure?

12-12 A snowball is dropped from a rooftop 20 m above the ground. If its temperature is initially −10°C, and if all of its kinetic energy is converted to internal energy, what is its final temperature?

12-13 A container with a mass of 0.6 kg is at a temperature of 20°C. When 2.5 kg of boiling water is poured into it, the final temperature is 90°C. What is the specific heat capacity of the container?

12-14 A calorimeter of mass 0.4 kg and a specific heat capacity of 0.63 kJ kg⁻¹ K⁻¹ contains a sample with a mass of 0.55 kg. If 2.45 kJ of energy is supplied electrically and the temperature rises 4°C, what is the specific heat capacity of the sample?

12-15 A 5-kg meteorite hits the ground at 2000 m s⁻¹. How much thermal energy is liber

ated if all its kinetic energy is converted to thermal energy?

12-16 The temperature of 15 kg of water increases at 0.003°C per second. At what rate is the internal energy of the water increasing? (Neglect the work done by the water.)

Section 12.3 | Phase Changes

12-17 How much heat is needed to melt a 10-kg block of ice that is initially at −10°C?

12-18 How much heat is required to heat 1 kg of water from 20°C at atmospheric pressure to boiling and to convert it entirely into steam?

12-19 If 0.15 kg of ice at 0°C is added to 0.25 kg of water at 20°C, (a) does all the ice melt? (b) What is the final temperature?

12-20 A picnic jug contains 1.3 kg of water and 0.6 kg of ice. If 35.6 W of heat enters through the insulation, how long does it take for all the ice to melt?

12-21 Ice at 0°C is added to a 1 kg of lemonade, cooling it from 20°C to 0°C. How much ice melts? (The heat capacity of lemonade equals that of water.)

12-22 A jeweler heats 0.1 kg of silver from 20°C until it melts. How much energy does this require?

12-23 A 0.003-kg droplet of molten lead falls onto a worktable and solidifies. How much heat does the droplet lose in the process if it was initially at its melting point?

12-24 When water boils, the heat added is less than the increase in the internal energy of the water. Explain why.

Section 12.4 | Heat Conduction

12-25 A mountain climber trapped in a storm builds a snow cave to keep warm. The walls of the cave are 1 m thick. What thickness of rock wool would provide an equivalent amount of insulation? (The thermal conductivity of packed snow is approximately 0.2 W m⁻¹ K⁻¹.)

12-26 People who leave their homes unoccupied in snowy areas often must arrange to have their rooftops shoveled to avoid collapse. Why is this less of a problem for occupied houses?

12-27 In cold regions, why does the frost extend

deeper into the ground in those years when there is little or no snow?

12-28 Why has styrofoam insulation become very widely used in recent years wherever space limitations are significant?

12-29 A cabin wall is made of wood 0.05 m thick and has an area of 12 m². If the outside surface of the wall is at 0°C and the inside surface is at 20°C, at what rate is heat lost through the wall?

12-30 At what rate will heat be conducted by a copper rod 4 m long with a cross-sectional area of 0.015 m² if one end is at 250°C and the other is at 40°C?

12-31 At what rate is heat lost by conduction through a rectangular pane of glass 0.003 m thick with sides 0.1 m and 0.2 m? Assume the inner surface is at 10°C and the outer surface is at 0°C.

12-32 (a) What is the R-value of a 1-m² slab of glass 0.5 cm = 0.005 m thick? (b) How much heat per hour passes through this slab if the temperature difference is 10°C between the two faces of the glass?

12-33 (a) What is the R-value for a 1-cm thickness of fiberglass with $\kappa = 0.038$ W m⁻¹ K⁻¹? (b) What is R for a 15-cm thickness of fiberglass?

12-34 The R-value of a 1-cm = 0.01-m thickness of a certain material is 0.2 m² K W⁻¹. If 50 W of thermal energy passes through a 1-m² area of the material, what is the temperature difference between the faces?

12-35 Equation 12.12 does not apply to thick insulation covering a pipe, since it holds only when the cross section is at least approximately uniform. However, one can still see the effect of insulating a water pipe qualitatively by considering a sheet of copper 0.002 m thick insulated with a felt layer 0.02 m thick. If water in contact with the copper is at 80°C, and the outer surface of the felt is at 15°C, what is the temperature of the other side of the copper sheet?

Section 12.5 | Heat Transfer by Convection

12-36 How much energy per second will a naked person with surface area 1.4 m² lose by convection in air at 0°C? Assume the average q is 7.1 W m⁻² K⁻¹ and that the skin temperature is 30°C.

12-37 A naked person with a surface area of 1.8 m², a skin temperature of 31°C, and an average q of 7.1 W m⁻² K⁻¹ loses 126 W by convection. What is the air temperature?

12-38 A windowpane is at 10°C and has an area of 1.2 m². If the outside air temperature is 0°C, at what rate is energy lost by convection? The q for the window is 4 W m⁻² K⁻¹.

12-39 When the wind is a factor, Eq. 12.14 can be used with the temperature far from the surface taken from the wind chill chart, Table 12.5. Suppose the temperature on the outside surface of a window is 10°C and the air temperature far from the window is −10°C. Find the ratio of the convective heat loss when the wind speed is 20 km h⁻¹ to the heat loss when there is no wind.

12-40 (a) When it is very cold outside, open fireplaces can cause more heat loss up a chimney than they deliver to the room they are in. What is responsible for this heat loss? (b) "Airtight" wood stoves admit only small, controlled amounts of air into a stove from the room. Why are they much more efficient than open fireplaces?

12-41 What is the motivation for using a ceiling fan in a high-ceilinged room in the winter?

Section 12.6 | Radiation

12-42 Why does the fiber glass insulation used in the walls of houses often have a layer of shiny aluminum foil on one side?

12-43 (a) A person's skin temperature is 35°C. What is the wavelength of maximum radiation intensity at this temperature? (b) To what portion of the electromagnetic spectrum does that wavelength correspond?

12-44 What is the wavelength of maximum radiation intensity for a surface at 2000°C?

12-45 Calculate the error made if Eq. 12.19 rather than Eq. 12.18 were used if $T + \Delta T = 319$ K and $T = 270$ K.

12-46 Estimate the error made if Eq. 12.19 rather than Eq. 12.18 were used if $T + \Delta T = 297$ K and $T = 293$ K.

12-47 A naked person with surface area 1.8 m² and skin temperature 33°C is in a room at 10°C. (Assume $e = 1$.) (a) At what rate does the person radiate energy? (b) What is the person's net rate of energy loss due to radiation?

12-48   An object is at 300 K, and an identical object is at 900 K. What is the ratio of the energies radiated? (Assume the emissivity is the same for both objects.)

12-49   A 2-m length of copper pipe containing hot water has its outer surface at 80°C. If the surroundings are at 20°C, at what rate does the pipe lose thermal energy due to radiation? (The surface area of the pipe is 0.12 m² and $e = 1$.)

12-50   A black-surfaced road at a temperature of 320 K receives radiant energy from the sun at a rate of 700 W m⁻². What is the net rate at which a square metre of road surface absorbs thermal energy?

PROBLEMS

***12-51**   The pendulum of a large clock consists of a thin steel rod with a heavy weight at the end. At 20°C the rod is 1.22 m long and the clock keeps accurate time. (a) By how much does the length change if the temperature rises to 40°C? (b) Does the clock run fast or slow? (c) What is the fractional change in the period of the pendulum? (*Hint*: See Chapter Nine.) (d) What is the error of the clock in seconds per day?

12-52   A car with a full 40-litre steel gasoline tank is parked in the sun. If its temperature rises 30°C, how much gasoline spills out? (For gasoline, $\beta = 9.50 \times 10^{-4}$ K⁻¹, and for steel, $\beta = 3.81 \times 10^{-5}$ K⁻¹.) (b) At what time of day is gasoline cheapest?

12-53   (a) Show that the coefficient of volume expansion β for an ideal gas is $1/T$, where T is the Kelvin temperature. (Assume that the pressure remains constant.) (b) What is β at 20°C?

12-54   Assuming that no heat is transferred to or from the surroundings, how much does the temperature of a river rise in going over a 30-m falls? (Assume the velocity of the water is the same above and below the falls.)

12-55   A tightly sealed small house has a total floor area of 90 m² and ceilings 2.5 m high. If the inside temperature is 21°C and the outside air is at

−10°C, what is the rate of energy loss if all the air in the house is exchanged with outside air every 3 hours? (The specific heat of air at constant pressure is 1.0 kJ kg⁻¹ K⁻¹; the density of air at 20°C is 1.20 kg m⁻³.)

***12-56**   A steel rod is initially at 20°C and has a length of 2 m. It has a cross-sectional area of 0.001 m². (a) If it is heated to 120°C, by how much does its length increase? (b) How large a force must be applied to its ends to restore the original length? (Young's modulus for steel is 2×10^{11} N m⁻².)

12-57   A 75-kg man utilizes energy at the rate of 10,000 kJ per day. Suppose that 10 percent of this energy is used for work and 90 percent is waste heat. If his body had no way of releasing that heat, by how much would his temperature rise per hour on the average? (The specific heat of animal tissue is approximately equal to that of water.)

12-58   How fast must a lead bullet travel so that it melts when fired into a thick slab of wood, assuming that no heat is lost to the wood? (Assume initially that $T_C = 20$°C.)

12-59   Using the data in Fig. 12.6, find the energy required to heat, at constant volume, 1 kg of hydrogen gas (a) from 30 to 40 K; (b) from 260 to 270 K.

12-60   A steel wool pad is rubbed on a steel frying pan with a force component of 10 N along the direction of motion. Each stroke is 0.1 m long, and there are 0.8 strokes per second. (a) At what rate is thermal energy generated? (b) If no heat is lost to the surroundings and the combined mass of the pan plus pad is 1.25 kg, by how much will their temperature rise after 1 minute?

12-61   A solar hot-water system employs several collectors, each 2 m by 1.5 m. Sunlight is incident at right angles onto a glass plate at the front of the collector at 400 W m⁻². This energy is absorbed by a black plate at the back of the panel and is transferred to water that flows through pipes attached to it. How much water in kilograms per minute flows through the collector if its temperature rises 30°C as it passes through?

12-62 When fiberglass insulation is installed in the walls of a house, the rolls are attached to the wooden studs so that an air space is left between the insulation and the outer walls. Explain how this minimizes problems with condensation.

12-63 The ice on a lake is 0.2 m thick. Its top surface is at −15°C, and its lower surface is at 0°C. (a) At what rate is heat conducted through the ice? (b) After 1 hour, how much thicker is the ice? (At 0°C, the density of ice is 920 kg m^{-3}. Neglect the reduction in the heat flow as the ice grows thicker.)

12-64 A student showers for 10 minutes using 10 litres of water per minute. The water is at 50°C and was heated electrically from 10°C. (a) How much energy was used to heat the water? (b) If electricity costs 10 cents per kilowatt hour, what is the cost of the shower?

12-65 The average temperature at the top of a mountain is lower than that at the bottom. How is this explained by considering the adiabatic expansion of rising air currents?

*12-66 The prevailing winds in the western United States are from the west. In many areas the region east of mountain ranges is hot and dry. Suggest a reason for this. (*Hint*: Typically, there is relatively great precipitation over the mountains. What effect does this have on the temperature of the air?)

*12-67 A pot has a copper bottom layer 0.005 m thick and an inner steel layer 0.002 m thick. The inside of the pot is at 100°C and the outside of the bottom is at 103°C. (a) What is the temperature of the copper–steel junction? (b) At what rate is heat conducted if the area of the bottom is 0.04 m^2?

*12-68 (a) At what rate is heat conducted across a wooden wall of area 20 m^2 and thickness 0.03 m if the temperature difference is 40°C? (b) How much heat is conducted per second if there is a layer of rock wool 0.04 m thick on one side of the wall?

12-69 A pot with a steel bottom 0.01 m thick rests on a hot stove. The area of the bottom is 0.1 m^2. The water inside the pot is at 100°C, and 0.05 kg are evaporated every 3 minutes. Find the temperature of the lower surface of the pot, which is in contact with the stove. (Assume that no heat is lost to the room.)

12-70 A styrofoam picnic chest has dimensions 0.5 × 0.3 × 0.35 m with walls 0.02 m thick. (a) If the temperature difference across the layer is 35°C, at what rate will heat be conducted? (b) How many kilograms of ice will melt each hour in the chest?

12-71 A homeowner turns down the thermostat from 23°C to 18°C. If the average outside temperature is 0°C, estimate the percentage reduction in fuel consumption.

12-72 The average outside temperature is 0°C; inside a house the temperature is 23°C. To reduce fuel bills by 10 percent, what thermostat setting should be chosen?

12-73 A surface at 20°C faces a cloudless nighttime sky. (a) What is the rate of radiation per square metre of the surface? (Assume $e = 1$.) (b) The amount of radiation from the sky is very small by comparison. Why?

12-74 The surface of the sun is at about 6000 K. (a) How much power does it radiate per square metre of surface area? (b) How much power reaches the upper atmosphere of the earth per square metre? (The diameter of the sun is 1.39 × 10^6 km, and the mean radius of the earth's orbit is 1.49 × 10^8 km.)

12-75 A man having a surface area 1.8 m^2 wears a garment 0.01 m thick with a thermal conductivity of 0.04 W m^{-1} K^{-1}. (a) If his skin temperature is 34°C and the outside of his garment is at −10°C, what is his rate of heat loss? (b) Is he adequately dressed? Explain.

12-76 A girl having a surface area of 1.2 m^2 wears a down jacket and pants 0.03 m thick. If her skin temperature is at 34°C and she can safely lose 85 W by conduction, what is the lowest temperature for which the clothing is adequate? (Assume that the outside of the clothing is at the same temperature as the air.)

12-77 A thin sheet of ice with an area of 0.15 m^2 on each side hangs from a roof. The ice is at 0°C and the surrounding air is at 10°C. The net rate at which radiant energy is transferred to the ice from the sunlight and from the surroundings is 20 W; $q = 9.5$ W m^{-2} K^{-1}. What mass of ice melts in 1 minute?

12-78 It is desired to insulate an attic floor to an R-value of 3 m^2 K W^{-1}. If rock wool is used, how thick must it be?

12-79 (a) If the R-value of the insulation in a 40-m^2 ceiling is 3.8 m^2 K W^{-1}, and the temperature difference across it is 10°C, how much energy is lost through the ceiling in 7 hours due to conduction? (b) A litre of heating oil provides 3.846×10^7 J of energy. At 39.6 cents per litre, what is the cost of this energy per hour?

12-80 What is the cost per hour of replacing the heat lost through a single-pane window 0.003 m thick and 1 m^2 in area if the inner and outer surface temperature differ by 10°C? (Assume heating oil provides 3.846×10^7 J of heat per litre and costs 39.6 cents per litre.)

12-81 A copper heating pipe 2 m long of outer radius 0.01 m has walls 0.002 m thick. It contains water at 80°C and is in a room with still air at 20°C. (Neglect radiation effects.) (a) Using $q = 9.5$ W m^{-2} K^{-1}, what is the temperature of the outer pipe surface? (b) At what rate is energy lost through the pipe walls?

*12-82 Show that when slabs with R-values R_1 and R_2 are in contact, the effective R-value is $R_1 + R_2$. (*Hint*: If the temperatures on either side are T_1 and T_2, respectively, find the temperature between the two slabs.)

ANSWERS TO REVIEW QUESTIONS

Q12-1, coefficient of linear expansion; **Q12-2**, 2α, $\beta = 3\alpha$; **Q12-3**, molar heat capacity; **Q12-4**, mass of 1 mole; **Q12-5**, pressure, volume; **Q12-6**, liquid, vapor, or gas; **Q12-7**, convection; **Q12-8**, contact; **Q12-9**, decreases; **Q12-10**, fourth.

SUPPLEMENTARY TOPICS

12.7 | TEMPERATURE REGULATION IN WARM-BLOODED ANIMALS

Most biological processes are temperature dependent, so the body temperature of an animal must be kept within a narrow range. Warm-blooded animals, such as birds and mammals, control their own temperatures by regulating the heat loss from their bodies. By contrast, cold-blooded animals are dependent on their environment for the maintenance of their body temperature. For example, snakes are often found sunning themselves on sun-warmed rocks. Many insects must beat their wings before takeoff to raise the temperature of their flight muscles. In this section, we are concerned only with the ways in which warm-blooded animals regulate their temperatures on a short-term basis.

In addition to the mechanisms used daily, biological adaptations to changing climatic conditions also occur on seasonal and evolutionary time scales. The heavy coats of animals, bird migration, and hibernation are all seasonal adaptations. On a longer time scale, nature has favored the development of larger animals in the coldest climates. Such animals have large ratios of volume to surface area, and the corresponding heat production to heat loss ratios are high.

In warm-blooded animals, the main object of temperature regulation is to keep vital organs and muscles at a nearly ideal temperature. Since heat loss occurs either at the body surface or through water evaporation from the lungs, the object is to adjust the flow of heat from the organs and muscles to the lung and body surfaces. The blood plays an important role in this process, because it carries heat from the internal to the external portions of the body. Also, the body's thermostat, the *hypothalamus*, which is located in the brain, uses the blood temperature to monitor the system. The hypothalamus acts to keep itself at a nearly constant temperature. In doing so, the temperature of other internal organs may vary much more widely. This is analogous to a house with a single thermostat in one room. The temperature in that room will be nearly uniform, while the temperature in other rooms may fluctuate considerably.

The source of body heat is the chemical metabolism of food. A resting 70-kg human generates about 80 W; during heavy exercise, the rate may be up to 20 times greater. Depending on the air temperature and the clothing worn, the heat generated may be needed to overcome convective and radiative losses, or it may be a waste product to be disposed of by the body.

A warm-blooded animal has a number of mechanisms to use in controlling its temperature. To raise its temperature, the body reduces the blood flow through the capillaries nearest the skin surface. Flesh is a poor conductor of heat, so this is effective in reducing heat losses. Also, body hair can be fluffed up to increase insulation. (Even humans have a vestige of this manifested as goose bumps; the body is attempting to fluff almost nonexistent hair.) Finally, heat production may be increased by shivering.

The body is cooled by convection and radiation from the skin and by the evaporation of sweat from the skin and of water from the lungs. If the interior temperature begins to increase, the body first increases blood flow near the skin surface to increase convective and radiative losses and then, if necessary, uses the evaporative loss mechanism. Humans and horses, among other animals, sweat from glands located over much of the body and thus benefit from evaporation over a large surface area. As much as 1.5 kg of sweat per hour may be evaporated from the human body. The latent heat of vaporization for sweat at 37°C is about equal to that of water at the same temperature, 2427 kJ kg^{-1}. Note that this is larger than the 2255 kJ kg^{-1} necessary to vaporize water at 100°C. Under many conditions the evaporation of sweat is the primary cooling mechanism used by the body.

Furry animals such as dogs do not sweat but take major advantage of evaporative cooling in the lungs. They exhale large volumes of air by panting. Panting itself generates heat but fortunately less than is lost by evaporation.

The various contributions to the rate of heat loss and production for a typical human adult are approximately as follows. If the area A is given in square metres, the skin temperature T_s and air temperature T_a are given in degrees Celsius, and the rate r of sweating is in units of kilograms per hour, then

H_m = rate heat is generated by metabolism:
80 to 1600 W

H_c = rate heat is lost by convection (still air):
$D_c A(T_s - T_a)$

H_r = rate heat is lost by radiation: $D_r A(T_s - T_a)$

H_s = rate heat is lost by evaporation of sweat: $D_s r$

H_l = rate heat is lost by evaporation from the lungs: D_l

The D's are constants:

$$D_c = 7.1 \text{ W m}^{-2} \text{ K}^{-1}$$
$$D_r = 6.5 \text{ W m}^{-2} \text{ K}^{-1}$$
$$D_s = 674 \text{ W h kg}^{-1}$$
$$D_l = 10.5 \text{ W}$$

The value of H_l is given for normal breathing rates; it increases in proportion to the rate of breathing. Typically, H_l is a small fraction of the heat loss, and we neglect its variation.

If the body temperature is held constant, then the heat losses are related by

$$H_m = H_c + H_r + H_s + H_l \qquad (12.20)$$

The following example illustrates the importance of sweating during moderate levels of activity.

Example 12.14

A person generates heat at a rate of 230 W. How much sweat is produced per hour if the surface area is 1 m²? Assume the body temperature is 37°C and that of the air is 28°C.

Using Eq. 12.20,

$$H_s = H_m - H_c - H_r - H_l$$
$$= 230 \text{ W} - (7.1)(1.0)(9) \text{ W}$$
$$\quad - (6.5)(1.0)(9) \text{ W} - 10.5 \text{ W}$$
$$= 97.1 \text{ W}$$

Since the rate at which heat is removed by sweating is $D_s r$, the sweat required is

$$r = \frac{H_s}{D_s} = \frac{97.1 \text{ W}}{674 \text{ W h kg}^{-1}} = 0.14 \text{ kg h}^{-1}$$

12.8 | LARGE- AND SMALL-SCALE ATMOSPHERIC ACTIVITY

The study of the behavior of the atmosphere, both on large and small scales, is a rich and complex one. Factors that affect the large-scale features of atmospheric circulation include the spherical shape and gravitational attraction of the earth, its rotation, the tilt of the earth's spin axis with respect to the plane of the earth's orbit around the sun, and of course, the heat from the sun. We have already seen how Coriolis forces affect the global air patterns (Section 7.9). Here we explore the effects of thermal processes.

As the land and ocean near the equator are heated by the sun, the air above is also heated by conduction and convection, causing it to expand. Objects less dense than the fluid in which they are immersed tend to rise, so this heated air rises. The rising air expands adiabatically; no heat is exchanged with the surrounding air, and work is done on the surroundings. In accordance with the first law of thermodynamics, this rising air cools somewhat, since its internal energy is decreasing. Moisture in the air condenses as rain, releasing its latent heat of vaporization. This additional heat causes further expansion and permits the upward flow to continue to greater heights.

The rising air leaves behind a low-pressure area near the surface. As a result, cooler, denser air from higher latitudes flows along the surface toward the equator and a compensatory high altitude flow of heated air occurs in the opposite direction. This upper atmospheric air has cooled somewhat by expansion and cools further as it leaves the warmest latitudes. At about 30° latitude, it descends and splits, feeding both the flows toward the equator and toward the poles (Fig. 12.18).

The Coriolis force causes the air flowing toward the equator to be deflected to the west. This is the origin of the trade winds that circle the earth along the equator. They were discussed in Section 7.9, and are shown again in Fig. 12.18.

The air descending at about 30° latitude is compressed as it descends. As a result it warms somewhat. This causes evaporation of whatever moisture the air contained, and as it reaches the surface, it is warm and dry. These areas are called the horse latitudes because horses being transported from Eu-

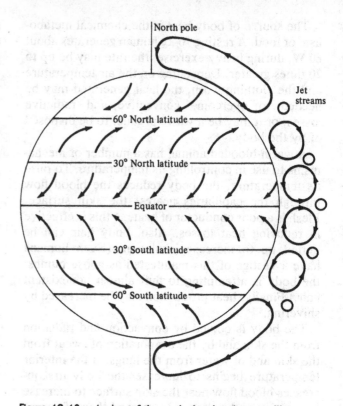

Figure 12.18.   A view of the earth showing the prevailing wind patterns. On the right are the air circulation profiles. Heated air rises at the equator, flows to higher latitudes, and cools, descending at about 30° latitude. This descending air splits, some returning to the equator, some moving farther poleward. At 60° latitude, a similar break in the motion of the air occurs with the air rising at this latitude. Also shown in cross section are the permanent jet streams, narrow high-speed west-to-east air streams.

rope often died of heat and thirst in this windless band. A band near the horse latitudes contains most of the earth's great deserts, including those of northern Africa, Arabia, and southern Australia, and even those of the American Southwest.

At the poles, the air is coldest and most dense. It descends until it reaches the surface and then travels toward the equator. This southward flow is deflected toward the west in both hemispheres. As these winds flow into the temperate zones the air warms, expands and rises. This occurs at about 60° latitude. The two great wind zones, the equatorial and polar zones, drive the wind flow in the temperate zone, between 30° and 60° latitude.

Another spectacular phenomenon occurs because of the large air flows across the earth. This is the jet streams, bands of very rapidly flowing air hundreds of kilometres wide and up to 2 km thick. They are at high altitude, 5 to 8 km up, and tend to occur where thermal and pressure gradients are large. Air near the equator has a larger moment of inertia about the rotation axis than air at higher latitudes. As air moves toward the poles, it must either lose angular momentum or increase its angular velocity. When conditions are favorable, the jet streams form. Because they flow so rapidly, they take up a very large angular momentum from the major air masses, allowing them to slow down. The major jet streams flow west to east at the boundaries between the temperate and polar zones and between the equatorial and temperate zones (Fig. 12.18).

The previous paragraphs suggest the richness and complexity of atmospheric behavior. If account is taken of less regular influences such as mountains, the larger land mass in the northern hemisphere, and the irregular boundaries and locations of land and sea, it is easy to see that the results are going to be even more complex.

Monsoons | A smaller-scale feature of atmospheric behavior that has a major effect on many people is the *monsoon*. Monsoons, from the Arabic word for season, are annual weather patterns that appear in many areas but are most dramatically displayed in the area of the Indian Ocean. For the warmer half of the year, the prevailing winds are from the southwest, off the Indian Ocean onto the Indian subcontinent. The weather is very wet, and there are periodic, heavy rainstorms. In the winter months, the prevailing wind is from the northeast, and the weather is very dry.

The Indian monsoon is a set of weather conditions that are superimposed on the prevailing trade winds. In fact, in summer the prevailing winds are reversed, flowing from the southwest. The monsoon occurs because of the difference in the heat capacities of the land and the ocean and because air above the ocean contains more moisture. In addition to its high heat capacity, the ocean water can circulate. In summer, this circulation is driven by winds that cause waves and mixing. In winter, the surface water cools and descends, and warmer, less dense, subsurface water rises. The ocean is a great reservoir of heat that is released during the winter months. The air above is heated, and it expands and rises relative to the air above land.

The average annual incident energy is a maximum near the equator. Because it is efficiently stored by the oceans, the air near the equator is being warmed year round. This heated air expands and rises. As we saw earlier, this leads to the northeasterly flow of air that is the trade wind.

In winter, the land, with its low heat capacity, cools more rapidly than the oceans. The air above is cooled and contracts. Meanwhile the air above the adjacent ocean areas is being heated; it expands and rises, lowering the pressure over the oceans. Eastern Tibet and western China is an area of high pressure in the winter. This high-pressure area, in conjunction with the low-pressure area over the Arabian Sea, contributes to a flow of air from the northeast to southwest over India. As we saw in Section 7.9, the Coriolis forces cause the air leaving high-pressure areas to circulate clockwise. This situation is reinforced by the larger-scale trade winds.

In winter, this cold northeast wind crosses India from central Asia. Even though it warms somewhat as it moves south, this causes more complete evaporation of the little moisture it carries. Thus in winter, India experiences a dry climate with prevailing northeast winds.

As winter draws to an end, the stored energy of the ocean is reduced and the ocean temperature drops to its lowest level. Then in spring and early summer, the land and water are both heated. Because of the lower heat capacity of the land, its temperature rises faster than that of the ocean. Now the warming land mass begins to heat the air above it, causing it to expand and rise compared to air above the cooler oceans, which is more dense and contains more moisture. When the effect of the warm land is strong enough, it produces a low-pressure area over eastern Tibet, replacing the winter high. There is a resulting flow of moist air from the ocean toward that low-pressure center, producing a moist southwest wind across much of India.

As the moist air starts across the relatively warm land, it is affected by the rising air above the land. It also rises and expands. As a result the moist air cools and its temperature drops sufficiently so that its moisture condenses and it rains. In the condensation process, the latent heat of vaporization is released. This additional heat causes further expansion and upward motion, enhancing and strengthening the summer monsoon. It is this overall pattern that brings the monsoon rains of summer to India.

At any point inland, the monsoon appears to have active and dormant phases. That is, a period of heavy rain is followed by a period of no rain and relatively dry descending air while the rainy area follows a track further inland. Then the cycle repeats itself. This periodic change is due to the effects of the rain itself. The water on the land surface reduces both the land temperature and the rate at which the land temperature increases. Much of the solar energy incident after the rain is absorbed by the evaporating surface water. This process requires absorption of the heat of vaporization, which is large, and may take some time to accomplish. During this period the ascension of air heated by the warming land is suppressed. This in turn reduces the pressure difference between the air above the land and water, temporarily reducing the flow of air inland from the sea.

The set of circumstances leading to a dormant phase does not stop the monsoon process; it only weakens it briefly. The summer phase of the monsoon does not stop until the heating of the land ends as fall begins.

12.9 | ADIABATIC EXPANSION OF AN IDEAL GAS

The ratio of the specific heats, $\gamma = C_P/C_V$, determines the behavior of an ideal gas when its volume changes with no heat entering or leaving the gas. We show now that this follows directly from the first law and the equation of state.

Consider a small adiabatic volume change dV. Since $Q = 0$, from the first law $dU = -W = -P\,dV$. From the definition of C_V, $dU = nC_V\,dT$. Thus we have $nC_V\,dT = -P\,dV$ or

$$dT = -\frac{P\,dV}{nC_V}$$

Also, from the equation of state, $PV = nRT$, it follows that $P\,dV + V\,dP = nR\,dT$, or

$$dT = \frac{P\,dV + V\,dP}{nR}$$

Equating the two expressions for dT, we find

$$(C_V + R)P\,dV + C_V V\,dP = 0$$

Now $C_V + R = C_P$ for an ideal gas, so dividing by $C_V PV$ and using the definition $C_P/C_V = \gamma$ yields

$$\frac{\gamma\,dV}{V} + \frac{dP}{P} = 0$$

Integrating, using $\int dx/x = \ln x$, we get $\gamma \ln V + \ln P = $ constant, or $\ln (PV^\gamma) = $ constant. Therefore,

$$PV^\gamma = \text{constant (adiabatic process in ideal gas)} \tag{12.21}$$

Note that for an ideal monatomic gas, $C_V = \frac{3}{2}R$, so $C_P = \frac{5}{2}R$ and $\gamma = \frac{5}{3}$.

A P–V plot shows curves corresponding to a constant quantity of an ideal gas (Fig. 12.19). The adia-

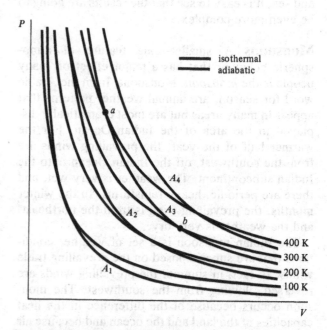

Figure 12.19. P–V plots for a given quantity of an ideal gas. Black curves show isothermal volume changes, $PV = nRT$. Colored curves show adiabatic processes, $PV^\gamma = $ constant, for $\gamma = 1.40$.

batic curves drop more steeply than the isothermal curves as V increases. Hence a given adiabatic curve such as A_3 crosses successive isothermals corresponding to decreasing temperatures as the volume increases, as seen at points a and b in Fig. 12.19. This is what we should expect. As the gas expands without any heat transfer, it does work and loses internal energy. Hence its temperature must decrease.

The use of this result is illustrated by the next example.

Example 12.15

A monatomic ideal gas initially at 0°C and a pressure of 1 atm is suddenly compressed to half its original volume. Find its new pressure and temperature.

Since the compression is very rapid, we can assume that there is not significant heat flow, and that the process is adiabatic. For an ideal monatomic gas, $\gamma = \frac{5}{3} = 1.67$. Thus when the pressure and volume change from P_0, V_0 to P, V, the pressure and volume satisfy $PV^\gamma = $ constant, or

$$PV^{1.67} = P_0V_0^{1.67}$$

$$P = P_0\left(\frac{V_0}{V}\right)^{1.67} = (1 \text{ atm})(2)^{1.67}$$

$$= 3.18 \text{ atm}$$

The pressure is more than three times its original value. Note that in an isothermal compression, PV remains constant, so P doubles when V is halved.

To find the new temperature, we use the ideal gas law, $PV = nRT$, or

$$T = \frac{PV}{nR} = \frac{(3.18 \, P_0)(0.5 \, V_0)}{nR}$$

$$= 1.59 \frac{P_0V_0}{nR} = 1.59T_0$$

The original temperature is 0°C, or $T_0 = 273$ K. Thus the final temperature is 1.59(273 K) = 434 K, or 161°C. The temperature rises rapdily when the gas is compressed.

EXERCISES ON SUPPLEMENTARY TOPICS

Section 12.9 | Adiabatic Expansion of an Ideal Gas

12-83 Suppose the gas in Example 12.15 is cooled back to 0°C at constant pressure after the compression. If the volume before the gas was compressed was V_0, what is its final volume?

12-84 An ideal diatomic gas with $\gamma = 1.4$ is at a temperature of 300 K and a pressure of 1 atm. It is suddenly compressed so that its volume is a third of its original volume. (a) Find its new pressure and temperature. (b) The gas is now cooled to 300 K at constant volume. What is its final pressure?

12-85 Show that in an adiabatic expansion of an ideal gas, $TV^{\gamma-1}$ is constant.

12-86 Show that in an adiabatic expansion of an ideal gas, $TP^{(1-\gamma)/\gamma}$ is constant.

12-87 An ideal gas expands adiabatically so that its temperature changes from T_1 to T_2. Show that the work it does is given by $C_V(T_1 - T_2)$.

12-88 For a monatomic ideal gas, $C_V = \frac{3}{2}$, while for a diatomic ideal gas $C_V = \frac{5}{2}$. An ideal gas at 300 K is compressed adiabatically to one-fourth its original volume. Find its final temperature if it is (a) monatomic; (b) diatomic.

PROBLEMS ON SUPPLEMENTARY TOPICS

12-89 A person produces thermal energy at a rate of 175 W. If all this heat is dissipated by evaporation of sweat, how much sweat per hour is required?

12-90 A naked person with a surface area of 1.5 m² and a skin temperature of 40°C is in a sauna at 85°C. (a) At what rate does the person absorb energy by radiation from the walls, assuming emissivity 1? (b) At what rate does the person radiate energy to the surroundings? (c) How much sweat must be evaporated per hour, assuming that no energy is transferred by convection? (Neglect the metabolic heat production.)

Additional Reading

T. C. Ruch and H. D. Patton (eds.), *Physiology and Biophysics*, vol. 3, W. B. Saunders Co., Philadelphia, 1973. Chapter 5 discusses temperature regulation in humans.

John R. Cameron and James G. Skofronick, *Medical Physics*, John Wiley & Sons, Inc., New York, 1978, Chapters 4 and 5.

J. Hansen et al., Climate Impact of Increasing Atmospheric Carbon Dioxide, *Science*, vol. 213, 1981, p. 957.

Phillip B. Allen, Conduction of Heat, *The Physics Teacher*, vol. 21, 1983, p. 569.

Albert A. Bartlett and Thomas J. Brown, Death in a Hot Tub: The Physics of Heat Stroke, *The American Journal of Physics*, vol. 51, 1983, p. 127.

Scientific American articles:

Robert L. Sproull, The Conduction of Heat in Solids, December 1962, p. 92.

David M. Gates, Heat Transfer in Plants, December 1965, p. 76.

G. Yale Eastman, The Heat Pipe, May 1968, p. 38.

Arthur H. Rosenfeld and David Hafemeister, Energy-Efficient Buildings, April 1988, p. 78.

G. Neugebauer and Eric E. Becklin, The Brightest Infrared Sources, April 1973, p. 28.

Jacob Gershon-Cohen, Medical Thermography, February 1967, p. 94.

David Turnbull, The Undercooling of Liquids, January 1965, p. 38.

Laurence Irving, Adaptations to Cold, January 1966, p. 94.

T. H. Benzinger, The Human Thermostat, January 1961, p. 134.

Bernd Heinrich and George A. Bartholomew, Temperature Control in Flying Moths, June 1972, p. 70.

Francis G. Carey, Fishes with Warm Bodies, February 1973, p. 36.

Joseph T. Eastman and Arthur L. DeVries, Antarctic Fishes, November 1986, p. 106.

Bernd Heinrich, Thermoregulation in Winter Moths, March 1987, p. 104.

Stephen H. Schneider, Climate Modeling, May 1987, p. 72.

Manuel G. Velarde and Christiane Normand, Convection, July 1980, p. 92.

H. Craig Heller, Larry I. Crawshaw, and Harold T. Hammel, The Thermostat of Vertebrate Animals, August 1978, p. 102.

Knut Schmidt-Nielsen, Countercurrent Systems in Animals, May 1981, p. 118.

Bernd Heinrich, The Regulation of Temperature in the Honeybee Swarm, June 1981, p. 146.

Eric A. Newman and Peter H. Hartline, The Infrared "Vision" of Snakes, March 1982, p. 116.

Peter J. Webster, Monsoons, August 1981, p. 108.

John T. Snow, The Tornado, April 1984, p. 86.

Jearl Walker, Gismos That Apply Non-Obvious Physical Principles to the Enjoyment of Cooking, *The Amateur Scientist*, June 1984, p. 146.

Jearl Walker, What Happens When Water Boils Is a Lot More Complicated than You Might Think, *The Amateur Scientist*, December, 1982, p. 12.

Jearl Walker, The Secret of a Microwave Oven's Rapid Cooking Is Disclosed, *The Amateur Scientist*, February 1987, p. 134.

Jearl Walker, Cooking Outdoors with Simple Equipment Demonstrates Aspects of Thermal Physics, *The Amateur Scientist*, August 1985, p. 114.

Jearl Walker, Thermal Oscillators: Systems That Seesaw, Buzz or Howl Under the Influence of Heat, *The Amateur Scientist*, February 1983, p. 146.

UNIT FOUR

FLUIDS

Fluids play a unique role in our lives and in our study of science, mainly because of their characteristic of flowing and the fact that they conform to the shape of their container. In this context, we can regard both liquids and gases as fluids.

Animals transport nutrients and remove wastes via the fluids of their circulatory systems. Similarly, the transport of materials in plants occurs in fluids. The flight of birds and planes involves fluid motion, as do the weather, waves, and ocean currents.

All these phenomena can be described by applying the principles of mechanics to fluids. However, because fluids do not remain in a fixed shape and because they may be compressed, a complete analysis can become very complicated. In order to simplify matters, in this unit we assume that fluids are *incompressible*; that is, they remain constant in density. For most liquids, this is a good first approximation. For gases, we must realize that our methods will only apply to those situations where the pressure and temperature variations are small.

In the first chapter of this unit (Chapter Thirteen), we also assume that there are no frictional forces between segments of a fluid moving with respect to one another. This is fine for fluids at rest and for some applications when fluids move. However, we see in Chapter Fourteen that these frictional, or *viscous*, effects are often important. In Chapter Fifteen, we discuss some important properties arising from the intermolecular forces in fluids.

CHAPTER 13
THE MECHANICS OF NONVISCOUS FLUIDS

In this chapter, we discuss fluids at rest and nonviscous (frictionless) fluids in motion. We first develop an understanding of why an object may either sink or float in a fluid at rest. We then develop *Bernoulli's equation*, which puts work and energy concepts into a form suitable for fluids. This is the central point of this chapter and can be used, for example, to understand why fluids in connected containers tend to have the same surface levels and how fluids flow from one place to another.

An important condition on this discussion is the assumption that the fluid is incompressible: a given mass of fluid always occupies the same volume though its shape may change. This condition is described mathematically by the *equation of continuity*, which simply states that the amount of fluid entering a tube must equal the amount leaving. This equation plays an important part in our discussions.

In mechanics, we found that if we could identify the forces acting on an object or objects, we could then predict the subsequent motion or describe the state of equilibrium. For our discussion of fluids, we use the same philosophy, but we need to take account of the fact that a given mass of fluid does not have a fixed shape. This complication is handled by using the *density* and *pressure* instead of the mass and force concepts we used previously.

The definitions of the density (the mass per unit volume) and the pressure (the force per unit area) in Sections 3.2 and 10.3, respectively, should be reviewed in preparation for this chapter. Typical densities of fluids are given in Table 13.1.

13.1 | ARCHIMEDES' PRINCIPLE

An object floating or submerged in a fluid experiences an upward or *buoyant* force due to the fluid. To understand this force, consider a segment of fluid of volume V and density ρ_0. The segment has a mass $m_0 = \rho_0 V$ and a weight $w_0 = m_0 g = \rho_0 V g$ (Fig. 13.1a). Only gravity and the surrounding fluid exert forces on the segment. Since it remains at rest, the force B exerted by the remainder of the fluid must balance the weight. *Hence the buoyant force B exerted by the surrounding fluid equals the weight of the fluid segment.*

Suppose now that this imaginary segment of fluid is replaced by a heavier object of volume V suspended by a string in the fluid (Fig. 13.1b). The surrounding fluid does not distinguish between the object and the fluid it replaces, so the buoyant force is the same. *Thus the buoyant force on the object is equal to the weight of the displaced fluid*:

$$B = w_0 = \rho_0 g V \quad \text{(Archimedes' principle)} \quad (13.1)$$

This was first deduced by Archimedes (287–212 B.C.) and is called *Archimedes' principle*.

The tension in the string is decreased when the object is placed in the fluid. If the density of the suspended object is ρ, its weight is $w = \rho g V$. The upward forces are the tension T and the buoyant force $B = \rho_0 g V$. Since it is equilibrium, $T + B = w$, and $T = w - B$, or

$$T = (\rho - \rho_0) g V \quad (13.2)$$

TABLE 13.1

Densities of some fluids at atmospheric pressure

Fluid	Density (kg m⁻³)	Temperature (°C)
Hydrogen (H_2)	0.0899	0
Helium (He)	0.178	0
Nitrogen (N_2)	1.25	0
Carbon dioxide (CO_2)	1.98	0
Oxygen (O_2)	1.43	0
Air	1.29	0
	1.20	20
	0.95	100
Water, pure	1000	0
	958	100
Sea water	1025	15
Alcohol, ethyl	791	20
Chloroform	1490	20
Ether	736	0
Linseed oil	930	0
Glycerin	1260	0
Mercury	13600	0
Whole blood	1059.5	25
Blood plasma	1026.9	25

The tension in the string is reduced by the weight of the displaced fluid. This consequence of Archimedes' principle provides a convenient way to determine densities, as seen in the next example.

Example 13.1

A piece of metal of unknown volume V is suspended from a string. Before submersion the tension in the string is 10 N. When the metal is submerged in water, the tension is 8 N. What is the density ρ of the metal?

Before submersion the tension is $T_i = \rho g V$. After submersion, the tension is $T_f = (\rho - \rho_0)gV$, where the density of water is $\rho_0 = 10^3$ kg m⁻³. Dividing the second equation by the first to eliminate V gives

$$\frac{T_f}{T_i} = \frac{\rho - \rho_0}{\rho}$$

Solving for ρ yields

$$\rho = \frac{\rho_0 T_i}{T_i - T_f}$$

$$= \frac{(1000 \text{ kg m}^{-3})(10 \text{ N})}{10 \text{ N} - 8 \text{ N}}$$

$$= 5000 \text{ kg m}^{-3}$$

An object less dense than a fluid will float partially submerged. If a portion V_S of its volume V is submerged, then the buoyant force is $\rho_0 g V_S$. This must equal the weight $\rho g V$ of the object, so $\rho_0 g V_S = \rho g V$, or

$$\frac{\rho}{\rho_0} = \frac{V_S}{V} \tag{13.3}$$

Thus the ratio of the densities is equal to the fraction of the volume submerged. This is illustrated in the following example of an iceberg.

Example 13.2

The density of ice is 920 kg m⁻³ while that of sea water is 1025 kg m⁻³. What fraction of an iceberg is submerged?

The fraction is

$$\frac{V_S}{V} = \frac{\rho}{\rho_0} = \frac{920 \text{ kg m}^{-3}}{1025 \text{ kg m}^{-3}} = 0.898$$

Almost 90 percent of the iceberg is submerged.

Balloons provide another illustration of Archimedes' principle.

Example 13.3

A child holds a helium-filled rubber balloon with a volume of 10 litres = 0.01 m³ in air at 0°C (Fig. 13.2a). Neglect the weight of the rubber and string and the buoyant force of the air on the child. (a) How great a force must she exert to keep the balloon from rising? (b) How many such balloons would it take to lift a 20-kg child?

(a) According to Table 13.1, at 0°C the density of helium is 0.178 kg m⁻³, and the density of air is 1.29 kg m⁻³. The weight of the helium $w = \rho_{He} g V$ is less than the upward buoyant force $B = \rho_{air} g V$, since

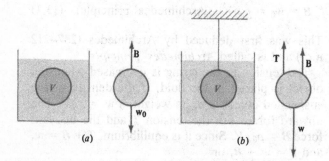

(a)   (b)

Figure 13.1. (a) An imaginary segment of fluid with the forces acting on it. (b) An object suspended by a string in a fluid and the forces acting on it.

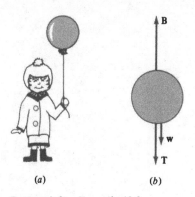

Figure 13.2.   Example 13.3.

air is denser. Hence the child must pull down on the balloon with a force T to keep it from rising (Fig. 13.2b). If the balloon remains at rest, $B = T + w$, and

$$T = B - w = \rho_{air}gV - \rho_{He}gV$$
$$= (1.29 \text{ kg m}^{-3} - 0.178 \text{ kg m}^{-3})(9.8 \text{ m s}^{-2})(0.01 \text{ m}^3)$$
$$= 0.109 \text{ N}$$

This is the force she must exert on the string. Alternatively, if she hung this much weight on the end of the string, the balloon would remain at rest.

(b) Her weight is $w = mg = (20 \text{ kg})(9.8 \text{ m s}^{-2}) = 196 \text{ N}$. Since each balloon can support 0.109 N, the number of balloons needed to balance her weight is

$$\frac{196}{0.109} = 1800$$

Note that it is easy to check that the neglected buoyant force of the air on the child is small. However, the weight of the rubber and string for the 1800 balloons would be a significant factor if somebody tried to verify this calculation experimentally.

13.2 | THE EQUATION OF CONTINUITY; STREAMLINE FLOW

Consider a situation where an incompressible fluid completely fills a channel such as a pipe or an artery. Then if more fluid enters one end of the channel, an equal amount must leave the other end. This principle, which can be put into various mathematical forms, is called the *equation of continuity*. It will be quite useful in many of our discussions.

Quantitative statements about fluid flow are made in terms of the *flow rate Q*, the volume of fluid flowing past a point in a channel per unit time:

$$Q = \frac{\Delta V}{\Delta t} \tag{13.4}$$

The S.I. units of flow rate are cubic metres per second (m³ s⁻¹). If an incompressible fluid enters one end of a channel at a rate Q_1, it must leave the other end at a rate Q_2, which is the same. Thus the equation of continuity can be written as

$$Q_1 = Q_2 \tag{13.5}$$

For example, if 1 m³ s⁻¹ enters, then 1 m³ s⁻¹ must leave.

This can be put into a more useful form if all the fluid in the channel is moving with a uniform velocity v. Consider a section of a tube with a constant cross-sectional area A (Fig. 13.3). In a time Δt, the fluid moves a distance $\Delta x = v \, \Delta t$, and the volume of fluid leaving the tube is $\Delta V = A \, \Delta x = Av \, \Delta t$. Alternatively, ΔV equals the flow rate Q times the time interval Δt, or $\Delta V = Q \, \Delta t$. Comparing these expressions for ΔV, we see that

$$Q = Av \tag{13.6}$$

The flow rate equals the cross-sectional area of the channel times the velocity of the fluid.

For a channel whose cross section changes from A_1 to A_2, this result together with $Q_1 = Q_2$ gives another form of the equation of continuity,

$$A_1v_1 = A_2v_2 \tag{13.7}$$

The product of the cross-sectional area and the velocity of the fluid is constant. If at some point A decreases, v must increase. For example, if the area is halved, then the velocity doubles.

Usually the flow velocity is not uniform in a channel. For example, in the next chapter we will encounter situations where the fluid near the walls of the channel is moving at a lower speed than the fluid

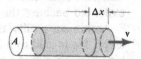

Figure 13.3.   The flow rate in a tube is $Q = Av$.

Archimedes was a mathematical and scientific genius whose equal did not appear until Newton, 2000 years later. Born the son of an astronomer, his relationship with King Hiero II of Syracuse afforded him both independent means and the attention of a man of power.

Archimedes is best remembered for his ingenious machines, which captured the popular imagination, played a role in the wartime defense of Syracuse from the Romans, and in the end resulted in larger than life stories about him. For example, the siege of Syracuse by the Romans during the Carthaginian war lasted three years, largely because of the defenses developed by Archimedes. It is said that he developed giant reflecting mirrors that focused sunlight on the Roman ships, setting them on fire. Giant cranes were also used to lift and upset ships. The war ended badly for Archimedes, as he is said to have been stabbed to death by one of the conquering Roman soldiers. At the time, he was doing geometry in the sand and refused to be disturbed.

Many of the stories about Archimedes' inventions are distorted because he himself considered them beneath the dignity of the pure scientist and never left any written record of them. His written testaments include treatises on geometry, where he approached the foundations of calculus, equilibrium and the center of gravity, and hydrostatics.

The principle of hydrostatics that carries his name grew from a problem concerning the gold content of a crown made for Hiero. Archimedes was asked to determine whether the crown was pure gold or was adulterated with silver. After much thought, he realized while at the public baths that he could measure the volume of the crown very accurately by placing it in water and measuring the amount displaced. He then compared the weight of the crown with the weight of an equal volume of gold. This discovery apparently had at least two immediate results. The idea so excited him that Archimedes dashed home naked shouting "Eureka, eureka," and the goldsmith was executed because the crown was not pure.

Archimedes fully understood and demonstrated the importance of the lever. He is said to have arranged a lever and pulley system with which the king himself pulled a large ship onto the shore. His work on the lever and on the importance of the center of gravity laid much of the groundwork for modern mechanics.

near its center. The equation of continuity still holds for such cases if it is written in terms of the average flow velocity $\bar{v}$. The flow rate is $Q = A\bar{v}$, and at two points in a channel, $A_1\bar{v}_1 = A_2\bar{v}_2$.

These relationships are illustrated in the following example.

Example 13.4

A water pipe leading up to a hose has a radius of 1 cm. Water leaves the hose at a rate of 3 litres per minute. (a) Find the velocity of the water in the pipe. (b) The hose has a radius of 0.5 cm. What is the velocity of the water in the hose?

(a) The velocity (strictly speaking, the average velocity) can be found from the flow rate and the area. The flow rate is the same in the hose and in the pipe. Using 1 litre = 0.001 m³ and 1 min = 60 s, the flow rate is

$$Q = \frac{\Delta V}{\Delta t} = \frac{0.003 \text{ m}^3}{60 \text{ s}}$$

$$= 5 \times 10^{-5} \text{ m s}^{-1}$$

We will call the velocity and area in the pipe v_1 and A_1, respectively. Then with $Q = Av$, we have

$$v_1 = \frac{Q}{A_1} = \frac{Q}{\pi r_1^2}$$

$$= \frac{5 \times 10^{-5} \text{ m s}^{-1}}{\pi (0.01 \text{ m})^2} = 0.159 \text{ m s}^{-1}$$

(b) The flow rate is constant, so $A_1 v_1 = A_2 v_2$, and the velocity v_2 in the hose is

$$v_2 = v_1 \frac{A_1}{A_2} = v_1 \frac{\pi r_1^2}{\pi r_2^2} = v_1 \left(\frac{r_1}{r_2}\right)^2$$

$$= (0.159 \text{ m s}^{-1}) \frac{1}{(0.5)^2} = 0.636 \text{ m s}^{-1}$$

The water flows faster in the narrower channel.

Streamline Flow
A type of fluid flow, called *streamline flow*, is most readily discussed quantitatively and is important in many applications. It is best defined by imagining a simple experiment. Suppose we use a very fine eyedropper to inject some ink into a fluid, without interrupting the flow (Fig. 13.4a). If the ink line formed in this way does not disperse or mix but remains narrow and well defined, the flow is called *streamline*. If several eyedroppers injected ink side by side, the ink pattern might look like Fig. 13.4b. Finally, we can imagine a *tube* of streamlines, as in Fig. 13.4c. The fluid in this

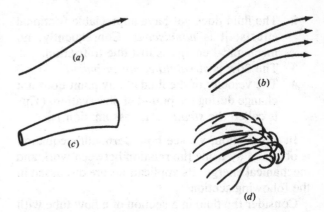

Figure 13.4. (a) A single streamline. (b) A group of adjacent streamlines. (c) A flow tube. The walls of the tube are composed of streamlines. (d) Turbulent flow.

tube is undergoing streamline flow. If, instead, the ink lines swirl and mix, the flow is said to be *turbulent* (Fig. 13.4d).

The tube is a useful concept because, by definition, the streamlines do not cross one another; no fluid flows into or out of the sides of the tube. Accordingly, the equation of continuity can be applied to this flow tube, and *the product* Av *is the same at all points in the flow tube*. The property of streamline flow is used in the next section.

13.3 | BERNOULLI'S EQUATION

We now consider Bernoulli's equation.* It states the consequences of the principle that the work done on a fluid as it flows from one place to another is equal to the change in its mechanical energy. Bernoulli's equation can be used under the following conditions:

1 The fluid is *incompressible*; its density remains constant.

---

* This important equation is usually said to have first been derived in the 1730s by Daniel Bernoulli (1700–1783). However, it may actually have been obtained somewhat earlier by his father Johann Bernoulli (1667–1748). In any case, the brilliant mathematician Leonhard Euler (1707–1783) provided the first completely rigorous derivation some years later. For a discussion of an unusual family squabble and episode in the history of science, see the preface by Hunter Rouse to the English translation of *Hydrodynamics* by Daniel Bernoulli and *Hydraulics* by Johann Bernoulli, Dover Publications, Inc., New York, 1968.

2   The fluid does not have appreciable frictional effects; it is *nonviscous*. Consequently, no mechanical energy is lost due to friction.

3   The flow is *streamline, not turbulent*.

4   The velocity of the fluid at any point does not change during the period of observation. (This is called the *steady-state* assumption.)

In this section, we see how Bernoulli's equation is obtained by using the relation between work and mechanical energy. Its applications are discussed in the following sections.

Consider the fluid in a section of a flow tube with a constant cross section A (Fig. 13.5a). According to the equation of continuity, the product Av remains constant. Thus the velocity v does not change as the fluid moves through the tube, and its kinetic energy remains the same. However, the potential energy changes as the fluid rises.

The net force on the fluid in the tube due to the surrounding fluid is the cross-sectional area A times the difference in pressures on the ends, or $(P_a - P_b)A$. If the fluid in the section moves a short distance Δx, then the work done on it is the product of the force and the displacement $(P_a - P_b)A \Delta x$. Since $A \Delta x$ is the volume ΔV of the fluid leaving the section (Fig. 13.5b), the work done on the fluid is

$$W = (P_a - P_b) \Delta V$$

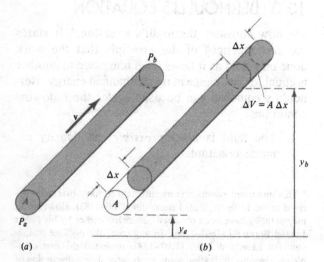

Figure 13.5.   (*a*) The fluid in a section of flow tube with a constant cross section has the same velocity everywhere. (*b*) The fluid has moved a short distance Δx.

This work done on the fluid must equal the increase $\Delta \mathcal{U}$ in its potential energy. $\Delta \mathcal{U}$ can be calculated if we note that the fluid leaving the section has a mass $\rho \Delta V$ and a potential energy $(\rho \Delta V)gy_b$, while the fluid entering at the bottom of the section has a potential energy $(\rho \Delta V)gy_a$. Thus $\Delta \mathcal{U} = \rho g \Delta V(y_b - y_a)$. Equating this to W, we have

$$P_a - P_b = \rho g(y_b - y_a)$$

or

$$P_a + \rho g y_a = P_b + \rho g y_b \qquad (v = \text{constant}) \quad (13.8)$$

Thus the pressure P plus the *potential energy per unit volume* $\rho g y$ of the fluid is the same everywhere in the flow tube if the velocity remains constant.

More generally, if the cross-sectional area of the flow tube changes, the fluid velocity v and *kinetic energy per unit volume* $\frac{1}{2}\rho v^2$ will also change. The work done on the fluid must then be set equal to the change in the potential plus kinetic energy of the fluid. The result is *Bernoulli's equation*,

$$P_a + \rho g y_a + \tfrac{1}{2}\rho v_a^2 = P_b + \rho g y_b + \tfrac{1}{2}\rho v_b^2 \quad (13.9)$$

The pressure plus the total mechanical energy per unit volume, $P + \rho g y + \frac{1}{2}\rho v^2$, *is the same everywhere in a flow tube.*

Bernoulli's equation is the main result of this chapter. As is clear from its derivation, it is a restatement of the relationship between work and energy in a form suitable for use in the physics of fluids. Examples of its uses are given in the following sections.

13.4 | STATIC CONSEQUENCES OF BERNOULLI'S EQUATION

We first examine the implications of Bernoulli's equation when the fluid is at rest, so $v = 0$ and $P + \rho g y$ is constant.

Fluid at Rest in a Container | Suppose fluid is at rest in a container shaped like the one in Fig. 13.6. We can find the pressure at a point B in terms of the pressure at the surface and the depth. To do this, we calculate $P + \rho g y$ at points A and B, choosing the y axis so that $y = 0$ at the bottom of the container. At A, the pressure is atmospheric

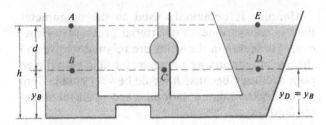

Figure 13.6. Fluid at rest in a container. As is explained in the text, the level of the surface of the fluid in each of the segments is the same.

pressure, P_{atm}; at B, the pressure is P_B. Thus $P_{atm} + \rho g h = P_B + \rho g y_B$ or, with $h - y_B = d$,

$$P_B = P_{atm} + \rho g d \qquad (13.10)$$

This result shows that the pressure at a depth d in a fluid at rest is equal to the surface pressure plus the potential energy density change $\rho g d$ corresponding to this depth. Equation 13.10 can also be interpreted as a statement of the force on a unit area a distance d below the surface of the liquid. The force per unit area P_B is the sum of two terms: P_{atm}, the pressure due to the atmosphere, and $\rho g d$, the pressure due to the weight of the liquid above the point B.

Calculating $P + \rho g y$ at points B and D gives $P_B + \rho g y_B = P_D + \rho g y_D$. Or, since $y_B = y_D$,

$$P_B = P_D$$

Thus the pressure at the same depth at two places in a fluid at rest is the same. In particular, since points A and E are both at atmospheric pressure, the surface of the liquid is at the same height at both points. Thus the surfaces of liquids at rest in connected containers of any shape must be at the same height if they are open to the atmosphere.

These ideas are illustrated in the next two examples.

Example 13.5

What is the pressure on a swimmer 5 m below the surface of a lake?

Using $d = 5$ m and $\rho = 1000$ kg m^{-3}, we find

$P_B = P_{atm} + \rho g d$
   $= 1.013 \times 10^5$ Pa + $(1000$ kg m$^{-3})(9.8$ m s$^{-2})(5$ m$)$
   $= 1.50 \times 10^5$ Pa

Example 13.6

The pressure 1 m above a floor is measured to be normal atmospheric pressure, 1.013×10^5 Pa. How much greater is the pressure at the floor if the temperature is 0° C?

Here, $d = 1$ m. From Table 13.1 the density of air at atmospheric pressure and 0° C is 1.29 kg m^{-3}. Thus

$P_B = P_{atm} + \rho g d$
   $= 1.013 \times 10^5$ Pa + $(1.29$ kg m$^{-3})(9.8$ m s$^{-2})(1$ m$)$
   $= (1.013 \times 10^5 + 12.6)$ Pa

Thus the pressure at the floor is greater by 12.6 Pa, or by about 1 part in 10^4, which is negligible for most purposes. The pressure change is small, unlike in the preceding example, because the density of the air is very small compared to that of a typical liquid. The properties of gases were discussed in Chapter Ten, with the assumption that the pressure in a gas-filled container is the same everywhere. This is usually a good approximation. However, if the pressure of a gas is measured at two very different heights, a considerable difference will be observed. For example, the atmospheric pressure at Aspen, Colorado, which is 2500 m above sea level, is about 80 percent of the sea-level pressure.

The Manometer | The open-tube manometer is a U-shaped tube used for measuring gas pressures. It contains a liquid that may be mercury or, for measurements of low pressures, water or oil. One end of the tube is open to the atmosphere, and the other end is in contact with the gas in which the pressure is to be measured (Fig. 13.7). The manometer can also be used to measure pressures in a liquid, provided that the liquid does not mix with the manometer fluid.

Measuring heights from the base of the U-tube, $P + \rho g y$ is $P + \rho g y_1$ at the left surface of the column

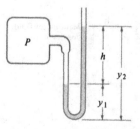

Figure 13.7. The open-tube manometer.

and $P_{atm} + \rho g y_2$ at the right surface. Equating these,

$$P + \rho g y_1 = P_{atm} + \rho g y_2$$

or

$$\begin{aligned} P &= P_{atm} + \rho g(y_2 - y_1) \\ &= P_{atm} + \rho g h \end{aligned} \qquad (13.11)$$

Thus a measurement of the height difference h of the two columns determines the gas pressure P. In a blood pressure gauge, the sphygmomanometer, the pressure measured is that in an air sack wrapped around the upper arm. We discuss such measurements in Section 13.6.

The pressure P in Eq. 13.11 is the *absolute pressure*. The difference between this and atmospheric pressure, $P - P_{atm}$, is the *gauge pressure*. The gauge pressure is then exactly equal to $\rho g h$.

Blood Pressure Measurements by Cannulation

In many experiments with anesthetized animals, the blood pressure in an artery or vein is measured by the direct insertion into the vessel of a *cannula*, which is a small glass or plastic tube containing saline solution plus an anticlotting agent. The saline solution, in turn, is in contact with the fluid in a manometer. It is necessary to have the surface of contact between the saline solution and the manometer fluid either at the same level as the insertion point of the cannula or to correct for the height difference (Fig. 13.8). Calculating $P + \rho g y$ at suitable points (Problem 13-57), it follows that the blood pressure P_B is given by

$$P_B = P_{atm} + \rho g h - \rho_s g h' \qquad (13.12)$$

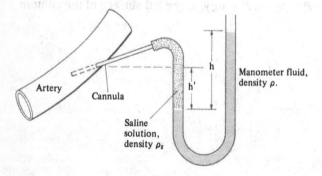

Figure 13.8. Measurement of blood pressure by cannulation.

Mercury is commonly used as the manometer fluid in measurements of arterial pressures. However, pressures in the veins are relatively low, and the use of mercury as a manometer fluid would give poor accuracy because h would be very small. Consequently the saline solution is used as the manometer fluid.

Physiologists often use electromanometers or *pressure transducers*. A transducer is a device that converts energy from one form to another; for example, a loudspeaker converts electrical energy to acoustical energy. In a pressure transducer, the manometer fluid pushes against a membrane instead of rising up a tube. The flexing of the membrane is proportional to the pressure, and the extent that the membrane is flexed is translated into an electrical signal. This signal drives a recorder that automatically gives a continuous record of the blood pressure.

13.5 | THE ROLE OF GRAVITY IN THE CIRCULATION

When animals evolved to the point where they spent a significant amount of time standing upright, a surprising number of changes in the circulatory system were required. Of particular importance is the venous system used to return blood from the lower extremities to the heart. Humans have adapted to the problems of moving blood upward a large distance against the force of gravity. Animals that have not, such as snakes, eels, and even rabbits, will die if held head upward; the blood remains in the lower extremities, and the heart receives no blood from the venous system.

Figure 13.9 shows what is observed if a person's large arteries are cannulated. In the reclining position, the pressures everywhere are almost the same. The small pressure drop between the heart and the feet or brain is due to the viscous forces. However, the pressures at the three points are quite different in the standing person, reflecting the large difference in their heights.

Because the viscous effects are small, we can use Bernoulli's equation, $P + \rho g h + \frac{1}{2}\rho v^2 = $ constant, to analyze this situation. The velocities in the three arteries are small and roughly equal, so the $\frac{1}{2}\rho v^2$

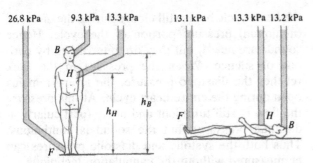

26.8 kPa   9.3 kPa 13.3 kPa   13.1 kPa   13.3 kPa 13.2 kPa

Figure 13.9. Schematic view of the results of cannulation of arteries in various parts of the human body when standing and reclining. The pressures shown are averaged over the heart cycle.

term can be ignored. Hence the gauge pressures at the heart P_H, at the foot P_F, and at the brain P_B are related by

$$P_F = P_H + \rho g h_H = P_B + \rho g h_B \quad (13.13)$$

where ρ is the density of blood.

In discussions of the circulatory system, it is convenient to measure pressures in *kilopascals*, kPa, where 1 kPa = 10^3 Pa is a multiple of the basic S.I. pressure unit. Many discussions of the circulatory system use an older unit, the *torr*; 1 torr = 0.1333 kPa. In Eq. 13.13, typical values for adults are $h_H = 1.3$ m and $h_B = 1.7$ m. With $\rho = 1.0595 \times 10^3$ kg m^{-3}, we find

$$
\begin{aligned}
P_F - P_H &= \rho g h_H \\
&= (1.0595 \times 10^3 \text{ kg m}^{-3})(9.8 \text{ m s}^{-2})(1.3 \text{ m}) \\
&= 1.35 \times 10^4 \text{ Pa} = 13.5 \text{ kPa}
\end{aligned}
$$

p_H is typically 13.3 kPa, so $P_F \approx 26.8$ kPa. In a similar way we find $P_B = 9.3$ kPa. This explains why the pressures in the lower and upper parts of the body are very different when the person is standing, although they are about equal when reclining.

This situation poses several problems. The most important are the tendency for blood to drain out of the venous side of the upper body back to the heart and the difficulty of lifting blood from the lower extremities up to the heart. To retard drainage from the venous side of the upper body, particularly from the brain where constant volume and flow rate are extremely important, the muscles surrounding the veins contract and cause constriction. In the lower extremities, because the veins have a much larger

capacity for passive expansion and blood storage than do arteries, the problem is to pump the blood "uphill." The veins in the extremities contain valves that open when blood flows toward the heart and close if the blood moves away from the heart. Blood is returned to the heart, at least partially, by the pumping action associated with breathing and by the flexing of skeletal muscle, as in walking. These muscle contractions squeeze the veins, and the valves ensure that the resultant blood flow is toward the heart. The importance of this is illustrated by the fact that a soldier who is required to stand at strict attention may faint because of insufficient venous return. Once horizontal, the pressures are equalized, and the soldier regains consciousness.

Effects of Acceleration | When a person in an erect position experiences an upward acceleration a, the effective weight becomes $m(g + a)$. Applying Bernoulli's equation to the brain and heart with g replaced by $(g + a)$,

$$P_B + \rho(g + a)h_B = P_H + \rho(g + a)h_B$$

or

$$P_B = P_H - \rho(g + a)(h_B - h_H) \quad (13.14)$$

Thus the blood pressure in the brain will be reduced even farther. It has been found that if a is two or three times g, a human will lose consciousness because of the collapse of arteries in the brain. This factor limits the speed with which a pilot can pull out of a dive (Chapter Five). A related experience is the feeling of light-headedness that sometimes occurs when one suddenly stands up. Since muscular movement is required to activate the venous return mechanism, blood will tend to collect in the lower veins until normal activity is resumed.

13.6 | BLOOD PRESSURE MEASUREMENTS USING THE SPHYGMOMANOMETER

Since the upper arm of a human is at about the same level as the heart, blood pressure measurements made there give values close to those near the

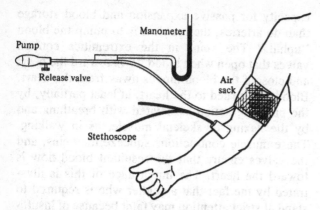

Figure 13.10. The use of the sphygmomanometer for measuring blood pressures.

heart. Also, the fact that the upper arm contains a single bone makes the brachial artery located there easy to compress. The pressure needed to do this is measured with the familiar instrument called the *sphygmomanometer*, which is convenient and painless (Fig. 13.10).

During a complete heart pumping cycle, the pressure in the heart and circulatory system goes through both a maximum (as the blood is pumped from the heart) and a minimum (as the heart relaxes and fills with blood returned from the veins). The sphygmomanometer is used to measure these extreme pressures. Its use relies on the fact that blood flow in the arteries is not always streamline. When the arteries are constricted and the blood flow rate is large, the flow becomes turbulent. This turbulent flow is noisy and can be heard with a stethoscope.

In the sphygmomanometer, the gauge pressure in an air sack wrapped around the upper arm is measured using a manometer or a dial pressure gauge. The pressure in the sack is first increased until the brachial artery is closed entirely. The pressure in the sack is then slowly reduced, while a stethoscope is used to listen for noises in the brachial artery below the sack. When the pressure is slightly below the *systolic* (peak) pressure produced by the heart, the artery will open briefly. Because it is only partially opened, the flow velocity is high and turbulent and therefore noisy. This resulting noise is heard as a tapping sound.

When the pressure in the sack is lowered further, the artery remains open during longer portions of

the heart cycle but is still closed during the *diastolic* (minimum) pressure portion of the cycle. Hence sounds are heard, but they are interrupted by periods of silence. When the pressure in the sack reaches the diastolic pressure, the artery remains open during the entire heart cycle. At this pressure the flow is still turbulent and noisy (particularly at diastolic pressure), but the sound is continuous. Thus both the systolic and diastolic pressures can be measured without the cannulation technique.

Blood pressures are usually presented as systolic/diastolic ratios. Typical readings for a resting healthy adult are about 120/80 in torr and 16/11 in kPa. The borderline for high blood pressure (hypertension) is usually defined to be 140/90 in torr and 19/12 in kPa. Pressures appreciably above that level require medical attention, because prolonged high blood pressure can lead to serious damage of the heart or other organs before a person is aware of any problem. Increasing emphasis has been placed in recent years on mass screenings to discover people with undetected high blood pressure.

13.7 | DYNAMIC CONSEQUENCES OF BERNOULLI'S EQUATION

Sometimes the velocity terms in Bernoulli's equation, Eq. 13.9, are comparable to or larger than the gravitational terms. In this section and the next, we discuss examples where these dynamic terms are important.

A very simple demonstration of the effect of flow rate on pressure can be performed by the reader. Tear a piece of paper in half and, holding the halves side by side about 2 cm apart, as in Fig. 13.11, blow

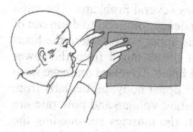

Figure 13.11. A simple test of Bernoulli's equation. When you blow between two pieces of paper, they move closer together.

Figure 13.12. Hancock Building in Boston, Massachusetts. In 1973, a prominent feature of the Boston skyline was this unoccupied skyscraper with its windows covered with plywood (white rectangles) because of the unfortunate tendency of the windowpanes to blow out during high winds. The pressure differences predicted by Bernoulli's equation provide a partial explanation of this phenomenon. Major design changes were required to complete and occupy the building. (Bill Chaplis / © AP / Wide World Photos)

between them. Since the flow is horizontal, the terms in Bernoulli's equation containing y are equal and cancel. If the pressure and velocity between the sheets are P_B and v_B, respectively, and those outside the sheets are P_0 and v_0, then

$$P_B + \tfrac{1}{2}\rho v_B^2 = P_0 + \tfrac{1}{2}\rho v_0^2$$

If we rearrange these terms, we find

$$P_0 - P_B = \tfrac{1}{2}\rho(v_B^2 - v_0^2)$$

Now v_B is larger than v_0, so the right-hand side is positive and P_0 must be greater than P_B. This pressure difference results in the sheets moving toward one another, as you will observe if you try it.

The fact that the pressure drops when the velocity increases for a fluid moving at a constant height is a consequence of energy conservation. The kinetic energy can increase only if work is done. That means that a net force must act on a segment of the moving fluid and that the pressure must be lower at the end where the velocity is higher.

This pressure drop associated with increasing fluid velocities has many everyday implications. For example, you may have been in a car that was pulled toward a large truck as it passed you on a highway. The air rushes around the vehicles and the portion passing between them is forced through a small area. From the continuity equation, Eq. 13.7, this air moves faster as a result. In the region of high velocity, the pressure is reduced and the vehicles are pulled toward each other. From the point of view of the drivers, it is rather like blowing between sheets of paper.

Part of the problem with windows blowing out in Boston's Hancock Building was due to the relatively low pressure outside (compared to inside), which occurred when the wind was blowing (Fig. 13.12).

The next example illustrates what happens when both the kinetic energy and potential energy terms play a role. Additional examples of Bernoulli's equation are given in the next section.

Example 13.7

Water enters a basement through a pipe 2 cm in radius at an absolute pressure of 3 atm. A hose with a 0.5-cm radius is used to water plants 10 m above the basement. Find the velocity of the water as it leaves the hose.

Applying Bernoulli's equation to the flow in the hose and in the pipe,

$$P_h + \rho g y_h + \tfrac{1}{2}\rho v_h^2 = P_p + \rho g y_p + \tfrac{1}{2}\rho v_p^2$$

or

$$v_h^2 = v_p^2 + 2g(y_p - y_h) + \frac{2(P_p - P_h)}{\rho} \qquad \text{(i)}$$

We know the difference in heights, $(y_p - y_h) = -10$ m. Water leaves the hose at atmospheric pressure, so $P_h = 1$ atm. We can eliminate v_p with the aid of the equation of continuity, $A_p v_p = A_h v_h$. Thus

$$v_p = v_h \frac{A_h}{A_p} = v_h \frac{\pi r_h^2}{\pi r_p^2}$$

$$= v_h \left(\frac{r_h}{r_p}\right)^2 = v_h \left(\frac{0.5}{2}\right)^2 = \frac{v_h}{16}$$

Substituting in Eq. i and solving for v_h, we find

$$v_h^2 = \frac{2(256)\{g(y_p - y_h) + [(P_p - P_h)/\rho]\}}{255}$$

$$= (2.008) \left[(9.8 \text{ m s}^{-2})(-10 \text{ m}) \right.$$

$$\left. + \frac{(3 \text{ atm} - 1 \text{ atm})(1.01 \times 10^5 \text{ Pa atm}^{-1})}{(1000 \text{ kg m}^{-3})} \right]$$

$$v_h = 14.45 \text{ m s}^{-1}$$

This is velocity of the water as it leaves the hose.

13.8 | FLOW METERS

In this section, we apply the complete Bernoulli equation to two kinds of flow meters. With minor modifications, they can be used to measure the flow in blood vessels, the airspeed of planes, and many other flow rates.

The Venturi Tube | In a *venturi tube*, fluid flows through different cross-sectional areas in different portions of the tube. When the tube narrows, the fluid velocity increases. Then, according to Bernoulli's equation, the pressure drops. Measurement of this pressure change determines the fluid velocity. The pressure measurement can be made with narrow vertical columns inserted into the main tube (Fig. 13.13a) or with electrical sensors.

Before using Bernoulli's equation, we must clear up a difficulty that arises because the liquid in the columns is at rest while the liquid in the tube is

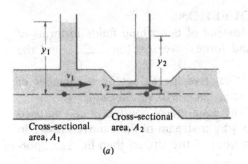

(a)

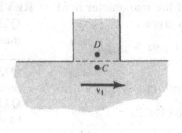

(b)

Figure 13.13. (a) Venturi tube. (b) Enlarged view of the region where column 1 connects to the flow tube.

moving. Bernoulli's equation cannot be applied directly to relate the pressures at points C and D in Fig. 13.13b because the fluid at the two points is not in the same streamline. However, if the pressures were unequal, fluid would flow from one point to the other. Since this does not occur, $P_C = P_D$. Thus the pressure in the columns is the same as the pressure in the streamline.

Bernoulli's equation requires that $P + \rho g y + \frac{1}{2}\rho v^2$ is the same everywhere in a flow tube. Applying Bernoulli's equation to points at the same height in the flow stream just below the columns,

$$P_1 + \frac{1}{2}\rho v_1^2 = P_2 + \frac{1}{2}\rho v_2^2$$

From the continuity equation, $A_1 v_1 = A_2 v_2$, or

$$v_2 = \frac{A_1}{A_2} v_1 \qquad (13.15)$$

Using this expression for v_2, the preceding equation can be written as

$$P_1 - P_2 = \frac{1}{2}\rho v_1^2\left(\frac{A_1^2}{A_2^2} - 1\right) \qquad (13.16)$$

Thus a measurement of $P_1 - P_2$ and knowledge of the areas determines v_1; v_2 can also be found using Eq. 13.15.

The following example shows how this flow meter can be used to measure the velocity of the blood in an artery.

Example 13.8

The flow of blood through a large artery in a dog is diverted through a venturi flow meter. The wider part of the flow meter has an area $A_1 = 0.08$ cm², which equals the cross-sectional area of the artery. The narrower part of the flow meter has an area $A_2 = 0.04$ cm². The pressure drop in the flow meter is 25 Pa. What is the velocity v_1 of the blood in the artery?

The ratio of the areas A_1/A_2 is dimensionless and has the value $0.08/0.04 = 2$. From Table 13.1, the density of whole blood is 1059.5 kg m⁻³. Dropping the units, Eq. 13.16 becomes

$$25 = \frac{1}{2}(1059.5)v_1^2(2^2 - 1)$$

Solving for v_1,

$$v_1 = \sqrt{\frac{(2)(25)}{(1059.5)(2^2 - 1)}} = 0.125 \text{ m s}^{-1}$$

The Prandtl Tube

Figure 13.14 shows a *Prandtl tube* inserted in a flow stream. It interrupts the flow pattern very little except at point A, where the fluid has zero velocity. At point B the velocity is assumed to be the streamline flow velocity v. From Bernoulli's equation, neglecting the small difference in heights at A and B,

$$P_A - P_B = \frac{1}{2}\rho v^2$$

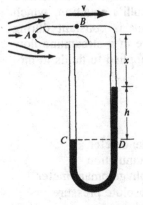

Figure 13.14. A Prandtl tube in a constant velocity flow stream. The right arm of the U-tube connects to the chamber opening at B. The left connects to the opening at A, where the fluid has zero velocity.

where ρ is the fluid density. If the manometer fluid has density ρ_m, then $P_C = P_D$ gives

$$P_A + \rho g(h + x) = P_B + \rho g x + \rho_m g h$$

or

$$P_A - P_B = (\rho_m - \rho)gh$$

Comparing the two expressions for $P_A - P_B$,

$$\tfrac{1}{2}\rho v^2 = (\rho_m - \rho)gh \qquad (13.17)$$

Thus a manometer reading gives a direct measurement of the flow velocity. As in the venturi tube, electromanometers may be employed instead of the open-tube manometer.

SUMMARY

The fundamental variables used in describing fluids are the density and pressure. The density is the mass per unit volume. The pressure is the force per unit area that a segment of fluid exerts on adjacent segments.

The definition of the pressure leads directly to Archimedes' principle: the buoyant force on an object in a fluid is equal to the weight of the fluid displaced.

If a fluid may be treated as incompressible, the flow satisfies the continuity equation. This equation states that when fluid flows in a tube, the flow rate Q must be constant even if the tube dimensions change, so the product Av is constant.

With the additional assumption that frictional or viscous forces are unimportant, we can equate the work done on a fluid to its change in mechanical energy. The result is Bernoulli's equation, which states that $P + \rho g y + \tfrac{1}{2}\rho v^2$ is constant during steady-state flow everywhere in a streamline flow tube. This equation can be applied to fluids in motion or at rest.

Checklist

Define or explain:

buoyant force	manometer
Archimedes' principle	cannulation
equation of continuity	sphygmomanometer
streamline flow	absolute pressure
Bernoulli's equation	gauge pressure
flow rate	venturi tube
flow tube	Prandtl tube
turbulent flow	

REVIEW QUESTIONS

Q13-1   Instead of describing fluids in terms of masses and forces, we use the _____ and the _____.

Q13-2   What two forces act on a segment of fluid at rest to keep it in equilibrium?

Q13-3   The equation of continuity can be used to explain why a stream of fluid moves faster in _____ portions of the stream than in _____ portions.

Q13-4   If a stream of fluid has its cross-sectional area halved in a certain region, its average velocity is _____.

Q13-5   In Bernoulli's equation, the terms $\rho g y + \tfrac{1}{2}\rho v^2$ represent the _____.

Q13-6   In static fluids, the pressure difference between two points in the fluid is determined by the fluid density g and the _____.

Q13-7   A person suffering from "light-headedness" can be relieved by _____.

Q13-8   When using the sphygmomanometer, why is the blood pressure usually measured in the upper arm?

Q13-9   In fluid motion, regions of high average velocity tend to have _____ pressures.

Q13-10   In a pipe with a constriction in it, will the fluid pressure in the constriction be higher or lower than in the wider part of the pipe?

EXERCISES

Section 13.1 | Archimedes' Principle

13-1   A 75-kg man just floats in fresh water with virtually all of his body below the surface. What is his volume?

13-2   An object weighs 100 N in air and 75 N in water. What is the relative density of the object?

13-3   A log of mass 40 kg is dropped into a river at 0°C. If the relative density of the log is 0.8, what will be the volume of the log above the surface?

13-4   A man has a mass of 80 kg. In pure water, he floats fully submerged. (a) When he is in the air, what is the buoyant force on him due to the atmosphere? (Use the tabulated densities at 0°C.) (b) When he is submerged in sea water, what is the buoyant force on him due to the water?

13-5   An oil tanker has a draft (depth under water) of 25 m in salt water. Assuming its sides are vertical, find its draft in fresh water.

13-6 The Goodyear blimp "America" has a volume of 5400 m^3. The mass of the empty blimp structure is 4250 kg. Assume the temperature is 0°C. (a) When the blimp is filled with helium, how large is the buoyant force on it? (b) What additional mass can be taken onto the blimp and still have it lift off the ground?

Section 13.2 | The Equation of Continuity; Streamline Flow

13-7 A water main with a radius of 0.15 m contains water with an average velocity of 3 m s^{-1}. What is the flow rate in the water main?

13-8 In a decorative fountain in a garden, water is shot nearly vertically from a pipe. The stream of water broadens out as it rises. Explain why.

13-9 A hose delivers 20 litres of water per minute. The diameter of its nozzle is 1 cm. What is the average velocity of the water as it leaves the nozzle?

13-10 The radius of a water pipe decreases from 0.2 m to 0.1 m. If the average velocity in the wider portion is 3 m s^{-1}, find the average velocity in the narrower region.

13-11 A garden hose with a cross-sectional area of 2 cm^2 has a flow of 200 cm^3 s^{-1}. What is the average velocity of the water?

13-12 A blood vessel of radius r splits into four vessels, each with radius $r/3$. If the average velocity in the larger vessel is v, find the average velocity in each of the smaller vessels.

Section 13.3 | Bernoulli's Equation

13-13 Can Bernoulli's equation be used to describe the flow of water through a rapids in a stream? Explain.

13-14 A baseball is thrown by a pitcher and curves as it approaches the batter. Can Bernoulli's equation be applied to this problem using a reference frame (a) moving with the ball; (b) fixed with respect to the ground? Explain.

13-15 If water moves through pipes of constant cross section from the basement to the first floor, will the pressure stay the same? Explain.

13-16 Does it matter if one uses gauge or absolute pressures in applying Bernoulli's equation? Explain.

13-17 In deriving Bernoulli's equation, we equated the work done on the fluid in a tube to its change in potential and kinetic energy. (a) If dissipative forces are present, how does that affect the pressure changes as a fluid moves along the tube? (b) Are dissipative forces more or less significant as the flow velocity increases? Explain.

Section 13.4 | Static Consequences of Bernoulli's Equation

13-18 Deep-sea photographs have been made at depths of 8000 m. (a) What is the pressure at this depth? (b) What is the force on the camera window if it measures 0.1 m by 0.15 m?

13-19 What is the pressure difference between the heart and brain of a giraffe if the brain is 2 m above the heart? (Assume that the velocity of the blood is the same in both locations.)

13-20 Estimate the drop in the pressure of the atmosphere as one goes from sea level to the top of a hill 500 m high if the temperature is 0°C.

13-21 How high can water rise in the pipes of a building if the gauge pressure at the ground floor is 2 × 10^5 Pa?

13-22 A submarine dives to a depth of 100 m in sea water. What gauge pressure is necessary to expel water from its ballast tanks?

13-23 A certain pressure can support a column of pure water 0.7 m high. The same pressure will support a column of saline solution 0.6 m high. What is the density of the saline solution?

13-24 A large artery is cannulated, and a saline solution of density 1300 kg m^{-3} is used as the manometer fluid. What is the blood pressure (gauge pressure) if the height difference in the manometer tubes is 0.67 m?

Section 13.5 | The Role of Gravity in the Circulation

13-25 When a man stands, his brain is 0.5 m above his heart. If he bends so that his brain is 0.4 m below his heart, by how much does the blood pressure in his brain change?

13-26 Explain why we are uncomfortable when we bend with our heads lower than our heart.

13-27 A pilot is accelerating downward at four times the acceleration of gravity during a maneuver. If he is erect, what is the blood pressure in his brain?

13-28   A jet pilot pulls his plane out of a dive in such a way that his upward acceleration is $3g$. What would you predict as the blood pressure in the brain?

13-29   At what acceleration would you expect the blood pressure in the brain to drop to zero for an erect person? (Assume there are no body mechanisms operating to compensate for such conditions.)

13-30   (a) If an elevator accelerates upward at 9.8 m s^{-2}, what is the average blood pressure in the brain? What is the average blood pressure in the feet? Assume the person is standing. (b) If the elevator accelerates downward at 9.8 m s^{-2}, what is the average blood pressure in the brain and feet?

Section 13.6 | Blood Pressure Measurements Using the Sphygmomanometer

13-31   If a sphygmomanometer were used to measure the blood pressure in the leg of a man sitting at rest, would the results give the pressure at the heart? Explain.

13-32   Suppose a man ran into a doctor's office and immediately had his blood pressure measured. Would a reading above the normal 120/80 in torr (or 16/11 in kPa) indicate he is suffering from high blood pressure? Explain.

Section 13.7 | Dynamic Consequences of Bernoulli's Equation

13-33   (a) In Example 13.7, what is the flow rate? (b) Find the flow rate when the hose is 20 m above the basement.

13-34   Water flows through a horizontal pipe that gradually tapers. At a point where the radius is R, the velocity is 2 m s^{-1} and the pressure is 3 atm. At a point where the radius is $R/2$, find (a) the velocity; (b) the pressure.

Section 13.8 | Flow Meters

13-35   A venturi tube has a radius of 1 cm in its narrower portion and 2 cm in its wider sections. The velocity of water in the wider sections is 0.1 m s^{-1}. Find (a) the pressure drop; (b) the velocity in the narrower portion.

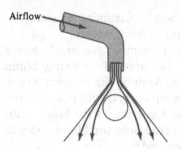

Figure 13.15.   A Ping-Pong ball stays in an inverted funnel when air is blown through it. Exercise 13-38.

13-36   A Prandtl tube flow meter is used to measure the aortic blood velocity of a dog. If water is the manometer fluid, what is the height difference in the manometer tube when the blood velocity is 0.1 m s^{-1}?

13-37   Suppose a venturi tube is equipped with vertical columns, as in Fig. 13.13. Show that

$$g(y_1 - y_2) = \tfrac{1}{2}v_1^2 \left(\frac{A_1^2}{A_2^2} - 1 \right)$$

13-38   In a standard classroom demonstration, a Ping-Pong ball will stay in an upside-down funnel when a stream of air passes through the funnel from the small end (Fig. 13.15). Explain briefly why the ball does not fall.

PROBLEMS

13-39   A block of oak weighs 90 N in air. A lead weight weighs 130 N when immersed in water. When attached together, they weigh 100 N in water. What is the density of the wood?

13-40   Find the initial acceleration of an iron ball with a density 8 times that of water when placed in (a) water; (b) mercury. (c) What is the direction of the acceleration in each case?

13-41   A man rows out to the center of a lake with a number of large rocks in the boat. He then throws them overboard. When he finishes, has the lake level risen, fallen, or remained the same? Explain.

13-42   An ice cube floats in a glass filled to the top with water. What happens to the water level as the ice cube melts? Explain.

13-43 A hot air balloon is a sphere of radius 8 m. The air inside it has a temperature of 60° C. How large a mass can the balloon lift when the outside air temperature is 20° C? (Assume the air is an ideal gas.)

13-44 A submarine has a mass of 2×10^7 kg and floats in sea water so that 10 percent of its volume is above the surface. How large a mass of water must be taken into its tanks so that it can submerge?

13-45 A garden hose with its nozzle closed has a tiny hole. A fine stream of water shoots from the hole and rises 10 m. What is the pressure in the hose?

13-46 A *hydrometer* is an instrument used to measure the density of battery acid and other liquids. It consists of a weighted sphere and an attached cylinder, and it is used by floating the hydrometer in the liquid of interest (Fig. 13.16). Find the density of the liquid in terms of the mass of the hydrometer M, the radius of the sphere R, the radius of the cylinder r, the length of the cylinder L, and the length of the cylinder above the surface x.

13-47 A *hydraulic jack* is constructed as shown in Fig. 13.17. The cross-sectional areas of the pistons are A_1 and A_2. Show that in equilibrium the forces F_1 and F_2 are related by

$$\frac{F_1}{A_1} = \frac{F_2}{A_2}$$

13-48 A hydraulic lift similar to that in Fig. 13.17 with pistons of cross-sectional areas

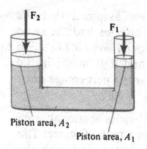

Piston area, A_2

Piston area, A_1

Figure 13.17. A hydraulic jack. Problems 13-47 and 13-48.

1500 cm^2 and 75 cm^2 is used to lift a dentist's chair of weight 1500 N. (a) What force is necessary on the small piston to raise the chair? (b) What distance must the small piston be moved to raise the chair 0.1 m?

13-49 A tank contains oxygen gas at 0° C. The pressure at the bottom of the tank is 100 atm. If the tank is 1 m tall, what is the pressure at the top? (Assume the average density of the oxygen is 143 kg m^{-3}.)

13-50 A *barometer* is constructed by filling a long tube with mercury and then inverting it, open side down, in a container of mercury exposed to the atmosphere (Fig. 13.18). (a) Show that atmospheric pressure P_{atm} is equal to $\rho g h$, where ρ is the density of mercury. (b) What is the height h when $P_{atm} = 1.013 \times 10^5$ Pa?

13-51 During a whole-blood transfusion, the needle is inserted in a vein where the pressure is 2000 Pa. At what height must the blood container be placed, relative to the vein, so that the blood just enters the vein?

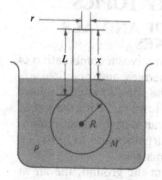

Figure 13.16. A hydrometer. Problem 13-46.

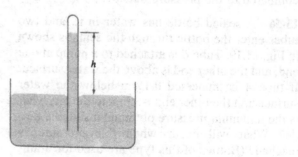

Figure 13.18. A mercury barometer. Problem 13-50.

13-52 In Section 13.5, we assumed that the blood in the various large arteries had the same velocities. Suppose the velocity were 0.2 m s^{-1} in the artery near the heart and 0.01 m s^{-1} in the artery near the foot. How large a percentage error would that introduce in $P_F - P_H$?

*13-53 A *siphon tube* of cross-sectional area 3×10^{-4} m^2 is used to drain a tank of water. The tube is initially filled with water, and with the ends closed, one end is placed in the tank 0.25 m below the water surface. The other end is outside the tank and at a distance of 0.5 m below the immersed end. (a) What is the velocity of the water flowing out of the tube shortly after the ends are opened? (b) Is the flow continuous? (c) What is the velocity of the water when the water surface in the tank is 0.1 m above the immersed end?

*13-54 A siphon tube is filled with gasoline and closed at each end. One end is inserted in a gasoline tank 0.3 m below the surface of the gasoline. The other end is placed 0.2 m below the end in the tank and both ends of the tube are opened. The tube has an inner cross-sectional areas of 4×10^{-4} m^2. The density of gasoline is 680 kg m^{-3}. (a) What is the velocity of the gasoline in the tube shortly after it is opened? (b) What is the corresponding rate of flow?

13-55 An artery or vein may become partially blocked or *occluded*, when some material reduces the vessel radius over a small portion of its length. (a) Does the velocity in the occluded region change? (b) Does the pressure in the occluded region change? (c) Describe the possible sequence of events in the flexible vessel if the pressure inside the vessel becomes very small compared to the pressure outside.

13-56 A sealed bottle has water in it, and two tubes enter the bottle through the seal, as shown in Fig. 13.19. Tube B is attached to a pump at one end, and the other end is above the water surface. If tube A is immersed 0.15 m below the water surface and the other end is open to the air, what is the minimum pressure obtained inside the bottle? What will occur when this pressure is reached? (Bottles of this type are used for draining unwanted fluids from the body, such as those

Figure 13.19. Problem 13-56.

that collect in and around the lungs in some diseases.)

13-57 The blood pressure in an artery is measured by cannulation (Fig. 13.8). The cannula contains saline solution of density ρ_s, and the manometer fluid has density ρ. Show that the blood pressure is given by Eq. 13.12.

ANSWERS TO REVIEW QUESTIONS

Q13-1, density; pressure; **Q13-2**, weight, buoyant force; **Q13-3**, narrower, wider; **Q13-4**, doubled; **Q13-5**, mechanical energy per unit volume; **Q13-6**, height difference; **Q13-7**, lowering their head; **Q13-8**, it is close to the pressure in the heart; **Q13-9**, low; **Q13-10**, lower.

SUPPLEMENTARY TOPICS

13.9 | THE FLIGHT OF ANIMALS AND AIRPLANES

A full discussion of flight involves a combination of elaborate mathematical theories and practical experimentation because the flow patterns about wings are very complex. However, with the aid of Bernoulli's equation, we can derive some qualitative results applicable to airplanes and to birds, insects, and other flying animals.

If we watch a plane from the ground, the air at any point is disturbed briefly as the plane passes and

Figure 13.20. (a) Streamline flow about a wing. (b) Turbulence, loss of lift, and stalling result from large angles of attack. (Gary S. Settles and Jason Listak / Photo Researchers, Inc.)

then returns to its original state. Since the fluid motion is not constant in time, we may not apply Bernoulli's equation to our observations. However, to an observer on the plane, the fluid flow is steady in time. *Thus Bernoulli's equation holds true, provided we apply it in a coordinate frame at rest relative to the plane.*

Fig. 13.20*a* shows the flow of air of initial velocity v and density ρ about a stationary airplane wing. The streamlines above the wing are closer together than those below the wing. According to the continuity equation, this indicates that the velocity v_a of the air above the wing is greater than that below, v_b (Fig. 13.21). Since Bernoulli's equation says that $P + \rho gy + \frac{1}{2}\rho v^2$ is constant in a streamline, the pressure P_a above the wing must be less than the pressure P_b below. (We can neglect the ρgy terms, since the wing thickness is small.) Then the upward

lift force F_L on a wing area A is

$$F_L = (P_b - P_a)A = \tfrac{1}{2}A\rho(v_a^2 - v_b^2) \quad (13.18)$$

This expression describes the lift force on the wing, but it does not explain its origin. It is clear from Figs. 13.20 and 13.21 that the air is deflected

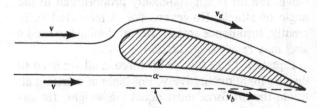

Figure 13.21. The air above the wing moves at a speed v_a, which is greater than the speed below the wing v_b. Both v_a and v_b are proportional to v.

Figure 13.22. The angle of attack is increased just before the jet takes off. (Colouria Media / Alamy Limited)

downward by the wing. According to Newton's third law of motion, this means that the air exerts an equal and opposite upward reaction force on the wing. This downward deflection of the air occurs even with flat or upside-down wings.

Equation 13.18 is only useful if the velocities v_a and v_b can be measured, because there is no simple way to predict these from the initial air flow velocity v. However, we would expect that both v_a and v_b are proportional to the initial air velocity v. Hence $v_a^2 - v_b^2$ is proportional to v^2, and the lift force can be rewritten as

$$F_L = \tfrac{1}{2}AC_L\rho v^2 \qquad (13.19)$$

The proportionality factor C_L is called the *lift coefficient*. In a few idealized cases, it can be predicted theoretically using advanced mathematical techniques, but it is usually measured experimentally. The lift coefficient depends in a complicated way on the shape of the wing and on its *angle of attack* α, the angle between the wing and the direction of the airflow. When the angle of attack is small, the lift is approximately proportional to the angle of attack. However, if α is increased sufficiently, turbulence sets in, the lift diminishes, and a stall may result (Fig. 13.20*b*).

Equation 13.19 for the lift force is all we need to discuss flight qualitatively. For flight at constant altitude the lift force must equal the weight. Jet aircraft have high flight speeds, so the area A and the angle α can be made small, thereby reducing dissipative drag forces. However, this also has the effect of making the takeoff velocities quite high. In order to take off at moderate speeds, jets must make an abrupt increase in the angle of attack after reaching a critical speed (Fig. 13.22). This increases the lift coefficient and permits takeoff. Propeller planes, which fly at lower speeds, have proportionately larger wing areas as well as larger angles of attack. This makes the lift coefficient large enough to permit takeoff at lower speeds.

Because the wings of flying animals provide both propulsion and lift, their design and motion are complex. The lift force is still determined by $F_L = \tfrac{1}{2}AC_L\rho v^2$ but A, C_L, and v vary during different phases of the wing motion (Fig. 13.23).

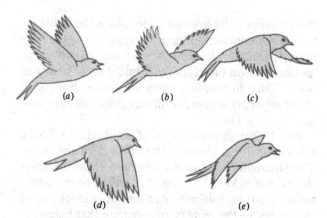

Figure 13.23. During level flight, the downstroke provides the greatest propulsive and lift force. The front of the wing is lower than the trailing edge during the sequence (*a*) through (*d*). During the upstroke, the wing is pulled forward and up, nearly parallel to the plane of the wing. Little propulsive or lift force is obtained, but little flying speed is lost, and little energy is required to execute the motion. (Adapted from Alexander, *Animal Mechanics*.)

Figure 13.24. A large bird builds up speed before taking off. (John Devries / Photo Researchers, Inc.)

Scaling and Flight

Small birds, such as sparrows, and larger ones, such as ducks, take off and land quite differently. We can understand this by once again using the scaling model. We use the simplest form of scaling, which assumes that the volume or weight of a bird varies as the cube of a characteristic length l. (The more complicated scaling procedure of Chapter Eight, which employs the buckling strength criterion $l \propto r^{2/3}$, leads to results very similar to those we obtain here.)

The cross-sectional area A of a wing varies as l^2, so the lift force $F_L = \frac{1}{2}AC_L\rho v^2$ varies as Av^2 or l^2v^2. In level flight, F_L must equal the weight of the bird, $w \propto l^3$. Equating these, we have $l^2v^2 \propto l^3$, or

$$v \propto l^{1/2} \qquad (13.20)$$

This result means that a large bird has a greater minimum flying speed than a small bird. A small bird can jump into the air and achieve flying speed with a beat or two of its wings. A large bird first builds up speed by taxiing along the ground or water (Fig. 13.24) or by descending from a high perch.

Birds of greatly different sizes are compared in the next example.

Example 13.9

The minimum flying speed for a swift is about 21 km h^{-1}. An ostrich has a characteristic length about 25 times that of the swift. According to the scaling model, what is its minimum flying speed?

The minimum flying speed varies as $l^{1/2}$, so

$$\frac{v(\text{ostrich})}{v(\text{swift})} = \frac{l(\text{ostrich})^{1/2}}{l(\text{swift})^{1/2}} = 25^{1/2} = 5$$

Thus $v(\text{ostrich}) = 5v(\text{swift}) = 5(21 \text{ km h}^{-1}) = 105$ km h^{-1}. It is not hard to see why ostriches cannot fly!

The largest present-day flying animal is the albatross, which has a wingspan of 3.3 m. Larger flying reptiles (pterosaurs) existed during the age of dinosaurs. The largest discovered to date had a wingspan of 15.5 m! It is speculated that such large creatures could not take off except by scaling cliffs and soaring off them like gliders. Their continued stay aloft would then depend on their ability to locate rising air currents or columns (Fig. 13.25).

13.10 | MODELS OF THE EARTH'S CRUST

How does the earth support large-scale features such as mountains and missing mass areas such as

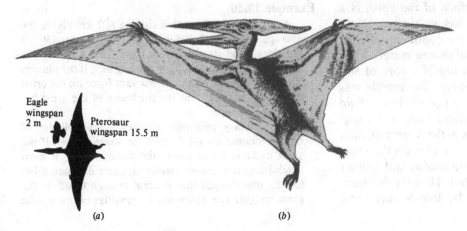

Eagle wingspan 2 m

Pterosaur wingspan 15.5 m

(a)

(b)

Figure 13.25. The pterosaur. (a) The size scale. (b) An artist's reconstruction of the pterosaur hunting its prey.

ocean basins? In both cases there is a significant difference from the average in the weight being supported by the underlying structures of the earth. Understanding these forces and means of support goes hand in hand with modern discussions of moving, solid continental plates.

Two effects are responsible for the support of mountain ranges. One is essentially Archimedes' principle, as was realized after a topographical survey of northern India was conducted in 1860. Distances were measured both by triangulation and by astronomical methods. In several instances large differences were found between the results of the two methods of measurement. These differences were traced ultimately to Archimedes' principle.

Triangulation employs line-of-sight measurements, while the astronomical method uses measurements of a star's position from two locations. Although it was first thought that the line-of-sight measurements were wrong because of the accumulation of errors as the data were added, it was discovered that the astronomical measurements were the problem.

These measurements require knowing the direction of the highest point in the sky or the *zenith* at each location. The zenith was assumed to be along the extension of a plumb line. In fact, errors occurred because the weight at the end of the plumb line was attracted toward the Himalayas more strongly at locations closest to the mountains. Thus the determination of the direction of the zenith had to be corrected for the proximity of the massive mountains. When attempts were made to do this, it was found that the mass of the mountains was less than expected.

It was known that the surface of the earth is a solid layer, the *crust*, which has an average thickness of about 33 km beneath the continents. Below the crust is a very deep layer of denser material, the *mantle*, which in turn lies on top of a core of still different composition and density. The mantle was thought to behave as a plastic or highly viscous fluid that could be deformed and flow. This model suggests that the solid crust floats in the denser mantle. Using Archimedes' principle, one expects then that the crust is thicker beneath mountains and thinner below ocean basins (Fig. 13.26a). Thus the displacement of high-density mantle by low-density crust

reduced the gravitational forces on the plumb lines used in the astronomical survey.

An equivalent description is in terms of the principle of *isostasy*. The earth is in *isostatic equilibrium*: the weight of any imaginary, narrow column extending up from the earth's center is the same as that of any other column of equal cross section. If this were not true, adjustments in the core, mantle, and crust would occur to restore equilibrium. This principle is equivalent to Archimedes' principle, since an object floating in a fluid displaces its own weight. Hence any column containing the object weighs as much as a similar adjoining column that contains only the fluid.

Surface variations such as mountains and ocean trenches will usually be reflected in local variations in the crust and mantle, not the core. This is because such features are on the order of 1 to 10 km high while the mantle is about 3000 km thick. It is unlikely that small features at the surface will affect the core.

This model suggests that beneath mountains one should find that the crust extends down, or intrudes, into the mantle. In terms of Archimedes' principle, a sufficient amount of the less dense, solid crust must displace fluid mantle material below the normal crust depth so that the buoyant force supports the mountains. In terms of isostasy, enough crust must replace mantle to bring an imaginary cylinder through that part of the surface back to equilibrium.

This buoyant support of raised masses on the earth's surface is illustrated in the following example.

Example 13.10

A plateau on the earth's surface is 2 km above the average continental surface. The crust is normally 33 km thick, and its density is $\rho_c = 2800$ kg m^{-3}; the density of the mantle is $\rho_m = 3300$ kg m^{-3}. If the plateau is entirely supported by the buoyant force on the crust due to the mantle, find the thickness of the crust beneath the plateau.

The isostasy principle requires every cylinder of cross-sectional area A to have the same weight. If the crust extends 2 km above the surroundings, it must extend into the denser mantle an extra distance d below its usual depth that is great enough to offset the extra weight. The difference in densities of the mantle

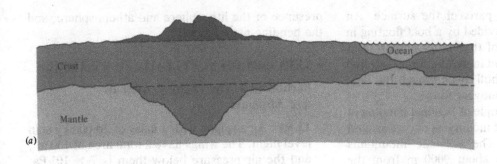

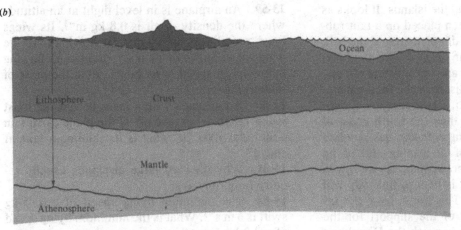

Figure 13.26. (*a*) The buoyant or isostatic model of support of surface structures on the earth. The crust thickens beneath mountains, floating on the denser, fluidlike mantle. The same model predicts that the crust thins beneath oceans. (*b*) The regional bending model suggests that the solid lithosphere bends downward beneath mountainous regions. In this model, the crust and part of the mantle are both solid. Elastic forces support the additional weight of the mountains.

and crust is (3300 − 2800) kg m⁻³ = 500 kg m⁻³. Thus isostasy requires

$$(500 \text{ kg m}^{-3})gdA = (2800 \text{ kg m}^{-3})g(2 \text{ km})A$$

$$d = 11.2 \text{ km}$$

This is the extra depth. Adding it to the average crust depth of 33 km and the 2 km for the plateau itself, we find 46.2 km for the total depth of the mantle below the plateau.

Isostasy predicts that the thickness of the earth's crust beneath the Himalayan crust should be about 80 km thick. In fact it is only about 55 km thick. This discrepancy means either that the isostatic model is totally invalid or that it does not explain all of the support.

A model for the additional support was developed in the 1930s. This model fits in with the modern evidence of crustal plates being formed in one location and moving across the earth's surface, although it was not originally expressed in terms of plates. It suggests that local surface variations are partially compensated for on a regional basis (Fig. 13.26*b*) and also builds on the fact that the mantle is much more solid than was earlier thought.

It is now known that the surface of the earth is covered by a solid layer called the *lithosphere*, beneath which is a liquid layer called the *athenosphere*. Unlike the crust–mantle boundary, their boundary does not display a density change; rather, it is more like a solid–fluid boundary. The crust and mantle are still believed to be layers of different densities, but the strict characterization of the crust as solid and mantle as fluid has been abandoned. In some areas parts of the crust are fluid, and in others much of the mantle is solid. The average thickness of the lithosphere is about 75 km.

The model suggests that beneath mountains the rigid lithosphere bends, just as a board does when weight is placed on it. This bending extends beyond the local region of the mountains themselves and results in a force sufficient to support the mountains partially. In other words, the mountains are supported in part by other parts of the surface. An interesting analogy is provided by a boat floating in the water. A small part of the hull is supported in part by buoyant forces and in part by forces exerted by the remainder of the hull, even though the boat overall is supported by buoyant forces.

A very distinctive example of regional bending of the lithosphere to support mountains occurs around the Hawaiian Islands. The volcanic mountains forming the islands rise about 9000 m from the ocean floor. The ocean floor has a trench several hundred metres deep around the islands. It looks as though a heavy ball had been placed on a taut rubber sheet and the sheet had dimpled around the ball.

The Himalayas provide an example of a combination of the regional bending and the isostatic effects. They are the result of a collision of the Indian plate, which, millions of years ago, was thousands of kilometres south of what was then the south coast of Asia, Tibet. That continuing collision has resulted in the bending downward of the leading edge of the Indian plate beneath the Tibetan plate. As we saw in Chapter Eight, a plate that is bent in this way will produce an upward force. This force, from the Indian plate, provides some of the support for the Himalayas. Since the crust beneath the Himalayas is about 55 km thick, the isostatic model accounts for the remainder.

The Alps of Europe and the Canadian Rockies appear to be largely supported by regional bending of the lithosphere. On the other hand, the Tibetan plateau, which abuts the Himalayas on the north side and averages 5 km in height, is supported by a very thick crust that extends far into the mantle. To a rather good approximation, the isostatic model describes the support of the Tibetan plateau. It also appears to explain the support of the Andes mountains in South America. These mountains seem to be supported by an extensive intrusion of the crust into the mantle.

It is interesting to note that the use of Archimedes' principle by itself does not fully account for the variations in the thickness of the crust. Nevertheless, it describes the observations well enough so that when one finds places where its predictions fail, it is worth further study to examine why this happens. It is just this sort of reasoning that has led to our current understanding of surface plates, the

presence of the lithosphere and athenosphere, and the bending plate model.

EXERCISES ON SUPPLEMENTARY TOPICS

Section 13.9 | The Flight of Animals and Airplanes

13-58   An airplane with a mass of 20,000 kg is in level flight. The wings have a total area of 100 m^2, and the air pressure below them is 7×10^4 Pa. What is the pressure above the wings?

13-59   An airplane is in level flight at an altitude where the density of air is 0.8 kg m^{-3}. Its wings have a total area of 100 m^2. Air flowing over the wings has a speed of 80 m s^{-1}, and the air flowing below has a speed of 65 m s^{-1}. Find the mass of the airplane.

13-60   An airplane with a mass of 9000 kg must reach 120 m s^{-1} to take off. If the plane carries an additional 7000 kg, what is its minimum takeoff speed?

13-61   Why do very large airplanes usually require long runways?

13-62   The minimum flying speed of a 0.05-kg swift is 6 m s^{-1}. What is the minimum flying speed of a 3.2-kg goose?

13-63   The swift has a wingspread of about 0.25 m, while the pterosaur had a wingspread of about 16 m. The swift has a minimum flying speed of 6 m s^{-1}. (a) Using scaling, estimate the minimum flying speed of the pterosaur. (b) Comment on the validity of the scaling model for this case.

Section 13.10 | Models of the Earth's Crust

13-64   The crust is normally 33 km thick and its density is $\rho_c = 2800$ kg m^{-3}; the density of the mantle is $\rho_m = 3300$ kg m^{-3}. The average height of the Himalayan Mountains is 7 km. What is the predicted thickness of the crust if the isostatic model fully explains the support of the mountains? (The crust beneath the Himalayas is actually about 55 km thick.)

13-65   The Tibetan plateau averages 5 km above the average continental surface, and the crust varies between 65 km and 70 km in thickness. Does the isostatic model explain the support of the Tibetan plateau? (Use the data in the preceding exercise.)

13-66 (a) The crust beneath the Andes mountains is about 70 km thick. What would be the average height of the Andean mountains if they were supported entirely by buoyant forces? (Use the data in Exercise 13.64.) (b) The highest peaks in the Andes are about 6.8 km high. Does it appear that the isostatic model fully accounts for the support of these mountains?

13-67 Assume that the isostatic model can be used to predict the thickness of the crust beneath ocean basins. What is the maximum average depth of such a basin if buoyant forces entirely support the crust? (Use the data in Exercise 13-64. The density of sea water is 1025 kg m^{-3}.)

PROBLEMS ON SUPPLEMENTARY TOPICS

13-68 The power required for a hummingbird (or a helicopter) to hover is

$$\mathcal{P}_H = \sqrt{\frac{w^3}{2\rho A}}$$

where w is the weight of the bird, A is the area swept out by its wings as they swing back and forth, and ρ is the density of air. (a) Show that the right-hand side has the dimensions of power. (b) Can another expression of the form $w^a\rho^b A^c$ be found that has dimensions of power?

13-69 Using the formula for the power expended in hovering flight in Problem 13-68, show how this power scales with the characteristic length of a bird.

13-70 A hovering hummingbird of mass 3×10^{-3} kg has wings that sweep out an area of 3×10^{-3} m^2. (a) Using the formula in Problem 13-68, find the power expended at 20° C. (b) The bird's muscles have a mass of 0.75×10^{-3} kg. Compare their power output with the 80 W kg^{-1} maximum output of human muscle.

13-71 Apply the scaling law $l^3 \propto r^2$ to the flight of birds. How is Eq. 13.20 modified?

Additional Reading

R. McNeill Alexander, *Animal Mechanics*, University of Washington Press, Seattle, 1968, Chapters 5 and 6.

R. A. R. Tricker and B. J. K. Tricker, *The Science of Movement*, Mills and Boon Ltd., London, 1967.

Arthur C. Guyton, *Circulatory Physiology*: *Cardiac Output and Its Regulation*, W. B. Saunders Co., Philadelphia and London, 1963. Chapter 6 discusses flow meters and their use.

John R. Cameron and James G. Skofronick, *Medical Physics*, John Wiley & Sons, Inc., New York, 1978. Chapter 6 discusses pressures in the body.

Alan P. Lightman, If Birds Can Fly Why Can't I? *Science 83*, October 1983, p. 22. Scaling and flight.

Lloyd Hunter, The Art and Physics of Soaring, *Physics Today*, April 1984, p. 34.

William F. Allman, Pitching Rainbows, *Science 82*, October 1982, p. 32. The physics of the curve ball in baseball.

Klaus Weltner, A Comparison of Explanations of the Aerodynamic Lifting Force, *The American Journal of Physics*, vol. 55, 1987, p. 50.

C. R. O'Dell, The Physics of Aerobatic Flight, *Physics Today*, November 1987, p. 24.

Robert G. Watts and Ricardo Ferrar, The Lateral Force on a Spinning Sphere: Aerodynamics of a Curve Ball, *The American Journal of Physics*, vol. 55, 1987, p. 40.

Scientific American articles:

Wallace O. Fenn, The Mechanism of Breathing, January 1960, p. 138.

J. V. Warren, The Physiology of the Giraffe, November 1974, p. 96.

Stanley J. Dudrick and Jonathan E. Rhoads, Total Intravenous Feeding, May 1972, p. 73.

D. James Baker, Jr., Models of Oceanic Circulation, January 1970, p. 114.

Suk Ki Hong and Hermann Rahn, The Diving Women of Korea and Japan, May 1967, p. 34.

Eric Denton, The Buoyancy of Marine Animals, July 1960, p. 118.

John P. Campbell, Vertical-Takeoff Aircraft, August 1960, p. 41.

John H. Storer, Bird Aerodynamics, April 1952, p. 24.

Carl Welty, Birds as Flying Machines, March 1955, p. 88.

Clarence D. Cone, Jr., The Soaring Flight of Birds, April 1962, p. 130.

David S. Smith, The Flight Muscles of Insects, June 1965, p. 76.

Alfred Gessow, The Changing Helicopter, April 1967, p. 38.

Felix Hess, The Aerodynamics of Boomerangs, November 1968, p. 124.

Vance A. Tucker, The Energetics of Bird Flight, May 1969, p. 70.

C. J. Pennynick, The Soaring Flight of Vultures, December 1973, p. 102.

Torkel Weis-Fogh, Universal Mechanisms for the Generation of Lift in Flying Animals, November 1975, p. 80.

Wann Langston, Jr., Pterosaurs, February 1981, p. 122.

Jearl Walker, Boomerangs! How to Make Them and Also How They Fly, *The Amateur Scientist*, March 1979, p. 162.

Jearl Walker, More on Boomerangs, Including Their Connection with the Dimpled Golf Ball, *The Amateur Scientist*, April 1979, p. 180.

Jearl Walker, Introducing the Musha, the Double Lozenge, and a Number of Other Kites to Build and Fly, *The Amateur Scientist*, February 1978, p. 156.

Ronald E. Rosenzweig, Magnetic Fluids, October 1982, p. 136. The strange properties of a liquid with magnetic particles in suspension.

Michael A. Markowski, Ultralight Airplanes, July 1982, p. 62.

Mark Drela and John S. Langford, Human-Powered Flight, November 1985, p. 144.

Jearl Walker, A Field Formula for Calculating the Speed and Flight Efficiency of a Soaring Bird, *The Amateur Scientist*, March 1985, p. 122.

A. Trevor Hodge, Siphons in Roman Aqueducts, June 1985, p. 114.

Peter Molnar, The Structure of Mountain Ranges, July 1986, p. 70.

CHAPTER 14
VISCOUS FLUID FLOW

Real fluids in motion always exhibit some effects of frictional or viscous forces. Whenever the work done against these dissipative forces is comparable to the total work done on the fluid or to its mechanical energy change, Bernoulli's equation cannot be used. Bernoulli's equation always applies for fluids at rest, since viscous forces then have no effect, but an estimate of the viscous forces must be made for moving fluids. For example, Bernoulli's equation can adequately describe the flow of blood in the large main arteries of a mammal, but not in the narrower blood vessels.

The *viscosity* of a fluid is a measure of its resistance to flow under an applied force. The greater the viscosity, the larger the force required to maintain the flow, and the more energy that is dissipated. Molasses has a high viscosity, water a smaller viscosity, and air a still smaller viscosity.

We begin this chapter by defining viscosity. We then examine the effects of viscous forces on the flow of a fluid in a tube. Viscosity is also responsible for the drag force experienced by a small object moving slowly through a fluid. Consequently, viscous forces determine the velocities of molecules and small particles in solution in a centrifuge.

14.1 | VISCOSITY

Viscosity is readily defined by considering a simple experiment. Figure 14.1 shows two flat plates separated by a thin fluid layer. If the lower plate is held fixed, a force is required to move the upper plate at a constant speed. This force is needed to overcome the viscous forces due to the liquid and is greater for

a highly viscous fluid, such as molasses, than for a less viscous fluid, such as water.

The force F is observed to be proportional to the area of the plates A and to the velocity of the upper plate Δv and inversely proportional to the plate separation Δy:

$$F = \eta A \frac{\Delta v}{\Delta y} \qquad (14.1)$$

When the layers lack the symmetry of Fig. 14.1, the ratio $\Delta v/\Delta y$ for the *velocity gradient* must be replaced by dv/dy, and Eq. 14.1 becomes

$$F = \eta A \frac{dv}{dy} \qquad (14.2)$$

The proportionality constant η (Greek letter "eta") is the viscosity. The larger the viscosity, the larger the force needed to move the plate at a constant speed. From Eq. 14.1, the dimensions, denoted by brackets [ ], of the viscosity are

$$[\eta] = \left[\frac{F/A}{\Delta v/\Delta y}\right] = \left[\frac{MLT^{-2}/L^2}{LT^{-1}/L}\right] = [ML^{-1}T^{-1}] \quad (14.3)$$

where M, L, and T stand for mass, length and time, respectively. The S.I. unit of viscosity is $1 \text{ kg m}^{-1} \text{ s}^{-1} = 1 \text{ Pa s}$.

Table 14.1 lists some typical viscosities. Usually as the temperature decreases, liquids become more viscous, as is readily observed in engine oil, honey, and other viscous fluids. By contrast, gases usually become less viscous as the temperature is lowered.

Because viscous forces are usually small, fluids are often used as lubricants to reduce friction. This is illustrated in the following example.

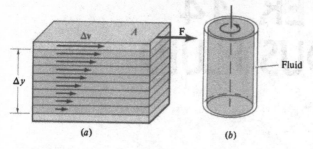

Figure 14.1. (a) Apparatus for measuring viscosity. (b) To prevent fluid leaking out, an actual measurement of viscosity uses rotating and fixed concentric cylinders.

Laminar Flow

In the type of flow illustrated by Fig. 14.1, because of the intermolecular forces, each layer moves at almost the same rate as the adjacent layer; the velocity changes continuously. Thus the fluid in contact with the moving plate has the same velocity as the plate, as indicated by the arrows. The fluid layer just below moves slightly more slowly, and each successive layer lags a bit more. The layer next to the stationary plate is at rest. This layered structure, or *laminar flow*, is the kind of streamline flow characteristic of viscous fluids at low velocities. When the fluid velocity is increased sufficiently, the flow changes its character and becomes disorganized or turbulent.

Turbulent flow is frequently undesirable because it dissipates more mechanical energy than does laminar flow. Airplanes and cars are often designed so that the flow of air around them is as steamlined as possible. Also, nature has arranged that the flow in blood vessels is normally laminar rather than turbulent. These ideas are discussed further in later sections.

Example 14.1

An air track used in physics lecture demonstrations supports a cart that rides on a thin cushion of air 1 mm = 10^{-3} m thick and 0.04 m² in area. If the viscosity of the air is 1.8×10^{-5} Pa s, find the force required to move the cart at a constant speed of 0.2 m s⁻¹.

Figure 14.1a can be used to model this apparatus, with the upper surface representing the moving cart. With Eq. 14.1, the force required is

$$F = \eta A \frac{\Delta v}{\Delta y}$$

$$= (1.8 \times 10^{-5} \text{ Pa s})(0.04 \text{ m}^2) \frac{(0.2 \text{ m s}^{-1})}{(10^{-3} \text{ m})}$$

$$= 1.44 \times 10^{-4} \text{ N}$$

This is a very small force and is consistent with the observation that an air track is nearly frictionless.

14.2 | LAMINAR FLOW IN A TUBE

Many interesting applications of the physics of fluids involve laminar flow in cylindrical tubes such as copper pipes or human arteries. In this section, we consider a formula for the flow rate called *Poiseuille's law*. It was first discovered experimentally by a physician, Jean Louis Marie Poiseuille

TABLE 14.1

Typical values of viscosity in units of pascal-seconds (Pa s)

Temperature (°C)	Castor Oil	Water	Air	Normal Blood[a]	Blood Plasma[a]
0	5.3	1.792×10^{-3}	1.71×10^{-5}		
20	0.986	1.005×10^{-3}	1.81×10^{-5}	3.015×10^{-3}	1.810×10^{-3}
37	—	0.6947×10^{-3}	1.87×10^{-5}	2.084×10^{-3}	1.257×10^{-3}
40	0.231	0.656×10^{-3}	1.90×10^{-5}		
60	0.080	0.469×10^{-3}	2.00×10^{-5}		
80	0.030	0.357×10^{-3}	2.09×10^{-5}		
100	0.017	0.284×10^{-3}	2.18×10^{-5}		

[a] The relative viscosities (η/η_{water}) of blood and of plasma remain nearly constant for temperatures between 0°C and 37°C.

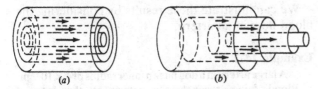

Figure 14.2. Laminar flow in a tube. The fluid in contact with the wall is at rest and successive thin cylindrical layers move with increasing speeds. The fluid at the center has the maximum velocity. If initially the fluid in the tube is as in (a), then a short time later the layers will have moved as in (b).

(1799–1869), who was investigating the flow in blood vessels. Poiseuille's law relates the flow rate to the viscosity of the fluid, the pressure drop, and the radius and length of the tube. We use it extensively in the next section in discussing the flow in blood vessels.

Consider a fluid moving through a tube slowly enough so that there is no turbulence and the flow is laminar. Just as in the case of the two flat surfaces discussed in the preceding section, the fluid in contact with the wall of the tube clings to it and is at rest. The thin, cylindrical layer of fluid adjacent to this stationary layer moves very slowly, and successive thin layers move at increasing velocities (Fig. 14.2). Hence the fluid at the center has the maximum velocity, v_{max}.

In a horizontal tube with a constant cross section, the equation of continuity implies that the average velocity $\bar{v}$ remains the same, since $Q = A\bar{v}$ must be constant. Nevertheless, the pressure drops as the fluid moves along the tube. This is because work is done against the viscous forces. If the cross section varies or if the tube is not horizontal, additional pressure changes arise in accordance with Bernoulli's equation (Fig. 14.3).

We can find the explicit velocity variation with the distance r from the axis of the tube by relating the viscous force and the pressure drop. Consider a tube with constant radius R and length l (Fig. 14.4a). The pressure drop between its ends is $\Delta P = P_1 - P_2$. If we consider a cylinder of fluid of radius r', the net driving force on it is the pressure drop times the cross-sectional area, $\Delta P\,\pi r'^2$. The surface area around the cylinder is $2\pi r'l$, so the viscous force on it is $-\eta A\,dv'/dy = -\eta(2\pi r'l)dv'/dr'$. Equating this viscous force to $\Delta P\,\pi r'^2$, we find

$$dv' = \frac{-\Delta P\, r'\,dr'}{2\eta l}$$

If we integrate the right side from r to R, the velocity goes from v to 0, since the fluid at the wall of the tube is at rest. Then we have

$$\int_v^0 dv' = \frac{-\Delta P}{2\eta l}\int_r^R r'\,dr' \quad \text{or} \quad v'\Big|_v^0 = \frac{-\Delta P}{2\eta l}\frac{r'^2}{2}\Big|_r^R$$

Thus

$$v = \frac{\Delta P}{4\eta l}(R^2 - r^2) \tag{14.4}$$

This formula for the velocity variation with r is used in sketching the velocity vectors shown in Fig. 14.2. It contains a great deal of information. We look first at the maximum velocity, which as expected occurs at $r = 0$. Its value is

$$v_{max} = \frac{\Delta P\, R^2}{4\eta l} \tag{14.5}$$

Next we calculate the flow rate Q through the tube. A thin cylindrical shell of thickness dr' has a cross-sectional area $2\pi r'dr'$ and a flow rate $dQ' = v'dA' = 2\pi r'v'dr'$ (Fig. 14.4b). Using Eq. 14.4 for

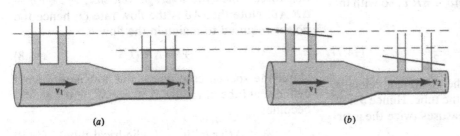

(a)   (b)

Figure 14.3. Pressures in a horizontal tube containing a moving fluid. (a) Ideal nonviscous fluid. In accordance with Bernoulli's equation, the pressure drops when the tube narrows and the average velocity increases. (b) Viscous fluid. Additional pressure drops occur due to the work done against viscous or frictional forces.

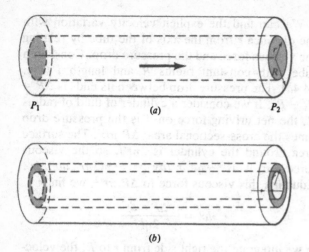

P_1 (a) P_2

(b)

Figure 14.4. (a) In equilibrium, the net force on the ends of the fluid in the cylinder must balance the viscous force opposing its motion. (b) The total flow rate is found by summing the flow rates in thin cylindrical shells.

the velocity and integrating from $r' = 0$ to $r' = R$, we obtain the flow rate (see Problem 14-40)

$$Q = \frac{\Delta P \, \pi R^4}{8\eta l} \quad \text{(Poiseuille's law)} \quad (14.6)$$

This is *Poiseuille's law*. It indicates that high viscosity leads to low flow rates, which is reasonable. The flow rate is proportional to the pressure gradient $\Delta P/l$. Note the analogy with the case of heat flow discussed in Chapter Twelve; the heat flow rate is proportional to the temperature gradient $\Delta T/l$. Also, the flow rate is proportional to R^4, which is somewhat surprising; the rate is extremely dependent on the radius of the tube. This implies, for example, that in blood vessels, moderate adjustments in the radius can produce large changes in the flow rates. Thus increasing R to $1.19R$ means a factor of $(1.19)^4 = 2$ increase in the flow rate.

Finally, we recall that the average velocity is related to the flow rate by $Q = A\bar{v} = \pi R^2 \bar{v}$, so with the formulas above,

$$\bar{v} = \frac{\Delta P \, R^2}{8\eta l} = \frac{v_{max}}{2} \quad (14.7)$$

The average velocity is half the maximum velocity, which occurs at the center of the tube. Hence a flow meter placed in the center measures twice the average velocity.

We can illustrate these results by considering the blood flow in an artery.

Example 14.2

A large artery in a dog has an inner radius of 4×10^{-3} m. Blood flows through the artery at the rate of 1 cm³ s⁻¹ = 10^{-6} m³ s⁻¹. Find (a) the average and maximum velocities of the blood; (b) the pressure drop in a 0.1-m-long segment of the artery.

(a) The average velocity is

$$\bar{v} = \frac{Q}{A} = \frac{Q}{\pi R^2}$$

$$= \frac{10^{-6} \text{ m}^3 \text{ s}^{-1}}{\pi (4 \times 10^{-3} \text{ m})^2}$$

$$= 1.99 \times 10^{-2} \text{ m s}^{-1}$$

The maximum velocity occurs at the center of the artery and is

$$v_{max} = 2\bar{v} = 2(1.99 \times 10^{-2} \text{ m s}^{-1})$$

$$= 3.98 \times 10^{-2} \text{ m s}^{-1}$$

(b) From Table 14.1, $\eta = 2.084 \times 10^{-3}$ Pa s. Thus the pressure drop is found from $\bar{v} = \Delta P \, R^2/8\eta l$, or

$$\Delta P = \frac{8\eta l \bar{v}}{R^2}$$

$$= \frac{8(2.084 \times 10^{-3} \text{ Pa s})}{(4 \times 10^{-3} \text{ m})^2} (0.1 \text{ m})(1.99 \times 10^{-2} \text{ m s}^{-1})$$

$$= 2.07 \text{ Pa}$$

Power Dissipation

We can readily compute the power dissipated in a tube by viscous forces. That power is, of course, equal to the power that must be supplied to maintain the flow.

Referring again to Fig. 14.4a, the net force on a segment is the pressure drop in the segment times the cross-sectional area, $F = (P_1 - P_2)A = \Delta P \, A$. The average power required to maintain the flow is this force times the average velocity, $\mathcal{P} = F\bar{v} = \Delta P \, A\bar{v}$. Note that $A\bar{v}$ is the flow rate Q; hence the power required to maintain the flow is

$$\mathcal{P} = \Delta P \, Q \quad (14.8)$$

For the special case where the flow is through a cylindrical tube of radius R, $A = \pi R^2$, and Eq. 14.6 becomes

$$\mathcal{P} = \Delta P (\pi R^2) \bar{v} \quad \text{(cylindrical tube)} \quad (14.9)$$

This result is particularly suitable for flow in blood vessels, as we show in the following example.

Example 14.3

What is the power required to maintain the blood flow in the dog's artery described in Example 14.2?

Using the results of Example 14.2 in Eq. 14.9, we find the power is

$$\begin{aligned}
\mathscr{P} &= \Delta P(\pi R^2)\bar{v} \\
&= (2.07 \text{ Pa})\pi(4 \times 10^{-3} \text{ m})^2(1.99 \times 10^{-2} \text{ m s}^{-1}) \\
&= 2.07 \times 10^{-6} \text{ W}
\end{aligned}$$

The metabolic rate of a dog is 10 W or greater, so the power expended in pumping blood through the large arteries is negligible. We see in Section 14.4 that most of the pressure drop and loss of energy due to viscous forces occurs in the small arterial subbranches and in the capillaries.

14.3 | TURBULENT FLOW

Poiseuille's laws hold true only for laminar flow. However, often the flow is not laminar but turbu-lent; it is similar to the wake of a fast boat, with swirls and eddies. The ink lines we used to describe streamline flow in Chapter Thirteen would become mixed or blurred. Some examples of turbulent flow are shown in Fig. 14.5.

We noted earlier that the mechanical energy dis-sipated is typically much larger in turbulent flow than in laminar flow. Hence it is often desirable to ensure that the flow does not become turbulent.

It is much harder to analyze turbulent flow than laminar flow. For example, Poiseuille's law for the laminar flow rate in a tube has no analog for turbu-lent flow. In practice, turbulent flow is treated using a variety of empirical rules and relationships devel-oped from extensive experimental studies.

In order to determine whether the flow is laminar and thus whether Poiseuille's law can be applied, we can make use of one of these empirical rules. It states that the value of a dimensionless quantity called the *Reynolds number* N_R determines whether the flow is turbulent or laminar. Consider a fluid of viscosity η and density ρ. If it is flowing in a tube of radius R and has an average velocity $\bar{v}$, then the

(a)

(b)

(c)

Figure 14.5. (*a*) Laminar flow; (*b*) turbulent flow of water. (*c*) First laminar, then turbulent flow of cigarette smoke. [(a and b) Gary S. Settles and Jason Listak / Photo Researchers, Inc.; (c) Phillip Hayson / Photo Researchers, Inc.)]

Reynolds number is defined by

$$N_R = \frac{2\rho\bar{u}R}{\eta} \text{ (flow in a tube of radius } R)(14.10)$$

In *tubes*, it is found experimentally that if

$$
\begin{aligned}
N_R &< 2000, &&\text{flow is laminar} \\
N_R &> 3000, &&\text{flow is turbulent} \quad (14.11) \\
2000 < N_R &< 3000, &&\text{flow is unstable (may} \\
&&&\text{change from laminar to} \\
&&&\text{turbulent, or vice versa)}
\end{aligned}
$$

Thus whether the flow is laminar or turbulent is determined by a particular combination of variables; doubling the tube radius and halving the average velocity will leave the character of the flow unchanged.

The Reynolds number also indicates whether the flow around an obstacle, such as a ship hull or an airplane wing, will be turbulent or laminar. In general, the Reynolds number at which turbulence sets in depends significantly on the shape of the obstacle and is *not* given by Eqs. 14.10 or 14.11.

In the preceding section, we computed the flow rate in an artery using Poiseuille's law, which is valid only if the flow is laminar. We now compute the Reynolds number for that case to see whether the flow is laminar or turbulent.

Example 14.4

In Example 14.2, the radius of the artery is 4×10^{-3} m, the average velocity of the blood is 1.99×10^{-2} m s^{-1}, and the viscosity is 2.084×10^{-3} Pa s. Also, the density of the blood from Table 13.1 is 1.0595×10^{3} kg m^{-3}. Find the Reynolds number and determine whether the flow is laminar.

The Reynolds number is

$$
\begin{aligned}
N_R &= \frac{2\rho\bar{u}R}{\eta} \\
&= \frac{2(1.0595 \times 10^{3} \text{ kg m}^{-3})}{2.084 \times 10^{-3} \text{ Pa s}} \\
&\quad \times (1.99 \times 10^{-2} \text{ m s}^{-1})(4 \times 10^{-3} \text{ m}) \\
&= 80.9
\end{aligned}
$$

This is much less than 2000, so the flow is laminar.

In turbulent flow, some energy is dissipated as sound and some as heat. The noise associated with turbulent flow in arteries facilitates blood pressure

measurements as we described in Chapter Thirteen, and it makes possible the detection of some heart abnormalities.

14.4 | FLOW IN THE CIRCULATORY SYSTEM

We now apply some of these ideas to the flow of blood in blood vessels. To do this, it is useful to summarize briefly some aspects of the cardiovascular system.

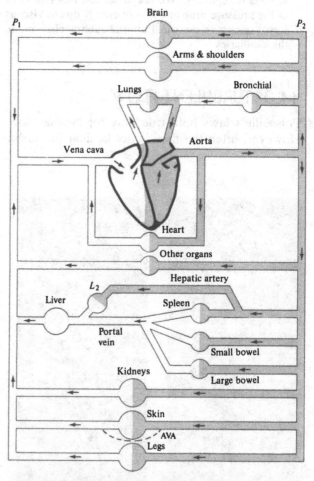

Figure 14.6. Schematic diagram of the mammalian circulatory system. The circles represent vascular beds. The small arrows represent the direction of blood flow. The colored shaded areas are those with oxygen-rich blood. The arterial system is on the right at pressure P_2, and the venous system on the left is at pressure P_1.

TABLE 14.2

Detailed structure of the mesenteric (intestinal) vascular bed of a small dog. This is one of many such vascular beds in the body.

Structure	Number N	Inner Radius R (m)	Total Inner Cross-Sectional Area $N\pi R^2$ (m²)	Length l (m)	Equivalent Flow Resistance R_{fl}/N (kPa s m⁻³)
Mesenteric artery	1	1.5×10^{-3}	7.0×10^{-6}	6.0×10^{-2}	6.67×10^3
Main branches	15	5.0×10^{-4}	1.2×10^{-5}	4.5×10^{-2}	2.55×10^5
Secondary branches	45	3.0×10^{-4}	1.3×10^{-5}	3.91×10^{-2}	5.69×10^5
Tertiary branches	1,900	7.0×10^{-5}	2.9×10^{-5}	1.42×10^{-2}	1.65×10^6
Terminal arteries	26,600	2.5×10^{-5}	5.2×10^{-5}	1.1×10^{-3}	5.61×10^5
Terminal branches	328,500	1.5×10^{-5}	2.32×10^{-4}	1.5×10^{-3}	4.79×10^5
Arterioles	1,050,000	1.0×10^{-5}	3.3×10^{-4}	2.0×10^{-3}	1.01×10^6
Capillaries	47,300,000	4.0×10^{-6}	2.378×10^{-3}	1.0×10^{-3}	4.38×10^5
Venules	2,100,000	1.5×10^{-5}	1.484×10^{-3}	1.0×10^{-3}	4.93×10^4
Terminal branches	160,000	3.7×10^{-5}	6.73×10^{-4}	2.4×10^{-3}	4.27×10^4
Terminal veins	18,000	6.5×10^{-5}	2.39×10^{-4}	1.5×10^{-3}	2.53×10^4
Tertiary veins	1,900	1.4×10^{-4}	1.17×10^{-4}	1.42×10^{-2}	1.03×10^5
Secondary veins	60	8.0×10^{-4}	1.47×10^{-4}	4.19×10^{-2}	9.33×10^2
Mesenteric vein	1	3.0×10^{-3}	2.8×10^{-5}	6.0×10^{-2}	4.0×10^2

The Blood

The circulatory system transports the substances required by the body and the waste products of metabolism. In order to perform a large number of functions, the blood contains many different constituents, including red blood cells, white blood cells, platelets, and proteins. However, for our purposes, it is sufficient to treat the blood as a uniform fluid, with viscosity $\eta = 2.084 \times 10^{-3}$ Pa s and density $\rho = 1.0595 \times 10^3$ kg m⁻³ at normal body temperature. Only more subtle physical properties of the circulatory system require a fuller description.

The Cardiovascular System

The cardiovascular system includes the heart and an extensive system of *arteries*, *vascular beds* containing *capillaries*, and *veins* (Fig. 14.6). The arteries carry blood to the organs, muscles, and skin, and the veins transport the return flow. Each large artery branches to form several smaller arteries, which in turn branch further. The blood ultimately reaches the vascular beds, where materials are exchanged with the surrounding tissues. The branching process is then reversed in the venous system, culminating in the *vena cava*, which returns blood to the heart. Table 14.2 gives the number and dimensions of several types of blood vessels in one vascular bed. Table 14.3 lists the properties of the human cardiovascular system.

An interesting component of the cardiovascular

TABLE 14.3

Properties of the human cardiovascular system for a typical adult. All pressures listed are gauge pressures (1 atm = 1.013×10^5 Pa = 101.3 kPa).

Mean pressure in large arteries	12.8 kPa
Mean pressure in large veins	1.07 kPa
Volume of blood (70-kg man)	5.2 litres = 5.2×10^{-3} m³
Time required for complete circulation (resting)	54 seconds
Heart flow rate (resting)	9.7×10^{-5} m³ s⁻¹
Viscosity of blood (37°C)	2.084×10^{-3} Pa s
Density of blood (37°C)	1.0595×10^3 kg m⁻³

system is the artereovenous anastomosis (AVA), or shunt. Found in the skin and in some other parts of the body, an AVA is a direct connection between small vessels in the arterial and venous systems—in other words, a shunt allowing the blood to bypass the capillaries. Muscle fibers in its walls can constrict or dilate the shunt, adjusting the blood flow as conditions change. When the body needs to release heat or to increase the skin temperature, shunts in the skin are open, allowing a large quantity of blood to go directly from the arteries into the extensive system of veins just below the skin without passing through the capillaries. This can increase the blood flow rate by a factor of 10 or more resulting in a rapid transfer of heat from the veins to the skin and to the surroundings.

Flow Resistance

The *flow resistance* R_f is defined, in general, as the ratio of the pressure drop to the flow rate:

$$R_f = \frac{\Delta P}{Q} \qquad (14.12)$$

When the flow is laminar, we can compare this with Eq. 14.6. Then we see that

$$R_f = \frac{8\eta l}{\pi R^4} \qquad \text{(laminar flow)} \qquad (14.13)$$

The flow resistance is seldom computed for physiological systems because of the complexity of the systems. Instead, it is usually arrived at by measuring ΔP and Q and hence determining R_f. Note that $R_f = \Delta P/Q$ defines a flow resistance whether the flow is laminar or not. However, Eq. 14.13 is valid only for laminar flow.

From its definition, it follows that the units of flow resistance are those of pressure divided by a volume per unit time. The basic S.I. unit is the pascal-second per cubic metre; we shall use kilopascal-seconds per cubic metre (kPa s m^{-3}). In texts and literature on physiology, pressures are usually measured in torr and lengths in centimetres, so the unit of flow resistance is

$$1 \text{ torr s cm}^{-3} = 1.333 \times 10^5 \text{ kPa s m}^{-3}$$

In the units we are using it is necessary to use Q in cubic metres per second (m^3 s^{-1}) and ΔP in kilopascals (kPa).

From the following example, we see that the flow resistance in a large artery is small. This explains why the pressure drop in such arteries is small.

Example 14.5

The aorta of an average adult human has a radius of 1.3×10^{-2} m. What are the resistance and pressure drop over a 0.2-m distance, assuming a flow rate of 10^{-4} m^3 s^{-1}?

From Table 14.3, $\eta = 2.084 \times 10^{-3}$ Pa s, so the flow resistance of the aorta is

$$R_f = \frac{8\eta l}{\pi R^4} = \frac{8}{\pi} \frac{(2.084 \times 10^{-3} \text{ Pa s})(0.2 \text{ m})}{(1.3 \times 10^{-2} \text{ m})^4}$$
$$= 3.72 \times 10^4 \text{ Pa s m}^{-3}$$
$$= 37.2 \text{ kPa s m}^{-3}$$

The pressure drop over the 0.2-m distance is then

$$\Delta P = R_f Q$$
$$= (37.2 \text{ kPa s m}^{-3})(10^{-4} \text{ m}^3 \text{ s}^{-1})$$
$$= 0.00372 \text{ kPa}$$

This is very small compared to the total pressure drop in the system, which is about 13.3 kPa. Most of the flow resistances and pressure drops occur in the smaller arteries and vascular beds of the body (Table 14.4).

TABLE 14.4

Approximate flow rates and resistances for the resting, reclining adult. The total flow rate from the aorta is 9.7×10^{-5} m^3 s^{-1}, and the average pressure drop across the beds is 11.7 kPa. (Refer to Fig. 14.6 for the relationships of the various beds.)

Vascular Bed	Flow Rate (m^3 s^{-1})	Flow Resistance (kPa s m^{-3})
Brain	12.5×10^{-6}	9.3×10^5
Arm and shoulders	6.8×10^{-6}	1.7×10^6
Lungs	97.0×10^{-6}	9.0×10^3
Bronchial	1.0×10^{-6}	1.2×10^7
Heart	4.2×10^{-6}	2.8×10^6
Other organs	10.0×10^{-6}	1.2×10^6
Liver, L_1	25.0×10^{-6}	4.0×10^4
Liver, L_2	5.0×10^{-6}	2.2×10^6
Spleen	8.3×10^{-6}	1.3×10^6
Small bowel	8.8×10^{-6}	1.2×10^6
Large bowel	2.9×10^{-6}	3.7×10^6
Kidneys	18.3×10^{-6}	6.4×10^5
Skin	5.5×10^{-6}	2.1×10^6
Legs	13.7×10^{-6}	8.5×10^5

When several blood vessels with flow resistances $R_{f1}, R_{f2}, \ldots$ are connected at each end, they have a common pressure drop ΔP, and they are said to be in *parallel*. The total flow Q is divided among them, with $Q_1 = \Delta P/R_{f1}$ through R_{f1}, $Q_2 = \Delta P/R_{f2}$ through R_{f2}, and so on. Adding up these flow rates,

$$Q = \Delta P \left[\frac{1}{R_{f1}} + \frac{1}{R_{f2}} + \frac{1}{R_{f3}} + \cdots \right]$$

If we were to replace these several resistances with a single equivalent resistance R_p, we would have $Q = \Delta P/R_p$. Hence for several resistances in parallel,

$$\frac{1}{R_p} = \frac{1}{R_{f1}} + \frac{1}{R_{f2}} + \frac{1}{R_{f3}} + \cdots \qquad (14.14)$$

When there are N equal parallel resistances, the equivalent resistance formula simplifies to

$$R_p = \frac{R_{f1}}{N} \qquad (14.15)$$

The flow resistance of a collection of arteries, such as the mesenteric bed of the dog, can be measured or calculated. The calculation can be done by considering each category of artery separately.

Example 14.6

From Table 14.2, the radius of a single capillary is 4×10^{-6} m, and its length is 10^{-3} m. What is the net resistance of the 4.73×10^7 capillaries in the mesenteric vascular bed of a dog if they are assumed to be in parallel?

With $\eta = 2.084 \times 10^{-3}$ Pa s, the resistance of one capillary is

$$
\begin{aligned}
R_{f1} &= \frac{8\eta l}{\pi R^4} \\
&= \frac{8(2.084 \times 10^{-3} \text{ Pa s})(10^{-3} \text{ m})}{\pi (4 \times 10^{-6} \text{ m})^4} \\
&= 2.073 \times 10^{16} \text{ Pa s m}^{-3} \\
&= 2.073 \times 10^{13} \text{ kPa s m}^{-3}
\end{aligned}
$$

There are $N = 4.73 \times 10^7$ capillaries in parallel, so their effective resistance is

$$R_f = \frac{R_{f1}}{N} = \frac{2.073 \times 10^{13} \text{ kPa s m}^{-3}}{4.73 \times 10^7}$$

$$= 4.38 \times 10^5 \text{ kPa s m}^{-3}$$

The effective resistance of all the capillaries in one vascular bed was calculated in the preceding

example by assuming that all the capillaries are in parallel, which is only approximately true. We also assumed that Poiseuille's law holds true for the flow in calculating the resistance of a single capillary. Again, this is an approximation, since the radii of the capillaries are comparable to the sizes of some of the constituents of the blood. Nevertheless, the results of such calculations are in rough agreement with the values found by measuring the pressure drop and flow rate and using $R_f = \Delta P/Q$.

Similar calculations for other portions of the vascular bed yield the results in the last column of Table 14.2. These results can be used to obtain the resistance of several sections of the vascular bed or of the entire bed. Suppose we know the resistances of N sections, each of which leads into the next. The total pressure drop is $\Delta P = \Delta P_{f1} + \Delta P_{f2} + \cdots + \Delta P_{fN}$. Each pressure drop, for example, $\Delta P_1 = QR_{f1}$, is the total flow rate Q times the resistance of that section. Adding all the pressure changes yields $\Delta P = Q(R_{f1} + R_{f2} + \cdots + R_{fN})$. Thus the effective flow resistance R_s of these sections, which are said to be in *series*, is the sum of the resistances

$$R_s = R_{f1} + R_{f2} + \cdots + R_{fN} \qquad (14.16)$$

If we add all the resistances of the arterial sections of the vascular bed of Table 14.2, we find $R_s = 45.3 \times 10^5$ kPa s m^{-3}. The same procedure can be used for the venous portion of the bed, and these results are summarized in Fig. 14.7. The arterial portion of this vascular bed has 87 percent of the total resistance and hence of the pressure drop. The capillaries have 9 percent of the resistance, and the venous portion has only 4 percent. Similar results

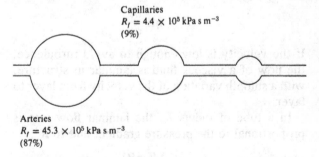

Capillaries
$R_f = 4.4 \times 10^5$ kPa s m^{-3}
(9%)

Arteries
$R_f = 45.3 \times 10^5$ kPa s m^{-3}
(87%)

Figure 14.7. Simplified flow resistance diagram for the mesenteric vascular bed of a dog. The total equivalent resistance is $(45.3 + 4.4 + 2.3) \times 10^5$ kPa s m^{-3} = 52.0×10^5 kPa s m^{-3}.

are found in other vascular beds; the arteries have the largest resistance, the capillaries a relatively small resistance, and the veins least of all.

The fact that most of the pressure drop and resistance occur in the arterial systems has important consequences for how the body regulates the circulation. The smallest arterial subdivisions, the arterioles, as well as some of the larger branches in the vascular beds, have surrounding muscle fibers. These can contract, reducing the radii of the vessels and hence increasing the flow resistance. Because the resistance varies as the fourth power of the radius, the body has a very effective way of adjusting the blood flow and responding to changing requirements.

Since the blood in the arteries is at a high pressure, severing an artery can lead to a serious loss of blood. The risk of this occurring is reduced by the fact that many arteries are deep within the body. When there is a drop in arterial pressure as a result of hemorrhaging, the body responds by constricting the vessels in many of the vascular beds. This temporarily conserves the reduced blood supply for use in the heart and the brain. However, the buildup of metabolic waste products and the shortage of oxygen eventually cause the vessels in the vascular beds to dilate. This lowers the blood pressure further, and the body is then in an unstable and poorly functioning condition referred to as shock.

SUMMARY

Viscous or frictional forces in fluids must be considered whenever the work done against them is appreciable. Viscous forces are proportional to the viscosity of the fluid and to the velocity gradient,

$$F = \eta A \frac{dv}{dy}$$

If the velocity is low enough to avoid turbulence, the flow of a viscous fluid is laminar in structure, with a smooth variation of the velocity from layer to layer.

In a tube of radius R, the laminar flow rate is proportional to the pressure gradient and to R^4:

$$Q = \frac{\Delta P \, \pi R^4}{8 \eta l}$$

The velocity of the fluid is a maximum at the center of the tube and decreases gradually in successive lamina to zero at the walls.

Turbulence sets in when the fluid velocity is increased sufficiently. The Reynolds number, a dimensionless combination of variables, can be used to predict whether the flow will be laminar or turbulent.

In many applications, such as the cardiovascular system, it is convenient to define the flow resistance R_f as

$$R_f = \frac{\Delta P}{Q}$$

For laminar flow

$$R_f = \frac{8 \eta l}{\pi R^4} \qquad \text{(laminar flow)}$$

When there are several flow resistances in parallel, the equivalent flow resistance is give by

$$\frac{1}{R_p} = \frac{1}{R_{f1}} + \frac{1}{R_{f2}} + \frac{1}{R_{f3}} + \cdots$$

When there are N equal parallel resistances, the equivalent flow resistance is

$$R_p' = \frac{R_{f1}}{N}.$$

If N resistances are in series, the effective resistance is

$$R_s = R_{f1} + R_{f2} + \cdots + R_{fN}$$

Checklist

viscous force	Poiseuille's law
viscosity	vascular bed
velocity gradient	power dissipation
laminar flow	flow resistance
turbulent flow	parallel
pressure gradient	series
dimensional analysis	Reynolds number

REVIEW QUESTIONS

Q14-1   The viscosity characterizes the force between moving _____ of fluid.

Q14-2   Is there a viscous force between a moving fluid and the container walls?

Q14-3 Streamline flow of a viscous fluid is called _____ flow.

Q14-4 Dimensional analysis can sometimes be used to obtain equations for various quantities. Can we also obtain the numerical coefficient in this way?

Q14-5 Poiseuille's law describes the _____ of fluid through a channel.

Q14-6 The Reynolds number is used to categorize the type of fluid flow. Roughly speaking, low Reynolds numbers correspond to _____ flow.

Q14-7 Each category of arterial sections in a vascular bed consists of a number of nearly identical arteries in _____ with each other.

Q14-8 The arterial sections of a vascular bed are in _____ with each other.

Q14-9 Is the flow resistance defined only for laminar flow?

Q14-10 If a fluid is forced through a channel, which type of flow requires the least energy to sustain, laminar or turbulent flow?

EXERCISES

Use 1.2 kg m^{-3} for the density of air and 1000 kg m^{-3} for the density of water.

Section 14.1 | Viscosity

14-1 In Fig. 14.1, at what point in the fluid is its velocity half that of the upper plate? Explain.

14-2 Why do automobile manufacturers recommend the use of "multiviscosity" engine oil in cold weather?

14-3 An experimental car rides on an air cushion 0.06 m thick with an area of 15 m^2. How much power is expended against viscous forces at a speed of 20 m s^{-1} if the viscosity of the air is 1.8 × 10^{-5} Pa s?

14-4 The air track cart in Example 14.1 has a mass of 0.5 kg. If its initial speed is 1 m s^{-1}, estimate the change in its speed after it has traveled 2 m.

14-5 The force needed to maintain a constant velocity of 0.3 m s^{-1} on an air track is found to be 0.005 N. The area of the cart is 0.05 m^2. How thick is the air layer? (Assume the viscosity is 1.8 × 10^{-5} Pa s.)

Section 14.2 | Laminar Flow in a Tube

14-6 Two arteries have the same flow rate, but one has twice the radius of the other. What is the ratio of the pressure drops over a given distance? (Assume laminar flow.)

14-7 A blood vessel of radius 10^{-3} m has a pressure gradient $\Delta P/l$ of 600 Pa m^{-1}. (Assume laminar flow.) (a) What is the flow rate of blood at 37°C in the vessel? (b) What is the maximum velocity of the blood in the vessel?

14-8 An artery has an inner radius of 2 × 10^{-3} m. If the temperature is 37°C, the average velocity of the blood is 0.03 m s^{-1} and the flow is laminar, find (a) the maximum velocity; (b) the flow rate; (c) the pressure drop in 0.05 m, if the artery is horizontal.

14-9 The pressure drop along a length of a horizontal artery is 100 Pa. The radius of the artery is 0.01 m, and the flow is laminar. (a) What is the net force on the blood in this portion of the artery? (b) If the average velocity of the blood is 1.5 × 10^{-2} m s^{-1}, find the power expended in maintaining the flow.

14-10 The radius of an artery is increased by a factor of 1.5. (a) If the pressure drop remains the same, what happens to the flow rate? (b) If the flow rate stays the same, what happens to the pressure drop? (Assume laminar flow.)

14-11 A hypodermic needle of length 0.02 m and inner radius 3 × 10^{-4} m is used to force water at 20°C into air at a flow rate of 10^{-7} m^3 s^{-1}. (a) What is the average velocity of the water in the needle? (Assume laminar flow.) (b) What is the pressure drop necessary to achieve the flow rate?

14-12 A fire truck pumps water through a hose with a narrow nozzle at a rate of 2 litres per second. The pressure drop in the hose is 3 atm. (a) How much power is expended in maintaining the flow? (b) Only part of this energy is expended against dissipative forces. Where does the remaining energy go?

14-13 Does Eq. 14.8 for the power dissipation require (a) laminar flow; (b) constant velocity; (c) constant height? Explain.

14-14 For a fixed flow rate, as the viscosity increases, what happens to (a) the pressure drop; (b) the power dissipation?

14-15 The flow rate in a tube is increased steadily, so that it changes from laminar to turbulent. What can you say about the power dissipation (a) while the flow is laminar; (b) once it has become turbulent?

Section 14.3 | Turbulent Flow

14-16 The average velocity of water at 20°C in a tube of radius 0.1 m is 0.2 m s^{-1}. (a) Is the flow laminar or turbulent? (b) What is the flow rate?

14-17 A water pipe of radius 0.02 m delivers water at a flow rate of 0.01 m^3 s^{-1} at 20°C. (a) What is the average velocity of the water? (b) Is the flow laminar or turbulent? (c) Is there enough information to determine the maximum velocity of the water in the pipe?

14-18 Calculate the Reynolds number for Exercise 14-11. Is the flow laminar as assumed?

14-19 (a) What is the greatest average velocity of blood flow at 37°C in an artery of radius 2×10^{-3} m if the flow is to remain laminar? (b) What is the corresponding flow rate Q?

14-20 (a) Draw an imaginary plane at right angles to the laminar flow in a cylinder. Is the pressure the same everywhere on this plane? Explain. (b) Does the pressure vary on this plane if the flow becomes turbulent? Why?

Section 14.4 | Flow in the Circulatory System

14-21 A blood vessel of radius R branches into several vessels of smaller radius r. If the average fluid velocity in the smaller vessel is half that in the large vessel, how many vessels of radius r must there be?

14-22 Which of the various portions of the arterial system in the vascular bed of Table 14.2 will have (a) the largest pressure drop; (b) the smallest?

14-23 A small artery has a length of 0.11 cm = 1.1×10^{-3} m and a radius of 2.5×10^{-5} m. (a) Calculate its resistance. (b) If the pressure drop across the artery is 1.3 kPa, what is the flow rate?

14-24 A glass tube has a radius of 10^{-3} m and a length of 0.1 m. (a) What is its resistance to the flow of a liquid with a viscosity of 10^{-3} Pa s? (b) If the pressure drop along the tube is 10^3 Pa, what is the flow rate?

PROBLEMS

14-25 A glass plate 0.25 m^2 in area is pulled at 0.1 m s^{-1} across a larger glass plate that is at rest. What force is necessary to pull the upper plate if the space between them is 0.003 m thick and filled with (a) water with $\eta = 1.005 \times 10^{-3}$ Pa s; (b) oil with $\eta = 0.01$ Pa s? (c) Why might oil be preferred to water as a lubricant?

14-26 The average flow rate of blood in the aorta is 4.20×10^{-6} m^3 s^{-1}. The aorta is 1.3×10^{-2} m in radius. (a) What is the average blood velocity in the aorta? (b) What is the pressure drop along 0.1 m of the aorta? (c) What is the power required to pump blood through this portion of the aorta?

14-27 Water at 20°C flows in a pipe of radius 0.02 m. For each metre of length, there is a pressure drop of 100 Pa, and a power dissipation of 0.8 W. (a) Find the flow rate. (b) Find the average velocity. (c) Is the flow laminar? Explain.

14-28 A fluid is pumped through a pipe at a flow rate of 0.01 m^3 s^{-1}. The power loss is 1.5 W per metre of pipe length. What is the flow resistance per metre?

14-29 What is the power loss in a pipe carrying fluid at 0.15 m^3 s^{-1} if the flow resistance is 4×10^4 Pa s m^{-3}?

14-30 (a) Estimate the power lost due to viscous effects in a gas pump hose if the viscosity of gasoline is 0.8×10^{-3} Pa s. (b) Will the actual power dissipated be considerably larger? Explain. (The density of gasoline is 670 kg m^{-3}.)

14-31 When fluid is pumped through a pipe of radius R at a flow rate Q, the viscous power loss is $\mathscr{P}_0$. What is the power loss at the same flow rate if 10 pipes of the same length but radius $R/8$ are used?

14-32 Two pipes, each of radius R and length L, feed into a single pipe of radius 1.5 R and length 1.5 L. What is the total flow resistance of this configuration for a fluid of viscosity η? (Assume laminar flow.)

14-33 (a) Using the resistances in Table 14.4, compute the pressure drops across the legs and lungs. (b) Explain the differences. What does this imply about the right ventricle, which pumps blood to the lungs?

14-34 Which of the vascular beds in Table 14.4, excluding the lungs, dissipates (a) the most power; (b) the least?

14-35 The pressure drop along a tube is increased gradually, and the corresponding flow rates are measured. (a) How would one get the flow resistance from these data? (b) What would happen to the flow resistance once the pressure became large enough so the flow became turbulent? Explain.

14-36 In Table 14.2, it is noted that the total cross-sectional area of all the capillaries in a particular vascular bed is 2.378×10^{-3} m^2, while the corresponding area for the main branches is only 1.2×10^{-5} m^2. How can this be reconciled with the fact that the main branches have a much smaller resistance?

14-37 The pressure drop along a copper tube is 10^3 Pa, and the flow rate of a liquid in this tube is 0.01 m^3 s^{-1}. (a) Find the flow resistance. (b) How much power is required to maintain this flow? (c) Does this calculation assume laminar flow? Explain.

14-38 When a calf is at rest, its heart pumps blood at a rate of 6×10^{-5} m^3 s^{-1}. The pressure drop from the arterial to venous systems is 12 kPa. (a) What is the flow resistance of its circulatory system? (b) How much work does the heart do in pumping the blood? (c) An experimental artificial heart powered by an electrical pump is implanted in place of the animal's heart. If the pump has an efficiency of 50 percent, how much electrical power does it require?

14-39 (a) Calculate the flow resistance of a typical human capillary 2×10^{-6} m in radius and 10^{-3} m long. (b) Estimate the number of capillaries in a human using this result, given that the net flow rate through the aorta is 9.7×10^{-5} m^3 s^{-1} and that the pressure drop from the arterial system to the venous system is 11.6 k Pa. Assume that all the capillaries are in parallel and that 9 percent of the pressure drop occurs in the capillaries.

c14-40 Show that integrating $dQ' = v'dA' = 2\pi r v' dr'$ leads to Eq. 14.6.

c14-41 (a) When a fluid in a tube undergoes laminar flow as described by Eq. 14.4, what is the flow rate for the portion of the fluid from $r = 0$ to $r = R/2$? (b) What is the ratio of this flow rate to the total flow rate through the tube? (c) What is the corresponding ratio for the cross-sectional areas?

ANSWERS TO REVIEW QUESTIONS

Q14-1, layers; **Q14-2**, yes; **Q14-3**, laminar; **Q14-4**, no; **Q14-5**, flow rate; **Q14-6**, laminar; **Q14-7**, parallel; **Q14-8**, series; **Q14-9**, no; **Q14-10**, laminar flow.

SUPPLEMENTARY TOPICS
14.5 | VISCOUS DRAG FORCES

Anyone who has held a hand out of a car window has discovered that an object moving through a fluid experiences a force that increases rapidly with the velocity. At very low velocities, this *drag force* results primarily from viscous forces that are proportional to the velocity v. At slightly higher but still relatively low speeds, the object accelerates the fluid moving around it, causing the force to vary approximately as v^2. In this section, we consider *low-speed*, or *viscous, drag forces*. "High-speed" drag is discussed in the next section.

Viscous drag forces result because the layer of fluid adjacent to an object is at rest with respect to the object. When the object moves through the fluid, this layer experiences a frictional force from the more rapidly moving layer next to it. Successive adjacent layers near the object produce frictional forces on each other, and the net result is to retard the motion of the object through the fluid.

An exact derivation of the viscous drag force is very difficult and has been carried out only for the simplest cases. However, given the observed direct proportionality at low speeds of the force and the velocity, we can obtain the general low-velocity form of the force law by again using a method called *dimensional analysis*.

The basic condition under which the drag force has the form we shall obtain is that the object moves very slowly through the fluid and the Reynolds number is very small. Figure 14.8 shows a spherical object of radius R moving with a small velocity v

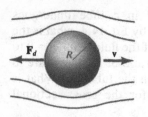

Figure 14.8. A spherical object of velocity **v**. F_d is the viscous drag force. Also shown are the laminar flow lines.

through a fluid of viscosity η and density ρ_0. Apart from dimensionless factors, the only physical quantities which could enter an expression for the drag force F_d are R, η, ρ_0, and v.

To construct from these variables a force proportional to v, we assume that the formula involves a factor of v and unknown powers of R, η, and ρ_0:

$$F_d = \phi v R^a \eta^b \rho_0^c \qquad (14.17)$$

where ϕ is a dimensionless numerical factor and the powers a, b, and c must be chosen so that F_d has the correct dimensions.

The dimensions of η were given in Eq. 14.3; ρ_0 is a mass per unit volume, and $[F] = [ma]$. Thus the physical quantities in Eq. 14.17 have the following dimensions:

$$[F] = [MLT^{-2}], \qquad [v] = [LT^{-1}], \qquad [R] = [L]$$
$$[\rho_0] = [ML^{-3}], \qquad [\eta] = [ML^{-1}T^{-1}]$$

From Eq. 14.17, we require

$$[MLT^{-2}] = [LT^{-1}][L]^a[ML^{-1}T^{-1}]^b[ML^{-3}]^c$$

We must choose a, b, and c so that the units of both sides of the equation match. To get T^{-2} on the right, we must make $b = 1$. Then to obtain M, we assign $c = 0$. Finally, to obtain L, we choose $a = 1$. Thus the viscous drag on an object must have the form

$$F_d = \phi R v \eta \qquad (14.18)$$

Note that the density ρ_0 does not enter the result. This is not too surprising, since the fundamental viscous force law $F = \eta A \, dv/dy$ does not depend upon the fluid density.

This result is valid whenever the velocity is small enough. In terms of the Reynolds number for a sphere of radius R, the requirement is

$$N_R = \frac{\rho_0 v R}{\eta} < 1 \quad \text{(sphere of radius } R) \qquad (14.19)$$

If $N_R \gtrsim 1$, the drag force becomes proportional to v^2 ($\gtrsim$ means "greater than or approximately equal to"). This occurs at velocities well below the onset of turbulence and is due, as noted earlier, to the kinetic energy imparted to the fluid.

For a sphere, ϕ is known to be exactly 6π, so

$$F_d = 6\pi R v \eta \quad \text{(sphere)} \qquad (14.20)$$

This is called *Stokes' law*. For complex shapes, Eq. 14.18 can still be used if ϕ is determined by experiment. R must be interpreted as some characteristic length of the object, such as the average radius of a red blood cell.

It is sometimes possible to get information about the size or shape of a small object if the viscous drag force on the object is determined from its motion. This idea underlies some of the applications of the centrifuge, which are discussed in Section 14.7.

To illustrate the use of Stokes' law, we obtain the maximum or terminal velocity v_T for a small sphere of radius R and density ρ falling through a fluid of viscosity η and density ρ_0. Terminal velocity is reached when the drag force $\mathbf{F}_d$ exactly balances the weight $\mathbf{w}$ and the buoyant force $\mathbf{B}$ (Fig. 14.9).

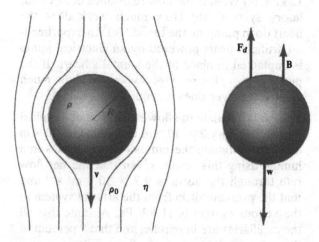

Figure 14.9. A sphere falling through a viscous fluid. Terminal velocity is reached when $F_d = w - B$.

The volume of the sphere is $V = \frac{4}{3}\pi R^3$, and its weight is $w = \rho g V$. The upward buoyant force is the weight of the fluid displaced $B = \rho_0 g V$. From Stokes' law, the viscous drag force at the terminal velocity v_T is $F_d = 6\pi R v_T \eta$. Thus terminal velocity is reached when $F_d = w - B$, or

$$6\pi R v_T \eta = \tfrac{4}{3}\pi R^3 \rho g - \tfrac{4}{3}\pi R^3 \rho_0 g$$

Solving for v_T, the terminal velocity of the sphere is

$$v_T = \frac{2}{9}\frac{R^2}{\eta} g(\rho - \rho_0) \qquad (14.21)$$

If v_T and R are measured, this equation provides a way of finding the viscosity of the fluid. The terminal velocity of a dust particle is found in the next example.

Example 14.7

(a) What is the terminal velocity in air at 20°C of a spherical dust particle of radius 10^{-5} m and density 2×10^3 kg m^{-3}? (b) What is the Reynolds number at terminal velocity? (c) Find the drag force at terminal velocity.

(b) At 20°C, the density of air is 1.20 kg m^{-3}, which is negligible compared to that of the particle. Using $\eta = 1.81 \times 10^{-5}$ Pa s from Table 14.1 and assuming the velocity is low enough that Stokes' law applies,

$$\begin{aligned}
v_T &= \frac{2}{9}\frac{R^2}{\eta} g(\rho - \rho_0)\\
&= \frac{2}{9}\frac{(10^{-5}\text{ m})^2}{(1.81 \times 10^{-5}\text{ Pa s})}\\
&\quad \times (9.8\text{ m s}^{-2})(2 \times 10^3\text{ kg m}^{-3})\\
&= 2.41 \times 10^{-2}\text{ m s}^{-1}
\end{aligned}$$

(b) The Reynolds number is

$$\begin{aligned}
N_R &= \frac{\rho_0 v R}{\eta}\\
&= \frac{(1.22\text{ kg m}^{-3})(2.41 \times 10^{-2}\text{ m s}^{-1})(10^{-5}\text{ m})}{(1.81 \times 10^{-5}\text{ Pa s})}\\
&= 0.0162
\end{aligned}$$

This is much less than 1, so Stokes' law and Eq. 14.21 for v_T apply.

(c) The drag force is

$$\begin{aligned}
F_d &= 6\pi R v \eta\\
&= 6\pi(10^{-5}\text{ m})(2.41 \times 10^{-2}\text{ m s}^{-1})(1.81 \times 10^{-5}\text{ Pa s})\\
&= 8.23 \times 10^{-11}\text{ N}
\end{aligned}$$

Equation 14.21 for the terminal velocity is valid only for very small objects, such as dust particles in air or macromolecules in solution. For larger objects the terminal velocity predicted by this equation corresponds to a Reynolds number much larger than 1, so that Stokes' law is not applicable. However, Eq. 14.21 is useful for finding the motion of molecules or small particles in a centrifuge, as is discussed in Section 14.7.

In this section, we obtained the viscous drag force using dimensional analysis. This method is very useful in many scientific problems where the exact theory is difficult to apply or is not even known, and we use it again in this chapter. However, it has limitations. For example, if several lengths enter a problem, it may not be possible to determine what combinations enter the formula, since $(l_1/l_2)^3$, $(l_1/l_2)^{1/2}$, and e^{-l_1/l_2} are all dimensionless quantities. In general, we must have only three dimensionally independent variables so that unique combinations can be formed that determine the units of mass, time, and length. Another drawback is that dimensionless constant factors such as ϕ occasionally turn out to be numerically very large or small.

14.6 | "HIGH-SPEED" DRAG FORCES

At the beginning of the preceding section, we noted that as the speed of an object moving in a fluid increases so that $N_R = \rho_0 v R/\eta \gtrsim 1$, the drag force is no longer proportional to v. Instead, it is approximately proportional to v^2. The term "high speed" is somewhat misleading, since the v^2 dependence is observed whenever N_R is appreciably more than 1, and this happens at surprisingly low speeds. For example, for a sphere of radius 1 cm in air, N_R is 1 at $v = 1.5$ mm s^{-1}. Thus high-speed drag applies to essentially all problems involving the motion of macroscopic objects.

The formula for the high-speed drag force on a sphere in a fluid can again be found using dimensional analysis. The force is assumed to be proportional to v^2 and to unknown powers of the radius of the sphere R, the viscosity of the fluid η, and the density of the fluid ρ_0. The calculation is left as a problem. The result is that F_d is proportional to

$R^2\rho_0 v^2$, or that

$$F_d = C_D A \frac{\rho_0 v^2}{2} \qquad (14.22)$$

Here factors are grouped for convenience: $A = \pi R^2$ is the cross-sectional area of the moving sphere, $\rho_0 v^2/2$ is the kinetic energy per unit volume of fluid with velocity v, and C_D is the *drag coefficient* that must be obtained from measurements. The viscosity η is absent, which is consistent with the idea that the drag results from accelerating the fluid moving around the sphere and not from viscous effects.

The result just given holds true for objects of any shape. Figure 14.10 gives experimental values of C_D versus the Reynolds number for a long cylinder moving perpendicular to its axis. We see that C_D is nearly constant; it varies between 0.3 and 3.0 as N_R varies from 10 to 10^6. This occurs despite the fact that as N_R increases, the motion of the fluid around the cylinder changes from laminar to turbulent when $N_R \approx 100$.

Equation 14.22 can be used to obtain the terminal velocity of a macroscopic falling object. The result for an object of cross-sectional area A, length L, and mass ρAL is

$$v_T = \sqrt{\frac{(\rho - \rho_0)}{\rho_0} \frac{2gL}{C_D}} \qquad (14.23)$$

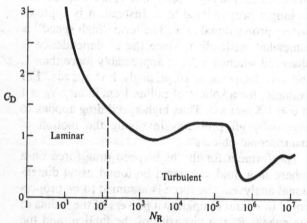

Figure 14.10. Drag coefficients versus Reynolds number for a long cylinder moving perpendicular to its axis. Here $N_R = \rho_0 vR/\eta$, where R is the radius of the cylinder.

Note that the cross-sectional area does not appear in the result. This derivation and numerical examples are left for the exercises and problems.

14.7 | CENTRIFUGATION

Centrifuges use the very large accelerations experienced by rapidly rotating objects to perform many tasks in biological and medical laboratories. For example, centrifuges can separate large and small particles and molecules. The speed of a molecule in a centrifuge is determined by the viscous drag force and the molecular mass. Accordingly, a measurement of this speed, together with other data, can be used to find the mass of the molecule.

A centrifuge consists basically of a sample holder that can be rotated (Fig. 14.11). If the sample rotates at a radius r and an angular velocity ω, its centripetal acceleration is $a_r = \omega^2 r$. We saw in Chapter Five that the effective weight of a rotating object of mass m is $\mathbf{w}^e = m(\mathbf{g} - \mathbf{a}_r)$. Since a_r may be up to $500,000g$ and is always much greater than g, the effective weight is given to a good approximation by $\mathbf{w}^e = -m\mathbf{a}_r$. Thus the sample will behave as though it were on a planet where $w^e = mg^e$ and the gravitational acceleration has a magnitude $g^e = \omega^2 r$. For example, molecules denser than a solvent will *sediment* or settle to the bottom of the holder at a much greater terminal or *sedimentation* velocity than in a stationary solution.

The sedimentation velocity $\mathbf{v}_s$ of particles experiencing a "gravitational acceleration" $\mathbf{g}^e$ is determined by their effective weight $\mathbf{w}^e$, the buoyant force $\mathbf{B}$ due to the fluid, and the low speed or viscous drag force $\mathbf{F_d}$ (Fig. 14.12). If the particles are spherical, Eq. 14.21, which was obtained from Stokes' law, can be used with g replaced by g^e to find this velocity. However, another expression for v_s is often more useful.

To obtain this expression we use the general form for the low-speed drag force, Eq. 14.17, with R representing an average dimension of the particle,

$$F_d = \phi R v \eta$$

If the particles have mass m and volume V, their density is $\rho = m/V$, and their effective weight is $w^e = mg^e$. If the density of the fluid is ρ_0, the buoy-

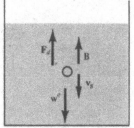

Figure 14.12. Forces on a particle in a centrifuge. The particle moves downward with a sedimentation velocity $\mathbf{v}_s$.

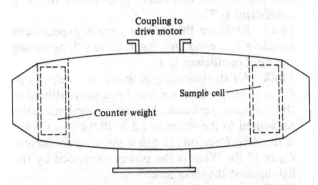

Coupling to drive motor

Sample cell

Counter weight

Figure 14.11. A centrifuge. Rotational speeds of up to 6000 revolutions per minute corresponding to 6835g are achieved with this unit. Other types of centrifuges achieve speeds of 60,000 revolutions per minute and 500,000g. (Jeff Greenberg / Photo Researchers, Inc.)

ant force is $B = \rho_0 g^e V = (\rho_0/\rho)mg^e$. The forces are balanced at a velocity v_s if $F_d = w^e - B$. Thus

$$\phi R v_s \eta = mg^e - \frac{\rho_0}{\rho} mg^e$$

or

$$v_s = \frac{mg^e}{\phi R \eta} \left(1 - \frac{\rho_0}{\rho}\right) \qquad (14.24)$$

This is the sedimentation velocity for molecules in a solution if the acceleration is $g^e = \omega^2 r$.

This result can be used in various ways. If the quantities on the right side are known, the sedimentation velocity can be calculated, and one can determine how long it will take for the material to collect at the bottom of the sample holder (Fig. 14.13). Alternatively, the sedimentation velocity can be measured by shining light through the spinning sample and exploiting the fact that proteins and many other materials absorb light at specific wavelengths. This velocity measurement then provides information about the other variables in Eq. 14.24. Also, the product ϕR can be inferred from diffusion experiments, and the densities are readily measured, so sedimentation velocities can provide a determination of molecular masses. If several molecules of different sizes are present, v_s will be different for each. This permits various components of a mixture to be identified.

Example 14.8

Hemoglobin has a density of 1.35×10^3 kg m^{-3} and a molecular mass of 68,000 u. The factor ϕR for hemoglobin in water is 9.46×10^{-8} m. If it is in a centrifuge with a centripetal acceleration of $10^5 g$, find its sedimentation velocity in water at 37°C.

In kilograms, the mass of the molecule is $(68,000 \text{ u}) \times (1.66 \times 10^{-27} \text{ kg u}^{-1}) = 1.129 \times 10^{-22}$ kg. The density of water is 10^3 kg m^{-3}. Thus the sedimenta-

Figure 14.13. (*a*), (*b*), and (*c*). Molecules sedimenting in a centrifuge at a velocity $v_s = 10^{-3}$ cm s^{-1}. A sharp boundary between the solution and pure solvent moves downward with velocity v_s. (*d*) In a mixture of two kinds of solutes, the larger molecules (black dots) will sediment faster than the smaller ones (colored dots).

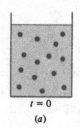
$t = 0$
(*a*)

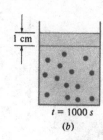
$t = 1000\ s$
(*b*)

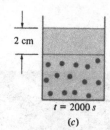
$t = 2000\ s$
(*c*)

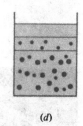
(*d*)

tion velocity is

$$v_s = \frac{mg^e}{\phi R\eta}\left(1 - \frac{\rho_0}{\rho}\right)$$

$$= \frac{(1.129 \times 10^{-22}\ \text{kg})(10^5)(9.8\ \text{m s}^{-2})}{(9.46 \times 10^{-8}\ \text{m})(0.695 \times 10^{-3}\ \text{Pa s})}\left(1 - \frac{1}{1.35}\right)$$

$$= 4.37 \times 10^{-7}\ \text{m s}^{-1}$$

At this velocity the molecules will travel 3.7 cm in a 24-hour period. We can see why it is quite common to run a centrifuge for many hours.

Example 14.9

A protein of density 1.3×10^3 kg m^{-3} has a sedimentation velocity of 10^{-6} m s^{-1} in a centrifuge with acceleration 10^6 m s^{-2}. At this sedimentation velocity the drag force is 2.07×10^{-16} N. Find the molecular mass of the protein.

Solving Eq. 14.24 for the molecular mass gives

$$m = \frac{\phi R\eta v_s}{g^e}\frac{1}{1 - (\rho_0/\rho)}$$

Since $\phi R\eta v_s$ is the drag force, and $\rho_0 = 10^3$ kg m^{-3}

$$m = \frac{2.07 \times 10^{-16}\ \text{N}}{10^6\ \text{m s}^{-2}}\frac{1}{1 - (1/1.3)}$$

$$= (7.98 \times 10^{-22}\ \text{kg})\left(\frac{1\ \text{u}}{1.66 \times 10^{-27}\ \text{kg}}\right) = 481,000\ \text{u}$$

EXERCISES ON SUPPLEMENTARY TOPICS

Section 14.5 | Viscous Drag Forces

14-42 A spherical blood cell of radius 5×10^{-6} m and density 1.3×10^3 kg m^{-3} is in water at 37°C. What is its terminal velocity? (Assume Stokes' law holds true.)

14-43 A large spherical molecule has a radius of 2×10^{-8} m and a density of 1.5×10^3 kg m^{-3}. (a) What is its terminal velocity when falling in water at 20°C? (b) What is the maximum velocity at which Stokes' law holds true?

14-44 For spherical dust particles of density 3×10^3 kg m^{-3}, find the maximum radius for which Stokes' law can be used to find the terminal velocity (a) in air at 20°C; (b) in water at 20°C.

14-45 The terminal velocity of a spherical oil droplet falling in air at 20°C is 2×10^{-7} m s^{-1}. What is the radius of the spherical droplet if its density is 930 kg m^{-3}? (Assume that Stokes' law holds true.)

Section 14.6 | "High-Speed" Drag Forces

14-46 A spherical pebble of radius 0.04 m and density 3×10^3 kg m^{-3} is dropped into a pond. Estimate its terminal velocity, assuming the drag coefficient is 1.

14-47 Estimate the force a person experiences standing in a wind blowing at 20 m s^{-1}, assuming the drag coefficient is 1.

14-48 A fish swimming in water at a velocity of 0.3 m s^{-1} experiences a drag force proportional to the velocity squared. The cross-sectional area presented to the water is 2.2×10^{-3} m^2. (a) What is the drag force on the fish if the drag coefficient C_D is 1? (b) What is the power expended by the fish against the drag force?

14-49 A baseball has a mass of 0.149 kg and a Ping-Pong ball has a mass of 3×10^{-3} kg. Their radii are 0.037 m and 0.018 m, respectively. Both are thrown in air with initial horizontal velocities of 15 m s^{-1}. (a) What is the ratio of drag forces on the two balls? (b) What is the initial acceleration of each ball due to the drag force, assuming $C_D = 1$?

14-50 A baseball has a mass of 0.149 kg and a radius of 0.037 m. (a) Calculate its terminal velocity in air at 0°C using Eq. 14.21. (b) Calculate the terminal velocity using Eq. 14.23, assuming

$C_D = 1$. (c) Explain the significance of the difference in the results in parts (a) and (b).

Section 14.7 | Centrifugation

14-51 A protein molecule has a mass of 10^5 u and a density of 1.35×10^3 kg m^{-3}. It is in a centrifuge with an acceleration of $2 \times 10^5 g$. If it is in water, find (a) its effective weight; (b) the buoyant force.

14-52 The sample in a centrifuge is 0.1 m from the axis of rotation. If its centripetal acceleration is 200,000g, how many times per minute does the centrifuge rotate?

14-53 Bushy stunt virus has a molecular mass of 1.06×10^7 u and a density of 1.35×10^3 kg m^{-3}. The factor ϕR in water is 3.58×10^{-7} m at 20°C. How much time is required for it to sediment 10^{-2} m if the acceleration in the centrifuge is $10^5 g$?

14-54 A red blood cell can be approximated by a sphere of radius 2×10^{-6} m and density 1.3×10^3 kg m^{-3}. How long will it take for it to sediment 1 cm $= 10^{-2}$ m in blood at 37°C (a) under the earth's gravitational acceleration; (b) in a centrifuge with an acceleration of $10^5 g$? (The density of blood is 1.0595×10^3 kg m^{-3}.)

14-55 Tobacco mosaic virus has a density of 1370 kg m^{-3} and $\phi R = 1.16 \times 10^{-6}$ m at 37°C. If the acceleration in a centrifuge is $2 \times 10^5 g$, the sedimentation velocity in water is observed to be 3.7×10^{-5} m s^{-1}. What is the molecular mass of the tobacco mosaic virus?

PROBLEMS ON SUPPLEMENTARY TOPICS

14-56 Red blood cells are usually not spherical in shape. What is the product ϕR in Eq. 14.17 for a cell mass 10^{-12} kg if the terminal velocity in water at 37°C is 10^{-5} m s^{-1}? (The density of the cell is 1.3×10^3 kg m^{-3}.)

14-57 Estimate the maximum velocity at which Stokes' law applies for a small fish in water.

14-58 Estimate the terminal velocity of an 800-N man falling through air (a) if he falls in a tuck position; (b) if he spreads his body and arms out. (Assume the drag coefficient C_D is 1.)

14-59 Assuming that the flow rate Q is proportional to the pressure gradient $\Delta P/l$, use dimensional analysis to derive the powers in Eq. 14.6.

14-60 Derive Eq. 14.22 using dimensional analysis.

14-61 When the drag force is proportional to the velocity squared, show that the terminal velocity of an object of density ρ falling through a fluid of density ρ_0 is given by Eq. 14.23.

14-62 For a spherical molecule of radius R in a fluid with viscosity η, the drag force is given both by $F_d = 6\pi\eta R v$ (Stokes' law) and by $F_d = \phi R v \eta$. What is the product ϕR for a spherical molecule with radius 10^{-8} m?

14-63 Nucleohistone has a mass of 2.1×10^6 u and a density of 1520 kg m^{-3}. (a) What is its volume? (b) If this molecule is spherical, what is its radius? (c) Assuming the molecule is spherical, use Stokes' law to find the product ϕR in water at 20°C. (d) The product ϕR is actually 4.33×10^{-7} m. Is this molecule spherical? Explain.

14-64 (a) What is the acceleration of a large air bubble in water at 20°C when it reaches half of its terminal velocity? (The density of water at 20°C is 990 kg m^{-3}, and the density of air is 1.20 kg m^{-3}.) (b) The acceleration in part (a) turns out to be a very large number. What does this imply about the time required to approach terminal velocity?

14-65 Figure 14.14 shows a viscous fluid trapped between the two gas bubbles as the gas and fluid move through a tube. Putting yourself in a frame of reference moving with the gas, draw arrows in the fluid showing its velocity at various points in the tube. Using your results, suppose the gas bubbles are actually red blood cells, the fluid blood plasma, and the tube a capillary. What does the velocity pattern you've drawn suggest about the role of the plasma in aiding diffusion of gases between the capillary and the red blood cells?

14-66 Some animals have very streamlined shapes and relatively low drag coefficients. For example, a dolphin has a drag coefficient C_D of 0.055. (a) If the dolphin presents an area of

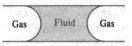

Figure 14.14. Problem 14-65.

0.11 m^2 to the water when swimming at 8.3 m s^{-1}, what is the drag force on it? (b) For the dolphin, about 15 percent of the 90-kg body mass is swimming muscle. Estimate the power output per kilogram of muscle for the dolphin. (c) Find the ratio of this result to the maximum power output of human muscles, 40 W kg^{-1}. (The large value of this ratio has led a number of researchers to study whether dolphin muscles are more efficient or if the flow along the body is less turbulent than expected.)

14-67 Assume that two swimmers, A and B, each swim 100 m in 80 s. A does so by swimming each 25-m stretch in 20 s. B swims the four segments in 15 s, 15 s, 25 s, and 25 s, respectively. Which swimmer does more work against drag forces?

14-68 An air bubble of radius 0.5 mm = 5×10^{-4} m rises in a liquid of density 900 kg m^{-3} and viscosity 8.37×10^{-3} Pa s. Find the terminal velocity of the bubble and justify your answer by checking the Reynolds number. Assume the air density is 1.2 kg m^{-3}. (Assume $C_D = 1$.)

Additional Reading

Richard B. Setlow and Ernest C. Pollard, *Molecular Biophysics*, Addison-Wesley Publishing Co., Reading, Mass., 1962. Chapter 4 discusses centrifugation.

R. McNeill Alexander, *Animal Mechanics*, University of Washington Press, Seattle, 1968, Chapters 5 and 6.

E. M. Purcell, Life at Low Reynolds Numbers, *American Journal of Physics*, vol. 45, 1977, p. 3.

Alan C. Burton, *Physiology and Biophysics of the Circulation*, Yearbook Medical Publishers, Inc., Chicago, 1965.

Vernon B. Mountcastle (ed.), *Medical Physiology*, Vol. 1, 12th ed., The C. V. Mosby Co., St. Louis, 1968.

Arthur C. Guyton, *Circulatory Physiology: Cardiac Output and Its Regulation*, W. B. Saunders Co., Philadelphia, 1963.

R. L. Whitmore, *Rheology of the Circulation*, Pergamon Press, Oxford and New York, 1968.

Gerald Aiello, Pierre LaFrance, Rogers C. Ritter, and James S. Trefil, The Urinary Drop Spectrometer, *Physics Today*, vol. 27, September 1974, p. 23.

J. Richard Shanebrook, Fluid Mechanics of Coronary Artery Bypass Surgery, *American Journal of Physics*, vol. 45, 1977, p. 677.

James A. Lock, The Physics of Air Resistance, *The Physics Teacher*, vol. 20, 1982, p. 158.

Richard A. Kerr, How Does Fluid Flow Become Turbulent? *Science*, vol. 221, 1983, p. 140.

M. Van Dyke, *Album of Fluid Motion*, Parabolic, Stanford, Calif., 1982. Three hundred photographs of many phenomena.

Cliff Frohlich, Aerodynamic Drag Crisis and Its Possible Effect on the Flight of Baseballs, *The American Journal of Physics*, vol. 51, 1984, p. 325.

Peter J. Brancazio, Trajectory of a Fly Ball, *The Physics Teacher*, vol. 23, 1986, p. 20.

Herman Erlichson, Maximum Projectile Range with Drag and Lift, with Particular Application to Golf, *The American Journal of Physics*, vol. 51, 1983, p. 347.

William R. Sears, Von Karman: Fluid Dynamics and Other Things, *Physics Today*, January 1986, p. 34. A pioneer of aerodynamics.

Scientific American articles:

Jesse W. Beams, Ultrahigh-Speed Rotation, April 1961, p. 134.

F. H. Harlow and J. E. Fromm, Computer Experiments in Fluid Dynamics, March 1965, p. 104.

R. W. Stewart, The Atmosphere and the Ocean, September 1969, p. 76.

D. James Baker, Jr., Models of Oceanic Circulation, January 1970, p. 114.

R. C. Chanaud, Aerodynamic Whistles, January 1970, p. 40.

Victor P. Starr and Norman E. Gant, Negative Viscosity, July 1970, p. 72.

Norman C. Chigier, Vortexes in Aircraft Wakes, March 1974, p. 76.

Kay Johansen, Aneurysms, July 1982, p. 110.

J. Edwin Wood, The Venous System, January 1968, p. 86.

James V. Warren, The Physiology of the Giraffe, November 1974, p. 96.

Donald R. Olander, The Gas Centrifuge, August 1978, p. 37.

E. Eugene Larrabee, The Screw Propeller, July 1980, p. 134.

Jearl Walker, Serious Fun with Polyox, Silly Putty,

Slime, and Other Non-Newtonian Fluids, *The Amateur Scientist*, November 1978, p. 186.

Jearl Walker, Delights of Forming Water into Sheets and Bells with Knives, Spoons, and Other Objects, *The Amateur Scientist*, August 1979, p. 188.

Jearl Walker, Easy Ways to Make Holograms and View Fluid Flow, and More About Funny Fluids, *The Amateur Scientist*, February 1980, p. 158.

Jearl Walker, The Charm of Hydraulic Jumps, Starting with Those Observed in the Kitchen Sink, *The Amateur Scientist*, April 1981, p. 176.

Albert C. Gross, Chester R. Kyle, and Douglas J. Malewicki, The Aerodynamics of Human-Powered Land Vehicles, December 1983, p. 142.

M. A. R. Koehl, The Interaction of Moving Water and Sessile Organisms, December 1982, p. 124. Effects of drag forces on shallow water organisms.

Paul W. Webb, Form and Function in Fish Swimming, July 1984, p. 72.

Alec N. Brooks, Allan V. Abbott, and David Gordon Wilson, Human-Powered Watercraft, December 1986, p. 120. Drag forces.

Chester R. Kyle, Athletic Clothing, March 1986, p. 104. Drag forces.

Jearl Walker, Fly Casting Illuminates the Physics of Fishing, *The Amateur Scientist*, July 1985, p. 122.

Jearl Walker, The Troublesome Teapot Effect, Or Why a Poured Liquid Clings to the Container, *The Amateur Scientist*, October 1984, p. 144.

CHAPTER 15
COHESIVE FORCES
IN LIQUIDS

When we consider pulling on a substance until it breaks, we usually think of solids. However, liquids also have a strong tendency to remain intact. For example, if pure water with no air dissolved in it is pressed between two smooth plates, enormous forces are necessary to separate the plates.

As in solids, the cohesiveness of liquids results from the attractions among the molecules. Because of these attractions, liquids have well-defined surfaces that, like stretched membranes or rubber sheets, tend to have a minimum surface area. Ripples in a quiet, smooth pool are suppressed because they require an increase in surface area. Aquatic insects are able to move on water surfaces because their weight is opposed by the resistance of the surface to deformation.

In addition to the attractive forces among themselves, the molecules of a liquid experience attractive or repulsive interactions with the molecules of other substances. Thus water rises near a vertical glass surface, whereas the opposite is true for mercury.

The cohesive properties of liquids can be changed by the addition of small amounts of other substances. For example, molecules in oils are *hydrophobic* (water hating), and oils will not dissolve in pure water. Molecules in soaps and detergents have both hydrophobic and *hydrophilic* (water-loving) portions. The hydrophilic part attaches itself to the water surface, and the hydrophobic portion surrounds oil or grease. This aids in the solution and removal of oil and grease.

In this chapter, we consider some effects of the cohesiveness of liquids. Topics discussed include the rise of liquids in narrow tubes or *capillaries*, the formation of bubbles, and the rise of sap in trees.

15.1 | SURFACE TENSION

One way to observe the effects of surface tension is to dip the apparatus shown in Fig. 15.1 into a liquid. This consists of a U-shaped wire, a slide wire of weight w_1, and a suspended weight w_2. A thin film of liquid fills the enclosed area between the wires. If the total weight $w = w_1 + w_2$ is properly chosen, the two surfaces of the film exert a force equal and opposite to the weight and the slide wire remains stationary. Thus in this situation the force F due to the surface tension is equal in magnitude to w.

The *surface tension* γ (Greek letter "gamma") is defined as the force per unit length exerted by *one* surface. Then if the straight wire of Fig. 15.1 has a length l, the net force upward due to the two surfaces is $F = 2\gamma l$. Thus the surface tension is

$$\gamma = \frac{F}{2l} \qquad (15.1)$$

Representative surface tensions are given in Table 15.1.

One may ask why the forces in Fig. 15.1 are attributed to the surfaces. The point is that the liquid film acts somewhat differently than a rubber sheet. If the apparatus is in equilibrium and the straight wire is moved up or down, it is in equilibrium again at each position, even though the film thickness has changed. Thus the thickness of the film is not important. If the film is stretched, molecules from the bulk of the fluid move to the surface, and the surface area is increased. Since the force remains the same while the bulk thickness varies, the force must be attributed to the surface of the film.

We can understand the reason for this behavior with the aid of a microscopic picture of the bound-

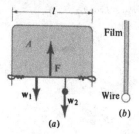

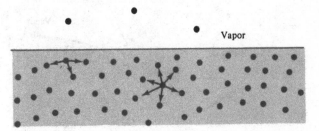

Figure 15.1. (a) A liquid film filling the area A exerts a force F, which balances $w = w_1 + w_2$. (b) A cross-sectional view of the sliding straight wire and the film attached to it. The film has two surfaces.

Figure 15.2. The molecules of a substance in the liquid and the coexistent vapor phase. The attractive forces on molecules near the surface and in the interior are denoted by arrows.

ary between a liquid and its vapor (Fig. 15.2). A molecule in the interior of the liquid experiences attractive forces due to all its neighbors, which lowers its potential energy. A molecule at the surface does not have as many neighbors, and its potential energy is not so low. Consequently, the molecules at the surface arrange themselves so that they have as many neighbors as possible. In this process, they minimize the surface area and the potential energy and produce the observed surface tension. The following example shows that these surface forces are relatively small.

TABLE 15.1

The surface tension for representative liquids in contact with air

Liquid	Surface Tension ($N m^{-1}$)	Temperature (°C)
Ethyl alcohol	2.23×10^{-2}	20
Olive oil	3.20×10^{-2}	20
Glycerine	6.31×10^{-2}	20
Water	7.56×10^{-2}	0
	7.28×10^{-2}	20
	6.62×10^{-2}	60
	5.89×10^{-2}	100
Mercury	0.465	20
Silver	0.800	970
Gold	1.000	1070
Copper	1.100	1130
Oxygen	1.57×10^{-2}	−193
Neon	5.15×10^{-3}	−247

Example 15.1

The U-shaped loop in Fig. 15.1 is dipped into water at 20°C. The slide wire is 0.1 m long and has a mass $m_1 = 1$ g $= 10^{-3}$ kg. (a) How large is the surface tension force? (b) If the wire is in equilibrium, how large is the mass m_2 suspended from the wire?

(a) According to Table 15.1, $\gamma = 7.28 \times 10^{-2}$ N m^{-1}. Thus the force due to the two surfaces of the film of water is

$$F = 2\gamma l = 2(7.28 \times 10^{-2} \text{ N m}^{-1})(0.1 \text{ m})$$
$$= 1.46 \times 10^{-2} \text{ N}$$

(b) In equilibrium the force F exerted by the film must equal the total weight $m_1 g + m_2 g$. Solving for m_2,

$$m_2 = \frac{F}{g} - m_1 = \frac{1.46 \times 10^{-2} \text{ N}}{9.8 \text{ m s}^{-2}} - 10^{-3} \text{ kg}$$
$$= 0.49 \times 10^{-3} \text{ kg} = 0.49 \text{ g}$$

Thus the surface forces support the weight of a total mass $m_1 + m_2$, which is approximately 1.5 g.

15.2 | CONTACT ANGLES AND CAPILLARITY

The surface of a liquid in contact with a solid surface forms an angle with respect to the solid surface (Fig. 15.3). The *contact angle* θ is determined by the competition between the liquid-liquid molecular forces and the liquid-solid forces and depends on the particular solid and liquid involved (Table 15.2). It also depends on how smooth and clean the solid surface is.

If θ is less than 90°, the liquid surface appears as in Fig. 15.3a and will rise in a narrow tube. If θ is greater than 90°, the liquid appears as in Fig. 15.3b

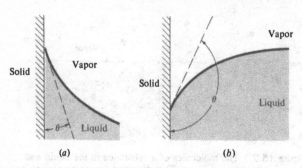

Figure 15.3. The contact angle θ for two liquids in contact with a solid surface. (a) $\theta < 90°$; (b) $\theta > 90°$.

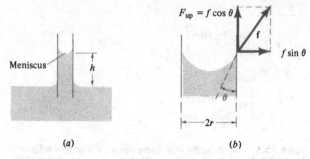

Figure 15.4. Liquid in a tube of radius r with a contact angle θ rises to a height h. The force on a small segment of the liquid in contact with the tube wall is **f**.

and will be depressed in a tube. If $\theta = 90°$, the liquid will neither rise nor fall. The rise or fall of a liquid in a narrow tube or capillary is referred to as *capillarity*, or *capillary action*.

We now look at how the contact angle determines the height of a liquid in a column. Figure 15.4 shows a liquid of density ρ in a tube of radius r. The contact angle is less than 90°. The net vertical force F_{up} is the vertical component of the surface tension times the length l of the liquid surface in contact with the tube; l equals the circumference $2\pi r$. Thus

$$F_{up} = 2\pi r \gamma \cos \theta \qquad (15.2)$$

The volume of the column of liquid up to the bottom of the curved liquid surface, or *meniscus*, is $V = \pi r^2 h$, and its weight is $w = \rho g V = \rho g \pi r^2 h$. The liquid rises until $F_{up} = w$, or

$$2\pi r \gamma \cos \theta = \rho g \pi r^2 h$$

This gives, for the height of the liquid in a capillary,

$$h = \frac{2\gamma \cos \theta}{\rho g r} \qquad (15.3)$$

TABLE 15.2

The contact angles for several liquid–solid interfaces

Interface	Contact Angle
Water–clean glass	0°
Ethyl alcohol–clean glass	0°
Mercury–glass	140°
Water–silver	90°
Water–paraffin	107°
Methylene iodide–Pyrex glass	30°

This result has several notable features. If $\theta = 90°$, then $h = 0$, and the fluid neither rises nor is depressed. If θ is greater than 90°, $\cos \theta$ is negative and so is h. This means that the liquid is depressed. The height h is proportional to γ; the greater the surface tension, the greater the capillary effect. Conversely, h depends on $1/r$, so the effect is most dramatic when r is small.

Although Eq. 15.3 was derived for a circular cross section, capillary rise occurs in tubelike structures or connected channels of any geometry. The height still depends on $\gamma/\rho g r$, where r is some typical dimension, although the overall numerical coefficient changes. For example, water will be easily absorbed by fine, porous fabric if the contact angle is less than 90°. We apply this result to trees in the next example.

Example 15.2

The sap in trees, which consists mainly of water in summer, rises in a system of capillaries of radius $r = 2.5 \times 10^{-5}$ m. The contact angle is 0°. The density of water is 10^3 kg m^{-3}. What is the maximum height to which water can rise in a tree at 20°C?

From Table 15.1, $\gamma = 7.28 \times 10^{-2}$ N m^{-1}. With $\cos \theta = 1$, the height the sap rises is

$$h = \frac{2\gamma \cos \theta}{\rho g r}$$

$$= \frac{2(7.28 \times 10^{-2} \text{ N m}^{-1})}{(10^3 \text{ kg m}^{-3})(9.8 \text{ m s}^{-2})(2.5 \times 10^{-5} \text{ m})}$$

$$= 0.594 \text{ m}$$

Since trees grow to heights of many metres, capillary action cannot account for the supply of water to the top of a tree.

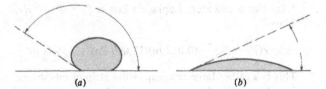

Figure 15.5. Water droplets on paraffin. (a) Pure water. (b) Wetting agent added.

Figure 15.5a shows the shape of a drop of water on paraffin. A wetting agent, a molecule with hydrophobic and hydrophilic portions, would cause the droplet on the paraffin to appear as shown in Fig. 15.5b. The hydrophilic part of the molecule attaches itself to the water surface, and the hydrophobic part stays away from the water surface but is attracted to the paraffin surface. Waterproofing agents have the opposite effect. They cause the angle of contact to be increased, and droplets are less likely to penetrate narrow fabric pores.

15.3 | LAPLACE'S LAW

Laplace's law relates the pressure difference across a closed elastic membrane or liquid film to the tension in the membrane or film. Its specific form depends on the shape of the closed surface.

We begin by considering a spherical membrane or rubber balloon filled with a fluid. The membrane wall exerts a force per unit length or wall tension γ (Fig. 15.6); this force per unit length depends on the thickness of the wall and therefore is associated with the membrane as a whole, *not* with each of the two surfaces as in the case of a liquid film. The pressure inside is P_i and that outside is P_0. The lungs and the ventricles of the heart may be approximated by such a model.

The total force to the left on the hemisphere of Fig. 15.6b due to the wall tension is the product of γ and the circumference $2\pi r$ of the hemisphere, or $2\pi r\gamma$. The forces due to the pressures are perpendicular to the surface at each point. All the components cancel except those to the right, which add up to the pressure difference $P_i - P_0$ times the *projected area* πr^2. The two forces must balance in

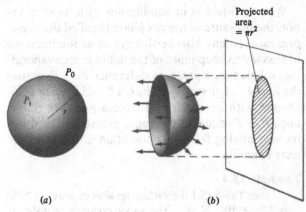

Figure 15.6. (a) A spherical membrane or balloon with inner and outer pressures P_i and P_0. (b) The sphere is cut in half by an imaginary plane. The arrows to the left represent the forces exerted by the wall. The arrows normal to the surface represent the forces due to the pressure difference.

equilibrium, so

$$2\pi r\gamma = (P_i - P_0)\pi r^2$$

or

$$P_i - P_0 = \frac{2\gamma}{r} \qquad \text{(spherical membrane)} \quad (15.4)$$

This is called *Laplace's law for a spherical membrane*. It is named after Marquis Pierre Simon de Laplace (1749–1827), a French physicist and mathematician.

Laplace's law implies that it requires a greater pressure difference to sustain a small sphere than a larger one. It holds true not only for the model discussed, a membrane or a balloon, but also for a spherical liquid drop. Both situations are illustrated by the next two examples.

Example 15.3

A rubber balloon is inflated to a radius of 0.1 m. The pressure inside is 1.001×10^5 Pa, and the pressure outside is 10^5 Pa. What is the wall tension γ?

Solving Laplace's law for γ,

$$\gamma = \frac{r}{2}(P_i - P_0) = \left(\frac{0.1 \text{ m}}{2}\right)(1.001 \times 10^5 \text{ Pa} - 10^5 \text{ Pa})$$

$$= (0.05 \text{ m})(10^2 \text{ Pa}) = 5 \text{ N m}^{-1}$$

This is the tension in the wall when the balloon is inflated to a radius of 0.1 m. Since the balloon is elastic, the wall tension will increase if the radius is increased.

When a liquid is in equilibrium with its own vapor, the pressure of the gas phase is called the *vapor pressure*. It may also be thought of as the pressure necessary to keep more of the liquid from evaporating; it balances a pressure difference $P_i - P_0$ across the liquid-vapor surface. Thus, a liquid drop in equilibrium with its vapor will have a pressure difference $P_i - P_0$ equal to the vapor pressure. The droplet size arising from this condition is found in the next example.

Example 15.4

From Table 15.1 the surface tension of water at 20°C is 7.28×10^{-2} N m^{-1}. The vapor pressure of water at 20° C is 2.33×10^3 Pa. What is the radius of the smallest spherical water droplet which can form without evaporating?

The pressure difference $P_i - P_0$ must be no more than 2.33×10^3 Pa. Solving Laplace's law for r, we have

$$r = \frac{2\gamma}{P_i - P_0} = \frac{2(7.28 \times 10^{-2} \text{ N m}^{-1})}{2.33 \times 10^3 \text{ Pa}}$$
$$= 6.25 \times 10^{-5} \text{ m}$$

In a soap bubble the film has two surfaces, each of which exerts a tension force. Hence if the derivation is repeated, there is an additional factor of 2, and we find

$$P_i - P_0 = \frac{4\gamma}{r} \quad \text{(spherical bubble)} \quad (15.5)$$

Also, for a cylindrical membrane of radius r, Laplace's law is

$$P_i - P_0 = \frac{\gamma}{r} \quad \text{(cylindrical tube)} \quad (15.6)$$

Again we observe the inverse dependence on the radius. In physiology, $P_i - P_0$ is called the *transmural* pressure, the pressure difference across the walls of a blood vessel. This is quite different from the driving pressure that forces fluid through the vessel.

Example 15.5

(a) An aorta has a transmural pressure of 13,000 Pa and a radius of 1.2 cm. What is the tension in its wall?
(b) A small capillary has a transmural pressure of 4000 Pa and a radius of 6×10^{-4} cm. What is its wall tension?

(a) For a cylinder, Laplace's law is $P_i - P_0 = \gamma/r$. Thus

$$\gamma = r(P_i - P_0) = (0.012 \text{ m})(13,000 \text{ Pa}) = 156 \text{ N m}^{-1}$$

This is a rather large tension. A flat strip of membrane 1 m long with this tension would be experiencing a 156-N force, tending to tear it apart. A 156-N force is equal to the weight of a 16-kg mass.

(b) For the small capillary,

$$\gamma = r(P_i - P_0) = (6 \times 10^{-6} \text{ m})(4000 \text{ Pa})$$
$$= 0.024 \text{ N m}^{-1}$$

The tension in the wall of the capillary is small because the radius is small. Hence the very thin capillary walls will not tear despite the large transmural pressure.

Equations 15.4, 15.5, and 15.6 can be deceptive in their apparent simplicity. Implicit in each result is the fact that the pressure and wall tension may depend on the radius. Suppose that we use a soap bubble as an example. Then the surface tension γ is constant as the radius changes and, because there are two surfaces, Eq. 15.5 applies. Suppose the outside pressure is reduced gradually to zero. Then $P_i - P_0$ is replaced by P_i, and Eq. 16.5 becomes

$$P_i = \frac{4\gamma}{r}$$

Now P_i is larger than $P_i - P_0$, so the left-hand side of this equation is larger than before. Since γ is constant, the right-hand side can only increase if r decreases! But this is contrary to our intuition; we know the soap bubble will become larger. The solution is that the inside pressure P_i does not remain constant as P_0 decreases. The following example illustrates this.

Example 15.6

The pressure outside a soap bubble of radius r is initially half the pressure inside, so $P_0 = \frac{1}{2}P_i$. The outside pressure is then reduced to $P_0' = 0$. Find the new pressure inside P_i' and the new radius r', assuming the surface tension γ and temperature remain constant.

Initially $P_0 = \frac{1}{2}P_i$ and $P_i - P_0 = \frac{1}{2}P_i$. Thus $P_i - P_0 = 4\gamma/r$ becomes

$$\frac{1}{2}P_i = \frac{4\gamma}{r} \quad \text{(i)}$$

When the outside pressure is reduced to zero, $P_i' - P_0' = P_i'$ and

$$P_i' = \frac{4\gamma}{r'} \qquad \text{(ii)}$$

Dividing Eq. ii by Eq. i, Laplace's law requires for equilibrium

$$\frac{P_i'}{P_i} = \frac{r}{2r'}$$

Since the temperature remains constant, the ideal gas law gives $P_i V = P_i' V'$. The volume of a sphere is $4\pi r^3/3$, so we find a second relationship between P_i and P_i',

$$\frac{P_i'}{P_i} = \frac{V}{V'} = \frac{r^3}{r'^3}$$

Equating the two expressions for P_i'/P_i, we find $r'^2 = 2r^2$, and $r' = 1.41r$. Thus the radius increases as expected.

15.4 | SURFACTANT IN THE LUNGS

The small air sacs of the lungs, the *alveoli*, expand and contract an average of 15,000 times per day in a normal adult (Fig. 15.7). It is across the membrane of the alveoli that oxygen and carbon dioxide are transported. The tension in the walls results from both the membrane tissue and a liquid on the walls containing a long lipoprotein, *surfactant*. We will see that the surfactant gives the membrane the elas-

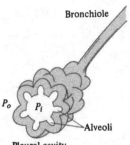

Figure 15.7. A cross section exposing alveoli at the end of a bronchiole, the smallest branch of a bronchial tube. The pressure inside the alveoli is P_i; the pressure in the fluid of the pleural cavity is P_0. The pleural cavity encloses the entire lung.

ticity needed to make the required adjustments in the wall tension.

The alveoli may be approximated by small spheres with tiny entrances. Thus we may use Laplace's law, Eq. 15.4, rewritten as

$$r(P_i - P_0) = r\,\Delta P = 2\gamma \qquad \text{(15.7)}$$

For a spherical membrane, the product of the radius and the pressure difference must be equal to 2γ for the membrane to be in equilibrium. In the alveoli, there is a special problem. During exhalation the pleural pressure P_0 increases, so ΔP decreases. At the same time, muscle contraction reduces the radii of the alveoli. If both r and ΔP decrease and γ is constant, the equilibrium condition, Eq. 15.7, cannot be satisfied, and the alveoli will collapse, because the inward force due to the walls exceeds the outward force due to the pressure difference. During inhalation the pleural pressure P_0 decreases and the radius increases. Again, if γ is constant, Eq. 15.7 is not satisfied, and the alveoli would tend to increase in size and rupture; the force due to the pressure difference would exceed the force due to the wall.

Nature solves this problem by having the surfactant present. Its long molecules prefer to lie nearly beside each other, making the membrane highly elastic. During inhalation, as the radius increases, the molecules are pulled apart and the wall tension increases. As $r\,\Delta P$ increases, so does γ, and Eq. 15.7 is satisfied. During exhalation the molecules slide back together, and the wall tension decreases along with $r\,\Delta P$. Thus the surfactant serves to change the wall tension so that equilibrium is maintained. Insufficient surfactant in the lungs is the cause of death of many newborn infants.

15.5 | THE HEART AS A PUMP

As our last example of how the physics of fluids can be used in understanding the circulatory system, we examine the mechanical properties of the heart. In particular, we calculate the work done by the heart in pumping blood and compare the result with the total metabolic energy expended.

In Section 14.2, we found that the power necessary to overcome viscous forces and maintain fluid flow is $\mathscr{P} = Q \, \Delta P$. We can use this result for the heart.

In a normal resting adult, the heart pumps 9.7×10^{-5} m^3 of blood per second. The pressure drop from the arterial to the venous systems is 11.7 kPa. Hence the power expended by the heart in overcoming viscous forces is

$$\begin{aligned}
\mathscr{P} &= Q \, \Delta P \\
&= (9.7 \times 10^{-5} \text{ m}^3 \text{ s}^{-1})(11.7 \text{ kPa}) \\
&= 1.1 \times 10^{-3} \text{ kW} = 1.1 \text{ W}.
\end{aligned}$$

Note that 1 Pa m^3 s^{-1} = 1 watt = 1 W.

The total metabolic energy used by the heart can be estimated by measuring its oxygen consumption. For a 70-kg resting man, it is found that the rate of energy usage by the entire heart is about 5.5 W. Of this, about 2.5 W are available to do useful work; the remainder is converted directly to heat during metabolism. We have just seen that 1.1 W are used to do mechanical work pumping blood. A significant fraction of the remaining 1.4 W is used to maintain the wall tension of the heart.

We can gain some insight into this wall tension by using a model that depicts the heart chamber that pumps blood to the body, the left ventricle, as a sphere. When the ventricle contracts, its wall must be under active tension to generate the increased blood pressure. The force per unit length or tension γ exerted by the wall was found in the preceding chapter to be related to the pressure difference $\Delta P = P_i - P_0$ and the radius r by Laplace's law, $\Delta P = 2\gamma/r$ or $\gamma = r \, \Delta P/2$. The total force produced along an imaginary cut in the wall (Fig. 15.6b) is then

$$F = 2\pi r \gamma = \pi r^2 \, \Delta P$$

The energy required by the heart muscle is related to this force, but the exact relationship is complex. However, we can see qualitatively what may happen. If a person suffers from high blood pressure, ΔP is large, and the power, $Q \, \Delta P$, the heart must expend to pump blood is larger than normal. The energy necessary to maintain the wall tension is also greater than normal. After months or even years, this high pressure may lead to enlargement of the heart. Since the wall force increases with r^2,

even more energy will be required, and the heart's oxygen requirements will be correspondingly larger. Congestive heart failure occurs when the oxygen supply is insufficient to meet the increased demands of the heart muscle.

15.6 | THE RISE OF SAP IN TREES; NEGATIVE PRESSURES

Sap is water plus the products of photosynthesis, including sugar. The fact that sap can reach the top of Douglas fir trees, 60 m or more high, has long been a puzzle. We have already seen that osmotic pressure (Chapter Ten) and capillary action (Example 15.2) cannot explain this phenomenon.

Negative pressures arising from the cohesive forces in water appear to provide the answer to this puzzle. These cohesive forces of water can be measured with an apparatus such as that of Fig. 15.8. When the piston is pulled upward the water expands very slightly, exerting a downward force on the piston. The force per unit area on the piston is found experimentally to be between 25 and 300 atm just before the column separates from the piston. This pressure is called negative pressure because the water is pulling *inward* on the piston instead of pushing *outward*. Because of the attractive forces among the molecules, the water and piston behave much like a solid rod that resists tension forces applied to its ends.

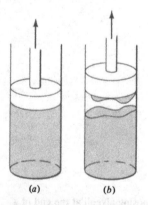

Figure 15.8. (a) Pure water, containing no dissolved gases, fills the volume beneath a piston in a chamber. The piston is pulled upward; the water pulls downward. (b) The water finally separates from the piston leaving water and its vapor.

In trees, the sap moves through the *xylem*, which forms channels with radii from 2.5×10^{-5} to 2.5×10^{-4} m. The xylem channels are filled with water up to the leaves. As water is evaporated from the leaf, the water column moves upward to keep itself intact. We can determine whether the experimentally observed maximum values of the negative pressure are consistent with the rise of water in tall trees.

If we suppose that the pressure at the base of a tree trunk is atmospheric pressure P_A, then the pressure at a height h above the ground is

$$P_h = P_A - \rho g h \qquad (15.8)$$

If h is large enough, P_h can become negative. For a tree 60 m in height, $P_h = -4.8$ atm. This is well within the range of the observed negative pressures in water. Thus it is believed that the negative pressure arising from the cohesive forces among the water molecules is responsible for the rise of sap to the tops of trees.

SUMMARY

Molecules at the surface of a liquid are subject to forces that attract them to the bulk of the liquid. Because of these forces the molecules of the liquid tend to stick together, producing the surface tension. The surface tension is defined as the force exerted by the surface of the liquid per unit length and is denoted by γ.

When a liquid is in contact with a solid, there is a competition between the liquid-liquid molecular forces and the liquid-solid molecular forces for those molecules near the region of contact. The results of this competition determine the shape of the liquid surface and the contact angle between the solid and liquid surfaces. If the liquid–liquid forces dominate, the liquid surface is depressed when a tube is lowered into the liquid. The liquid rises in the tube if the liquid–solid forces dominate.

Laplace's law describes the relation between the pressure difference across the surface of a closed membrane and the wall tension in the membrane. It is particularly useful in understanding the relation between the size of the membrane and the pressure as illustrated by the discussions of surfactant in the lungs and the heart's pumping capacity.

Checklist

Define or explain:

surface tension	meniscus
contact angle	Laplace's law
capillarity	alveoli
hydrophobic	ventricle
hydrophilic	negative pressure

REVIEW QUESTIONS

Q15-1   Is the surface tension γ defined as a force or as a force per unit length?

Q15-2   True or false? The molecules in the bulk of a fluid play absolutely no role in the surface tension.

Q15-3   The _____ between liquid and solid surfaces depends on the molecular forces between solid–liquid and liquid–liquid molecules.

Q15-4   If the contact angle at a liquid–solid interface is near zero, the liquid will _____ in a narrow tube made of the solid.

Q15-5   Wetting agents result in _____ contact angles between the solid and liquid.

Q15-6   A general feature of Laplace's law for the membrane shapes considered in the text is that it requires a _____ pressure difference to sustain a small radius surface than it does to sustain a large one.

Q15-7   The presence of surfactant in the lungs ensures that the wall tension of the alveoli varies with the _____.

Q15-8   The wall force in the heart, required to maintain blood flow, depends on the blood pressure and on the _____ of the heart.

Q15-9   The phenomenon described as _____ in trees is due to the cohesiveness, or stick-togetherness, of a pure liquid.

EXERCISES

Section 15.1 | Surface Tension

15-1   The surface tension of a liquid is measured using the apparatus of Fig. 15.1. If the straight wire is 0.05 m long and the weight of the wire plus attached weights is 2×10^{-3} N, what is the surface tension of the liquid?

15-2   If the surface tension of a liquid is 3×10^{-2} N m^{-1} and the length of the wire is 0.2 m,

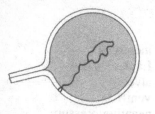

Figure 15.9.   Exercise 15-3.

what total weight will the liquid support in the apparatus of Fig. 15.1?

15-3   Figure 15.9 shows a loop of thread attached to a wire ring that has been dipped into a soap solution. Why does the loop assume a circular shape when the film inside is punctured?

Section 15.2 | Contact Angles and Capillarity

15-4   How high will water at 0°C rise in a tube of radius 10^{-3} m if it is made (a) of glass; (b) of paraffin?

15-5   How far will the meniscus of mercury be depressed in a glass tube of radius 10^{-4} m?

15-6   A glass tube of radius 1 mm = 10^{-3} m is used to construct a mercury barometer (Fig. 15.10). (a) How far will the surface be shifted by capillary effects? Is it raised or lowered? (b) If the height of the mercury column is 0.76 m, what fractional error is introduced if the capillary effects are ignored?

15-7   Normal atmospheric pressure supports a column of mercury 0.76 m high. A mercury barometer consists of a glass tube filled with mercury (Fig. 15.10). If capillary effects are to be less than 0.01 percent of the height of the column, what is the minimum radius of the tube?

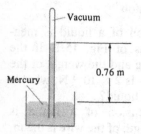

Figure 15.10.   Exercises 15-6 and 15-7.

15-8   How high will ethyl alcohol rise in a glass tube 0.04 mm = 4×10^{-5} m in diameter? (The density of ethyl alcohol is 791 kg m^{-3}.)

Section 15.3 | Laplace's Law

15-9   A soap bubble has a radius of 0.05 m. If the pressure difference between the inside and outside is 2 Pa, what is the surface tension of the soap film?

15-10   The radius of a small vein is 0.02 cm, and the transmural pressure is 2000 Pa. What is the tension in the wall?

15-11   A rubber water hose with a radius of 1 cm carries water at a gauge pressure of 6 atm. (a) What is the tension in the walls of the hose? (b) What force applied to a 2π-cm-wide strip of rubber would produce this large a wall tension?

15-12   How would you expect the weight of a garden hose to vary with its radius? (Assume the length and the maximum permissible water pressure are constant.)

15-13   A spherical balloon of radius 0.1 m is filled with helium at a gauge pressure of 1.01 atm. What is the tension in its wall?

15-14   Derive Eq. 15.5.

15-15   Derive Eq. 15.6

15-16   What is the pressure difference between the inside and outside of a droplet of glycerine of radius 10^{-4} m?

Section 15.4 | Surfactant in the Lungs

15-17   A typical alveolus has a radius of 10^{-4} m. The wall tension is 0.05 N m^{-1}. (a) What is the pressure difference between the inside and outside of the alveolus? (b) There is an outward normal force everywhere on the alveolar surface. Find the sum of the magnitudes of these forces. (The surface area of a sphere is $4\pi r^2$.)

15-18   At the end of exhalation the radius of the alveoli is 0.5×10^{-4} m. The gauge pressure inside the alveoli is -400 Pa, and in the pleural cavity it is -534 Pa. What is the wall tension in the alveoli? How does this compare with the wall tension of 0.05 N m^{-1} in the absence of surfactant?

Section 15.5 | The Heart as a Pump

15-19   Using the assumption that a ventricle may be approximated by a sphere, by what factor must the wall force increase if the ventricle radius increases by 10 percent?

15-20 A man exercising vigorously is using metabolic energy at a rate 10 times as large as when he is at rest. His arterial blood pressure rises by 50 percent above the resting level. Assuming the rate of blood flow is proportional to the metabolic rate, estimate (a) the blood flow rate for this person; (b) the work done by the heart against viscous forces in pumping the blood. (In a typical resting human, the blood flow rate is 9.7×10^{-5} m^3 s^{-1}.)

Section 15.6 | The Rise of Sap in Trees; Negative Pressures

15-21 If the pressure of sap in a tree is negative, will fluid flow out of a fine tube inserted into the xylem?

15-22 The pressure of sap in the xylem is measured at two points 1 m apart in height. What pressure difference is observed?

15-23 What is the negative pressure at the base of a tree 20 m high?

15-24 Show that if the pressure is measured in atmospheres and h in metres, Eq. 15.8 can be written as $P_h = 1 - (0.0967$ m$^{-1})h$.

PROBLEMS

15-25 A thin wire loop of weight w and radius r floats on a liquid with surface tension γ (Fig. 15.11). What force F must be exerted to remove the loop?

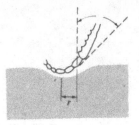

Figure 15.12. An insect leg supported by water. Problem 15-26.

15-26 Each leg of a six-legged insect standing on water at 20°C produces a depression of radius $r = 10^{-3}$ m (Fig. 15.12). The angle ϕ is 30°. (a) What is the surface tension force acting upward on each leg? (b) What is the weight of the insect?

15-27 A narrow cylindrical tube of radius r is inserted slightly into a liquid or surface tension γ (Fig. 15.13). If one blows into the top so that a hemispherical bubble forms at the lower end, show that the pressure in the tube P is given by $P = P_A + 2\gamma/r$, where P_A is the atmospheric pressure.

15-28 Two bubbles with radii r and R are at either end of a tube that is closed off by a clamp (Fig. 15.14). If the clamp is released, what happens to the two bubbles?

15-29 A soap bubble is formed by dipping one end of a tube of radius r in a soap solution and blowing on the other end until the bubble is hemi-

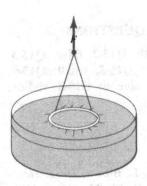

Figure 15.11. Problem 15-25.

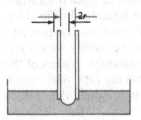

Figure 15.13. Problem 15-27.

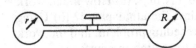

Figure 15.14. Problem 15-28.

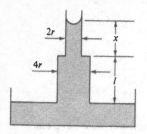

Figure 15.15. Problem 15-30.

spherical and has the same radius as the tube. Show that the pressure in the tube P is related to the atmospheric pressure P_A by

$$P = P_A + \frac{4\gamma}{r}$$

*15-30 A capillary tube is constructed as shown in Fig. 15.15. The lower segment of length l has radius $2r$ and the upper segment has radius r. How high in the upper segment will a liquid with surface tension γ (where $\gamma > 2rl\rho g$) climb if the contact angle is 0°?

15-31 When a glass tube is dipped into water at 20°C, the water rises to a height of 0.2 m. When the tube is dipped into a liquid of density 700 kg m^{-3}, the liquid is observed to rise to a height of 0.15 m and to make a contact angle of 0°. What is the surface tension of that liquid? (The density of water at 20°C is 990 kg m^{-3}.)

15-32 An alternative way of defining the surface tension is the potential energy per unit area or the energy that must be supplied to stretch a surface divided by the increase in area. (a) In Fig. 15.1, how much work must be done on the two surfaces of the film to lower the sliding wire a distance d? (b) What is the increase in area of the two surfaces? (c) Show that the ratio of the work done to the increase in area equals the surface tension γ.

15-33 A soap bubble is blown up from a radius of 3 cm to a radius of 5 cm. The surface tension of the film is 2.5×10^{-2} N m^{-1}. (a) How much work must be done against the atmosphere? (b) Using the result of the preceding problem, find the work that must be done to stretch the surface.

15-34 A wire with a radius of 0.05 mm is dipped vertically into water at 20°C. The water makes a contact angle of 0° with the wire. What length of wire is under the water when the buoyant force exactly balances the downward force exerted by the surface of the water on the wire?

15-35 (a) To what height will water rise in a vertical glass capillary tube of radius 3×10^{-5} m? (b) If the tube is only 0.2 m long, will the water overflow the top of the tube? (Assume that the top edges of the tube are smoothly rounded and that the water is at 0°C.)

15-36 Capillary rise or fall is not limited to cylindrical tubes. Show that when two flat plates separated by a distance d are placed vertically in a fluid, the fluid rises a height $h = (2\gamma \cos \theta)/\rho g d$ between the plates. (γ is the surface tension of the fluid, ρ is its density, and θ is the contact angle between the fluid and the plates.)

15-37 Use the result of the previous problem to find the height that water at 20°C rises between two flat glass plates separated by 0.3 mm = 3×10^{-4} m.

15-38 A person suffering from high blood pressure has an average difference between the arterial and venous systems of 20 kPa instead of the normal 11.7 kPa. Assume that the energy expended in maintaining the tension in the heart wall is proportional to the force it exerts. (a) If the heart is not enlarged, by what factor are its metabolic requirements increased? (b) If the heart is enlarged in radius by 5 percent, estimate the additional metabolic demands this implies.

ANSWERS TO REVIEW QUESTIONS

Q15-1, force per unit length; **Q15-2**, false; **Q15-3**, contact angle; **Q15-4**, rise; **Q15-5**, small; **Q15-6**, larger; **Q15-7**, radii of the alveoli; **Q15-8**, radius; **Q15-9**, negative pressure.

Additional Reading

Martin H. Zimmerman and C. L. Brown, *Trees: Structure and Function*, Springer-Verlag, New York, 1971.

Alan T. Hayward, Negative Pressure in Liquids: Can It Be Harnessed to Serve Man? *American Scientist*, vol. 59, 1971, p. 434.

P. F. Scholander, Tensile Water, *American Scientist*, vol. 60, 1972, p. 584.

R. McNeill Alexander, *Animal Mechanics*, University of Washington Press, Seattle, 1968, Chapters 5 and 6.

Scientific American articles:

James E. McDonald, The Shape of Raindrops, February 1954, p. 64.

V. A. Greulach, The Rise of Water in Plants, October 1952, p. 78.

John A. Clements, Surface Tension in the Lungs, December 1962, p. 120.

Thomas F. Robinson, Stephen M. Factor, Edmund H. Sonnenblick, The Heart as a Suction Pump, June 1986, p. 84. A new model for the heart.

Martin H. Zimmerman, How Sap Moves in Trees, March 1963, p. 132.

Robert E. Apfel, The Tensile Strength of Liquids, December 1962, p. 58.

Jearl Walker, Funny Things Happen When Drops of Oil or Other Substances Are Placed in Water, *The Amateur Scientist*, December 1983, p. 164.

Jearl Walker, What Causes the "Tears" That Form on the Inside of a Glass of Wine? *The Amateur Scientist*, May 1983, p. 162. Surface tension effects.

See also selected references on the heart in Chapter 14.

APPENDIX A

PERIODIC TABLE OF ELEMENTS

The symbol for each element is preceded by the atomic number; below is the atomic mass of the element as it occurs naturally on the earth. The atomic mass unit (u) is defined so the mass of a ^{12}C atom is exactly 12 u. The mass of carbon is listed as 12.01115 u because naturally occurring carbon is 98.89 percent ^{12}C and 1.11 percent ^{13}C. For artificially produced elements, the approximate atomic mass of the most stable isotope is given in brackets.

Period	Series	I	II	III	IV	V	VI	VII	VIII			O
1	1	1 H 1.00797										2 He 4.0026
2	2	3 Li 6.939	4 Be 9.0122	5 B 10.811	6 C 12.01115	7 N 14.0067	8 O 15.9994	9 F 18.9984				10 Ne 20.183
3	3	11 Na 22.9898	12 Mg 24.312	13 Al 26.9815	14 Si 28.086	15 P 30.9738	16 S 32.064	17 Cl 35.453				18 A 39.948
4	4	19 K 39.102	20 Ca 40.08	21 Sc 44.956	22 Ti 47.90	23 V 50.942	24 Cr 51.996	25 Mn 54.9380	26 Fe 55.847	27 Co 58.9332	28 Ni 58.71	
	5	29 Cu 63.54	30 Zn 65.37	31 Ga 69.72	32 Ge 72.59	33 As 74.9216	34 Se 78.96	35 Br 79.909				36 Kr 83.80
5	6	37 Rb 85.47	38 Sr 87.62	39 Y 88.905	40 Zr 91.22	41 Nb 92.906	42 Mo 95.94	43 Tc [99]	44 Ru 101.07	45 Rh 102.905	46 Pd 106.4	
	7	47 Ag 107.870	48 Cd 112.40	49 In 114.82	50 Sn 118.69	51 Sb 121.75	52 Te 127.60	53 I 126.9044				54 Xe 131.30
6	8	55 Cs 132.905	56 Ba 137.34	57–71 Lanthanide series*	72 Hf 178.49	73 Ta 180.948	74 W 183.85	75 Re 186.2	76 Os 190.2	77 Ir 192.2	78 Pt 195.09	
	9	79 Au 196.967	80 Hg 200.59	81 Tl 204.37	82 Pb 207.19	83 Bi 208.980	84 Po [210]	85 At [210]				86 Rn [222]
7	10	87 Fr [223]	88 Ra [226.05]	89–Actinide series**								
		104 [261]	105 [262]	106 [263]								

*Lanthanide series:

57 La 138.91	58 Ce 140.12	59 Pr 140.907	60 Nd 144.24	61 Pm [145]	62 Sm 150.35	63 Eu 151.96	64 Gd 157.25	65 Tb 158.924	66 Dy 162.50	67 Ho 164.930	68 Er 167.26	69 Tm 168.934	70 Yb 173.04	71 Lu 174.97

**Actinide series:

89 Ac [227]	90 Th 232.038	91 Pa [231]	92 U 238.03	93 Np [237]	94 Pu [242]	95 Am [243]	96 Cm [247]	97 Bk [247]	98 Cf [249]	99 Es [254]	100 Fm [257]	101 Md [256]	102 No [253]	103 Lw [260]

APPENDIX B

MATHEMATICAL REVIEW

This appendix reviews topics covered in high school or introductory college mathematics courses that are needed in various parts of this book. Students who are somewhat rusty in basic algebra, geometry, and trigonometry may find it helpful to study Sections B.1 to B.6 in detail; the remaining sections are provided mainly for reference at specific points in the book. A list of paperback mathematics review books is given at the end of the appendix for students who need additional preparation in this area. Answers to all the review problems are also given at the end of this appendix.

B.1 | POWERS AND ROOTS

A quantity x multiplied by itself n times is written as x^n. For example, $(2)(2)(2) = 2^3$; in words, this is 2 raised to the *exponent* or *power* 3. The basic rule in manipulating powers of a given number is that exponents add. For example, $(2^2)(2^3) = (2)(2) \cdot (2)(2)(2) = 2^5$. In symbols, the rule is

$$(x^n)(x^m) = x^{n+m} \tag{B.1}$$

From this rule, we see that $x^n x^0 = x^n$, so $x^0 = 1$ for any value of x. Also, $x^n x^{-n} = x^0 = 1$, so x^{-n} is the inverse of x^n:

$$x^{-n} = \frac{1}{x^n} \tag{B.2}$$

For example, $10^{-2} = 1/10^2 = 1/100 = 0.01$. Another useful rule is

$$(x^n)^m = x^{nm} \tag{B.3}$$

For example, $(10^2)^3 = (10)(10) \cdot (10)(10) \cdot (10)(10) = 10^6$; similarly, $(10^2)^{-3} = 10^{-6}$.

When two numbers are raised to the same power, their products and quotients obey simple rules:

$$(x^n)(y^n) = (xy)^n \tag{B.4}$$

$$\frac{x^n}{y^n} = \left(\frac{x}{y}\right)^n \tag{B.5}$$

For example, $(4)^2(2)^3 = (4 \cdot 2)^3 = (8)^3$, and $(4)^3(2)^{-3} = (4/2)^3 = (2)^3$.

A fractional exponent means that a root of a number is involved. For example, $x^{1/2}x^{1/2} = x^1 = x$, so $x^{1/2}$ is the square root of x. The quantity $x^{1/n}$ is the nth root of x:

$$x^{1/n} = \sqrt[n]{x} \tag{B.6}$$

For example, $(64)^{1/3} = \sqrt[3]{64} = 4$. More complicated fractional powers can be evaluated with the aid of Eq. B.3. For example, $(27)^{2/3} = (27^{1/3})^2 = (3)^2 = 9$. All the other rules listed above also apply to fractional powers.

REVIEW PROBLEMS

Evaluate or simplify the following quantities:

1. 2^4
2. 3^2
3. $(2^2)(2^3)$
4. $(x^5)(x^3)(x)$
5. 5^{-2}
6. $(5^{-3})(5^4)$
7. $(x^4)(x)(x^{-3})$
8. x^4/x^2
9. x^4/y^4
10. $(a^2x^4)^{1/2}$
11. $(a^3x^6)^{1/2}$
12. $(x^2y^6)^{1/2}$
13. $(x^4y^4)^{-1/2}$
14. $(1000)^{1/3}$

15. $(10,000)^{-1/4}$

16. $x^2(x^6)^{-1/3}$

17. $(125)^{-1/3}$

18. $\left(\dfrac{x^2}{64}\right)^{1/2}$

19. $(x^4 y^{-8})^{1/2}$

20. $(10^4)^{3/4}$

B.2 | SCIENTIFIC NOTATION

A number is said to be in scientific notation when it is written as a number between 1 and 10 times a power of 10. For example, 376 can be written as $3.76 \times 100 = 3.76 \times 10^2$, since $10^2 = 10 \times 10 = 100$. One advantage of this notation is compactness; 376,000,000 can be written as 3.76×10^8. Note that the power of 10 is the number of places the decimal point has been shifted to the left. Similarly, $0.0000376 = 3.76 \times 0.00001 = 3.76 \times 10^{-5}$. Here the number in this negative exponent indicates how many places the decimal point has been shifted to the right.

Scientific notation facilitates many kinds of numerical calculations. It is especially useful in manipulations involving very large or small numbers. As an illustration, consider 2×10^{20} times 3×10^{-15} divided by 8×10^8:

$$\frac{(2 \times 10^{20})(3 \times 10^{-15})}{8 \times 10^8} = \frac{(2)(3)}{8} \times 10^{20-15-8}$$

$$= 0.75 \times 10^{-3} = 7.5 \times 10^{-4}$$

The use of scientific notation also aids in the evaluation of roots, as in the following illustrations:

$$(2.32 \times 10^8)^{1/2} = (2.32)^{1/2}(10^8)^{1/2} = \sqrt{2.32} \times 10^4$$
$$= 1.52 \times 10^4$$

$$(2.32 \times 10^8)^{1/3} = (232 \times 10^6)^{1/3}$$
$$= (232)^{1/3}(10^6)^{1/3}$$
$$= \sqrt[3]{232} \times 10^2 = 6.14 \times 10^2$$

$$(9.37 \times 10^{-4})^{1/3} = (937 \times 10^{-6})^{1/3}$$
$$= (937)^{1/3}(10^{-6})^{1/3}$$
$$= \sqrt[3]{937} \times 10^{-2}$$
$$= 9.79 \times 10^{-2}$$

In the last two examples, we have rewritten the power of 10 so that it leads to an integer power of 10 when the root is calculated. Notice also from the first two examples that the cube root of a number greater than 1 is less than the square root; the fourth root is smaller still. The converse statement holds for numbers less than 1.

REVIEW PROBLEMS

Write the following numbers in scientific notation:

21. 27,631

22. 2,763,100

23. 15,000

24. 0.000000034

25. 1,600

26. 4,329.76

27. 0.003902

28. 0.08002

Express the following numbers in ordinary notation:

29. 2.34×10^{-3}

30. 1.76×10^6

31. 5.799×10^{-5}

32. 4.5×10^7

33. 0.067×10^4

34. 27.2×10^5

35. 0.0272×10^8

Evaluate the following expressions:

36. $(3 \times 10^6)(5 \times 10^4)$

37. $\dfrac{4 \times 10^8}{8 \times 10^6}$

38. $(5 \times 10^{10})(3 \times 10^{-8})(4 \times 10^6)$

39. $\dfrac{(4.4 \times 10^6)(3 \times 10^3)^2}{6 \times 10^{-4}}$

40. $\dfrac{(8.25 \times 10^4)(3.14)(5.2 \times 10^3)^2}{(6.25 \times 10^{-3})}$

41. $(4 \times 10^4)^{1/2}$

42. $(90,000)^{1/2}$

43. $(2.7 \times 10^7)^{1/3}$

44. $(8,000)^{1/3}$

45. $(4 \times 10^{-6})^{1/2}$

46. $(160,000)^{1/4}$

47. $(10^{10})^{1/2}$

48. $(10^{10})^{-1/2}$

49. $(10^{10})^{1/3}$

50. $(3.2 \times 10^8)^{1/3}$

B.3 | SIGNIFICANT FIGURES

The accuracy of any measurement is limited by errors of various types (see Section 1.1). It is important to keep track of these errors at least approximately in using or manipulating experimentally determined numbers. This is accomplished most readily with the rules for significant figures.

The principle involved is illustrated by the problem of determining the area A of a rectangular sheet of paper using a ruler whose smallest spacing is 0.1 cm. If we place one end of the ruler at the edge of the paper, the other edge might lie between the markings indicating 8.4 and 8.5 cm. We can, at best, then judge its position to one tenth of a spacing, so we might report our reading as 8.43 cm. However, a more elaborate measuring arrangement might well give a length closer to 8.44 or 8.42 cm; the last digit we report is somewhat uncertain. The number 8.43 is said to have three *significant figures*. In the same way we might find 6.77 cm for the other dimension of the rectangle. The area is then the product

$$A = (8.43 \text{ cm})(6.77 \text{ cm}) = 57.0711 \text{ cm}^2 = 57.1 \text{ cm}^2$$

Each of the factors in the product is uncertain in the third place, so only three places on the right have any meaning. Hence A is given to three significant figures. To clarify the reason for this, suppose the first factor is found to be closer to 8.42 cm when more careful measurements are made. Then the area becomes $A = (8.42 \text{ cm})(6.77 \text{ cm}) = 57.0034 \text{ cm}^2$, and the digits beyond 57.0 are changed. Clearly, these digits in the product are meaningless, and the area A is somewhat uncertain in the third digit. Note that our answer for A has been rounded up from 57.07 . . . to 57.1; a number below 57.05 would be rounded down to 57.0.

In all computations involving multiplication and division, the factor with the fewest significant figures determines the number of significant figures in the answer. For example, in

$$\frac{(8.2239)(2.7)(98.35)\pi^2}{2764} = 7.797899 \ldots$$

the first three factors in the numerator have five, two, and four significant figures, respectively; $\pi^2 = (3.1415926 \ldots)^2$ is known to an arbitrarily great accuracy; and the denominator is known to four significant figures. Accordingly, the answer obtained for this expression should be rounded to two figures, that is, to 7.8. However, it is a good idea to retain one or more extra places in *intermediate steps* of the calculation in order to avoid introducing additional errors in the process of rounding off the numbers. This is important in complex multistep calculations and is easy to do with an electronic calculator.

The significant figures procedure used in addition and subtraction differs from that for multiplication and division. It is illustrated by the sum

$$\begin{array}{r} 45.76 \\ + \ 0.123 \\ \hline 45.883 \end{array}$$

Here the 6 in the first number is somewhat uncertain, and the next place is completely unknown. Accordingly, the 3 in the sum is meaningless, and the answer is rounded to 45.88. *The answer contains as many places relative to the decimal point as the "least accurate number" in the sum.* Notice that in this example the least accurate number that limits the accuracy is 45.76, which has four significant figures; 0.123 has only three significant figures but is more accurate in the sense meant here.

Since the same ideas apply to subtraction, the difference of two nearly equal numbers may have very few significant figures. For example, consider

$$\begin{array}{r} 35.179 \\ -35.17813 \\ \hline 0.001 \end{array}$$

This result has essentially no accuracy, since it is uncertain by approximately 1 in the last place. If a new set of measurements changed the numbers slightly, their difference could well be 0.002 or -0.001.

Adding or subtracting numbers expressed in scientific notation requires that they be written with the same power of 10. For example,

$$\begin{aligned} 2.25 \times 10^6 + 6.4 \times 10^7 &= 2.25 \times 10^6 + 64 \times 10^6 \\ &= 66.25 \times 10^6 \\ &= 6.6 \times 10^7 \end{aligned}$$

Note that we have rounded 66.25 to 66 in accordance with the rules.

Significant Zeros | The number 1200 may have

two, three, or four significant figures, depending upon whether the zeros represent measurements or are merely used to locate the decimal point. Scientific notation avoids this ambiguity; 1.2×10^3, 1.20×10^3, and 1.200×10^3 have two, three, and four significant figures, respectively.

REVIEW PROBLEMS

Round off the following quantities to three significant figures and write them in scientific notation:

51. 27632.0	**54.** 3.33333
52. 0.3729	**55.** 2.45558×10^4
53. 4.6667	**56.** 0.000034567

How many significant figures are there in the final result for each of the following expressions?

57. $(3.2)(8.67)/(3.008)$
58. $(0.0002)(45.6)$
59. $(2.0 \times 10^5)(3.777 \times 10^{-4})$
60. $17.2 + 2.35 + 4.3333$
61. $88.45 + 9.24 - 6.05043$
62. $186.45 - 186.12$

Evaluate the following expressions in accordance with the rules for significant figures:

63. $3.28 \times 10^5 + 4.25 \times 10^7$
64. $3.7 \times 10^6 + 2.91 \times 10^7$
65. $1.91 \times 10^{-3} - 1.7 \times 10^{-5}$

B.4 | SOLUTION OF ALGEBRAIC EQUATIONS

The application of physical laws often leads to one or more algebraic equations that must be solved for the desired quantities. To do this, we must have as many equations as there are unknowns; for example, if we want to find two forces acting on an object, we must have two different equations relating them.

Equations in One Unknown | The basic rule in manipulating any algebraic equation is that both sides of the equation must be treated in the same way. If we add a number to one side, or multiply it by some factor, or square it, we must do the same thing to the other side.

To illustrate how a simple equation is solved, we first consider a *linear* equation, one in which the unknown quantity x appears only to the first power:

$$5x - 10 = 30$$

To solve for x, we first add 10 to both sides, giving

$$5x = 40$$

Dividing by 5 leads to the desired solution:

$$x = 8$$

A *quadratic* equation is one in which the highest power of the unknown is 2. Quadratic equations may or may not have a term linear in the unknown. An example of the latter situation is

$$16t^2 = 64$$

Dividing by 16 gives $t^2 = 4$. Taking the square root then gives two possible answers, $t = +2$ and $t = -2$, since either of these numbers squared is equal to 4. (Quadratic equations generally have two solutions.) Since t represents some number such as a time that is measured, it can only have one correct value. The circumstances of the specific problem will indicate which is the appropriate solution. For example, in Chapter One, in determining when a ball thrown straight up is at a specific height, we encounter quadratic equations in the time variable t. The two solutions of these equations correspond to the time when the ball is at that height on the way up and on the way down.

The quadratic equation

$$t^2 - 6t + 8 = 0$$

is somewhat more complicated than the preceding one, since it contains t to the first power as well as t^2. It can be solved by *factoring*, rewriting the equation as a product of two factors that is equal to zero:

$$(t - 2)(t - 4) = 0$$

This factoring can be verified by noting that when we multiply out the two factors, we obtain four terms, $t^2 - 4t - 2t + 8 = t^2 - 6t + 8$. Clearly the product can be zero only if either the first *or* the second factor is 0. Thus

$$t - 2 = 0, \qquad t = 2$$

or

$$t - 4 = 0, \qquad t = 4$$

The two solutions of this equation are $t = 2$ and $t = 4$.

The disadvantage of factoring is that one must guess the factors somehow. The *quadratic formula* is a general solution that can always be used without any guesswork. The equation

$$at^2 + bt + c = 0$$

has two solutions,

$$t = \frac{-b + \sqrt{b^2 - 4ac}}{2a}$$

and   (B.7)

$$t = \frac{-b - \sqrt{b^2 - 4ac}}{2a}$$

This can be applied to the example $t^2 - 6t + 8 = 0$ by setting $a = 1$, $b = -6$, and $c = 8$. We find then

$$t = \frac{-(-6) + \sqrt{(-6)^2 - 4(1)(8)}}{2(1)}$$

$$= \frac{6 + \sqrt{4}}{2} = 4$$

and

$$t = \frac{-(-6) - \sqrt{(-6)^2 - 4(1)(8)}}{2(1)}$$

$$= \frac{6 - \sqrt{4}}{2} = 4$$

These are the same solutions as found before.

Simultaneous Equations | Two different equations containing the same two unknowns are called *simultaneous equations*. The unknowns are found by combining the equations in such a way that a single equation is obtained that contains just one unknown. For example, consider these two equations for a force F and an acceleration a, $F - 6a = 20$ and $-F + 8a = 0$. If we add these equations, the F and $-F$ cancel:

$$\begin{array}{r} F - 6a = 20 \\ -F + 8a = 0 \\ \hline F - F - 6a + 8a = 20 + 0 \end{array}$$

This reduces to

$$2a = 20$$

or

$$a = 10$$

F is then found by substituting the value found for a into the first equation:

$$F - 6(10) = 20, \qquad F = 20 + 60 = 80$$

Sometimes one equation must be multiplied by a factor before the equations are added or subtracted in order to eliminate one unknown. For example, consider $x + 3y = 6$ and $2x - y = 5$. Neither the x's nor the y's will completely cancel if these equations are added. However, if we multiply the first equation by 2 and the second by -1, we find upon adding

them

$$\begin{array}{r} 2x + 6y = 12 \\ -2x + y = -5 \\ \hline 7y = 7 \end{array}$$

and $y = 1$. Substituting this value of y into either equation then gives $x = 3$.

The procedure just used is readily extended to three simultaneous equations containing three unknowns, x, y, and z. Two of the equations are combined to yield an equation containing only two unknowns, say, x and y, and another combination of two of the original equations is formed that again contains only x and y. The problem has then been reduced to two equations in two unknowns, and one then proceeds as in the example just given to find x and y.

REVIEW PROBLEMS

Solve the following equations for the unknown quantities.
66. $x - 7 = 3$
67. $3x + 7 = 4 + 6x$
68. $1 + 0.2x = 7$
69. $x^2 + 4 = 13$
70. $x^{1/2} + 4 = 13$
71. $-4x + 7 = 2x + 15$
72. $(x/3)^{1/2} = 2$
73. $0 = 64 - 16t^2$
74. $x^3 - 1 = 63$
75. $(x + 2)(x + 4) = 0$
76. $x^2 + 3x + 2 = 0$
77. $3x^2 + 2x - 5 = 0$
78. $x^2 + 4 = -4x$
79. $2x^2 = -3x$
80. $-3x + 2x^2 - 5 = 0$
81. $x + y = 5$, $x - y = 1$
82. $2 - T = 3a$, $T = 4a$
83. $x + 3y = 9$, $x - 2y = 10$
84. $2x - y = 10$, $x + y = 6$
85. $3x - 7y = 2$, $3x - 2y = 4$

B.5 | GRAPHS

Just as pictures are often more informative than words, graphs are often more useful than algebraic formulas in understanding what is happening in a

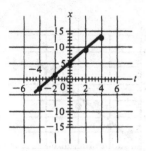

Figure B.1. The graph of $x = 5 + 2t$.

physical system. To illustrate how a graph is constructed, consider the equation for the position coordinate x of an object moving at a constant velocity at a time t:

$$x = 5 + 2t$$

We start by making a table of the values of x obtained from this equation for several values of t between -4 and $+4$:

time t	-4	-2	0	2	4
position x	-3	1	5	9	13

Using ordinary (Cartesian) graph paper, we draw a horizontal axis for the independent variable, t, and a vertical axis for the dependent variable, x. The tabulated values are then used to locate the points marked on the graph (Fig. B.1).

In this example, all the points fall on a single straight line because t appears only to the first power. If other powers are present, the graph of the equation will be a curve. Some examples of such curves are shown in Fig. B.2.

The choice of the dependent and independent variables is not fixed, and it depends on what one is trying to do. For example, the equation

$$x = 16t^2$$

gives the position of an object dropped from $x = 0$ at time $t = 0$. If we want to know when it will be at a position x, we must solve for t in terms of x:

$$t = \tfrac{1}{4}\sqrt{x}$$

Now x has become the independent variable. The graphs of the two forms of the equation look quite different (Fig. B.3), although both are curves rather than straight lines. We can also get a straight-line graph if we consider t^2 rather than t as a variable. This is particularly useful in analyzing experimental measurements, since it is easy to see if the data points all fall on a straight line as expected.

REVIEW PROBLEMS

Draw the graphs of the following equations:
86. $y = 3x - 7$
87. $x = 2t^2$
88. $y = 2x^4 - 3$

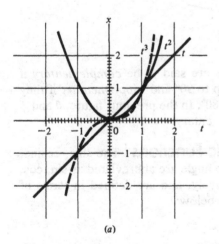
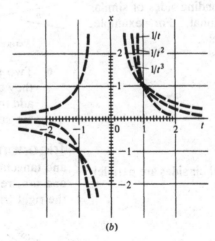

Figure B.2. (a) Graphs of $x = t$, $x = t^2$, and $x = t^3$. (b) Graphs of $x = 1/t$, $x = 1/t^2$, and $x = 1/t^3$. Note that $1/t^3$ becomes very small most rapidly as t increases and also grows most rapidly as t approaches zero.

Figure B.3. (a) A graph of $x = 16t^2$. (b) A graph of $t = \frac{1}{4}\sqrt{x}$. (c) Measured pairs of x and t^2 values are plotted. They fall close to a straight line drawn through them with a ruler. On a plot of x versus t, they would fall near a curved line that would be harder to draw accurately and to analyze numerically.

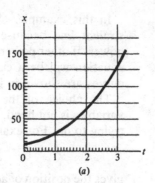
(a)

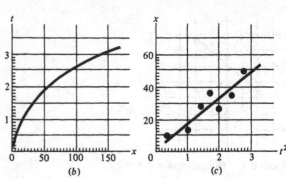
(b)   (c)

B.6 | PLANE GEOMETRY AND TRIGONOMETRIC FUNCTIONS

Plane Geometry | The following results from plane geometry are often useful:

1   The sum of the internal angles of any triangle is 180°. In a right triangle, where one angle is 90°, the other two angles must add up to 90°.

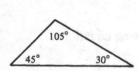

2   Two triangles are *similar* if two of their angles are equal. The corresponding sides of similar triangles are proportional. For example, $a/A = b/B$ in this figure:

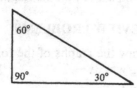

3   Two angles are equal if their sides are parallel.

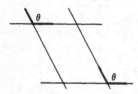

4   Two angles are equal if their sides are mutually perpendicular. For example, the angle between the weight vector **w** and the line perpendicular to the inclined plane equals the angle between the plane and the horizontal direction.

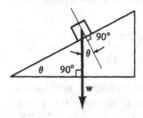

5   Two angles are equal if they are *vertical* angles.

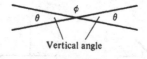
Vertical angle

6   Two angles are said to be *complementary* if they add up to 90° and *supplementary* if they add up to 180°. In the previous figure, θ and ϕ are supplementary.

Trigonometric Functions | The sine, cosine, and tangent of an angle are abbreviated as sin, cos, and tan, respectively, and are defined in terms of the right triangle below:

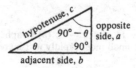

$$\sin \theta = \frac{\text{opposite side}}{\text{hypotenuse}} = \frac{a}{c} \qquad \text{(B.8)}$$

$$\cos \theta = \frac{\text{adjacent side}}{\text{hypotenuse}} = \frac{b}{c} \qquad \text{(B.9)}$$

$$\tan \theta = \frac{\text{opposite side}}{\text{adjacent side}} = \frac{a}{b} \qquad \text{(B.10)}$$

The Pythagorean theorem states that

$$a^2 + b^2 = c^2 \qquad \text{(B.11)}$$

Dividing by c^2,

$$\frac{a^2}{c^2} + \frac{b^2}{c^2} = 1$$

or

$$\sin^2 \theta + \cos^2 \theta = 1 \qquad \text{(B.12)}$$

The trigonometric functions of angles larger than 90° may be either positive or negative, depending on the angle. In the notation of the diagram below, they are defined by

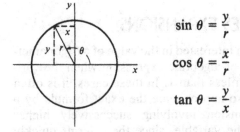

$$\sin \theta = \frac{y}{r}$$

$$\cos \theta = \frac{x}{r}$$

$$\tan \theta = \frac{y}{x}$$

By convention, r is always positive. However, for the angle shown, which is said to be in the second *quadrant*, x is negative and y is positive. Accordingly the sine is positive, and the tangent and cosine are negative. In the third quadrant, only the tangent is positive; and in the fourth, only the cosine is positive.

Many books contain a table of the trigonometric functions for angles up to 90°. For angles between 90° and 180°, one looks up the supplement, $180° - \theta$. Between 180° and 270°, one looks up $\theta - 180°$; and from 270° to 360°, one looks up $360° - \theta$. Minus signs are inserted wherever required in accordance with the discussion above. For example, sin 150° = sin 30°, cos 150° = −cos 30°, and tan 150° = −tan 30°. These rules are summarized in Fig. B.4. Many pocket calculators have these rules built in.

Graphs of the sine, cosine, and tangent (Fig. B.5) are useful in understanding the general behavior of these quantities. They all repeat after one full circle or cycle; their *period* is 360° or 2π radians. (Measuring angles in radians is discussed in Chapter Five.)

The average of the sine or cosine over a full cycle is zero, since for every positive value, there is a corresponding negative value. Notice that the sin θ and cos θ curves are identical if the cos θ curve is shifted 90° to the right. The same shift also makes the $\sin^2 \theta$ and $\cos^2 \theta$ curves (Fig. B.6) identical, so the average values of these quantities over a full cycle must be equal. Denoting the average by a bar, this means

$$\overline{\sin^2 \theta} = \overline{\cos^2 \theta}$$

Since we know from Eq. B.12 that $\sin^2 \theta + \cos^2 \theta = 1$, it follows that

$$\overline{\sin^2 \theta} + \overline{\cos^2 \theta} = 1$$

Therefore,

$$\overline{\sin^2 \theta} = \overline{\cos^2 \theta} = \tfrac{1}{2} \qquad \text{(B.13)}$$

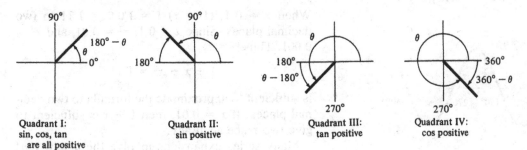

Figure B.4. A summary of the rules for finding the trigonometric functions. For example, if θ is in the third quadrant, a plus sign is used for tan θ, and a minus sign is used for sin θ and cos θ.

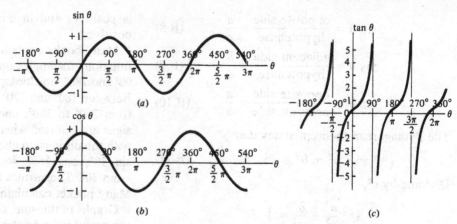

Figure B.5.   Graphs of (a) sin θ;
(b) cos θ; (c) tan θ.

Also, we can see from Fig. B.6 that the product, sin θ cos θ, has a corresponding negative value for each positive value, so averaging the product over a full cycle must give zero:

$$\overline{\sin \theta \cos \theta} = 0 \qquad (B.14)$$

REVIEW PROBLEMS

89. If two angles of a triangle are 29° and 111°, what is the third angle?

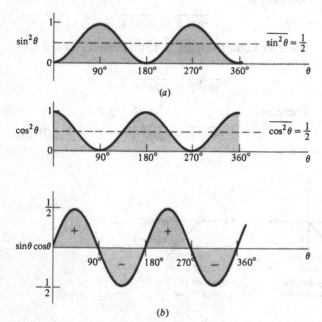

(a)

(b)

Figure B.6.   (a) $\sin^2 \theta$ and $\cos^2 \theta$ have the same average value $\frac{1}{2}$.
(b) The average value of sin θ cos θ is zero.

90. Find sin 120°; cos 120°; tan 120°.
91. Find sin 270°; cos 270°; tan 270°.
92. At what angle or angles between 0° and 360° is sin θ equal to 0, +1, −1? Give the corresponding angles for the cosine and tangent.

B.7 | SERIES EXPANSIONS

We are often interested in the value of a trigonometric function or algebraic expression when the variable is much less than 1. In these cases, it is often convenient to approximate the exact formula by a series expansion involving successively higher powers of the variable, since these terms quickly become very small.

As an example, we may consider the series expansion for $(1 - x)^{-1}$ derived in algebra texts:

$$\frac{1}{1 - x} = 1 + x + x^2 + x^3 + \cdots$$

When $x = 0.1$, $(1 - x)^{-1} = 1/0.9 = 1.11$ to two decimal places. Since $x = 0.1$, $x^2 = 0.01$, and $x^3 = 0.001$. Thus

$$1 + x + x^2 = 1.11$$

is sufficient to approximate the formula to two decimal places. If $x = 0.01$, then $1 + x$ is sufficient to give two place accuracy.

Many series expansions involve the quantity $n!$ (read "n factorial") defined by

$$n! = n(n - 1)(n - 2) \ldots (2)(1)$$

For example, $4! = 4 \times 3 \times 2 \times 1 = 24$. By definition,

$$1! = 1, \qquad 0! = 1$$

The following series expansions are often useful:

$$(1 \pm x)^{-1} = 1 \mp x + x^2 \mp x^3 + \cdots$$
$$(-1 < x < 1) \quad \text{(B.15)}$$

$$(1 \pm x)^n = 1 \pm nx + \frac{n(n-1)x^2}{2!}$$
$$\pm \frac{n(n-1)(n-2)x^3}{3!} + \cdots$$
$$(-1 < x < 1) \quad \text{(B.16)}$$

$$(1 \pm x)^{-n} = 1 \mp nx + \frac{n(n+1)x^2}{2!}$$
$$\mp \frac{n(n+1)(n+2)x^3}{3!} + \cdots$$
$$(-1 < x < 1) \quad \text{(B.17)}$$

$$e^x = 1 + x + \frac{x^2}{2!} + \frac{x^3}{3!} + \cdots \quad \text{(B.18)}$$

In the following series for the trigonometric functions, the angles must be measured in radians, where 1 rad $= 180°/\pi = 57.3°$:

$$\sin x = x - \frac{x^3}{3!} + \frac{x^5}{5!} - \cdots \quad \text{(B.19)}$$

$$\cos x = 1 - \frac{x^2}{2!} + \frac{x^4}{4!} - \cdots \quad \text{(B.20)}$$

$$\tan x = x + \frac{x^3}{3} + \frac{2x^5}{15} + \frac{17x^7}{314} + \cdots \quad \text{(B.21)}$$

REVIEW PROBLEMS

93. What is the percentage error in using $\sin x = x$, when $x = 10° = 0.1745$ rad? What is the error at $30°$?

94. For $x = 0.1$, $e^x = e^{0.1} = 1.105$. How many terms in the series expansion for e^x are needed to obtain this accuracy?

95. (a) Write out the first three terms in the series for $(1 + x)^{1/2} = \sqrt{1 + x}$. (b) What does this approximation give for $x = 0.1$? Compare this with the exact answer to five decimal places, 1.04881.

B.8 | DERIVATIVES

At the end of several chapters in this book, we present derivations of various equations that are based on arguments using differentiation. Here we list the derivatives used. Note that the derivative of a constant is zero. Also, when an expression is multiplied by a number, its derivative is multiplied by the same number. For example,

$$\frac{d}{dt}(3t^2) = 3\frac{d}{dt}(t^2)$$

In the following expressions, a and n are constants:

$$\frac{d}{dt}(t^n) = nt^{n-1} \qquad \text{(B.22)}$$

$$\frac{d}{dt}\left(\frac{1}{t}\right) = -\frac{1}{t^2} \qquad \text{(B.23)}$$

$$\frac{d}{dt}\left(\frac{1}{t^n}\right) = \frac{-n}{t^{n+1}} \qquad \text{(B.24)}$$

$$\frac{d}{dt}(e^{at}) = ae^{at} \qquad \text{(B.25)}$$

$$\frac{d}{dt}\sin at = a\cos at \qquad \text{(B.26)}$$

$$\frac{d}{dt}\cos at = -a\sin at \qquad \text{(B.27)}$$

If y depends on a variable u, and u depends in turn on t, then the *chain rule* states that

$$\frac{dy}{dt} = \frac{dy}{du}\frac{du}{dt} \qquad \text{(chain rule)}$$

REVIEW PROBLEMS

Find the derivatives of the following expressions:
96. $3t + 7$
97. $4t^3$
98. $1 - (1/t)$
99. $4e^{-3t}$
100. $10\sin 2\pi t$

B.9 | AREAS AND VOLUMES

At various points in this book, we have to make use of the formulas for the areas and volumes of simple shapes. They are listed here for reference.

Circle

>   radius = r
>   diameter = $2r$
>   circumference = $2\pi r$
>   area = πr^2

Square

>   side = a
>   area = a^2

Triangle

>   area = $\frac{1}{2}$(base)(height)

Cube

>   side = a
>   surface area = $6a^2$
>   volume = a^3

Sphere

>   radius = r
>   surface area = $4\pi r^2$
>   volume = $4\pi r^3/3$

Cylinder

>   radius = r, length = l
>   area of curved surface = $2\pi rl$
>   area of each end = πr^2
>   volume = $\pi r^2 l$

B.10 | THE EXPONENTIAL FUNCTION; LOGARITHMS

Many times, the rate at which a quantity changes is proportional to the quantity present. For example, the rate at which a population of bacteria increases is directly proportional to the size of the population itself, as is the rate of growth in the funds in a savings account. Similarly, the rate of change of the charge on a capacitor is sometimes proportional to the charge present. Students of calculus will recognize these as situations where the quantity, call it y, depends on time as

$$y = Cb^{Dt}$$

where b and D are numbers and C is a constant that is determined by the conditions of the situation when $t = 0$. This is called an exponential dependence of y on t.

The choice of b is arbitrary, although it will affect the value of D when it is determined. However, there is a particular choice of b that can be made that greatly simplifies the manipulations. This choice is $b = e = 2.718. \ldots$ For this seemingly unlikely choice, the rate of change of $y = Ce^t$ with t is exactly equal to y itself. For any other choice of b, the rate of change of $y = Cb^t$ with t is proportional to but not equal to y. Thus the function $y = e^t$ is very common in many scientific studies. The decreasing function $e^{-t} = 1/e^t$ is of similar importance when the rate of *decrease* of a quantity is proportional to the present amount of that quantity. This happens, for example, in the decay of radioactive nuclei.

The exponential function e^t is built into many pocket calculators, sometimes as the inverse of the *natural logarithm*. If $x = 10^t$, then the more familiar *common logarithm* (log, or logarithm to the base 10) is the power of 10, or t in this case. Symbolically,

$$\log x = \log (10^t) = t \qquad (B.28)$$

Conversely, the inverse common logarithm of t is 10^t.

Similarly, the natural logarithm (ln, or logarithm to the base e) is defined as the power of e needed to obtain a given quantity. Thus if $y = e^t$,

$$\ln y = \ln (e^t) = t \qquad (B.29)$$

The inverse natural logarithm of t (INV ln on many calculators) is then e^t.

Some simple rules can be obtained from the definitions B.28 and B.29 for the logarithms of products, quotients, and powers. The following rules are given for natural logarithms but apply equally well to common logarithms:

$$\ln (xy) = (\ln x) + (\ln y) \qquad (B.30)$$
$$\ln (x^n) = n(\ln x) \qquad (B.31)$$
$$\ln \left(\frac{1}{x^n}\right) = -n(\ln x) \qquad (B.32)$$
$$\ln \left(\frac{x}{y}\right) = (\ln x) - (\ln y) \qquad (B.33)$$

Note that there is no simple rule for the logarithms of sums or differences of quantities.

Using either tabulated values of e^t or values found with a calculator, we can construct a plot of

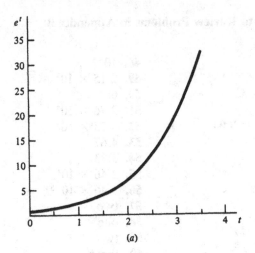

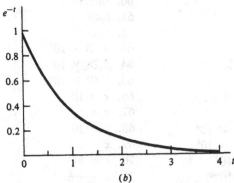

Figure B.7. (a) The graph of e^t. (b) The graph of e^{-t}. Note the difference in vertical scales in the two graphs.

e^t (Fig. B.7). Note how it grows very rapidly as t increases, much more rapidly than any power of t. Also, the plot of e^{-t} diminishes very rapidly for large t values, although it never reaches zero.

Several special values of e^{-t} are used in this book. To three significant figures, $e^{-1} = 0.368$ and $e^{-2} = 0.135$. Also, $e^{-t} = 0.500$ when $t = 0.693$.

A series expansion for e^x is given in Eq. B.18 above, and the derivative of e^x is given in Eq. B.25.

B.11 | TRIGONOMETRIC IDENTITIES

There are a variety of identities relating trigonometric quantities. The following formulas are used in this text:

$$\sin(a + b) = \sin a \cos b \pm \cos a \sin b \qquad (B.34)$$

$$\cos(a + b) = \cos a \cos b \mp \sin a \sin b \qquad (B.35)$$

$$\sin a + \sin b = 2 \sin \tfrac{1}{2}(a + b) \cos \tfrac{1}{2}(a - b) \qquad (B.36)$$

$$\cos a + \cos b = 2 \cos \tfrac{1}{2}(a + b) \cos \tfrac{1}{2}(a - b) \qquad (B.37)$$

B.12 | INTEGRALS

Integrals are used in several sections. The following brief list contains most of the *indefinite integrals* used in the text or needed for the problems. Definite integrals are discussed below.

$$\int t^n \, dt = \frac{t^{n+1}}{n + 1} \quad (n \neq -1) \qquad (B.38)$$

$$\int \frac{dt}{t} = \ln t \qquad (B.39)$$

$$\int e^{at} dt = \frac{1}{a} e^{at} \qquad (B.40)$$

$$\int \sin at \, dt = -\frac{1}{a} \cos at \qquad (B.41)$$

$$\int \cos at \, dt = \frac{1}{a} \sin at \qquad (B.42)$$

$$\int \frac{t \, dt}{(a^2 + t^2)^{1/2}} = (a^2 + t^2)^{1/2} \qquad (B.43)$$

$$\int \frac{dt}{(a^2 + t^2)} = \frac{1}{a} \tan^{-1} \frac{t}{a} \qquad (B.44)$$

(Here $\tan^{-1}$ is the *arctangent*; if $y = \tan^{-1} x$, then $x = \tan y$.)

$$\int \frac{t \, dt}{(a^2 + t^2)^{3/2}} = \frac{-1}{(a^2 + t^2)^{1/2}} \qquad (B.45)$$

$$\int \frac{a^2 \, dt}{(a^2 + t^2)^{3/2}} = \frac{t}{(a^2 + t^2)^{1/2}} \qquad (B.46)$$

$$\int u \, dv = uv - \int v \, du \quad \begin{array}{l}\text{(integration} \\ \text{by parts)}\end{array} \qquad (B.47)$$

$$\int t^n e^{at} \, dt = \frac{t^n}{a} - \frac{n}{a} \int t^{n-1} e^{at} \, dt \qquad (B.48)$$

$$\int t^n e^{-at} \, dt = -\frac{t^n}{a} + \frac{n}{a} \int t^{n-1} e^{-at} \, dt \qquad (B.49)$$

A *definite integral* is evaluated by substituting the values of the variable at the ends of the integration range into the indefinite integral. If $g(t)$ is the indefinite integral of $f(t)$, then

$$\int_a^b f(t)dt = g(t)\Big|_a^b = g(b) - g(a) \quad \text{(B.50)}$$

For example, according to Eq. B.38, $\int t\, dt = t^2/2$. Then

$$\int_a^b t\, dt = \frac{t^2}{2}\Big|_a^b = \frac{b^2}{2} - \frac{a^2}{2}$$

Also, repeated application of Eq. B.49 shows that

$$\int_0^\infty t^n e^{-at}\, dt = \frac{n!}{a^{n+1}} \quad \text{(B.51)}$$

(Here $n! = n(n-1)(n-2)\dots(2)(1)$ is *n-factorial*.)

REVIEW PROBLEMS

Evaluate the following quantities with the aid, where needed, of tables or a pocket calculator.

101. Find e^2, e^3, e^4.

102. Find $e^{0.5}$, $e^{1.5}$.

103. Find $\ln e^3$, $\ln 10$, $\ln 4$, $\ln 0.75$, $\ln 2$.

104. What is x if its natural logarithm is 0.5, 0.1, 1, -1, 2, 2.5?

105. What are the common logarithms of 10, 100, 1000, 5, 0.5, e?

106. What is x if its common logarithm is 0.5, 0, 1, -1, 2, 2.5?

Simplify the following expressions:

107. $\log(x^4)$

108. $\ln(x/y^2)$

109. $\ln(\sqrt{x})$

110. $\log(1/x^3)$

111. $\ln[x(a+b)]$

Additional Reading

Students needing additional mathematical preparation may find the following paperback books helpful:

Jerry B. Marion and Ronald C. Davidson, *Mathematical Preparation for General Physics*, W. B. Saunders Co., Philadelphia, 1972. Same level as this appendix.

Clifford E. Swartz, *Used Math*, Prentice-Hall, Inc., Englewood Cliffs, N.J., 1973. Includes more advanced material.

Michael Ram, *Essential Mathematics for College Physics*, John Wiley & Sons, New York, Inc., 1982; *Essential Mathematics for College Physics with Calculus*, John Wiley & Sons, Inc., New York, 1984.

Answers to Review Problems in Appendix B

1. 16
2. 9
3. $2^5 = 32$
4. x^9
5. $1/5^2 = 0.04$
6. 5
7. x^2
8. x^2
9. $(x/y)^4$
10. ax^2
11. $a^{3/2}x^3$
12. xy^3
13. $1/x^2y^2$
14. 10
15. 0.1
16. 1
17. $\frac{1}{5} = 0.2$
18. $x/8$
19. $x^2 y^{-4} = x^2/y^4$
20. 10^3
21. 2.7631×10^4
22. 2.7631×10^6
23. 1.5×10^4
24. 3.4×10^{-8}
25. 1.6×10^3
26. 4.32976×10^3
27. 3.902×10^{-3}
28. 8.002×10^{-2}
29. 0.00234
30. 1,760,000
31. 0.00005799
32. 45,000,000
33. 670
34. 2,720,000
35. 2,720,000
36. 1.5×10^{11}
37. 50
38. 6×10^9
39. 6.6×10^{16}
40. 1.12×10^{15}
41. 200
42. 300
43. 300
44. 20
45. 2×10^{-3}
46. 20
47. 10^5

48. 10^{-5}
49. 2.15×10^3
50. 684
51. 2.76×10^4
52. 3.73×10^{-1}
53. 4.67
54. 3.33
55. 2.46×10^4
56. 3.46×10^{-5}
57. two
58. one
59. two
60. three
61. four
62. two
63. 4.28×10^7
64. 3.28×10^7
65. 1.89×10^{-3}
66. $x = 10$
67. $x = 1$
68. $x = 30$
69. $x = \pm 3$
70. $x = 81$
71. $x = -\frac{4}{3}$
72. $x = 12$
73. $t = \pm 2$
74. $x = 4$
75. $x = -2$, $x = -4$
76. $x = -1$, $x = -2$
77. $x = 1$, $x = -\frac{1}{3}$
78. $x = -2$
79. $x = -\frac{2}{3}$, $x = 0$
80. $x = -1$, $x = \frac{5}{2}$
81. $x = 3$, $y = 2$
82. $a = \frac{4}{7}$, $T = \frac{8}{7}$
83. $y = -\frac{1}{3}$, $x = 9\frac{2}{3}$
84. $x = 5\frac{1}{3}$, $y = \frac{2}{3}$
85. $y = \frac{2}{3}$, $x = 1\frac{2}{3}$
86.

87. **88.**

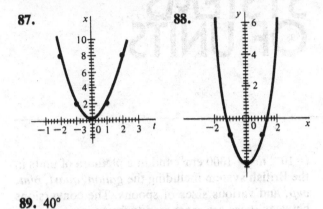

89. 40°
90. sin 120° = 0.866, cos 120° = −0.5,
    tan 120° = −1.732
91. sin 270° = −1, cos 270° = 0, tan 270° = ∞
92. sin θ = 0 at 0°, 180°, 360°
    sin θ = 1 at 90°
    sin θ = −1 at 270°
    cos θ = 0 at 90°, 270°
    cos θ = 1 at 0°, 360°
    cos θ = −1 at 180°
    tan θ = 0 at 0°, 180°, 360°
    tan θ = 1 at 45°, 225°
    tan θ = −1 at 135°, 315°

93. 0.52 percent at 10°, 4.7 percent at 30°
94. three items
95. (a) $1 + \frac{1}{2}x - \frac{1}{8}x^2$
    (b) 1.04875, which is 0.006 percent less than
       the exact answer.
96. 3
97. $12t^2$
98. $1/t^2$
99. $-12e^{-3t}$
100. $20\pi \cos 2\pi t$
101. 7.39, 20.1, 54.6
102. 1.65, 4.48
103. 3, 2.30, 1.39, −0.288, 0.693
104. 1.65, 1, 2.72, 0.368, 7.39, 12.2
105. 1, 2, 3, 0.699, −0.301, 0.434
106. 3.16, 1, 10, 0.1, 100, 316
107. $4 \log x$
108. $\ln x - 2 \ln y$
109. $\frac{1}{2} \ln x$
110. $-3 \log x$
111. $\ln x + \ln (a + b)$

APPENDIX C

SYSTEMS OF UNITS

In this text, we have used Système Internationale (S.I.) units almost exclusively. This is in keeping with a worldwide effort to develop a single set of units for scientific, commercial, and social use. Because this effort is far from complete and because historical material will always be important, a variety of units will be with us for a long time. In this appendix, we describe the c.g.s. and British systems of units to assist the reader in relating units in these systems to S.I. units. Some units that do not fall clearly into any of these systems are also discussed.

We assume the reader is familiar with the general scheme of conversion of units described in Chapter One of this textbook. A table of useful conversion factors can be found inside the front cover. Multiples and submultiples of S.I. units are constructed using prefixes given on the right front endpaper of this text.

C.1 | TIME, LENGTH, AND MASS

The single quantity with the same units in all systems is time. The basic unit of time is the *second*, with the *minute* and *hour* in common use. In scientific work, submultiples of the second are often convenient, and the prefixes of the S.I. system are useful for these cases.

The basic units of length are the *metre*, *centimetre*, and *foot* in the S.I., c.g.s., and British systems, respectively. There are 100 centimetres and 3.281 feet in 1 metre. Areas and volumes have the obvious units of m^2, cm^2, and ft^2 and of m^3, cm^3, and ft^3, respectively, in the three systems and require the use of conversion factors either two or three times. In the British system, the *inch* (= 1/12 foot) is often used, as is the *mile* (= 5280 feet).

Measurements of the volumes of liquids and gases are commonly expressed in the litre ($=10^{-3}$ $m^3 = 1000$ cm^3) and in a plethora of units in the British system including the *gallon*, *quart*, *pint*, *cup*, and various sizes of spoons. The conversions between these are most readily found in cookbooks and dictionaries. The *gallon* is equivalent to 3.786 litres.

The units of mass in the three systems are the *kilogram*, *gram*, and *slug*. The relationship between the kilogram and gram is obvious from the prefix, and the slug is equal to 14.59 kilograms. The atomic mass unit, denoted u, is accepted for use with the S.I. system; 1 u = 1.66×10^{-27} kg.

The acceleration of gravity, g, is important in all three systems:

$$g = 9.8 \text{ m s}^{-2} = 980 \text{ cm s}^{-2} = 32 \text{ ft s}^{-2}$$

Until recently, two length units were very commonly used in studies of light and in atomic physics. The *angstrom* and the *micron* are equal to 10^{-10} metres and 10^{-6} metres, respectively, and are simply names given to convenient submultiples of the metre.

In the same spirit, the *fermi*, equal to 10^{-15} metres, was used for years as the convenient length unit in nuclear studies. Similarly the *barn*, equal to 10^{-28} m^2, is a convenient measure of cross-sectional areas in subatomic particle collisions.

C.2 | UNITS OF FORCE, WEIGHT

The *newton*, the S.I. unit of force, is equivalent to 1 kg m s^{-2}, as can be seen from Newton's second law, $F = ma$. In the c.g.s. system, the force unit is the *dyne*; by the same reasoning, it is equal to 1 gm cm s^{-2}. Similarly, the *pound*, the British unit of force, is 1 slug ft s^{-2}. The numerical conversion factors are

$$1 \text{ N} = 10^5 \text{ dynes} = 0.2248 \text{ pound}$$

These can be simply obtained from $F = ma$, where $a = g$ and the force is interpreted as the weight.

Note that these units are names given to the force in the fundamental law $F = ma$. Thus the force units are derived from those for mass, length, and time given in Section C.1. In fact, with the exception of the units of electric charge, all the units of this section and those following are derived from those of mass, length, and time.

C.3 | OTHER UNITS OF MECHANICS

The derived S.I. unit of energy is the *joule*. This can be related to the units of mass, length, and time using $W = Fs$, that is work equals force times distance, or from the units of kinetic energy, $mv^2/2$. Thus the joule is equal to 1 N m = 1 kg m^2 s^{-2}. Similarly, the c.g.s. energy unit, the *erg*, is 1 dyn cm = 1 gm cm^2 s^{-2}. The British energy unit is the *foot-pound* = 1 ft lb = 1 slug ft^2 s^{-2}.

Unfortunately, the complete energy unit story is more complex. Historically, thermal energy was not recognized as the same entity as mechanical energy. Hence we have inherited a separate set of energy units from theoretical studies that are still in common use. A *calorie* is the heat necessary to raise the temperature of 1 gram of water by 1 K and is equal to 4.184 joules, or 4.184 × 10^7 ergs. The British Thermal Unit, the BTU, had an origin similar to the calorie, but involved raising the temperature of a pound of water by 1° F. It is equal to 777.2 ft lb = 1.054 × 10^3 joules.

In atomic physics, a commonly used energy unit is the *electron volt*. This is a small energy unit equal to 1.602 × 10^{-19} joule. It is accepted for use with the S.I. system.

There is no defined c.g.s. unit of power; it is just the erg s^{-1}. In the British system, the logical power unit is the foot-pound per second. However, the more common British unit is the *horsepower*, equal to 550 ft lb s^{-1}.

There is a wide variety of pressure units in common use. The standard units in the three systems are the *pascal*, dyn cm^{-2}, and lb in^{-2}. Atmospheric pressures are often measured in terms of the *standard atmosphere* = 1.013 × 10^5 pascals = 1.013 × 10^6 dyn cm^{-2} = 14.7 lb in^{-2}. Pressures are also often given in terms of the height of a column of liquid that is supported, usually water or mercury. In fact, the pressure of 1 mm Hg (1 millimetre of mercury) is given the name of *torr*; 1 torr = 133.3 pascals. One inch of water (1 in. H$_2$O) is equal to a pressure of 249.1 pascals.

In addition to the variety of systems of units, many combinations of units are used because they are numerically convenient. As an example, consider the conversion between two units of flow resistance, 1 Pa s m^{-3} = 7.50 × 10^{-9} torr s cm^{-3}. The smaller units are convenient in biological studies.

C.4 | ELECTRICAL UNITS

In the study of electricity and magnetism, a large number of units is introduced. However, if the unit of charge, the coulomb, is regarded as a fundamental unit, as are mass, length, and time, then all other units are derived from these four units.*

For example, the *volt* is a joule per coulomb; and, as described in the preceding section, 1 joule is equivalent to 1 kg m^2 s^{-2}. Fortunately, S.I. units are widely used in electrical and magnetic studies, and conversions from other unit systems are seldom required. One exception to this is the c.g.s. unit of magnetic field strength, the *gauss*, which equals 10^{-4} *tesla*. For example, the gauss is widely used in studies of the earth's magnetic field where the numbers are of a convenient size.

C.5 | SUMMARY

This appendix does not by any means exhaust all the systems of units or all of the combinations of units that are in use. However, if the reader will keep in mind that all units can be reduced to a combination of the units of mass, length, time, and charge, the task of relating and converting units will be greatly eased.

* If, in Coulomb's law, $F = kQ_1Q_2/r^2$, the constant k were chosen to be dimensionless, the coulomb could be expressed in terms of units of mass, length, and time. This is a perfectly valid procedure, and it is employed in some c.g.s. systems of electrical units. However, in this text (and in most other modern books), we assign units to k and regard the coulomb as a fundamental unit, and not one expressed in units of mass, length, and time.

ANSWERS TO ODD NUMBERED EXERCISES AND PROBLEMS

Chapter 1

1-1 4.05×10^3 m²

1-3   3.79 litres

1-5   (a) 7×10^{-9} m   (b) 7×10^{-3} m

1-7   40.5 hectares

1-11 $3.51 quart⁻¹

1-13 40 km h⁻¹

1-17 80 km h⁻¹

1-19 (a) 10.2 m s⁻¹

1-21 (a) −9.8 m s⁻¹   (b) −29.4 m

1-23 (a) 10 m s⁻¹   (b) 5 m s⁻¹   (c) 0

1-25 6.94 km h⁻¹

1-27 (a) Mary   (b) 0.03 h

1-31 positive at 0, T; negative at $T/2$

1-33 $\bar{v} = 10.1$ m s⁻¹; $\bar{v} < v$(max)

1-35 (a) −98 m s⁻¹   (b) −98 m s⁻¹

1-39 (a) $T_0 < t < 3T_0$ (b) $0 < t < T_0$, $3T_0 < t < 5T_0$
(c) $t > 5T_0$

1-41 (a) $-v_0/T$ (b) $-v_0/T$ (c) equal for constant a

1-43 (a) 0.001667 s   (b) 42,000 m s⁻²

1-45 27.8 h

1-47 (a) 50 m   (b) 20 m s⁻¹

1-49 (a) −0.6 m s⁻²   (b) 750 m

1-53 (a) −113 m s⁻²   (b) −11,300 m s⁻²

1-55 400 m s⁻²

1-57 45.9 m

1-59 (a) 400 m   (b) 2440 m   (c) 46.7 s

1-61 (a) 11.5 m   (b) 1.53 s   (c) 0.473 s, 2.59 s

1-63 (a) 39.4 m s⁻¹   (b) 74.1 m

1-65 2.5 m

1-67 (a) 0.204 s   (b) 38.1 m   (c) 38.5 m

1-71 neither; $a = g$ = constant

1-73 (a) 0.247 s   (b) ≈3 m s⁻¹

1-75 (a) T_1 to T_2 (b) 0 to T_0 (c) 0 to T_1 (d) T_2 to
T_3 (e) none   (f) T_0 to T_1, T_2 to T_3

1-77 no, it takes longer to come down

1-79 7 m s⁻¹

1-81 (a) 5 km h⁻¹   (b) 1 km h⁻¹

1-87 6 s

1-89 (a) 4.52 m s⁻²   (b) 2.55 s   (c) 11.5 m s⁻¹
(d) 200-m, yes; 1000-m, no

1-91 closest approach is 10 m

1-93 (a) 9.7 m s⁻²   (b) 30 m s⁻²   (c) 60 m should
have been 20 m

1-95 1720 m

1-97 (b) A (c) $(2\pi A/T)\cos 2\pi t/T$
(d) $-(2\pi/T)^2 A \sin 2\pi t/T$ (e) $(2\pi/T)^2$

1-99 (a) $2Bt - 3Ct^2$ (b) $2Bt - 6Ct$ (c) $2B/3t$

1-101 (a) 1.84 m   (b) 1.22 s

1-103 $v = 2.42$ m s⁻¹, $a = 98.0$ m s⁻²

1-105 62.5 m

1-107 $bT^3/3$

1-109 $v_f t + (v_f/b)(e^{-bt} - 1)$

1-111 $v_0 e^{-ct}$

1-115 (a) $(A/\omega)\sin \omega t$ (b) $(-A/\omega^2)\cos \omega t$

Chapter 2

2-1   (a) D   (b) G   (c) C   (d) 0   (e) A   (f) G
(g) C   (h) D

2-3   (b) 10.4, 17° above −x axis

2-5   (a) 4.47, 63.4° above +x axis
(b) 4.47, 63.4° below −x axis

2-7 (a) 7.21, 56° above **A** (b) 7.21, 56° above −**A**
(c) 7.21, 56° below **A**

2-9 24.9, 36° above −x axis

2-11 224 km, 27° N of W

2-13 (a) 8.54, 69° above **C** (b) 17.0, 28° below **A**

2-15 (a) 39.3 s (b) 12.7 m s^{-1}

2-17 $v_x = 28.2$ m s^{-1}, $v_y = 10.3$ m s^{-1}

2-19 (a) 500 km h^{-1} (b) 372.7 km h^{-1}, 63.4° south
of due west

2-21 p, 2 qt

2-21 (a) 41,700 m s^{-2} (b) $a_x = 36,100$ m s^{-2}, $a_y = 20,800$ m s^{-2}

2-25 3.79 × 10^{-3} m s^{-2}

2-27 (a) just before it hits the ground (b) at the
highest point reached (c) $a = g$ = constant

2-29 dropped bullet

2-31 24.75 m s^{-1}

2-33 (a) 7.50 m s^{-1} (b) g

2-35 (a) 1.79 × 10^5 m s^{-2}
(b) $a_x = 1.55 × 10^5$ m s^{-2}, $a_y = 8.93 × 10^4$ m s^{-2}

2-37 (a) 1.33 s (b) 11.5 m from building

2-39 (a) 141 m (b) 4.08 s

2-41 0.0304 m s^{-2}

2-43 (a) the second (b) speeds are equal

2-45 4.47 km h^{-1} (b) 0.5 m south of starting point
(c) 0.25 h

2-47 24.9 m s^{-1}

2-49 0.56 m; does not clear net

2-51 (a) 1.03 s (b) 30.8 s

2-53 $v_{ox} = 6.41$ m s^{-1}, $v_{oy} = 15.3$ m s^{-1}

2-57 (a) (50 m) sin (0.16 s^{-1})t, (50 m) cos (0.16 s^{-1})t
(b) (8 m s^{-1}) cos (0.16 s^{-1})t, −(8 m s^{-1}) sin (0.16 s^{-1})t
(c) (1.28 m s^{-2}) sin (0.16 s^{-1})t,
−(1.28 m s^{-2}) cos (0.16 s^{-1})t

2-59 (a) $pt\hat{x} + (qt^2/2)\hat{y}$ (b) $\mathbf{r} = (pt^2/2)\hat{x} + (qt^3/6)\hat{y}$

2-61 (a) 2.04 s (b) 2.89 s (c) 3.53 s

2-63 40.8 m

2-65 8.85 m s^{-1}

2-67 20.2 m s^{-1}

2-69 26.1 m s^{-1}

2-71 71.4°

2-75 (a) 2.97 m s^{-1} (b) 0.45 m

2-77 30 m

Chapter 3

3-1 37° below the 20-N force, 25 N

3-3 15° from either force, 19.3 N

3-5 490 N

3-7 (a) 4.90 N (b) 1.10 lb

3-9 54.5 kg

3-11 0.0741

3-13 1.0595 kg

3-15 (a) 1420 kg m^{-3} (b) density near edge of sun is
low compared to center

3-17 (a) 1.27 × 10^{17} kg m^{-3} (b) 1.27 × 10^{14} kg m^{-3}

3-19 1.002

3-21 127 kg

3-23 0.4515 kg

3-25 (a) 11.3 (b) 11.3 kg

3-27 no, no

3-29 (a) 0 (b) 19,600 N

3-31 w

3-33 stable, cables restore position

3-35 no, car is accelerated, net force is not zero

3-41 (a) 5 m s^{-2} (b) 0.06 s

3-43 one quarter of the original acceleration

3-45 3000 N

3-47 11,500 N

3-49 2.45 m s^{-2}

3-51 (a) 3320 m s^{-2} (b) 339

3-53 0.86 m s^{-2}

3-55 652.5 N

3-57 0.444

3-59 (a) 5500 kg m^{-1} (b) yes, if outer layers are
less dense

3-61 four times as great

3-63 296 N

3-65 $m_E/8$

3-67 (a) 61.2 kg N (b) 66.2 kg (c) 99.1 N

3-69 2w, upward

3-71 (a) 3 m s^{-2} (b) 1.045 mg, 17.0° to vertical

3-73 0.867

3-75 30 N

3-77 increase maximum frictional force

3-79 (a) 300 N (b) 150 N

3-83 1125 N

3-85 (a) 81.6 kg (b) 10 m s^{-2} (c) 816 N

3-87 (a) 5122 N (b) 1914 N

3-89 (a) 1.23 m s^{-2} (b) 32,000 N (c) 16,000 N

3-91 (a) 29.4 N (b) 3.92 m s^{-2}

3-93 (a) 49 N (b) 0.5

3-95 8.85 m s^{-2}

3-97 (a) 4.105 × 10^{12} N (b) 2.93 × 10^{16} N

3-99 5.12 m s^{-2}

3-101 (a) 1.55 mg, 1.225 mg (b) 0.225 mg

3-103 (a) 23.5 N   (b) 1.96 m s^{-2} (c) 0.98 m s^{-1}, 0.245 m

3-105 190 kg

3-107 (a) 6.24 m s^{-2} (b) 22.3 m s^{-1}

3-109 3.20 m s^{-2}

Chapter 4

4-1 w_1, 0; w_2, −6 N m; w_3, −40 N m; w_4, −75 N m

4-3 (a) $A \times A$, $A \times C$ (b) $A \times D$, $A \times E$
(c) $A \times B$ (d) $A \times D$, $A \times E$

4-5 equal in magnitude, opposite in direction; component of **E** perpendicular to **A** equals D

4-7 4 m, 1.732 m

4-9 (a) 30 N m, into page; 24 N m, into page; 21.2 N m, out of page;   (b) position (a)

4-11 $T_1 = 25.7$ N, $T_2 = 40.3$ N

4-13 $F_1 = 0.75$ N, $F_2 = 0.25$ N

4-15 (a) $w + w_1 + w_2$ (b) w_1/w_2

4-17 3.06 m

4-19 0.175 m

4-21 1.31 m

4-23 (a) $X = 0.25$ m, $Y = 0.25$ m   (b) 0.354 m

4-25 6

4-27 27°

4-31 500 N

4-33 0.667

4-37 (a) I   (b) III   (c) splenius

4-39 193 N

4-41 $T = 3000$ N, $H_x = 2598$ N, $H_y = 500$ N

4-43 24.1 N

4-45 $X = 0$, $Y = 2mL/(M + 2m)$

4-47 36°

4-49 3.33 kg

4-51 (a) $T = 264$ N, $R_x = 251$ N, $R_y = 46.7$ N
(b) 0.133

4-55 (a) $T = 2020$ N, $R_x = 1980$ N, $R_y = 70$ N
(b) $T = 3220$ N, $R_x = 3150$ N, $R_y = -5$ N

4-57 $4L/9$

4-59 $3h/4$

4-61 (a) 0.075 m   (b) 3 N

4-63 3 m from scale 1

4-62 $X = 0.229h$, $Y = 0.443h$

4-67 75°

4-69 42.4 N

Chapter 5

5-1 4

5-3 0.64 m s^{-2}

5-5 367 m

5-7 (a) 19,700 N   (b) 2010 kg

5-9 5100 m

5-11 0.546

5-13 31.3 m s^{-1}

5-17 14.3°

5-19 car may slide downward

5-21 up the embankment

5-23 42,300 rev min^{-1}

5-25 (a) 1.58 m s^{-2} (b) 370 N   (c) 512 N

5-27 (a) 5.73°   (b) 45°   (c) 720°

5-29 (a) 60°   (b) 135°   (c) 405°

5-31 (a) up   (b) down

5-33 (a) 12.5 rad s^{-1}; along axle away from us
(b) 2.5 rad s^{-2}

5-35 7670 rad s^{-1}, 73,200 rev min^{-1}

5-37 (a) no   (b) possibly   (c) yes

5-39 (a) 66.7 rad s^{-1} (b) 4.44 rad s^{-1} (c) 500 rad

5-41 0.245 kg m^2

5-43 before, since $I \approx I_{\text{bucket}}$; water does not spin much

5-45 0.289 l

5-47 (a) 0.00640 kg m^2 (b) 0.0960 N m

5-49 $g/4$

5-51 $7ml^2/48$

5-53 $2mR^2$

5-55 6.25×10^{19}

5-57 6.25×10^{12} must be removed

5-59 3.33×10^{-6} C

5-61 (a) -9.63×10^7 C   (b) $+9.63 \times 10^7$ C
(c) 8.35×10^{25} N

5-63 9.22×10^{-10} N

5-65 (a) 18.9 m s^{-2} (b) 1.06

5-67 (a) 22.8 m s^{-1} (b) 57.8 m s^{-1}, 0

5-69 (a) 0.0338 m s^{-2} (b) 698 N   (c) further reduces weight

5-71 16.0 s

5-73 (a) $4w$ (b) $w\sqrt{10}$

5-75 $(31/32)\pi p a R^4$

5-77 5.39 s

5-79 7.02 N m

5-81 (a) 0   (b) $\sqrt{3}\, kqQ/4a^2$, away from line joining $+q$ charges

5-83 25.7 mR^2

5-85 (a) $mb^2/6$ (b) $2mb^2/3$

5-89 4 AU

5-91 1.88 y

5-93 6.02×10^{24} kg

5-95 (a) 2.73×10^{-3} m s^{-2} (b) 2.71×10^{-3} m s^{-2}
(c) agree within 1 percent

Chapter 6

6-1 56.4 J
6-3 76°
6-5 80 J
6-7 2.21×10^5 J
6-9 (a) $x = 0$ (b) $\frac{1}{2}ka^2$ (c) 0
6-11 12.5 J
6-13 (a) 20,000 J (b) 20,000 N
6-15 (a) 2500 J (b) 2500 J
6-17 13.1 J
6-19 4230 N
6-21 (a) 39.2 J (b) 0 (c) -117.6 J
6-23 (a) $v_0^2/2g$ (b) $v_0/\sqrt{2}$
6-25 24.2 m s^{-1}
6-27 0
6-29 31.3 m s^{-1}
6-31 35.9 m s^{-1}
6-33 8.82×10^4 J
6-35 15,000 N
6-37 0.918
6-39 0.592
6-41 19.85 m s^{-1}
6-43 (a) 2123 km h^{-1} (b) 2063 km h^{-1}
6-45 (a) 49,000 J (b) 6.45×10^{-3} kg
6-47 2.35×10^{12} J
6-49 4.32×10^{14} J
6-51 (a) 29.4 J (b) 4.85 m s^{-2}
6-53 (a) $GM_s m/2R$ (b) $GM_E m/2R_E$ (c) 14.15
6-55 -6.60×10^{-8} J
6-57 3.17×10^4 m s^{-1}
6-59 2.37×10^3 m s^{-1}
6-61 1.85×10^{19} kg m^{-3}
6-63 1.227×10^7 m s^{-1}
6-65 8464
6-67 (a) 2.915×10^{-15} J (b) 1.822×10^4 eV
6-69 400 N
6-71 (a) $3.65 (b) 0.35
6-73 40 W
6-75 209 W
6-77 (a) 1.80 W (b) 5.14 N (c) 1080 J
6-79 (a) 200 W (b) 800 W
6-81 6.53×10^4 W
6-83 (a) 200 m^2 (b) comparable to roof of large one-story house

6-85 0.790 J
6-87 (a) 48.0 J (b) 96.0 J
6-89 (a) 1350 J (b) 2.149 N m (c) converted into thermal energy
6-91 $(4gd/5)^{1/2}$
6-93 (a) 36.3 J kg^{-1}, 132 W kg^{-1} (b) 3.23 J kg^{-1}, 131 W kg^{-1}
6-97 2.84 m s^{-1}
6-99 $mgl \sin \theta$
6-101 (a) 1.28 m (b) 0.573 m s^{-1} (c) 0.724 m
(d) 3.77 ms^{-1}
6-103 (a) 6×10^{15} kg (b) 311 GW
6-105 (a) 1.529×10^{15} J (b) 3.54×10^{10} W (c) 1.77
6-107 (a) 1.25×10^{18} J (b) 1.45×10^{13} W (c) 1.45
6-109 (a) 498 N (b) 8.53 km
6-114 1.46°
6-115 earth, 11,200 m s^{-1}; sun, 42,100 m s^{-1}
6-117 (a) $GM_s^2/4R_s$ (b) 9.50×10^{40} J
(c) 7.93×10^6 y
6-119 5.27×10^{-3} s
6-125 $ma^2t^2/2$
6-127 (a) 718 N (b) 5740 W
6-129 6.09 m s^{-1}
6-131 (a) 198 m (b) 58.0 s

Chapter 7

7-1 450,000 N
7-3 69.1 m s^{-1}
7-5 $2mv/\Delta t$ to left
7-7 decrease recoil velocity
7-9 change in momentum of blood
7-13 $mv_0/(m + M)$
7-15 (a) 8.26 m s^{-1} (b) 1650 N
7-17 0.005 m s^{-1}
7-19 $\phi = \theta$
7-21 (a) 3.34×10^{-11} m s^{-1} (b) 1.12×10^{-15}
7-23 $3v/2$
7-25 (a) earth–moon center of mass
(b) 4.66×10^6 m
7-27 0.932
7-29 (a) none (b) 1.33×10^5 J
7-31 1/2
7-33 no; gravity produces torque
7-35 (a) 16.7 rad s^{-1} (b) 4.33 kg m^2 s^{-1}
7-37 0.251 kg m^2 s^{-1}
7-39 to increase I, hence stability
7-43 500 s

7-45 2.05 rad s^{-1}

7-47   no; net gravitational force is not central, exerts torque

7-49 8220 m s^{-1}

7-51   no; torque about most other points is not zero

7-53 $v/2$

7-55 3.34×10^{-12} m s^{-1}

7-57   (a) car, 33.3 m s^{-1}; truck 6.67 m s^{-1}
(b) 6.67 m s^{-1}

7-59 1.09×10^{8} m s^{-1}

7-63   (a) 2.48 m s^{-1} (b) 0.314 m

7-65   (b) and (c)

7-67 m_2/m_1

7-69 $m/(m + M)$

7-71   (a) 18.1 m s^{-1}, $83.7°$ south of west
(b) 3.62×10^{5} J

7-73 0.2 rev s^{-1}

7-75   it will lengthen

7-77 $n^2h^2/8\pi^2 I$

7-79   (a) 1.71 rad s^{-1} (b) 1.71 rad s^{-1}

7-85 1470 N

7-89   (a) 114 J   (b) 55.3 J

7-97   counterclockwise

7-99   increase rate

Chapter 8

8-1 1.25×10^{7} N m^{-2}

8-3 0.0125

8-5 1.56×10^{-4} m

8-7 4.84×10^{-3} m

8-9 7.07×10^{4} N

8-11 1.27×10^{11} N m^{-2}

8-13   (a) 0.02 cm   (b) 0.004 cm

8-15   (a) 9800 N m^{-2}, 4.90×10^{-8}
(b) 9.80×10^{-8} m   (c) 5.10×10^{6} kg

8-17 $77,400$ N

8-19   (a) 3.18×10^{6} N m^{-2}, 1.59×10^{-5}
(b) 4.77×10^{-5} m

8-21 2.25×10^{7} N m^{-1}

8-23 151 N

8-25 78.5 N m

8-27   (a) 2.13×10^{-7} m^4 (b) 8.53×10^{-7} m^4,
5.33×10^{-8} m^4 (c) board B, $\perp$ to 2-cm dimension
(d) board A

8-29   (a) yes   (b) weight, normal force   (c) no;
torques add to zero

8-31   they produce a large torque with respect to the base

8-33 8.73 m

8-35 37.6 m, compared to 8.73 m

8-37   (a) 10^{6} N m^{-2}, 1.19×10^{-5} (b) 1.19×10^{-7} m

8-39 2.83×10^{4} N

8-41   (a) 1.25×10^{7} N m^{-2} (b) 0.125

8-43 $15,700$ N

8-45   (a) 205 m^3 (b) 0.005 m

8-47   (a) 3.89×10^{-3} m^2 (b) 2×10^{-4} m

8-49 16

8-51   (a) 8.80×10^{-5} m^4 (b) 7.41×10^{-7} m^4

8-53 R(solid)$/R$(hollow) $= 0.0914$

8-55 1.73 cm

8-61   areas would scale with weight

8-63 $m^{5/8}$

8-65   (a) $m^{-1/3}$ (b) $m^{-1/4}$

8-67   independent of mass, as in Chapter 6

8-69 25 m

Chapter 9

9-1   (a) 0 (b) $4R$

9-3   (a) $T/4$ to $T/2$, $3T/4$ to T (b) never
(c) 0 to $T/4$, $T/2$ to $3T/4$

9-5   (a) 0.1 m, 0 (b) 0, -0.314 m s^{-1}
(c) -0.1 m, 0

9-7 ± 0.354 m

9-9   (a) 0 (b) $\pm R$ (maximum displacement)

9-11 -148 m s^{-2}

9-13 2.25 N m^{-1}

9-15   (a) 0.327 m   (b) 1.15 s

9-17 1.36 Hz

9-19 0.248 m

9-21 12.2 m

9-23 1.49 m

9-25 4

9-27 1.050 Hz

9-29 6.35 s

9-31 2.65 m s^{-1}

9-33 8.94 m s^{-1}

9-35   (a) 4.90 N m^{-1} (b) 1.58 Hz   (c) 0.635 s
(d) 6.13×10^{-3} J

9-37 0.0707 m

9-39   (a) ± 0.447 m s^{-1} (b) ± 0.387 m s^{-1}

9-41   (a) 147 J   (b) 1.176×10^{5} N m^{-1} (c) 7.72 Hz

9-43   (a) 0.769 s   (b) 4.61 s

9-45 $1/100$

9-47   (a) x_0, 0, $-4\pi^2 f^2 x_0$ (b) $-x_0$, 0, $4\pi^2 f^2 x_0$

9-49 $x = R \sin (2\pi ft)$, $v = (2\pi f)R \cos (2\pi ft)$,
$a = -(2\pi f)^2 R \sin (2\pi ft)$

9-51 (a) 8.88 N m^{-1} (b) 7.5 Hz
9-53 (a) 19.7 N m^{-1} (b) 0.995 m
9-55 (a) $\simeq$ 0.7 Hz (b) $\simeq$ 4 km
9-57 5.95 m s^{-1}
9-59 (a) $7ml^2/48$, $l = 1$ m (b) 0.652 Hz
9-61 (a) longer (b) 14
9-69 (a) 1.31×10^{14} Hz (b) 1.32×10^{-11} m
  (c) 9790 m s^{-1}
9-71 2.57×10^{-6} kg m s^{-2}
9-73 (b) determines phase (point in cycle at $t = 0$)
9-77 $\simeq 10^5$ N m^{-1}
9-79 (a) 98,000 N m^{-1} (b) 7.05 Hz (c) yes
9-81 0.0621 m
9-83 (a) 22.2 Hz (b) well

Chapter 10

10-1 21.1° C
10-3 −40°
10-5 172.4° F
10-7 4.032 g
10-9 1.806×10^{24}
10-11 (a) 31.998 u (b) 53.15 g
10-13 2.31×10^{24}
10-15 (a) 200 kPa (b) 301.3 kPa
10-17 4.86×10^7 N
10-19 2030 N; no
10-21 (a) $\approx 10^5$ Pa (b) ≈ 1000 Pa
10-23 5
10-25 1.37
10-27 10,970 K
10-29 1.05 atm
10-31 10,100 m
10-33 393 m s^{-1}
10-35 pressure is doubled
10-37 0.9957
10-39 (a) 4.25×10^{-21} J (b) 205 K
10-41 746 s
10-43 3.74×10^6 Pa = 37.0 atm
10-45 196 moles m^{-3}
10-47 (a) −459.67° F (b) 459.67° R (c) 671.67° R
10-49 7.36×10^{22}
10-51 (a) 0.032 (b) 77,800 N
10-53 4.66 litres
10-55 9750 K
10-57 (a) 0.45 s (b) 4.5 times as large
10-59 7.88 atm
10-61 12.5 J

Chapter 11

11-1 (a) $P_1(V_3 - V_1)$ (b) $-P_1(V_3 - V_1)$
11-3 1.4 J
11-5 10^7 J
11-7 3.24×10^5 J
11-9 25 W
11-11 faster increase with piston fixed; all heat goes into internal energy change
11-13 violates second law
11-15 16.33 J K^{-1}
11-17 1.26 J K^{-1} s^{-1}
11-19 (a) no (b) increased
11-21 (a) all tails (heads) 1 way; 1 head (tail) and 5 tails (heads)—6 ways; 2 heads (tails) and 4 tails (heads)—15 ways; 3 heads and 3 tails—20 ways. (b) 3 heads and 3 tails most probable
11-25 raise it
11-27 (a) 58.1% (b) 3.3×10^6 J (c) 41.8%
11-29 500 K, 429 K
11-31 January, 1.07%; July, 6.08%
11-33 2.5
11-35 (a) 70,000 J (b) −80,000 J (c) 20,000 J
11-37 50%
11-39 (a) 2 or 12—1 way; 3 or 11—2 ways; 4 or 10—3 ways; 5 or 9—4 ways; 6 or 8—5 ways; 7—6 ways (b) 7
11-41 (a) 148 s (b) no; heat transfer from water is not efficient
11-43 (a) 43.9% (b) 1.52
11-45 (a) 0.874 (b) 11.45 kW (c) 80 kW
11-51 (a) 589 K (b) 1875 MW (c) 3.68×10^6 kg
11-53 (a) 7.43×10^{-3} litres s^{-1} (b) 214 litres
11-55 (a) 8.82 litres (b) 34.5 litres
11-57 (a) 25% (b) 231 W
11-59 1.24×10^6 J
11-61 2.68 g
11-63 no
11-65 0.375 W kg^{-1}
11-67 18.5 d

Chapter 12

12-1 5.08×10^{-3} m
12-3 4.6×10^{-4} m
12-5 lid expands more than glass
12-7 0.02991 m
12-9 different expansions would produce internal stresses

12-11   46.6 kJ
12-13   2.48 kJ kg^{-1} K^{-1}
12-15   10,000 kJ
12-17   3.54 × 10^3 kJ
12-19   (a) no   (b) 0° C
12-21   0.25 kg
12-23   2.74 kJ
12-25   0.2 m
12-27   snow acts as insulation
12-29   384 W
12-31   53.3 W
12-33   (a) 0.263 m^2 K W^{-1} (b) 3.95 m^2 K W^{-1}
12-35   79.999°C
12-37   21.2°C
12-39   1.5
12-41   push warm air down
12-43   (a) 9 × 10^{-6} m   (b) infrared
12-45   23.4%
12-47   (a) 895 W   (b) 240 W
12-49   55.5 W
12-51   (a) 3.1 × 10^{-4} m   (b) slow   (c) 1.27 × 10^{-4}
        (d) 11.0 s
12-53   3.41 × 10^{-3} K^{-1}
12-55   775 W
12-57   1.2 K h^{-1}
12-59   (a) 62.4 kJ   (b) 104 kJ
12-61   0.576 kg min^{-1}
12-63   (a) 127.5 J s^{-1} (b) 0.0015 m
12-65   the air does work as it expands, so it loses
        internal energy
12-67   (a) 102°C   (b) 3200 W
12-69   100.8°C
12-71   22%
12-73   (a) 418 W m^{-2} (b) no; average sky
        temperature is very low
12-75   (a) 317 W   (b) no
12-77   8.74 × 10^{-3} kg
12-79   (a) 2.65 × 10^6 J   (b) 0.39 cents h^{-1}
12-81   (a) 79.997°C   (b) 71.6 W
12-83   0.314V$_0$
12-89   0.260 kg h^{-1}

Chapter 13

13-1   0.08 m^3
13-3   0.01 m^3
13-5   25.6 m
13-7   0.21 m^3 s^{-1}

13-9   4.24 m s^{-1}
13-11   1 m s^{-1}
13-13   no; flow is turbulent
13-15   no; work is done against gravity
13-17   (a) pressure drop is greater   (b) more
        significant; more power is dissipated
13-19   20.8 k Pa
13-21   20.4 m
13-23   1170 kg m^{-3}
13-25   9.34 k Pa = 70.1 torr
13-27   25.8 k Pa
13-29   21.6 m s^{-2}
13-31   No
13-33   (a) 1.13 × 10^{-3} m^3 s^{-1} (b) 2.73 × 10^{-4} m^3 s^{-1}
13-35   (a) 75 Pa   (b) 0.4 m s^{-1}
13-39   750 kg m^{-3}
13-41   fallen
13-43   309 kg
13-45   9.8 × 10^4 Pa = 0.967 atm
13-49   99.986 atm
13-51   0.193 m
13-53   (a) 3.83 m s^{-1} (b) yes, until water level falls
        0.25 m   (c) 3.43 m s^{-1}
13-55   (a) yes, increases   (b) decreases
13-59   8878 kg
13-61   high takeoff velocity
13-63   (a) 48 m s^{-1} (b) doubtful validity
13-65   yes; model predicts 66 km
13-67   7.25 km
13-69 $l^{7/2}$
13-71 $l^{3/4}$

Chapter 14

14-1   halfway
14-3   1.8 W
14-5   5.4 × 10^{-5} m
14-7   (a) 1.13 × 10^{-7} m^3 s^{-1} (b) 0.0720 m s^{-1}
14-9   (a) 0.0314 N   (b) 4.71 × 10^{-4} W
14-11   (a) 0.354 m s^{-1} (b) 632 Pa
14-13   (a) no   (b) yes   (c) yes; only pressure drops
        due to dissipative forces are relevant
14-15   (a), (b) power dissipation is $Q \, \Delta P$
14-17   (a) 7.96 m s^{-1} (b) turbulent   (c) no
14-19   (a) 0.983 m s^{-1} (b) 1.24 × 10^{-5} m^3 s^{-1}
14-21 $2R^2/r^2$
14-23   (a) 1.49 × 10^{10} kPa s m^{-3}
        (b) 8.72 × 10^{-11} m^3 s^{-1}

14-25 (a) 8.38×10^{-3} N (b) 8.33×10^{-2} N (c) oil inhibits rust

14-27 (a) 8×10^{-3} m^3 s^{-1} (b) 6.37 m s^{-1} (c) $N_R = 2.5 \times 10^5$, so flow is turbulent

14-29 900 W

14-31 $409.6P_0$

14-33 (a) 11.6 kPa, 0.873 kPa (b) right ventricle does less work than left

14-35 (a) $R_f = \Delta P/Q$ (b) increase substantially

14-37 (a) 100 kPa s m^{-3} (b) 10 W (c) no

14-39 (a) 3.32×10^{14} kPa s m^{-3} (b) 3.08×10^{10}

14-41 (a) $7\pi \Delta PR^4/128\eta l$ (b) 7/16 (c) 1/4

14-43 (a) 4.33×10^{-10} m s^{-1} (b) 50 m s^{-1}

14-45 4.23×10^{-8} m

14-47 $\simeq 200$ N

14-49 (a) 4.23 (b) 3.90 m s^{-2}, 45.8 m s^{-2}

14-51 (a) 3.25×10^{-16} N (b) 2.41×10^{-16} N

14-53 805 s

14-55 3.39×10^7 u

14-57 10^{-5} m s^{-1}

14-63 (a) 2.29×10^{-24} m^3 (b) 8.18×10^{-9} m (c) 1.54×10^{-7} m (d) no, probably flattened like a pancake

14-65 carries material to and from walls

14-67 B does 21% more work

Chapter 15

15-1 0.02 N m^{-1}

15-3 minimize film area outside

15-5 -0.0535 m

15-7 0.0703 m

15-9 0.025 N m^{-1}

15-11 (a) 6060 N m^{-1} (b) 382 N

15-13 2560 N m^{-1}

15-15 3.35×10^{-3} N m^{-1}; 7%

15-17 4 Pa

15-19 21%

15-23 yes; negative pressure situation is destroyed

15-25 -0.934 atm

15-27 $w + 4\pi r\gamma$

15-33 3.86×10^{-2} N m^{-1}

15-35 (a) 41.5 J (b) 5.03×10^{-4} J

15-37 (a) 0.514 m (b) No

15-39 0.0495 m

Chapter 16

16-1 $(2kQ^2/9b^2)\hat{y}$

16-3 $-(kQ^2/2b^2)\hat{y}$

16-5 4.36×10^{-9} N

16-7 (a) e (b) 640 N

16-9 (a) 1.32×10^{13} N C^{-1} outward (b) 2.11×10^{-6} N, toward nucleus

16-11 5.69×10^{-4} N C^{-1}, opposite to **a**

16-13 $-(kQ/2b^2)\hat{y}$

16-15 -1.77×10^{-8} C

16-17 $x = 0$, $y = -0.243b$

16-19 no, force on a charge has a unique direction

16-21 (a) 10^{-6} C m^{-1} (b) 1.8×10^5 N C^{-1}

16-23 (a) 0.0050 (b) 0.41

16-25 (a) 86.4 V (b) -1.38×10^{-17} J

16-27 (a) 8.84×10^{-8} C m^{-2} (b) 400 V

16-29 (a) toward positive plate (b) toward negative plate (c) acquire some energy (d) 42.9

16-31 (a) 0.335 m (b) 0.335 m

16-33 (a) 16.8 MeV (b) 5.68×10^7 m s^{-1}

16-35 (a) 1.127×10^{-12} J (b) 3.67×10^7 m s^{-1}

16-37 (a) $E = 0$ (b) $\Delta V = E\ell$, where ℓ is the distance moved parallel to the field

16-39 cylinders centered on wire

16-41 3.13×10^{-11} m

16-43 $2qE$

16-45 (a) 0 (b) 1.6×10^{-23} N m (c) 0

16-47 10^{-7} F

16-49 6.25×10^{15}

16-51 3.23 m^2

16-53 4×10^8 V

16-55 (a) 0.325 m^2 (b) 1.44 cm

16-57 (a) 60 μF (b) 0.060 C

16-59 (a) 8.85×10^{-8} C (b) 4.43×10^{-5} J (c) 100 V, 4.43×10^{-6} J

16-61 (a) 1.5×10^{-6} m^2, 1.5×10^{-8} F (b) 6.075×10^{-11} F

16-63 (a) halved (b) halved (c) halved (d) halved

16-65 (a) 4.79×10^{-19} C (b) 2.99 (c) 1890 V

16-67 720 N C^{-1}, toward plate

16-69 (a) 1.76×10^{14} m s^{-2} (b) 10^{-8} s (c) 8.8×10^{-3} m (d) 5°

16-71 $0.701kQ/a^2$, 30° below $-x$ axis

16-73 (a) dark areas (b) dark (positive) areas

16-77 (a) $-2kqa\hat{y}/(x^2 + a^2)^{3/2}$ (b) 1/2

16-79 $2k\lambda/R$

16-83 $mv^2/2qE$

16-85 (a) $2kp_1p_2/R^3$ (b) kp_1p_2/R^3

16-87 (b) 0.316 e

16-91 five capacitors in parallel

16-93 1.33 μF

Chapter 17

17-1 (a) 720 C (b) 4.50×10^{21}

17-3 (a) no (b) no

17-5 3.43×10^{-4} m s^{-1}

17-7 4.75×10^{-4} kg

17-9 2.5 ohms

17-11 34.2 ohms

17-13 1.05×10^{-3} m

17-15 (a) r^2 (b) $1/R$

17-17 (a) no; R decreases as I increases. (b) no

17-19 11.5 ohms

17-21 20 ohms

17-23 (a) 6 A (b) 60 C (c) -720 J (d) 720 J
(e) 0 (f) 720 J (g) chemical energy in the battery

17-25 (a) 0.15 A (b) -1.5 V, 1.5 V, 1.5 V, -0.6 V, -0.9 V

17-27 (a) 3000 A, 3.6×10^4 W (b) 0.146 ohm
(c) 934 W (d) 25.6 W

17-29 (a) 144 ohms (b) 0.833 A

17-31 (a) 0.4 A (b) 4.8 W, -3.2 W (c) 0.64 W, 0.96 W

17-33 64.8 cents

17-35 (a) 7.02×10^6 J (b) 8.78×10^5 J

17-37 (a) 4.17 A (b) 1.15 ohm

17-39 460

17-41 (a) 240 ohms (b) 40 ohms

17-43 1 ohm

17-45 (a) 1.5 A (b) 3 V (c) 1 A

17-47 90-ohm series resistor

17-49 (a) 0.1 ohm (b) 10^{-7} s

17-51 0.02 s

17-53 (a) 0.012 A (b) 0.005 s

17-55 (a) 0.01 C (b) 0.0037 C

17-57 (a) 10 V (b) 100 V

17-61 (a) 7200 C (b) 4.50×10^{22} (c) 6.15×10^{23}

17-63 (a) 2.09×10^{-3} ohm (b) 0.00162 m
(c) $w(\text{A1})/w(\text{Cu}) = 0.462$

17-65 (a) 4600 W (b) 37.7 min

17-67 (a) 1.51×10^4 J (b) 5.16 K

17-69 (a) positive (b) 241 W (c) 12.06 V

17-71 (a) $\mathcal{E}/r$ (b) $\mathcal{E}/2r$

17-73 (a) 0.0516 ohm (b) 1.032 V (c) 20.6 W

17-75 0.00148 m = 0.148 cm

17-77 (a) 0.1 C (b) 10 ohms (c) 37 A

17-81 $\mathcal{E} = \mathcal{E}_1 R/(R + R_1)$

17-83 $\frac{1}{2}\ln 2 = 0.347$

17-85 1.295 ohm m

17-87 (a) 13.6 ohm m (b) 7.37×10^{-2} ohm^{-1} m^{-1}

17-89 (a) 1 A (b) 10 ohms (c) 14 V

17-91 3.427 W

Chapter 18

18-1 10^6

18-3 1.59×10^9 ohms

18-5 (a) 1.26×10^{-9} F (b) 1.59×10^6 ohms

18-7 (a) 1.2×10^7 N C^{-1}, into axon (b) 8.48

18-9 (a) 4.5×10^{-6} C m^{-2} (b) 9.0×10^{-4} C m^{-2}

18-11 10 μm

18-13 0.8 μm

18-15 8.17×10^{12}

18-17 74.1 mV

18-19 (a) 0.0289 A (b) 0.00260 W

18-21 1.5 mm

18-23 (a) -86.3 mV (b) -88.6 mV

18-25 (a) 0.2 s (b) 0.01 s

18-27 (a) 2.67×10^7 ohm m (b) 1.46×10^{10} m^2
(c) 8.28 μm

18-29 $\rho_a = 0.812$ ohm m, $\rho_{if} = 0.599$ ohm m

18-31 (a) 3.9×10^{-10} C (b) 2.44×10^9

18-37 (a) 75 (b) 75,000

Chapter 19

19-1 (a) P_4 (b) P_1

19-3 no; can have $\mathbf{v} \| \mathbf{B}$

19-5 (a) 0 (b) 0 (c) qvB/m, into page (d) qvB/m, out of page (e) qvB/m, $+y$ direction (f) qvB/m, $-y$ direction

19-7 (a) 5×10^{-4} N, into page (b) 0.05 m s^{-2}, into page

19-9 0.5 T

19-11 (a) 30 N

19-13 (a) 2 N, 2 N, 0 (b) 0

19-15 (a) 0.1 A m^2 (b) 0.01 N m (c) $\mathbf{B}$ in plane of loop

19-17 yes; $-x$ direction

19-19 3.77×10^{-7} T

19-21 1.257×10^{-3} T

19-23 6.28×10^{-3} T

19-25 (a) 8×10^{-6} T (b) 8×10^{-7} T

19-27 7.80×10^{-7} A

19-29 (a) 2×10^{-4} m (b) yes

19-31 0.25 A, parallel

19-33 (a) ev_dB, upward (b) v_dB, upward (c) av_dB
(d) av_dB (e) 2×10^{-5} V (f) out of page
(g) opposite in sign for a given current direction

19-35 (a) 0.24 A m^2 (b) 0.12 N m (c) $\boldsymbol{\mu} \| \pm \mathbf{B}$

19-37 2×10^{-6} N, toward left

19-39 (a) 10^{-5} T, into page (b) 1.67×10^{-5} T, into page (c) 2.33×10^{-5} T, out of page
(d) $x = 0.0333$ m

19-41 15.9 A

19-43 (a) 1.09×10^{-3} A (b) 13.4 T

19-45 $\pi k'I/a$

19-47 (a) 9.6×10^{-20} kg m s^{-1} (b) 5.75×10^{7} m s^{-1}

19-49 5 MeV

19-51 (a) D (b) D (c) D

19-53 (a) 1.67×10^{5} m s^{-1} (b) 8.66×10^{-3} m

19-55 (a) $evB/2m$ (b) $0.866\,v$, 0 (c) $v/2$, $mv/2eB$
(d) $1.732\pi mv/eB$ (e) helix

19-59 (a) $2k'Ir/a^2$ (b) $2k'I/r$
(c) $2k'I(r^2 - b^2)/[r(c^2 - b^2)]$ (d) 0

Chapter 20

20-1 (a) yes (b) no (c) yes

20-3 (a) same (b) large in copper, almost zero in rubber

20-5 3.14 A

20-7 (a) 48 V (b) 0

20-9 clockwise

20-11 $2\omega BA/\pi$

20-13 150 V

20-15 0.075

20-17 1

20-19 induced EMF can lead to sparks

20-21 (a) clockwise (b) counterclockwise

20-27 0.32 H

20-31 (a) qvB (b) $qvB\ell$ (c) $-B\ell v$; same

20-33 Viewed from above: (a) counterclockwise
(b) zero (c) clockwise

20-35 (a) proportional to ω (b) reduces it
(c) increases I (d) I^2R becomes large.

20-39 (a) $4\pi K_m k'IN/\ell$ (b) $2\pi K'_m N^2 I^2/\ell^2$
(c) $1/(8\pi k')$

20-43 (a) 1.333 H (b) 6 H

20-45 (a) $(Li_0/T)e^{-t/T}$ (b) $\frac{1}{2}Li_0^2 e^{-2t/T}$

20-47 (a) 1592 bits cm^{-1} (b) 4421 bits cm^{-1}

20-49 5.04×10^{6} bits s^{-1}

20-51 6

20-53 (a) 1.2 A (b) 0.02 s (c) 0.759 A (d) 1.2 A

20-55 2.392 J

20-59 28.3 A

20-61 (a) 200 W (b) 1.67 A (c) 2.36 A

20-63 ground plus either "hot" line

20-65 (a) 159 Hz (b) 70.7 V

20-67 (a) 39.8 μF (b) 66.7 ohms (c) 240 V

20-69 100

20-71 (a) 0.796 A (b) 1.125 A

20-73 (a) 75.4 ohms (b) 125 ohms (c) 1.92 A

20-75 (a) 101 ohms (b) 1.19 A

20-77 1.592×10^{8} Hz

20-79 250 V

20-81 (a) 13 ohms (b) 426 W

20-83 (a) 15.8 ohms (b) 2 W

20-85 R_v should be much larger to avoid altering currents and voltages significantly

20-87 9.9×10^{-3} ohm

20-91 5.77 s

20-93 (a) 1.29×10^{-9} F (b) 1.75 ohm
(c) 0.452 ohm

Chapter 21

21-1 0.344 m

21-3 (a) 10^{10} Hz (b) 5×10^{9} waves
(c) 1.5×10^{8} m

21-5 214 m

21-7 (a) 6×10^{14} Hz (b) 3.77×10^{15} rad s^{-1}
(c) 1.257×10^{7} m^{-1}

21-11 $(0.1$ m$) \sin[(3.14$ m$^{-1})x - (15.7$ s$^{-1})t]$

21-13 173 m s^{-1}

21-15 156 N

21-21 (a) $2A$ (b) $2A \cos \omega t$

21-23 (a) $0, \pi/k, 2\pi/k, \ldots$ (b) $\pi/2k, 3\pi/2k, \ldots$

21-27 (a) 435 m s^{-1} (b) 2.91×10s^{-4} kg ms^{-1}

21-29 (a) 3.5 m (b) 1.75 m

21-31 6.51 m

21-33 (a) 0.25 m (b) 0.132 m

21-37 (a) 5 Hz

21-39 0.0866 m

21-41 0.25

21-43 all kinetic energy; string is still moving

21-47 3.42 m s^{-1}

21-49 40.0 s

21-51 (a) 1.52×10s^{-3} s

21-53 (a) 80% (b) 20%

21-55 (a) ωA (b) $\omega^2 A^2 \Delta m/2$ (c) $\omega^2 A^2 \Delta m/2$

21-57 $2A \cos \phi/2$

21-59 1058 Hz

21-61 29.9 m s^{-1}

21-63 8.99×10^{4} Hz

21-65 (a) $+3.47$ m s^{-1}, -3.41 m s^{-1} (b) No

21-67 5.28×10^{-8} m

21-69 (a) 497.1 Hz (b) 502.9 Hz (c) 5.8 Hz

21-73 0.0157 m s^{-1}
21-77 13.7 Hz
21-79 53,300 Hz

Chapter 22

22-1 2.07×10^{11} kg m^{-1} s^{-2}
22-3 8.71 m
22-5 365 Hz
22-7 40.7 m
22-9 1498 m
22-11 0.0516 m
22-13 in water, c is larger, λ larger
22-15 132 Hz, 265 Hz, 397 Hz, 529 Hz
22-17 2.65 m, 0.0823 m
22-19 9.09 Pa
22-21 0.0166
22-23 4
22-25 14.7
22-27 1.73×10^{-3}·Pa
22-29 3×10^{-7} W m^{-2}
22-31 17,200 Hz
22-37 10
22-39 60 dB
22-41 8×10^{-13} W
22-43 no pressure differences or shielding by the head for sources overhead
22-49 (a) 0.103 m (b) 4.4×10^{-3} s
22-51 (a) 86.0 Hz (b) 1.828 m
22-53 (a) 1.26×10^4 W (b) 1.26×10^3 J
22-55 49.5 dB
22-57 (a) 10^{-8} W m^{-2} (b) 50.5 dB
(c) 6.28×10^{-6} W
22-59 (a) 0.0430 m (b) 1720 Hz
22-63 (a) 99.9% (b) 0.11%
22-65 9×10^6
22-67 $\simeq 2$ mm

Chapter 23

23-1 2.25×10^8 m s^{-1}
23-3 (a) 450 nm (b) yellow
23-5 375 nm
23-7 0.0204
23-9 0.997
23-11 1.649
23-13 (a) 15° (b) 11°
23-15 1.183

23-17 air near road is less dense, has smaller n; sunlight bends upward
23-19 57°
23-21 1.91×10^{-5} m
23-23 5.98×10^{-5} m
23-25 no, two beams are not coherent
23-27 625 nm
23-29 500
23-31 (a) to separate lines (b) to sharpen lines
23-33 693 nm
23-35 916 nm
23-37 0.258 m
23-39 0.154 m
23-41 30°
23-43 (a) 0.2 (b) 0.8
23-45 63.4°
23-47 10°
23-49 77°
23-51 11.34 m
23-53 (a) 13.4° (b) $s' = 0.74$ m
23-55 $d \sin \theta = (m + \frac{1}{2})\lambda$
23-61 (a) $(1768/m)$ nm (b) look for lines at smaller angles
23-65 2.68×10^{-3} m
23-69 (a) all of it (b) resolution is reduced in both cases
23-71 150 nm
23-75 spot is 0.117 m from plate
23-77 all wavelengths interfere destructively

Chapter 24

24-1 4 m
24-3 20 cm
24-5 -0.5 m
24-7 1.50 m
24-9 blue, 0.0775 m; red, 0.0795 m
24-11 -0.333 m
24-13 (a) -0.4 m (b) 5; erect
24-15 (a) 0.0508 m (b) -0.0169 (c) 1.42 m
24-17 four times larger
24-19 0.250 m
24-21 (a) 4.75 diopters (b) 0.211 m
24-23 (a) -0.1818 m (b) -0.286 m
24-25 10^{-3} m
24-27 0.2 m
24-29 (a) 0.133 m from objective (b) 0.00412 m
(c) -277

24-31 edges of retina have most rods
24-33 (a) 510 nm, 620 nm   (b) 450 nm, 560 nm
24-35 (a) 5.75×10^{-7} m   (b) 5.75×10^{-6} m
24-37 real images are inverted; processing in nervous system
24-39 80.1 m
24-41 (a) 0, $-f$, ∞, $3f$, $3f/2$
24-45 -1.20 m
24-47 $2f$
24-51 6.80×10^{-3} m
24-53 0.1 m away
24-57 0.0357 m
24-59 64
24-61 (a) 1.34×10^{-6} m   (b) 2.15×10^{-5} m
24-63 3.5 diopters
24-65 (a) 3.5 diopters   (b) 1 m
24-67 0.1667 m
24-69 (a) 480 nm   (b) 28%
24-71 (a) 0.52, 0.48, 0; 580 nm   (b) 0.44, 0.13, 0.43; extraspectral
24-75 (a) 0.125 m   (b) 0.5 m
24-77 -20
24-79 (a) red, blue   (b) red, green   (c) red

Chapter 25

25-1 2000 km h^{-1}
25-3 100 s
25-5 (a) 3.75×10^{-8} s   (b) 6.75 m
25-7 0.872 m
25-9 $0.866c$
25-11 8 light-years
25-13 $0.995c$
25-15 $0.866c$
25-17 (a) 5.35×10^{-9} u   (b) 1.78×10^{-10}
25-19 8.37×10^{-4} u
25-21 (a) 2150 MeV   (b) 1210 MeV
25-23 (a) $0.995c$ (b) $9.95mc$
25-25 (a) 932 MeV   (b) 932 MeV
25-27 (a) 1.005 y   (b) 10.05 y   (c) both
25-29 (a) 5 h   (b) 1.25 h   (c) 6.25 h   (d) 4 h
25-31 3.50×10^{-7} kg
25-33 (a) 1.12   (b) 1.35×10^{8} m s^{-1}
   (c) 1.45×10^{8} m s^{-1}
25-37 2.25×10^{-10} m
25-41 (a) 167 m   (b) A flashes first
25-43 (a) 0.8 h   (b) 1.33 h
25-45 (a) $0.822c$ (b) 0

25-47 (a) $0.806c$ (b) $-0.263c$
25-49 (a) 4 m   (b) 10^{-8} s   (c) 5.8 m
25-51 $v_x = 0.8c$, $v_y = 0.54c$, $v = 0.965c$

Chapter 26

26-1 4.53×10^{14} Hz
26-3 9.65×10^{14} Hz
26-5 removal of electrons leaves positive charge
26-7 48.6 m
26-9 (a) 3.10 eV   (b) 1.77 eV
26-11 (a) 6.24×10^{12} Hz   (b) 1.25×10^{14} Hz
   (c) infrared, blue
26-13 (a) 3.08×10^{-20} J   (b) 3.51×10^{-11} m
26-15 5.32×10^{20} Hz
26-17 (a) 1.21×10^{19} Hz   (b) 2.48×10^{-11} m
26-19 (a) 2.42×10^{20} Hz   (b) 1.24×10^{-12} nm
   (c) 0.00334 eV s m^{-1} = 5.35×10^{-22} kg m s^{-1}
26-21 (a) 7.95×10^{-8} W m^{-2} (b) 4.00×10^{-6} W
26-23 1995 m
26-25 (a) 1.62×10^{-27} kg   (b) 13.1 N m^{-1}
26-27 (a) 277 nm   (b) 0.48 eV   (c) 0.48 eV
26-29 (a) 2.42×10^{19} Hz   (b) 2.32×10^{19} Hz
26-31 (a) 3.34×10^{-4} eV s m^{-1} = 5.35×10^{-23} kg m s^{-1} (b) 3.93×10^{-14} J = 24.5 eV
   (c) 99,975.5 eV   (d) 5.92×10^{15} Hz
26-33 $\Delta\lambda$ varies as $1/m$, and the nuclear mass is much larger

Chapter 27

27-1 4.73×10^{-14} m
27-3 2975 m
27-5 486 nm
27-7 151 eV
27-9 6.63×10^{-24} kg m s^{-1} (for both)
27-11 3.70×10^{-63} m
27-13 (a) 6.63×10^{-34} m   (b) no, λ is too small
27-15 (a) 0.821 nm   (b) 224 eV
27-17 yes
27-19 (a) 13.6 eV   (b) 54.4 eV   (c) 122 eV
27-21 $n = 2$
27-23 4.05×10^{-6} m
27-25 6.4 ev
27-31 1.16×10^{-3} m s^{-1}
27-33 $\geq 3.52 \times 10^{-31}$ m
27-35 (a) 1.06×10^{-24} kg m s^{-1}
   (b) 1.16×10^{6} m s^{-1}, 5.28×10^{-24} m s^{-1}

27-37 (a) 6.8 eV (b) $2a_0 = 1.06 \times 10^{-10}$ m

27-39 (a) -7.21×10^5 eV (b) 1.60×10^{-14} m (c) 4

27-41 12.75 eV, 12.1 eV, 10.2 eV, 2.55 eV, 1.89 eV, 0.661 eV

27-43 (a) $n^2\hbar^2/2I$, $n = 0, 1, 2, \ldots$

27-45 (a) 6.17×10^4 Hz (b) 2.56 eV (c) $4 \rightarrow 2$

Chapter 28

28-1 (a) 0, 1, 2, 3 (b) $4s, 4p, 4d, 4f$
(c) $0, \hbar, 2\hbar, 3\hbar$

28-3 (a) $0, \pm e\hbar B/2m, \pm 2e\hbar B/2m$
(b) 5.79×10^{-4} eV (c) absorbed

28-5 32

28-7 (a) $r = 0$ (b) $r \approx 5a_0$ (c) $r = 0, 2a_0$

28-9 (a) equal magnitudes, opposite signs (b) no

28-11 14

28-13 all have one s electron outside closed shells

28-15 48 eV

28-17 small ionization energies

28-19 H electron closes shell in halogen atoms

28-21 $n = 3, l = 0, m_l = 0, s = 1/2, m_s = \pm 1/2$

28-23 11.1 eV

28-25 (a) 0.5 (b) 0.1

28-27 (a) $8a_0$ (b) $8a_0$

28-29 (a) 483 eV (b) mutual repulsion of 1s electrons (c) yes; additional shielding

28-31 (a) -272 eV (b) 3.79

28-33 (a) 2×10^{11} W (b) 10^{17} W m^{-2}

28-37 (a) 68.3 MeV (b) 9.6 Mev

28-39 22.4 MeV

28-43 (a) $4a_0$ (b) $2a_0$

28-45 (b) 9.01×10^{-15}

28-47 (a) $\psi(a) = \psi(-a) = 0$ (c) $a^{-1/2} \cos n\pi x/2a$, $n = 1, 3, 5, \ldots$; $a^{-1/2} \sin n\pi x/2a$, $n = 2, 4, 6, \ldots$; $E_n = n^2\hbar^2\pi^2/8ma^2$

28-49 $13e^{-4} = 0.238$

28-51 (a) $1.5 a_0$ (b) $1/a_0$ (c) r and $1/r$ are large in different regions of space

Chapter 29

29-1 (a) 1.30 eV (b) -6.10 eV (c) 4.80 eV

29-3 (a) -5.76 eV (b) 3.13 eV

29-5 no; it is symmetrical

29-9 (b) 4 (c) 2

29-11 2.66×10^{14} Hz

29-13 yes; photons are emitted or lattice excited

29-17 4.46×10^{-29} C m

29-19 yes; nonbonding orbital is negative, H nuclei positive

29-21 (a) graphite, sp^2; diamond, sp^3 (b) yes; no bonding between planes in graphite

29-23 12.0 eV

29-25 1.18 T

29-27 5.11×10^7 Hz

29-31 63.8 Hz

29-35 broader peaks

29-37 3 to 2 to 2

29-41 $f_p > f_e$

29-43 (a) counterclockwise (b) reduces f_p

Chapter 30

30-1 8 h

30-3 17.6 d

30-5 5.6 to 5.7 d

30-7 18.95%

30-9 15.5 d

30-11 (a) $\frac{1}{4}$ (b) $\frac{1}{4}$

30-13 11,500 y

30-15 too old

30-17 1300 y

30-19 1.1×10^{-14}

30-21 1.48×10^4 m

30-23 8, 19, 35, 126

30-25 7.86 MeV

30-27 (a) 1397 MeV (b) 6.98 MeV

30-29 (a) 30 MeV (b) 0

30-31 (a) 1.44 MeV (b) -1.547×10^{-3} u

30-33 (a) $^3_1$H (b) $^2_1$H (c) α

30-35 (a) 4.84×10^{20} Hz (b) 6.20×10^{-13} m

30-37 (a) no, expect $N > Z$ for stable nucleus (b) positron, increase N/Z

30-39 6.93×10^6

30-41 6.64

30-43 40.4 y

30-45 (a) straight line (b) decay rate is not a simple exponential (c) straight line, less rapid decrease

30-47 (a) 24.7 MeV (b) 1.99×10^6 kg

30-49 (b) $^9_5$B and $^9_3$Li have unfilled lower levels (c) β^-

30-51 (a) 8.64 fm (b) 176.3 MeV

30-53 1319 MeV

30-57 geological stability (against earthquakes)

30-61 electrical repulsion is three times larger

30-63 (a) 8.21×10^{13} J kg^{-1} (b) 0.0203 kg s^{-1}

30-65 (a) 7.72×10^8 K (b) some atoms have above-average energies

Chapter 31

31-1 a single γ can ionize atoms; one microwave quantum cannot

31-3 (a) α particles (b) 0.0045 cm

31-7 nuclear mass is much larger than electron mass

31-9 $K(d) = 2K(p)$

31-11 determine range

31-13 (a) 5 cm (b) 0.5 cm

31-15 1.61×10^{15}

31-17 (a) 3.7×10^4 (b) 8.29×10^{-10} J
(c) 8.29×10^{-10} W

31-19 8.11×10^{-7} Ci

31-21 6.20 R

31-23 (a) 4.50 min (b) 6.43 min

31-25 4.1×10^{-4} Sv y^{-1}

31-27 (a) 12 (b) 50

31-29 less important because of smaller total dose to genetic pool

31-31 2600 y^{-1}

31-33 one to 5 years doubles cancer rate, 0.25 to 1.5 years doubles mutation rate

31-35 (a) 160,000 (b) 5

31-37 $88,000,000

31-39 2000

31-43 (a) low-energy X rays have shorter ranges
(b) reduce skin dose

31-45 (a) 7.40×10^{11} s^{-1} (b) 5.89×10^{10} m^{-2} s^{-1}

31-47 100 rad, 100 rem

31-49 1420 cm^3

31-51 (a) 0.616 J (b) 3.08 rad (c) 28

31-53 (a) 4 (b) 0.4 (c) no; masked by naturally occurring cancers

31-55 (a) 4.30 (b) 1.14×10^{-5} (c) 1.26×10^{-6}

31-57 count rate increases as slabs are added

INDEX

884

FUNDAMENTAL CONSTANTS

The numerical values of most constants have been rounded off to three significant figures for convenience.

Quantity	Symbol	Numerical Value
Speed of light (in vacuum)	c	3.00×10^8 m s^{-1}
Gravitational constant	G	6.67×10^{-11} N m^2 kg^{-2}
Avogadro's number	N_A	6.02×10^{23} molecules mole^{-1}
Universal gas constant	R	8.31 J K^{-1} mole^{-1}
Boltzmann constant	k_B	1.38×10^{-23} J K^{-1}
		8.62×10^{-5} eV K^{-1}
Stefan's constant	σ	5.67×10^{-8} W m^{-2} K^{-4}
Atomic mass unit	u	1.66×10^{-27} kilograms
Coulomb constant	k	9.00×10^9 N m^2 C^{-2}
	$\varepsilon_0 = \frac{1}{4}\pi k$	8.85×10^{-12} C^2 N^{-1} m^{-2}
Biot-Savart constant	k'	10^{-7} T m A^{-1}
Electron charge	$-e$	-1.60×10^{-19} coulombs
Electron mass	m_e	9.11×10^{-31} kilograms
Proton charge	e	1.60×10^{-19} coulombs
Proton mass	m_p	1.673×10^{-27} kilograms
Neutron mass	m_n	1.675×10^{-27} kilograms
Planck's constant	h	6.63×10^{-34} J s
		4.14×10^{-15} eV s
	$\hbar = h/2\pi$	1.055×10^{-34} J s
		6.58×10^{-16} eV s
Rydberg constant	R_H	1.10×10^7 metres^{-1}
Bohr radius	a_0	5.29×10^{-11} metres
Bohr magneton	μ_B	9.27×10^{-24} J T^{-1}

SOLAR AND TERRESTRIAL DATA

The numerical values given have been rounded off to three significant figures for convenience.

Standard atmospheric pressure	1 atm
	1.013×10^5 Pa
	1.013 bars
	760 mm Hg
	760 torr
Acceleration of gravity, g	9.81 m s^{-2}
Magnetic field (Washington, D.C.)	5.7×10^{-5} teslas
Speed of sound (dry air, 20°C)	344 m s^{-1}
Mass of earth	5.98×10^{24} kilograms
Volume of earth	1.09×10^{21} m^3
Mean radius of earth	6.38×10^6 metres
Mean density of earth	5.52×10^3 kg m^{-3}
Mean angular rotational speed of earth	7.29×10^{-5} rad s^{-1}
Earth to sun, mean distance	1.50×10^{11} metres
Earth to moon, mean distance	3.84×10^8 metres
Mean orbital speed of earth about the sun	2.98×10^4 m s^{-1}
Sun, mean radius	6.95×10^8 metres
mass	1.99×10^{30} kilograms
Moon, mean radius	1.74×10^6 metres
volume	2.20×10^{19} m^3
mass	7.35×10^{22} kilograms
mean density	3.34×10^3 kg m^{-3}
acceleration of gravity	1.62 m s^{-2}

ATOMIC MASSES OF THE ELEMENTS AS THEY OCCUR ON THE EARTH.

The mass of a carbon-12 atom is defined as exactly 12 u. Brackets indicate the approximate mass of the most stable isotope of artificially produced elements.

Atomic Number	Element	Symbol	Atomic Mass (u)	Atomic Number	Element	Symbol	Atomic Mass (u)
1	hydrogen	H	1.00797	54	xenon	Xe	131.30
2	helium	He	4.0026	55	cesium	Ca	132.905
3	lithium	Li	6.939	56	barium	Ba	137.34
4	beryllium	Be	9.0122	57	lanthanum	La	138.91
5	boron	B	10.811	58	cerium	Ce	140.12
6	carbon	C	12.01115	59	praseodymium	Pr	140.907
7	nitrogen	N	14.0067	60	neodymium	Nd	144.24
8	oxygen	O	15.9994	61	promethium	Pm	[145]
9	fluorine	F	18.9984	62	samarium	Sm	150.35
10	neon	Ne	20.183	63	europium	Eu	151.96
11	sodium	Na	22.9898	64	gadolinium	Gd	157.25
12	magnesium	Mg	24.312	65	terbium	Tb	158.924
13	aluminum	Al	26.9815	66	dysprosium	Dy	162.50
14	silicon	Si	28.086	67	holmium	Ho	164.930
15	phosporus	P	30.9738	68	erbium	Er	167.26
16	sulfur	S	32.064	69	thulium	Tm	168.934
17	chlorine	Cl	35.453	70	ytterbium	Yb	173.04
18	argon	Ar	39.948	71	lutetium	Lu	174.97
19	potassium	K	39.102	72	hafnium	Hf	178.49
20	calcium	Ca	40.08	73	tantalum	Ta	180.948
21	scandium	Sc	44.956	74	tungsten	W	183.85
22	titanium	Ti	47.90	75	rhenium	Re	186.2
23	vanadium	V	50.942	76	osmium	Os	190.2
24	chromium	Cr	51.996	77	iridium	Ir	192.2
25	manganese	Mn	54.9380	78	platinum	Pt	195.09
26	iron	Fe	55.847	79	gold	Au.	196.967
27	cobalt	Co	58.9332	80	mercury	Hg	200.59
28	nickel	Ni	58.71	81	thallium	Tl	204.37
29	copper	Cu	63.54	82	lead	Pb	207.19
30	zinc	Zn	65.37	83	bismuth	Bi	208.980
31	gallium	Ga	69.72	84	polonium	Po	[210]
32	germanium	Ge	72.59	85	astatine	At	[210]
33	arsenic	As	74.9216	86	radon	Rn	[222]
34	selenium	Se	78.96	87	francium	Fr	[223]
35	bromine	Br	79.909	88	radium	Ra	226.05
36	krypton	Kr	83.80	89	actinium	Ac	[227]
37	rubidium	Rb	85.47	90	thorium	Th	232.038
38	strontium	Sr	87.62	91	protactinium	Pa	[231]
39	yttrium	Y	88.905	92	uranium	U	[238.03]
40	zirconium	Zr	91.22	93	neptunium	Np	[237]
41	niobium	Nb	92.906	94	plutonium	Pu	[242]
42	molybdenum	Mo	95.94	95	americium	Am	[243]
43	technetium	Tc	[99]	96	curium	Cm	[247]
44	ruthenium	Ru	101.07	97	berkelium	Bk	[247]
45	rhodium	Rh	102.905	98	californium	Cf	[249]
46	palladium	Pd	106.4	99	einsteinium	Es	[254]
47	silver	Ag	107.870	100	fermium	Fm	[257]
48	cadmium	Cd	112.40	101	mendelevium	Md	[256]
49	indium	In	114.82	102	nobelium	No	[259]
50	tin	Sn	118.69	103	lawrencium	Lw	[260]
51	antimony	Sb	121.75	104	Rutherfordium	Rf	[261]
52	tellurium	Te	127.60	105	(unnamed)		[262]
53	iodine	I	126.9044	106	(unnamed)		[263]

crèmes brûlées

José Maréchal

PHOTOGRAPHIES DE CHARLOTTE LASCÈVE
Stylisme de Élodie Rambaud

LES PETITS PLATS
MARABOUT
ORIGINAUX & AUTHENTIQUES
DEPUIS L'AN 2000

sommaire

cuisson et caramélisation

cuisson

Je préconise dans mes recettes une température de 95 °C plutôt que 100 °C, qui est la plus juste température de cuisson des crèmes brûlées, car selon la puissance, l'affichage électronique ou le thermostat de votre four, des écarts de température au-dessus des 100 °C pourraient nuire à la cuisson de vos crèmes.

En effet, comme la crème anglaise, la crème brûlée ne doit pas bouillir car sa prise se fait uniquement grâce à la liaison des jaunes d'œufs.

Si vous n'êtes pas très sûr de la précision de votre four, soyez prudent en diminuant un peu la température.

Cuire ensuite vos crèmes au bain-marie, dans un plat à rebord rempli à moitié d'eau, et soyez patient quelques minutes de plus pour une cuisson maîtrisée.

caramélisation

1) LE CHALUMEAU : cet outil de « poche » est incontestablement le plus pratique : il permet une coloration du caramel plus uniforme et plus rapide, ainsi vos crèmes restent bien figées et froides à l'intérieur. Il fonctionne avec des recharges de gaz à briquet que vous trouvez chez tous les buralistes.

2) SOUS LE GRIL DU FOUR : préchauffer le gril du four, placer vos crèmes sur une plaque remplie à moitié d'eau froide, les saupoudrer de sucre puis les placer sous le gril en surveillant attentivement. Tourner la plaque de temps en temps pour unifier la caramélisation.

3) LE FER CHAUFFÉ À BLANC : le fer est l'outil de nos ancêtres. Les premières crèmes brûlées datent du XVIIe siècle, mais cet outil a su traverser les années. Il est encore utilisé aujourd'hui autour des bonnes tables.

L'odeur du caramel fumant et ses reflets irréguliers nous rappellent des souvenirs d'enfance… Héritage de nos grands-mères, il conserve toute sa force de nous régaler.

Attention cependant de choisir des moules adaptés au diamètre de celui-ci.

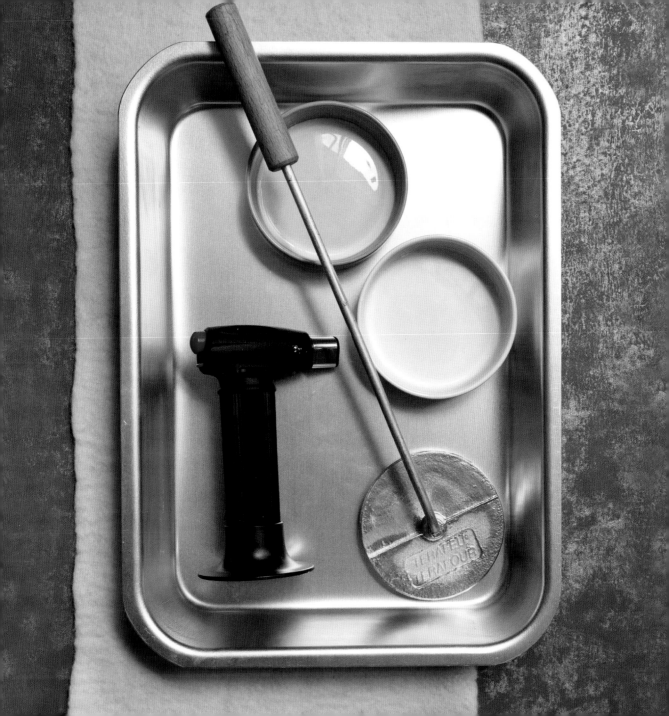

le lait…

LE LAIT DE VACHE

Entier, ½ écrémé ou écrémé, associé plus ou moins à la crème fraîche, il aura pour but d'alléger plus ou moins vos crèmes, et notamment celles à base de produits riches tels que le Nutella ou les carambars.

LE LAIT DE SOJA

Relativement riche et fabriqué à partir des graines de soja, le lait de soja peut être employé en tant qu'ingrédient de remplacement de nombreuses recettes à base de lait de vache telles que les crèmes brûlées.

LE LAIT DE COCO

Le lait de coco est fabriqué en broyant la pulpe avec de l'eau bouillante. Il ne faut pas le confondre avec le jus présent dans le fruit (eau de coco). Je vous recommande d'utiliser du lait de coco en boîte (liquide) plutôt que celui en poudre qui est de moins bonne qualité. Avec son taux élevé de matières grasses, il est préférable de l'utiliser seul ou à la place de la crème dans vos recettes de crèmes brûlées.

LE LAIT D'AMANDE OU DE PISTACHE

Souvent difficile à se procurer, voici une astuce pour le fabriquer soi-même :

1-Enfermez des amandes fraîchement moulues dans un torchon fin.

2-Nouez solidement et immergez le tout dans de l'eau.

3-Malaxez plusieurs fois afin d'en extraire le lait.

4-Pressez le torchon au maximum pour ne rien perdre.

Pour vos recettes de crèmes brûlées, vous pouvez plus simplement faire infuser les fines poudres d'amandes et de pistaches dans la crème et le lait chaud.

le sucre...

LE SUCRE CRISTALLISÉ BLANC

De betterave ou de canne, le sucre cristallisé blanc se présente sous la forme de cristaux plus ou moins gros qui même ajoutés à une crème continuent de croquer sous la dent.

Il est donc préférable de l'utiliser plutôt pour caraméliser vos crèmes, si vous le souhaitez, à la place de la cassonade.

LE SUCRE EN POUDRE (OU SUCRE SEMOULE)

C'est le sucre obtenu après broyage et tamisage du sucre cristallisé blanc. Il se dissout plus facilement aux préparations. Battu avec les jaunes d'œufs (blanchir), il évitera la cuisson des jaunes et ainsi les petites impuretés dans vos crèmes.

LA CASSONADE

La cassonade est le sucre cristallisé roux obtenu directement à l'issue de la première cuisson du jus de canne. Il est couramment utilisé pour caraméliser les crèmes brûlées car il a une couleur dorée et des notes aromatiques de vanille et de rhum.

LA VERGEOISE

Provenant d'un sirop de betterave, la vergeoise est un sucre à consistance moelleuse présentant deux sortes de coloration : la vergeoise blonde et la vergeoise brune, plus foncée et à l'arôme particulier.

Particulièrement appréciée dans le nord de la France et en Belgique, son utilisation pour caraméliser vos crèmes apportera une saveur plus particulière et une coloration plus soutenue (voir recette chicorée, marrons, raisins au rhum...).

crèmes brûlées classiques… (3 recettes de base)

1 - DÉLICATE ET PRESQUE LÉGÈRE
(compter une quinzaine de minutes
de cuisson en plus pour cette recette)
35 cl de crème liquide
12 cl de lait
70 g de sucre en poudre
4 jaunes d'œufs
½ gousse de vanille
60 g de cassonade

2 - DOUCE ET UN PEU PLUS GOURMANDE
35 cl de crème liquide
10 cl de lait
90 g de sucre en poudre
5 jaunes d'œufs
½ gousse de vanille
60 g de cassonade

3 - SOYEUSE ET UN PEU PLUS CRÉMEUSE
50 cl de crème liquide
70 g de sucre en poudre
5 jaunes d'œufs
½ gousse de vanille
60 g de cassonade

préparation

Couper la gousse de vanille dans le sens de la longueur,
racler les graines dans le lait (ou la moitié de la crème
pour la version n°3) et faire chauffer dans une casserole à feu doux.

Pendant ce temps, fouetter énergiquement dans un saladier les jaunes
d'œufs et le sucre en poudre afin que le mélange blanchisse. Incorporer
la crème froide (l'autre moitié pour la version 3) et bien mélanger.

Enfin, ajouter le lait chaud (ou la crème pour la version n°3)
et mélanger de nouveau afin de bien dissoudre l'ensemble.

Faire reposer la préparation dans un récipient adapté,
au réfrigérateur 2 heures au moins.

cuisson

Allumer le four à 95 °C (th. 3) (voir techniques page 4).

Répartir délicatement la crème dans des petits pots en porcelaine
ou en terre cuite puis les disposer bien à plat dans le four.
Cuire pendant 1 h à 1 h 15 (selon la contenance des petits pots).
Les crèmes doivent être tremblantes et juste prises.

Une fois cuites et légèrement refroidies, réserver les crèmes au réfrigérateur.

caramélisation

Au moment de servir, saupoudrer les crèmes de cassonade puis les
caraméliser à l'aide d'un chalumeau (ou voir autres techniques page 4).

crème Catalane

50 cl de lait
125 g de sucre en poudre
1 zeste de citron
1 bâton de cannelle (ou 2 pincées
en poudre)
4 jaunes d'œufs
20 g de Maïzena
60 g de cassonade

préparation et cuisson

Chauffer dans une casserole à feu doux le lait, la cannelle et le zeste de citron.

Pendant ce temps, fouetter énergiquement dans un saladier les jaunes d'œufs et le sucre en poudre puis incorporer la Maïzena.

Filtrer le lait chaud sur le mélange, bien dissoudre l'ensemble et remettre la crème dans une casserole sur feu doux sans cesser de mélanger jusqu'à épaississement.

Répartir délicatement la crème chaude dans des petits pots en porcelaine ou en terre cuite.

Mettre les crèmes Catalane 2 heures au moins au réfrigérateur.

caramélisation

Au moment de servir, saupoudrer les crèmes de cassonade puis les caraméliser à l'aide d'un chalumeau (ou voir autres techniques page 4).

pots de crème à la vanille et spéculos

35 cl de crème liquide
12 cl de lait
70 g de sucre en poudre
4 jaunes d'œufs
½ gousse de vanille
4 à 6 spéculos

préparation

Couper la gousse de vanille dans le sens de la longueur, racler
les graines dans le lait et faire chauffer dans une casserole à feu doux.

Pendant ce temps, fouetter énergiquement dans un saladier
les jaunes d'œufs et le sucre en poudre afin que le mélange
blanchisse. Incorporer la crème froide et bien mélanger.

Enfin, ajouter le lait chaud et mélanger de nouveau
afin de bien dissoudre l'ensemble.

Faire reposer la préparation dans un récipient adapté,
2 heures au moins au réfrigérateur.

cuisson

Allumer le four à 95 °C (th. 3) (voir techniques page 4).

Répartir délicatement la crème dans des petits pots
en porcelaine ou en terre cuite.

Déposer délicatement sur chaque crème un spéculos puis cuire au
four, bien à plat, pendant 1 h à 1 h 15 (selon la contenance des petits
pots). Les crèmes doivent être tremblantes et juste prises.

Une fois cuites et légèrement refroidies, réserver les crèmes
au réfrigérateur 1 h au moins avant de les servir.

cheese cream

25 cl de lait
150 g de fromage blanc
50 g de mascarpone
3 jaunes d'œufs
½ citron vert
60 g de sucre en poudre

préparation

Prélever à l'aide d'un épluche-légumes les zestes
de citron vert puis les hacher finement.

Dans une casserole, chauffer le lait et les zestes à feu doux.

Pendant ce temps, réunir dans un saladier les jaunes d'œufs et le sucre
en poudre puis fouetter énergiquement afin que le mélange blanchisse.

Incorporer au fouet le mascarpone puis le fromage blanc.

Enfin, verser le lait chaud en mélangeant bien afin de dissoudre l'ensemble.

Faire reposer la préparation dans un récipient adapté,
2 heures au moins au réfrigérateur.

cuisson

Allumer le four à 95 °C (th. 3) (voir techniques page 4).

Répartir délicatement les crèmes dans des petits pots en porcelaine ou en
terre cuite puis les disposer dans un plat à rebord rempli à moitié d'eau. Cuire
au bain-marie pendant 1 h à 1 h 15 (selon la contenance des petits pots).

Une fois cuites et légèrement refroidies, réserver
les crèmes au réfrigérateur avant de les déguster.

nougat cream

LA CRÈME
30 cl de lait
20 cl de crème
5 jaunes d'œufs
160 g de nougat
30 g de miel

LA NOUGATINE
50 g de pistaches
50 g d'amandes
50 g de noisettes
75 g de miel
40 g de sucre en poudre

préparation de la nougatine

Dans une casserole bien propre, cuire à feu moyen, sans remuer, le sucre, le miel et un peu d'eau (l'eau doit juste recouvrir le sucre). Pendant ce temps, mixer grossièrement les fruits secs.

Dès qu'une coloration commence à apparaître, mélanger légèrement le caramel afin qu'il devienne homogène puis ajouter les fruits secs.

Retirer du feu et verser la nougatine sur une toile de cuisson ou un papier sulfurisé légèrement graissé en l'étalant le plus finement possible. Laisser refroidir à température ambiante.

À l'aide d'un rouleau à pâtisserie, casser la nougatine en petits morceaux avant de la passer au mixeur quelques secondes afin d'obtenir une poudre grossière.

préparation de la crème

Chauffer le lait, le miel et le nougat coupé en petits morceaux dans une casserole à feu doux. Mélanger attentivement afin de bien dissoudre l'ensemble.

Hors du feu, incorporer la crème liquide puis les jaunes d'œufs.

Bien mélanger puis faire reposer la préparation dans un récipient adapté, 2 heures au moins au réfrigérateur.

cuisson

Allumer le four à 95 °C (th. 3) (voir techniques page 4).

Répartir délicatement la crème dans des petits pots en porcelaine ou en terre cuite puis les disposer bien à plat dans le four. Cuire pendant 1 h à 1 h 15 (selon la contenance des petits pots).

Les crèmes doivent être tremblantes et juste prises.

Une fois cuites et légèrement refroidies, réserver les crèmes au réfrigérateur. Au moment de servir, recouvrir chaque petit pot de cette poudre de nougatine.

crème façon diplomate

40 cl de lait
10 cl de crème liquide
1 œuf entier
2 jaunes d'œufs
75 g de sucre en poudre
½ gousse de vanille
100 g de fruits confits en cubes
80 g de brioche
80 g de raisins de Corinthe

préparation

Couper la gousse de vanille dans le sens de la longueur, racler les graines dans le lait et la crème puis chauffer le tout dans une casserole à feu doux.

Pendant ce temps, fouetter énergiquement dans un saladier les jaunes d'œufs, l'œuf entier et le sucre en poudre afin que le mélange blanchisse.

Verser dessus la crème chaude en mélangeant bien afin de dissoudre l'ensemble.

cuisson

Allumer le four à 150 °C (th. 5).

Tailler la brioche en petits dés puis les répartir avec les fruits confits et les raisins de Corinthe dans vos petits pots.

Les garnir enfin de crème vanillée puis les disposer dans un plat à rebord rempli à moitié d'eau.

Cuire au bain-marie pendant 25 à 35 minutes (selon la contenance des petits pots).

Une fois cuites et légèrement refroidies, réserver les crèmes au réfrigérateur avant de les déguster.

caramélisation

Juste avant de servir ces crèmes, vous pouvez, si vous le souhaitez, les napper d'un sirop d'érable ou d'un caramel liquide, elles n'en seront que plus gourmandes !

crème brûlée « pas comme les autres »

50 cl de crème liquide
80 g de sucre en poudre
6 jaunes d'œufs
½ gousse de vanille
60 g de cassonade

préparation

Couper la gousse de vanille dans le sens de la longueur, racler les graines dans la moitié de la crème et faire chauffer dans une casserole à feu doux.

Pendant ce temps, fouetter énergiquement dans un saladier les jaunes d'œufs et le sucre en poudre afin que le mélange blanchisse. Incorporer le reste de crème froide et bien mélanger.

Enfin, ajouter la crème chaude et mélanger de nouveau afin de bien dissoudre l'ensemble.

Faire reposer la crème dans un récipient adapté, 2 heures au moins au réfrigérateur.

cuisson

Allumer le four à 95 °C (th. 3) (voir techniques page 4).

Répartir délicatement la crème dans des moules en silicone puis les disposer bien à plat dans le four. Cuire pendant 1 h à 1 h 15 (selon la contenance des moules). Les crèmes doivent être tremblantes et juste prises.

Une fois cuites et légèrement refroidies, mettre les crèmes 2 à 3 heures au congélateur.

caramélisation

Une quinzaine de minutes avant de passer au dessert, démouler les crèmes congelées, les rouler dans la cassonade en insistant un peu pour qu'il s'incruste bien sur toute leur surface puis disposer les crèmes sur les assiettes de service.

Caraméliser uniformément les crèmes à l'aide d'un chalumeau puis les laisser décongeler quelques minutes avant de les servir.

crème brûlée au foie gras

200 g de foie gras frais (cru)
20 cl de crème liquide
20 cl de lait
4 jaunes d'œufs
2 pincées de sel
2 pincées de quatre épices
1 c. à café de sucre en poudre
1 c. à soupe de porto
60 g de cassonade ou de sucre vergeoise

préparation

Chauffer le lait dans une casserole à feu doux.

Pendant ce temps, couper le foie gras en cubes puis le mixer, à l'aide d'un blendeur ou d'un mixeur avec la crème froide, les jaunes d'œufs, le sel, le sucre en poudre, le quatre épices et le porto.

Enfin, ajouter le lait chaud et mixer de nouveau pour dissoudre l'ensemble.

Filtrer la crème au foie gras à l'aide d'une passoire fine dans un récipient adapté et la faire reposer 2 heures au moins au réfrigérateur.

cuisson

Allumer le four à 95 °C (th. 3) (voir techniques page 4).

Répartir délicatement la crème dans des petits pots en porcelaine ou en terre cuite puis les disposer bien à plat dans le four. Cuire pendant 30 à 40 minutes (selon la contenance des petits pots). Les crèmes doivent être tremblantes et juste prises.

Une fois cuites et légèrement refroidies, réserver les crèmes au réfrigérateur.

caramélisation

Au moment de servir, saupoudrer les crèmes de cassonade ou de sucre vergeoise vergeoise puis les caraméliser à l'aide d'un chalumeau (ou voir autres techniques page 4).

crème brûlée à la carotte et à l'orange

250 g de carottes cuites
20 cl de jus d'orange
30 cl de crème liquide
6 jaunes d'œufs
75 g de sucre en poudre
60 g de cassonade

préparation

Couper les carottes cuites en rondelles. Les mixer à l'aide d'un blendeur ou d'un mixeur plongeant avec la crème. Réserver.

Chauffer le jus d'orange dans une casserole à feu doux.

Pendant ce temps, fouetter énergiquement dans un saladier les jaunes d'œufs et le sucre en poudre afin que le mélange blanchisse. Incorporer la crème de carottes puis le jus d'orange chaud et bien mélanger pour dissoudre l'ensemble.

Faire reposer la crème dans un récipient adapté, 2 heures au moins au réfrigérateur.

cuisson

Allumer le four à 95 °C (th. 3) (voir techniques page 4).

Répartir délicatement la crème dans des petits pots en porcelaine ou en terre cuite puis les disposer bien à plat dans le four.
Cuire pendant 1 h à 1 h 15 (selon la contenance des petits pots).
Les crèmes doivent être tremblantes et juste prises.

Une fois cuites et légèrement refroidies, réserver les crèmes au réfrigérateur.

caramélisation

Au moment de servir, saupoudrer les crèmes de cassonade puis les caraméliser à l'aide d'un chalumeau (ou voir autres techniques page 4).

crème brûlée à la betterave et aux framboises

15 cl de lait
25 cl de crème liquide
50 g de sucre en poudre
6 jaunes d'œufs
90 g de betterave cuite
60 g de framboises (fraîches
ou surgelées)
60 g de cassonade

préparation

Éplucher et couper les betteraves en cubes. Les mixer à l'aide d'un blendeur ou d'un mixeur plongeant avec la crème et les framboises. Réserver.

Chauffer le lait dans une casserole à feu doux.

Pendant ce temps, fouetter énergiquement dans un saladier les jaunes d'œufs et le sucre en poudre afin que le mélange blanchisse. Incorporer la crème betterave-framboises puis le lait chaud et bien mélanger pour dissoudre l'ensemble.

Filtrer la crème à l'aide d'une passoire fine et la faire reposer dans un récipient adapté, 2 heures au moins au réfrigérateur.

cuisson

Allumer le four à 95 °C (th. 3) (voir techniques page 4).

Répartir délicatement la crème dans des petits pots en porcelaine ou en terre cuite puis les disposer bien à plat dans le four. Cuire pendant 1 h à 1 h 15 (selon la contenance des petits pots). Les crèmes doivent être tremblantes et juste prises.

Une fois cuites et légèrement refroidies, réserver les crèmes au réfrigérateur.

caramélisation

Au moment de servir, saupoudrer les crèmes de cassonade puis les caraméliser à l'aide d'un chalumeau (ou voir autres techniques page 4).

crème brûlée au thé vert et au sésame

5 sachets de thé vert
35 cl de crème liquide
12 cl de lait
90 g de sucre en poudre
5 jaunes d'œufs
30 g de sucre en poudre
30 g de cassonade
50 g de sésame noir

préparation

Dans une casserole, chauffer le lait et la crème à feu doux avec les sachets
de thé et laisser infuser hors du feu quelques minutes de plus.

Pendant ce temps, réunir dans un saladier les jaunes d'œufs et 90 g de sucre
en poudre puis fouetter énergiquement afin que le mélange blanchisse.

Filtrer la crème chaude sur le mélange œufs-sucre puis
mélanger de nouveau afin de bien dissoudre l'ensemble.

Faire reposer la crème dans un récipient adapté,
2 heures au moins au réfrigérateur.

cuisson

Allumer le four à 95 °C (th 3) (voir techniques page 4).

Répartir délicatement la crème brûlée au thé vert dans des petits pots
en porcelaine ou en terre cuite puis les disposer bien à plat dans
le four. Cuire pendant 1 h à 1 h 15 (selon la contenance des petits
pots). Les crèmes doivent être tremblantes et juste prises.

Une fois cuites et légèrement refroidies, réserver les crèmes au réfrigérateur.

caramélisation

Caraméliser légèrement le sésame dans une poêle avec les 30 g de sucre.

Au moment de servir, saupoudrer les crèmes de cassonade
puis les caraméliser partiellement (voir photo) à l'aide d'un
chalumeau puis, parsemer joliment les crèmes de sésame.

crème au citron et à la bergamote

30 cl de crème liquide
10 cl de lait
3 jaunes d'œufs
50 g de sucre en poudre
1 citron
10 g d'arôme bergamote

préparation

Prélever à l'aide d'un épluche-légumes les zestes
du citron puis les émincer finement.

Dans une casserole, chauffer le lait, les zestes et l'arôme bergamote à feu doux.

Pendant ce temps, réunir dans un saladier les jaunes d'œufs et le sucre
puis fouetter énergiquement afin que le mélange blanchisse.

Filtrer à l'aide d'une passoire fine la crème chaude sur le mélange
œufs-sucre puis mélanger de nouveau afin de bien dissoudre l'ensemble.

Faire reposer la crème dans un récipient adapté,
2 heures au moins au réfrigérateur.

cuisson

Allumer le four à 95 °C (th. 3) (voir techniques page 4).

Répartir délicatement la crème au citron et à la bergamote dans des
petits pots en porcelaine ou en terre cuite puis les disposer bien à
plat dans le four. Cuire pendant 1 h à 1 h 15 (selon la contenance des
petits pots). Les crèmes doivent être tremblantes et juste prises.

Une fois cuites et légèrement refroidies, réserver les
crèmes au réfrigérateur avant de les déguster.

Verveine

6 sachets
35 cl de crème liquide
12 cl de lait
90 g de sucre en poudre
5 jaunes d'œufs
60 g de sucre cassonade ou vergeoise

Tilleul.

8 sachets
35 cl de crème liquide
12 cl de lait
90 g de sucre en poudre
5 jaunes d'œufs
60 g de sucre cassonade ou vergeoise

1 - Dans une casserole, pour chacune des recettes, chauffer le lait et la crème à feu doux avec les sachets ou les branches d'herbes (+ le miel pour la recette miel romarin) et laisser infuser hors du feu quelques minutes de plus.

2 - Pendant ce temps, réunir dans un saladier les jaunes d'œufs et le sucre en poudre puis fouetter énergiquement afin que le mélange blanchisse.
Filtrer la crème chaude sur le mélange œufs-sucre puis mélanger de nouveau afin de bien dissoudre l'ensemble.
Faire reposer la crème dans un récipient adapté, 2 heures au moins au réfrigérateur.

Thym

5 petites branches de thym
35 cl de crème liquide
12 cl de lait
90 g de sucre en poudre
5 jaunes d'œufs
60 g de sucre cassonade ou vergeoise

Miel et Romarin

2 branches de romarin
35 cl de crème liquide
12 cl de lait
30 g de sucre en poudre
60 g de miel
5 jaunes d'œufs
60 g de sucre cassonade ou vergeoise

4 - Une fois cuites et légèrement refroidies, réserver les crèmes au réfrigérateur. Au moment de servir, saupoudrer les crèmes de sucre cassonade ou vergeoise puis les caraméliser à l'aide d'un chalumeau.

3 - Allumer le four à 95 °C (th. 3) (voir techniques page 4). Répartir délicatement la crème dans des petits pots en porcelaine ou en terre cuite puis les disposer bien à plat dans le four. Cuire pendant 1 h à 1 h 15 (selon la contenance des petits pots). Les crèmes doivent être tremblantes et juste prises.

crème brûlée au gingembre confit

35 cl de crème liquide
10 cl de lait
60 g de sucre en poudre
5 jaunes d'œufs
60 g de gingembre confit (2 x 30 g)
50 g de cassonade ou de sucre vergeoise

préparation

Émincer puis hacher finement la moitié du gingembre confit.

Dans une casserole, chauffer le lait, la crème et le gingembre haché à feu doux.

Pendant ce temps, fouetter énergiquement dans un saladier
les jaunes d'œufs et le sucre afin que le mélange blanchisse.

Ajouter la crème chaude en mélangeant bien afin de dissoudre l'ensemble.

Faire reposer la crème dans un récipient adapté,
2 heures au moins au réfrigérateur.

cuisson

Allumer le four à 95 °C (th. 3) (voir techniques page 4).

Répartir délicatement la crème au gingembre dans des petits pots
en porcelaine ou en terre cuite puis les disposer bien à plat dans
le four. Cuire pendant 1 h à 1 h 15 (selon la contenance des petits
pots). Les crèmes doivent être tremblantes et juste prises.

Une fois cuites et légèrement refroidies, réserver les crèmes au réfrigérateur.

caramélisation

Au moment de servir, saupoudrer les crèmes de cassonade ou de sucre
vergeoise, les caraméliser à l'aide d'un chalumeau (ou voir autres techniques
page 4) puis déposer sur chacune d'elles une fine tranche de gingembre confit.

crème brûlée « Indian Style »

35 cl de crème liquide
10 cl de lait
90 g de sucre en poudre
5 jaunes d'œufs
2 cl d'eau de fleur d'oranger
10 g de graines de cardamome
(ou 4 à 5 pincées en poudre)
50 g de cassonade ou de sucre vergeoise

préparation

Dans une casserole, chauffer le lait, la crème et la cardamome à feu doux.

Ajouter la fleur d'oranger et laisser infuser hors
du feu quelques minutes de plus.

Pendant ce temps, fouetter énergiquement dans un saladier
les jaunes d'œufs et le sucre en poudre afin que le mélange blanchisse.

Filtrer la crème chaude sur le mélange œufs-sucre
en mélangeant bien afin de dissoudre l'ensemble.

Faire reposer la crème dans un récipient adapté,
2 heures au moins au réfrigérateur.

cuisson

Allumer le four à 95 °C (th. 3) (voir techniques page 4).

Répartir délicatement la crème dans des petits pots en porcelaine
ou en terre cuite puis les disposer bien à plat dans le four.
Cuire pendant 1 h à 1 h 15 (selon la contenance des petits pots).
Les crèmes doivent être tremblantes et juste prises.

Une fois cuites et légèrement refroidies, réserver les crèmes au réfrigérateur.

caramélisation

Au moment de servir, saupoudrer les crèmes de cassonade
ou de sucre vergeoise puis les caraméliser à l'aide d'un
chalumeau (ou voir autres techniques page 4).

crème brûlée au lait de coco et fruits de la passion

40 cl de lait de coco
4 jaunes d'œufs
60 g de sucre en poudre
1 fruit de la passion
+ 2 pour la cuisson, comme sur la photo
(facultatif)
40 g de cassonade

préparation

Couper le fruit de la passion en deux puis récupérer
à l'aide d'une petite cuillère les graines et la pulpe.

Dans une casserole, chauffer le lait de coco, les graines et la pulpe
à feu doux puis laisser infuser hors du feu quelques minutes de plus.

Pendant ce temps, fouetter énergiquement dans un saladier les jaunes
d'œufs et le sucre en poudre afin que le mélange blanchisse.

Filtrer le lait de coco sur le mélange œufs sucre en mélangeant
de nouveau afin de bien dissoudre l'ensemble.

Faire reposer la crème dans un récipient adapté,
2 heures au moins au réfrigérateur.

cuisson

Allumer le four à 95 °C (th. 3) (voir techniques page 4).

Répartir délicatement la crème coco-passion dans des petits
pots en porcelaine ou en terre cuite puis les disposer bien à plat
dans le four. (Si vous le souhaitez, comme sur la photo, déposer
délicatement ½ fruit de la passion dans chacun des petits pots.)

Cuire pendant 1 h à 1 h 15 (selon la contenance des petits pots).
Les crèmes doivent être tremblantes et juste prises.

Une fois cuites et légèrement refroidies, réserver les crèmes au réfrigérateur.

caramélisation

Au moment de servir, saupoudrer les crèmes de cassonade puis les
caraméliser à l'aide d'un chalumeau (ou voir autres techniques page 4).

crème brûlée aux raisins et au rhum

LES RAISINS AU RHUM
70 g de sucre en poudre
70 g d'eau
5 cl de rhum brun
80 g de raisins secs

LA CRÈME
30 cl de crème liquide
10 cl de lait
3 jaunes d'œufs
50 g de sucre en poudre
40 g de sucre vergeoise

préparation des raisins au rhum (à réaliser la veille, c'est mieux !)

Dans une petite casserole, chauffer l'eau et le
sucre en poudrejusqu'à ébullition.

Hors du feu, ajouter les raisins secs et le rhum puis laisser
mariner les raisins dans le sirop jusqu'à leur utilisation.

préparation de la crème

Dans une casserole, chauffer le lait à feu doux.

Pendant ce temps, fouetter énergiquement dans un saladier les jaunes
d'œufs et le sucre en poudre afin que le mélange blanchisse. Incorporer la
crème froide et 2 ou 3 cuillère à soupe du sirop au rhum. Bien mélanger.

Enfin ajouter le lait chaud et mélanger de nouveau
afin de dissoudre l'ensemble.

Faire reposer la crème dans un récipient adapté,
2 heures au moins au réfrigérateur.

cuisson

Allumer le four à 95 °C (th. 3) (voir techniques page 4).

Égoutter les raisins secs, les répartir dans des petits pots en porcelaine
ou en terre cuite puis les recouvrir de crème. Les disposer bien à plat
sur une plaque et cuire au four pendant 1 h à 1 h 15 (selon la contenance
des petits pots). Les crèmes doivent être tremblantes et juste prises.

Une fois cuites et légèrement refroidies, réserver les crèmes au réfrigérateur.

caramélisation

Au moment de servir, saupoudrer légèrement les crèmes de sucre vergeoise
puis les caraméliser à l'aide d'un chalumeau (ou voir autres techniques page 4).

crème brûlée aux fruits frais… à partager

35 cl de crème liquide
10 cl de lait
90 g de sucre en poudre
5 jaunes d'œufs
½ gousse de vanille
60 g de cassonade
400 g environ de fruits frais
(fruits rouges, kiwis, mangues, ceux qui
vous font envie… Tout est permis !)

préparation

Couper la gousse de vanille dans le sens de la longueur, racler
les graines dans le lait et faire chauffer dans une casserole à feu doux.

Pendant ce temps, réunir dans un saladier les jaunes d'œufs et le
sucre puis fouetter énergiquement afin que le mélange blanchisse.
Incorporer la crème froide et bien mélanger. Enfin, ajouter le lait
chaud et mélanger de nouveau afin de bien dissoudre l'ensemble.

Faire reposer la crème dans un récipient adapté,
2 heures au moins au réfrigérateur.

cuisson

Allumer le four à 95 °C (th. 3) (voir techniques page 4).

Répartir délicatement la crème dans des petits pots en porcelaine
ou en terre cuite puis les disposer bien à plat dans le four.
Cuire pendant 1 h 15 à 1 h 30 (selon la contenance des pots).
Les crèmes doivent être tremblantes et juste prises.

Une fois cuites et légèrement refroidies, réserver les crèmes au réfrigérateur.

Laver, éplucher ou tailler les fruits que vous aurez choisis.

caramélisation

Au moment de servir, saupoudrer les crèmes de cassonade, les caraméliser
à l'aide d'un chalumeau (ou voir autres techniques page 4) puis disposer
soigneusement les fruits frais sur la moitié de leur surface.

crème brûlée façon tatin

LES POMMES CARAMÉLISÉES
3 pommes (golden, reinette,
jauna gold…)
25 g de beurre demi-sel
50 g de sucre en poudre

LA CRÈME
35 cl de crème liquide
12 cl de lait
70 g de sucre en poudre
4 jaunes d'œufs

½ gousse de vanille
40 g de cassonade ou de sucre vergeoise

préparation des pommes caramélisées

Éplucher, épépiner et tailler les pommes en quartiers plus ou moins gros en fonction de la hauteur de vos moules. Faire caraméliser légèrement dans une poêle 50 g de sucre en poudre. Ajouter les pommes et le beurre, remuer et cuire à feu doux 2 à 3 minutes. Laisser refroidir.

préparation de la crème

Couper la gousse de vanille dans le sens de la longueur, racler les graines dans le lait puis chauffer dans une casserole à feu doux. Pendant ce temps, fouetter énergiquement dans un saladier les jaunes d'œufs et le sucre afin que le mélange blanchisse. Incorporer la crème froide et bien mélanger. Enfin, ajouter le lait chaud en mélangeant de nouveau afin de bien dissoudre l'ensemble.

Faire reposer la crème dans un récipient adapté,
2 heures au moins au réfrigérateur.

cuisson

Allumer le four à 95 °C (th. 3) (voir techniques page 4).

Répartir soigneusement les pommes caramélisées dans des petits pots en terre cuite puis les recouvrir aux ¾ de crème vanillée. Les disposer bien à plat dans le four et cuire pendant 1 h à 1 h 15 (selon la contenance des pots). Les crèmes doivent être tremblantes et juste prises.

Une fois cuites et légèrement refroidies, réserver les crèmes au réfrigérateur.

caramélisation

Au moment de servir, saupoudrer légèrement les crèmes de cassonade ou de sucre vergeoise puis les caraméliser à l'aide d'un chalumeau (ou voir autres techniques page 4).

crème brûlée mi-figues mi-raisins

50 cl de crème liquide
70 g de sucre en poudre
6 jaunes d'œufs
½ gousse de vanille
6 à 8 figues fraîches ou surgelées
2 grappes de raisin ou une boîte
de raisins au sirop
40 g de cassonade

préparation

Couper la gousse de vanille dans le sens de la longueur, racler les graines dans la crème puis faire chauffer dans une casserole à feu doux.

Pendant ce temps, fouetter énergiquement dans un saladier les jaunes d'œufs et le sucre afin que le mélange blanchisse. Incorporer enfin la crème chaude en mélangeant bien pour dissoudre l'ensemble.

Faire reposer la crème dans un récipient adapté, 2 heures au moins au réfrigérateur.

cuisson

Allumer le four à 95 °C (th. 3) (voir techniques page 4).

Tailler les figues en quartiers, éplucher et épépiner les raisins si besoin.

Les répartir soigneusement en deux parties égales dans des moules en porcelaine ou en terre cuite puis les recouvrir de crème vanillée.

Les disposer bien à plat sur une plaque et cuire au four pendant 1 h à 1 h 15 (selon la contenance des moules). Les crèmes doivent être tremblantes et juste prises.

caramélisation

Une fois cuites et légèrement refroidies, réserver les crèmes au réfrigérateur. Au moment de servir, saupoudrer légèrement les crèmes de cassonade puis les caraméliser à l'aide d'un chalumeau ou sous le gril du four.

crème brûlée aux marrons

40 cl de crème liquide
4 jaunes d'œufs
30 g de sucre en poudre
200 g de crème de marrons
quelques marrons au sirop (facultatif)
50 g de sucre vergeoise

préparation

Chauffer la crème dans une casserole à feu doux.

Pendant ce temps, fouetter énergiquement dans un saladier
les jaunes d'œufs et le sucre afin que le mélange blanchisse.
Incorporer la crème de marrons et bien mélanger.

Enfin, ajouter la crème chaude et mélanger de
nouveau afin de bien dissoudre l'ensemble.

Faire reposer la crème dans un récipient adapté,
2 heures au moins au réfrigérateur.

cuisson

Allumer le four à 95 °C (th. 3) (voir techniques page 4).

Répartir délicatement la crème et quelques brisures de marrons (facultatif)
dans des petits pots en porcelaine ou en terre cuite puis les disposer
bien à plat dans le four. Cuire pendant 1 h à 1 h 15 (selon la contenance
des petits pots). Les crèmes doivent être tremblantes et juste prises.

Une fois cuites et légèrement refroidies, réserver les crèmes au réfrigérateur.

caramélisation

Au moment de servir, saupoudrer les crèmes de sucre vergeoise puis les
caraméliser à l'aide d'un chalumeau (ou voir autres techniques page 4).

crème brûlée au pamplemousse et au miel

50 cl de crème liquide
20 g de sucre en poudre
50 g de miel
6 jaunes d'œufs
2 ou 3 pamplemousses
40 g de cassonade

préparation

Chauffer la crème et le miel dans une casserole à feu doux.

Pendant ce temps, fouetter énergiquement dans un saladier
les jaunes d'œufs et le sucre. Incorporer enfin la crème chaude
en mélangeant bien pour dissoudre l'ensemble.

Faire reposer la crème dans un récipient adapté,
2 heures au moins au réfrigérateur.

Peler les pamplemousses à vif.

À l'aide d'un couteau, prélever les segments sans la peau
puis les éponger sur un papier absorbant.

cuisson

Allumer le four à 95 °C (th. 3) (voir techniques page 4).

Disposer soignesement les pamplemousses bien à plat dans des moules
en porcelaine ou en terre cuite puis, les recouvrir délicatement de
crème au miel et cuire au four pendant 1 h à 1 h 15 (selon la contenance
des moules). Les crèmes doivent être tremblantes et juste prises.

Une fois cuites et légèrement refroidies, réserver les crèmes au réfrigérateur.

caramélisation

Au moment de servir, saupoudrer les crèmes de cassonade puis les
caraméliser à l'aide d'un chalumeau ou sous le gril du four.

crème brûlée citronnelle aux fraises

35 cl de crème liquide
12 cl de lait
90 g de sucre en poudre
5 jaunes d'œufs
½ bâton de citronnelle
250 g de fraises
40 g de cassonade ou de sucre vergeoise

préparation

Émincer finement le bâton de citronnelle.

Dans une casserole, chauffer le lait, la crème et la citronnelle à feu doux puis laisser infuser hors du feu quelques minutes de plus.

Pendant ce temps, fouetter énergiquement dans un saladier les jaunes d'œufs et le sucre afin que le mélange blanchisse.

Filtrer la crème chaude sur le mélange et bien dissoudre l'ensemble.

Faire reposer la crème dans un récipient adapté, 2 heures au moins au réfrigérateur.

cuisson

Allumer le four à 95 °C (th. 3) (voir techniques page 4).

Répartir délicatement la crème citronnelle dans des petits pots en porcelaine ou en terre cuite puis les disposer bien à plat dans le four. Cuire pendant 1 h à 1 h 15 (selon la contenance des petits pots). Les crèmes doivent être tremblantes et juste prises.

Une fois cuites et légèrement refroidies, réserver les crèmes au réfrigérateur.

caramélisation

Au moment de servir, saupoudrer les crèmes de cassonade ou de sucre vergeoise, les caraméliser à l'aide d'un chalumeau (ou voir autres techniques page 4). Laver et découper les fraises puis les déposer joliment sur les crèmes.

crème brûlée au Nutella

30 cl de lait
20 cl de crème liquide
5 jaunes d'œufs
40 g de sucre en poudre
150 g de Nutella
60 g de cassonade

préparation

Chauffer le lait, la crème et le Nutella dans une casserole à feu doux.
Mélanger attentivement afin de bien dissoudre le Nutella.

Fouetter énergiquement dans un saladier les jaunes d'œufs
et le sucre en poudre afin que le mélange blanchisse puis incorporer
la crème chaude en mélangeant bien afin de dissoudre l'ensemble.

Faire reposer la crème dans un récipient adapté,
2 heures au moins au réfrigérateur.

cuisson

Allumer le four à 95 °C (th. 3) (voir techniques page 4).

Répartir délicatement la crème dans des petits pots en porcelaine
ou en terre cuite puis les disposer bien à plat dans le four.
Cuire pendant 1 h à 1 h 15 (selon la contenance des petits pots).
Les crèmes doivent être tremblantes et juste prises.

Une fois cuites et légèrement refroidies, réserver les crèmes au réfrigérateur.

caramélisation

Au moment de servir, saupoudrer les crèmes de cassonade puis les
caraméliser à l'aide d'un chalumeau (ou voir autres techniques page 4).

crème brûlée au cointreau et au chocolat blanc

35 cl de crème liquide
120 g de chocolat blanc
6 jaunes d'œufs
5 cl de cointreau
60 g de cassonade

préparation

Dans une casserole, chauffer la crème à feu doux.

Pendant ce temps, réunir le chocolat en petits morceaux dans un saladier.

Verser dessus la crème chaude en mélangeant bien afin de dissoudre l'ensemble puis incorporer les jaunes d'œufs et enfin le cointreau.

Transvaser la crème dans un récipient adapté et la faire reposer 2 heures au moins au réfrigérateur.

cuisson

Allumer le four à 95 °C (th. 3) (voir techniques page 4).

Répartir délicatement les crèmes au chocolat blanc dans des petits pots en porcelaine ou en terre cuite puis les disposer bien à plat dans le four. Cuire pendant 1 h à 1 h 15 (selon la contenance des petits pots). Les crèmes doivent être tremblantes et juste prises.

Une fois cuites et légèrement refroidies, réserver les crèmes au réfrigérateur.

caramélisation

Au moment de servir, saupoudrer les crèmes de cassonade puis les caraméliser à l'aide d'un chalumeau (ou voir autres techniques page 4).

petits pots crémeux aux 3 chocolats

CRÈME AU CHOCOLAT NOIR
25 cl de lait
25 cl de crème liquide
125 g de chocolat noir
5 jaunes d'œufs
70 g de sucre en poudre

CRÈME AU CHOCOLAT BLANC
40 cl de crème liquide
130 g de chocolat blanc
6 jaunes d'œufs

CRÈME AU CHOCOLAT AU LAIT
40 cl de crème liquide
15 cl de lait
140 g de chocolat au lait
4 jaunes d'œufs
60 g de sucre en poudre

pour les crèmes au chocolat noir et au lait

Dans une casserole, chauffer le lait et la crème à feu doux.

Pendant ce temps, fouetter énergiquement dans un saladier les jaunes d'œufs et le sucre afin que le mélange blanchisse.

Ajouter le chocolat coupé en petits morceaux à la crème chaude, bien mélanger afin de dissoudre l'ensemble puis le verser sur le mélange œufs-sucre.

pour les crèmes au chocolat blanc

Dans une casserole, chauffer la crème à feu doux.

Pendant ce temps, réunir dans un saladier le chocolat coupé en petits morceaux.

Verser dessus la crème chaude, bien mélanger afin de dissoudre l'ensemble puis incorporer les jaunes d'œufs.

Transvaser les différentes crèmes dans des récipients adaptés et les faire reposer 2 heures au moins au réfrigérateur.

cuisson

Allumer le four à 95 °C (th. 3) (voir techniques page 4).

Répartir délicatement les crèmes au chocolat dans des petits pots en porcelaine ou en terre cuite puis les disposer dans un plat à rebord rempli à moitié d'eau. Cuire au bain-marie pendant 1 h à 1 h 15 (selon la contenance des petits pots). Les crèmes doivent être tremblantes et juste prises.

Une fois cuites et légèrement refroidies, réserver les crèmes au réfrigérateur avant de les déguster.

crème à la pistache et au cacao

35 cl de crème liquide
12 cl de lait
70 g de sucre en poudre
4 jaunes d'œufs
60 g de pâte à pistache colorée ou
1 petite cuillère à soupe d'arôme pistache
30 cl de sauce ou de glaçage au cacao

préparation

Dans une casserole, à feu doux, chauffer le lait et la pâte ou l'arôme pistache.

Pendant ce temps, fouetter énergiquement dans un saladier
les jaunes d'œufs et le sucre afin que le mélange blanchisse.
Incorporer la crème froide et bien mélanger.

Enfin, ajouter le lait chaud à la pistache et mélanger
de nouveau afin de bien dissoudre l'ensemble.

Faire reposer la crème dans un récipient adapté,
2 heures au moins au réfrigérateur.

cuisson

Allumer le four à 95 °C (th. 3) (voir techniques page 4).

Répartir délicatement la crème à la pistache dans des petits pots
en porcelaine ou en terre cuite puis les disposer bien à plat dans
le four. Cuire pendant 1 h à 1 h 15 (selon la contenance des petits
pots). Les crèmes doivent être tremblantes et juste prises.

Une fois cuites et légèrement refroidies, réserver les crèmes au réfrigérateur.

Au moment de servir, tiédir si besoin la sauce ou le glaçage au
cacao et napper joliment les crèmes selon votre gourmandise.

crème craquante menthe choco

35 cl de crème liquide
10 cl de lait
80 g de sucre en poudre
5 jaunes d'œufs
10 feuilles de menthe fraîche
2 cl de sirop de menthe
125 g de chocolat noir

1 pinceau

préparation

Dans une casserole, chauffer le lait, la crème et
les feuilles de menthe à feu doux.

Ajouter le sirop de menthe et laisser infuser hors
du feu quelques minutes de plus.

Pendant ce temps, fouetter énergiquement dans un saladier
les jaunes d'œufs et le sucre afin que le mélange blanchisse.

Filtrer la crème chaude sur le mélange œufs-sucre
en mélangeant bien afin de dissoudre l'ensemble.

Faire reposer la crème dans un récipient adapté,
2 heures au moins au réfrigérateur.

cuisson

Répartir la crème dans des petits pots en porcelaine ou en terre cuite
puis les disposer dans un plat à rebord rempli à moitié d'eau. Rajouter
délicatement un peu de crème dans chaque petit pot jusqu'aux rebords
puis cuire au bain-marie pendant 1 h à 1 h 15 (selon la contenance des
petits pots). Les crèmes doivent être tremblantes et juste prises.

Une fois cuites et légèrement refroidies, réserver les crèmes au réfrigérateur.

présentation

Lorsque les crèmes sont bien froides, faire fondre le chocolat noir
au bain-marie ou au four à micro-ondes avec quelques gouttes d'huile neutre.

À l'aide d'un pinceau, napper délicatement chacune
d'elles d'une fine pellicule de chocolat.

Remettre les petits pots au réfrigérateur une quinzaine de
minutes au moins pour que le chocolat soit bien craquant.

crème brûlée aux carambars

30 cl de lait
20 cl de crème liquide
5 jaunes d'œufs
20 carambars (160 g)
60 g de cassonade

préparation

Chauffer le lait, la crème et les carambars dans une casserole
à feu doux. Mélanger délicatement afin de bien dissoudre les
caramels puis y incorporer, hors du feu, les jaunes d'œufs.

Faire reposer la crème dans un récipient adapté,
2 heures au moins au réfrigérateur.

cuisson

Allumer le four à 95 °C (th. 3) (voir techniques page 4).

Répartir délicatement la crème dans des petits pots en porcelaine
ou en terre cuite puis les disposer bien à plat dans le four.
Cuire pendant 1 h à 1 h 15 (selon la contenance des petits pots).
Les crèmes doivent être tremblantes et juste prises.

Une fois cuites et légèrement refroidies, réserver les crèmes au réfrigérateur.

caramélisation

Au moment de servir, saupoudrer les crèmes de cassonade puis les
caraméliser à l'aide d'un chalumeau (ou voir les autres techniques page 4).

crème brûlée à la chicorée

35 cl de crème liquide
10 cl de lait
90 g de sucre en poudre
5 jaunes d'œufs
25 g de chicorée liquide
40 g de sucre vergeoise brun

préparation

Dans une casserole, chauffer le lait à feu doux.

Pendant ce temps, fouetter énergiquement dans un saladier les jaunes d'œufs et le sucre en poudre afin que le mélange blanchisse. Incorporer la crème froide, la chicorée et bien mélanger.

Enfin, ajouter le lait chaud et mélanger de nouveau afin de bien dissoudre l'ensemble.

Faire reposer la préparation dans un récipient adapté, 2 heures au moins au réfrigérateur.

cuisson

Allumer le four à 95 °C (th. 3) (voir techniques page 4).

Répartir délicatement la crème à la chicorée dans des petits pots en porcelaine ou en terre cuite puis les disposer bien à plat dans le four. Cuire pendant 1 h à 1 h 15 (selon la contenance des petits pots). Les crèmes doivent être tremblantes et juste prises.

Une fois cuites et légèrement refroidies, réserver les crèmes au réfrigérateur.

caramélisation

Au moment de servir, saupoudrer les crèmes de sucre vergeoise, puis les caraméliser à l'aide d'un chalumeau (ou voir autres techniques page 4).

espresso crémeux

25 cl de crème liquide
15 cl de café espresso chaud
60 g de sucre en poudre
4 jaunes d'œufs
du lait entier
quelques gouttes d'extrait de café
(facultatif)

1 shaker et quelques glaçons

préparation

Réunir dans un saladier les jaunes d'œufs et le sucre puis
fouetter énergiquement afin que le mélange blanchisse.
Incorporer la crème froide puis bien mélanger.

Enfin, ajouter le café chaud en mélangeant de nouveau
afin de bien dissoudre l'ensemble.

Faire reposer la crème dans un récipient adapté,
2 heures au moins au réfrigérateur.

cuisson

Répartir délicatement la crème au café dans des petites tasses puis les
disposer dans un plat à rebord rempli à moitié d'eau. Cuire au bain-marie
pendant 1 h à 1 h 15. Les crèmes doivent être tremblantes et juste prises.

Une fois cuites et légèrement refroidies, réserver les crèmes au réfrigérateur.

présentation

Au moment de servir, secouer vivement dans un shaker un peu
de lait entier et de l'extrait de café avec 2 ou 3 glaçons, récupérer
la mousse de lait et napper vos espresso crémeux.

crème brûlée au caramel salé

125 g de sucre en poudre
5 jaunes d'œufs
30 cl de lait
20 cl de crème liquide
5 g de sel de Guérande
40 g de cassonade ou de sucre vergeoise

préparation

Dans une casserole bien propre, cuire à feu moyen, sans remuer,
le sucre avec un peu d'eau (l'eau doit juste recouvrir le sucre).

Dès qu'une coloration commence à apparaître, mélanger
légèrement afin qu'elle devienne homogène.

Lorsque le caramel commence à prendre une teinte brune légèrement
prononcée, retirer du feu, ajouter le sel et verser délicatement le lait.

Remettre sur feu doux en mélangeant attentivement
afin de bien dissoudre le caramel dans le lait.

Hors du feu, incorporer la crème liquide puis les jaunes d'œufs.

Bien mélanger puis filtrer la crème dans un récipient adapté
et la faire reposer 2 heures au moins au réfrigérateur.

cuisson

Allumer le four à 95 °C (th. 3) (voir techniques page 4).

Répartir délicatement la crème dans des petits pots en porcelaine
ou en terre cuite puis les disposer bien à plat dans le four.
Cuire pendant 1 h à 1 h 15 (selon la contenance des petits pots).
Les crèmes doivent être tremblantes et juste prises.

Une fois cuites et légèrement refroidies, réserver les crèmes au réfrigérateur.

caramélisation

Au moment de servir, saupoudrer les crèmes de cassonade puis les
caraméliser à l'aide d'un chalumeau (ou voir les autres techniques page 4).

remerciements

Un grand merci à Charlotte et Élodie pour leur énergie, leur bon goût mais aussi pour leur gourmandise !

Je tiens également à remercier mes complices de cuisine, Carine,
Jérome et particulièrement André pour leur disponibilité.

Et bien sûr, merci à Christophe, à l'équipe du Café Noir et à l'équipe de Marabout.

shopping

Astier de Villatte
173 rue St Honoré 75001 Paris
www.astierdevillatte.com
01 01 42 60 74 13

Jeannine Cros
11, rue d'Assas - 75006 – Paris
01 45 48 00 67

Mora
13, Rue Montmartre 75001 Paris
www.mora.fr
01 45 08 19 24

Merci
111 bd Beaumarchais Paris 11
01 42 77 78 92

Adonde
www.adonde.fr

L'atelier de Madame M.
www.atelier.madame.m.free.fr

Gargantua
www.gargantua.ch

Conran shop
www.conranshop.fr

Le petit atelier de Paris.
www.lepetitatelierdeparis.com

WMF
renseignements au 01 44 74 18 81

© Hachette Livre - Marabout 2009

Dépôt légal : octobre 2010

ISBN : 978-2-501-06326-5

40-5015-9

Imprimé en Chine par Leo Paper